PRACTICAL ORGANIC CHEMISTRY

By the same authors
INTRODUCTION TO
PRACTICAL ORGANIC CHEMISTRY
With Diagrams

PRACTICAL ORGANIC CHEMISTRY

by

FREDERICK GEORGE MANN
S.C.D. (CANTAB.), D.SC. (LOND.), F.R.I.C., F.R.S.
FELLOW AND LECTURER, TRINITY COLLEGE, CAMBRIDGE,
UNIVERSITY READER IN ORGANIC CHEMISTRY

and

BERNARD CHARLES SAUNDERS
M.A., SC.D. (CANTAB.), D.SC. (LOND.), F.R.I.C.
FELLOW AND CHARLES KINGSLEY LECTURER, MAGDALENE COLLEGE, CAMBRIDGE,
UNIVERSITY LECTURER IN CHEMISTRY

LONGMANS, GREEN AND CO
LONDON : NEW YORK : TORONTO

LONGMANS, GREEN AND CO LTD
6 & 7 CLIFFORD STREET LONDON WI
ALSO AT MELBOURNE AND CAPE TOWN

LONGMANS, GREEN AND CO INC
55 FIFTH AVENUE NEW YORK 3

LONGMANS, GREEN AND CO
215 VICTORIA STREET TORONTO I

ORIENT LONGMANS LTD
BOMBAY CALCUTTA MADRAS

First Published 1936
Second Edition 1938
New Impressions 1941, 1942, 1943, 1944, 1946, 1947, 1949
Third Edition 1952

PRINTED IN GREAT BRITAIN
BY WESTERN PRINTING SERVICES LTD., BRISTOL

PREFACE TO THIRD EDITION

FOR the production of this edition, we have made a thorough and critical revision of the whole contents of the book, based on our experience of its use in the laboratory and on the general advance in organic chemical practice. In addition to this general revision, however, we have extended the book in three main directions.

The book as originally planned was intended to meet the needs primarily of pupils in the senior forms at schools and of undergraduates up to the level of a Pass Degree. We have extended Parts II and III dealing with Preparations and with the Reactions and Identification of Organic Compounds so that the book should now cater fully for the needs of students working for Honours Degrees. In particular, the Preparations now include examples of most of the more simple standard reactions: for this purpose we have now added, for example, preparations illustrating the Benzidine Transformation, the Ullmann Condensation, the Benzilic Acid Rearrangement, the Reformatsky Reaction, the Clemmensen Reduction, the Fischer Indolisation Reaction, the Mannich Reaction, and the Diels-Alder Reaction. It is probable that preparative work on a much smaller scale than has hitherto been customary in teaching laboratories will become more common in future. To meet this need, we have added a short section to Part I (pp. 41–46), describing the design and use of apparatus for this purpose, and we have also included some examples of these small-scale preparations as alternatives to the larger preparations in Part II.

In Part III, dealing with the Reactions and Identification of Organic Compounds, greater emphasis has now been placed on the preparation of suitable crystalline derivatives. Quite apart from the importance of these derivatives for purposes of identification, encouragement is thereby given to the student to gain experience in small-scale preparative work.

We have also added an entirely new section dealing with semimicroanalysis. In our original Introduction (p. ix) we justified the retention of macro-methods of quantitative analysis on the grounds that they formed an excellent introduction to micromethods and also afforded a valuable training in exact manipulation generally. By now, however, the macro-estimation particularly of carbon and hydrogen and of nitrogen has disappeared entirely from most laboratories. On the other hand, the micro-methods developed so largely by Pregl, and which usually require no more than 5 mgm. of material, necessitate prolonged training and an impeccable experimental technique, and give consistently reliable results only in the hands of full-time analysts. They are consequently unsuitable for students. The semi-micro methods of analysis, which usually require 20–50 mgm. of material, form an ideal compromise for student-training, for the necessary technique can be acquired after only a few attempts. These methods moreover provide the student with very valuable manipulative exercise, and serve as an introduction to the handling of even smaller quantities of material which may arise in his post-graduate work. This section on Semi-microanalysis has been designed and written by Dr. P. Sykes, and is based on his experience of teaching such methods in the Cambridge laboratories. We wish to thank him sincerely for a very valuable contribution to this work.

In the original planning of this book we were at pains to ensure that the preparations in particular were designed to afford a minimum expenditure of time, materials and heating. We hope that the economy thus introduced will be especially appreciated in view of the recent heavily increased cost of chemicals, fuel and laboratory service. This increased cost, incidentally, must necessarily increase the attraction of the small-scale preparations referred to above.

We are grateful to our colleagues for many valuable discussions and suggestions: in particular we would mention Dr. F. B. Kipping, Dr. P. Maitland, Dr. G. W. Kenner and Mr. J. Harley-Mason.

We should also like to express once again our sincere thanks for the considerable help we have received from our laboratory assistants, Mr. F. C. Baker and Mr. F. E. Smith.

F.G.M.
B.C.S.

PREFACE TO SECOND EDITION

THE two chief additions which have now been made are the Sodium Carbonate-Zinc Method as an alternative to Lassaigne's Sodium Fusion Method for detecting elements in organic compounds, and the Tables of Physical Constants which have been included in the Appendix. These Tables have been compiled to cover a very much wider scope of organic compounds than those described in this book. In addition to the general utility of these Tables, we hope that they will be of value to students wishing to extend their practice in the identification of organic compounds beyond the range given in Part III of this book. This range has been deliberately limited in order to enable students to obtain a firm grasp of the methods of identifying simple compounds, and these methods have therefore been based almost entirely on chemical reactions alone. When the range of organic compounds to be identified is extended, and particularly when higher homologues are being investigated, identification by the physical properties of derivatives becomes increasingly necessary, and the Tables of Physical Constants should considerably facilitate this extension.

We wish to express our gratitude to the chemists who have made suggestions with regard to the subject-matter of this book: many of these suggestions have now been incorporated in this edition. We would warmly welcome further suggestions for improving its contents.

F.G.M.
B.C.S.

INTRODUCTION

THIS laboratory manual of organic chemistry has been compiled primarily to cover the work required for Part I of the Natural Sciences Tripos at Cambridge University, the General B.Sc. course at London University, and the Pass Degree courses at other universities. At the same time, however, it has been carefully arranged to cover adequately the needs of students proceeding to the M.B. examinations in organic chemistry at the various universities. Moreover, since the introductory work has been given in considerable detail, the book is suitable for senior pupils at schools (more particularly for Higher Certificate and University Entrance Scholarship candidates), and should therefore be sufficient to cover both their school and university needs.

This work is based largely on the authors' experience with the teaching of practical organic chemistry to very large classes of students at Cambridge University. For such classes experimental directions involving the utmost economy in chemicals and apparatus, and also in the students' time, are obviously required. Therefore the whole of the experimental work described in this book has been repeatedly checked by the authors themselves (and for the most part by their classes also) in order to obtain the desired results with a minimum expenditure of materials and time. In the section on Organic Preparations in particular, this detailed investigation of each preparation has frequently enabled unexpected simplifications and economies to be introduced, more particularly as many text-books still contain experimental directions which have frequently remained unchanged since their original publication in chemical journals many years ago, and in which, moreover, occasional errors both in fact and in transcription have thus remained uncorrected. It is almost universally found that departments of organic chemistry are more costly to maintain than other science departments, primarily because of the heavy consumption of organic reagents and solvents, and the economies which have now been effected will, we think, be appreciated by most teachers of practical organic chemistry.

Teachers of chemistry (and of the sciences generally) will have found that many students appear to dissociate their practical work sharply in their minds from their theoretical knowledge. Many students of organic chemistry moreover remain familiar with a particular preparation, but fail to appreciate the value or significance of the process of which that preparation is merely one example: for instance, a student may often have a detailed knowledge of the preparation of acetanilide, but be unable to give a general account of the methods of acetylation, or of the practical value of the process of acetylation itself. Consequently in the following pages the description of most experiments (and particularly of the preparations) is preceded by a short account in small print of the chief theoretical considerations involved: in the case of preparations based on one of several alternative methods, a brief account is similarly given of these methods and of their comparative practical value. This combination of theory and practice will, it is hoped, both simplify and elucidate the practical study of organic chemistry, and enable the student to visualise his practical work as an orderly whole and not as a vast number of isolated and unrelated experiments.

Part III, on the Reactions and Identification of Organic Compounds, has been strictly limited to the commoner members of each of the more important classes of organic compounds. This work, consisting chiefly of reactions carried out on the test-tube scale, should be of great value to the student, who, if he carries out the reactions intelligently, should thereby effectively consolidate his theoretical knowledge. Yet students frequently attempt far too ambitious a programme of reactions and more particularly of qualitative analysis, and thus often become lost in the very detailed work on which such programmes are based. We consider therefore that students should master thoroughly the more simple programme given in Part III before proceeding to wider and more detailed systems for the identification of organic compounds.

The comparatively wide prevalence of micro-methods of quantitative organic analysis, applied more particularly to the estimation of the constituent elements in an organic compound, may cause the advisability of including the macro-methods in Part IV to be questioned. Quite apart, however, from the fact that the micro-methods still find no place in many laboratories, we consider that thorough practice in the macro-methods of quantitative analysis to be not only an excellent introduction to the micro-methods themselves, but also a valuable training in exact manipulation generally.

Part V, on Simple Enzyme Reactions, is rather a new departure in practical books of this type. The importance of this section to medical students, biochemists, physiologists, etc., is obvious. We consider, however, that students of chemistry who are not reading any biological subject should have some practical knowledge of a branch of organic chemistry which is of the greatest scientific importance, and the industrial application of which will undoubtedly increase very widely in the future. At present it rarely occurs to such students that an organic reaction can be usefully promoted by the application of anything but the flame of a Bunsen burner!

If students are carefully trained in accurate work, accidents in the laboratory should be of very rare occurrence. Since, however, they can never be entirely eliminated, it is hoped that the First Aid directions given in the Appendix will prove of value, particularly to the junior staff of laboratories, who by virtue of their duties as demonstrators are frequently the first to be called upon to help injured students.

We wish to express our very sincere thanks to Dr. W. H. Mills, F.R.S., and to Dr. Hamilton McCombie, for much advice and help in the compilation of this book; to Prof. C. S. Gibson, F.R.S., for suggestions with regard to the needs of medical students; and to Prof. E. L. Hirst, F.R.S., for advice upon certain preparations in the carbohydrate series. We are also greatly indebted to Dr. F. B. Kipping and Dr. P. Maitland for many suggestions based on the experience obtained from their own first-year medical and Tripos classes. We gratefully acknowledge the help we have received from Dr. P. J. G. Mann of the Cambridge University Biochemical Department, who read over the section on Enzymes and made many valuable suggestions, and from Dr. F. J. W. Roughton, F.R.S., and Dr. G. A. Millikan, who kindly furnished the details of experiments concerning carbonic anhydrase.

Our warm thanks are due also to our Laboratory and Lecture Assistants, Mr. F. C. Baker and Mr. F. E. Smith, who have given us great help in the many repetitions of the preparations and the quantitative analyses respectively which were required before this book could attain its final form.

The notes on First Aid have been based on the memorandum *Safeguards in the Laboratory*, compiled by the Science Masters' Association and the Association of Women Science Teachers. This report has, however, been considerably modified and amplified for our purpose, and we are greatly indebted to Dr. F. B. Parsons, M.D., for very kindly supervising our final draft and thus ensuring its medical accuracy.

The authors will welcome criticisms and suggestions from teachers of practical organic chemistry.

Cambridge.   F. G. Mann
    May 1936   B. C. Saunders

CONTENTS

CONTENTS

ABBREVIATIONS

The following abbreviations are used throughout this book:

b.p.	boiling-point
f.p.	freezing-point
m.p.	melting-point
d.	density (gms. per c.c.)
gm(s).	gram(s)
mgm.	milligram(s)
Gm.Mol.	gram-molecule
N.	Normal
Atm.	Atmosphere-pressure

The abbreviations c.c. and ml. are used for general measurement and quantitative determinations respectively.

The density of liquids, unless otherwise stated, is given at 15°C.

The experiments described in Part I have been numbered, as they form a graded series to illustrate the chief manipulative processes employed in practical organic chemistry. The experiments in Parts II–V have not been numbered, as in general a selection must be made from them. In each part of the book, the experiments have been arranged as far as possible in logical order, although occasionally (as in Part IV) this is not necessarily the order of increasing difficulty.

PART I

METHODS AND MANIPULATION

In this part of the book, a brief account is given of the chief manipulative processes which are used in practical organic chemistry. Most of these processes are those which First and Second Year students are likely to use repeatedly in their work. The remainder are not of such frequent occurrence, but are processes with which students should be familiar for future work: the discussion of the latter processes is given in small print.

It should be emphasised that all the processes here described are considered essentially from the practical standpoint. The student should always acquaint himself with the theoretical basis of these operations, for which he should consult any standard text-book of physical chemistry: this applies particularly to such processes as the distillation of constant boiling-point mixtures, steam-distillation, ether extraction, *etc.*

The experimental operations in organic chemistry which occur with greatest frequency are those which are concerned, directly or indirectly, with the isolation and purification of organic compounds. It is necessary therefore to describe in detail the chief methods of purification. Before doing so, however, the *criteria of purity* (and their observation) must first be discussed, so that when the purification has been attempted, its success can at once be checked and confirmed.

Criteria of Purity. Solid Compounds. The property of an organic compound which is most frequently determined as a criterion of purity is the *melting-point*, because in general it may be said that a pure compound has usually a sharp melting-point (*i.e.*, the substance melts entirely within a range of about 1°C.), whereas an impure substance has an indefinite melting-point, and will therefore melt slowly and indecisively over a range of several degrees. The actual possibilities which may be revealed by a melting-point determination may be summarised as follows:

A. *Melting-point sharp.*

   (1) Substance chemically pure. This is almost invariably the cause of a sharp melting-point.
   (2) Substance is a eutectic mixture of two or more compounds The chance of a given mixture containing two compounds

in just the proportion to give a sharp-melting eutectic mixture is so remote that this possibility may be neglected. [Occasionally arbitrary mixtures of two substances which (usually) are chemically related may melt fairly sharply at temperatures intermediate between the melting-points of the two components, but this phenomenon is rarely encountered.]

B. *Melting-point indefinite.*

(1) The substance is *impure*. This is almost invariably the cause of an indefinite melting-point.

(2) The substance is *pure*, but on warming undergoes slight thermal decomposition before the melting-point is reached, and the decomposition products then act as impurities and depress the melting-point.

Experimental Determination of Melting-point. The general method consists in placing the finely powdered compound in a capillary tube, and heating the latter in a bath of a suitable liquid, the temperature of the bath when the compound melts being then noted. The capillary tubes should be very thin-walled tubes, about 8 cm. long, and about 1 mm. in diameter. They can be prepared very easily by heating the centre of a clean dry soft-glass test-tube* in a large brush flame of a Bunsen burner, whilst the ends of the tube are uniformly rotated by the hands. When the central portion of the tube over a length of about 5 cm. has become both soft and moderately thickened by the heating, the ends of the tube are drawn as far apart as the arms permit, the soft portion of the tube being thus drawn out into a long capillary. The latter is then cut into suitable lengths (rejecting any flawed or otherwise unsuitable portions), and one end of each portion is then sealed. This is done by inserting the end of the capillary tube horizontally into the extreme edge of a small steady Bunsen flame for a few seconds, rotating the capillary meanwhile: no difficulty should thus be experienced in obtaining a uniformly sealed strong end to the capillary tube (Fig. 1(A)).

A clean dry porous plate is then broken into fragments† about

---

* A laboratory demonstration of this operation is far better than any written description. The tubes may be bought from many dealers (*e.g.*, J. W. Towers & Co. Ltd., Victoria House, Widnes, Lancs; also The Scientific Glass-Blowing Co., 12–14 Wright Street, Oxford Road, Manchester 15), but students should learn to make their own capillary tubes.

† A microscope slide may be used in place of the fragment of unglazed porcelain. The slide has the advantage that it can be washed after each determination and so used repeatedly: the rough surface of the porcelain, however, lends itself much more readily to the pulverisation of the organic material.

3 cm. square. (A supply of the fragments in a dust-tight box should always be freely available in the laboratory.) To fill the capillary with the compound the melting-point of which is to be determined, about 0·1 gm. of the compound is placed on one of the fragments of plate, and crushed to a fine powder by gently rubbing it with the flat end of a porcelain spatula or (better) with the slightly bent end of a small flat narrow metal (*e.g.*, nickel) spatula. When a very fine powder has been obtained, sufficient is transferred to the capillary tube (by pushing the open end of the tube through the powder and backing the latter if necessary with the spatula) so that, when the closed end of the tube is tapped on the bench, a length of about 5 mm. of fairly tightly packed material has accumulated at the bottom. This is a rapid operation when the compound gives a fine dense powder: some compounds however, even when pure, have a waxy consistency, and are not easily inserted into a tube of the usual width, in which case a slightly wider capillary (say 2 mm. in diameter) may have to be used. The student should soon be able by experience to select a suitable tube having once obtained the "feel" of the material when crushed on the porcelain. Should the material be inclined to stick in the tube, it can often be rapidly conducted to the bottom by vibrating the tube gently by the cross-wise action of a blunt file or the milled edge of a coin.

The usual apparatus for heating the substance is shown in Fig. 1(B), and consists of a long-necked hard-glass flask **D** to which a thermometer **E** is fitted by means of a cork having a shallow vertical groove **F** cut or filed as shown to allow expansion of the contents of **D**. The best liquid for placing in **D** is medicinal paraffin, which possesses the following very suitable properties: (*a*) it has a low specific heat and therefore the temperature can be easily increased using only a small flame, (*b*) even when hot it

(A)

(B)   (C)

FIG. 1.

is almost non-inflammable, and therefore should the flask break whilst still over the flame, the oil seldom ignites, (c) the oil is non-corrosive, and owing to its low specific heat causes remarkably slight burns even if spilt, while at a high temperature, on the hands. The oil may be safely heated up to about 220°, when it begins to decompose slightly, giving off smoky fumes. For substances melting above this temperature, the flask **D** should contain concentrated sulphuric acid containing a crystal of potassium nitrate to prevent charring and consequent darkening in colour at higher temperatures. Fresh sulphuric acid can be safely heated to about 280°, but its use should generally be avoided in elementary classes. Alternatively, silicone* can be used in place of sulphuric acid for compounds of high melting-point. It is a straw-coloured non-corrosive liquid which can be safely heated to *ca.* 300° without decomposition or ignition.

The capillary tube is then placed as shown against the thermometer **E**, to which it will adhere by the capillary attraction of the oil, the column of powdered material being thus beside the bulb of the thermometer. The oil in **D** is then *slowly* heated, and the temperature, or range of temperature, over which the compound melts carefully noted. It is essential for an accurate determination that the temperature of the oil in **D** should rise *very slowly* as the compound is about to melt. It will therefore frequently save time, particularly if the compound is likely to have a high melting-point, to fill two capillaries with the substance. The temperature of **D** is then raised quickly using one tube, in order to determine the melting-point approximately: the temperature is then allowed to fall about 30°, the second capillary is then substituted for the first, and an accurate determination with the temperature very slowly rising is then made. It is important to note that a second determination is never made by noting the temperature at which the molten material in the capillary solidifies as the oil cools, or by reheating the tube after this solidification has occured. A freshly-filled capillary should always be used for each subsequent determination.

The more accurate apparatus shown in Fig. 1(C) is strongly recommended when laboratory conditions enable students to retain their own apparatus over a complete course of work. A glass tube **T**, bent as shown, is fixed by the rubber-bands **RB** to the thermometer **G**. The glass stirrer **S** is then placed so that the shaft is in the tube **T**, and is connected by a piece of string through the tube as shown, a knot or a

* Marketed as "DC550 Fluid" by Midland Silicones Ltd., Oldbury, Birmingham.

cork preventing the stirrer from falling completely to the bottom of the beaker **H** which contains the oil. The apparatus is kept permanently fixed to a small retort stand, which holds the beaker on a gauze-covered ring **I**, and the thermometer and tube by the clamp **J**. The capillary is then placed as before against the thermometer, and the oil gently heated: meanwhile by means of the string the stirrer is kept steadily in motion and the oil well mixed. The thorough mixing of the oil in this apparatus, and the better control of its temperature, give therefore more accurate results than those obtained with the simple apparatus shown in Fig. 1(B).

In the electrically heated type of melting-point apparatus, the capillary is placed in a fine perpendicular hole in a metal cylinder, and the material in the base of the capillary is viewed with the aid of a lens through a similar fine horizontal hole in the cylinder, the material being illuminated by a small electric bulb placed at the rear end of this hole. The temperature of the cylinder can be increased at various speeds by the use of electric resistances.

Experiment 1. Determination of Melting-points.

The student should determine the melting-point of the following compounds:

A (I). *Pure Compounds.* (*a*) Phenyl Benzoate   M.p.   70°
                 (*b*) Benzoic Acid   121°
                 (*c*) Salicylic Acid   157°
     By working in the above order, time will not be wasted by having to allow the apparatus to cool between consecutive determinations.

B (I). *Impure Substances.* Prepare an intimate mixture of (*b*) with about one-third of its weight of (*c*).

  (II). *Pure Compounds*, decomposing slightly before melting. Lactose. Melts slowly between about 205 and 215°, with preliminary darkening and subsequent decomposition.

NOTE. When it is suspected that an indefinite melting-point is caused by a pure substance undergoing preliminary decomposition, a fairly accurate result may often be obtained by repeating the determination, having first heated the oil to within 5–10° of the melting-point before placing the capillary in position. The compound is thus exposed to the high temperature for such a short time before melting that only slight preliminary decomposition occurs.

Identification by Mixed Melting-points. It will be clear that melting-point determinations afford a ready method of identifying minute quantities of a solid compound, if the *probable* identity of this compound is already suspected. Thus if there is reason to believe that a particular substance is, for example, benzoic acid, a small quantity of the substance is mixed with a known sample of benzoic acid, and the melting-point of the mixture determined. If the mixture has the normal sharp melting-point of benzoic acid, then the unknown substance must be benzoic acid itself: if the mixture has an indefinite melting-point, then the unknown substance is not identical with benzoic acid and by acting as an impurity is causing the indefinite melting-point. Identification by "mixed melting-points" is a valuable and frequently used process in organic research work.

Experiment 2. Identification by Mixed Melting-points.

Students should be provided with known (labelled) samples of one of the following series of compounds, the samples being finely ground so that no obvious difference in crystal form, *etc.*, is apparent. They should determine the melting-point of each compound in order to assure themselves that these melting-points lie too near together to enable any one compound to be identified by a simple melting-point determination. They should then be given an unknown compound **A** (preferably in coarse crystals), told that it is one member of the series, and then identify it by mixed melting-point determinations.

SERIES I		SERIES II	
Acetanilide	M.p. 113°	Benzoic acid	M.p. 121°
Acetyl-*o*-toluidine	112°	Succinic anhydride	120°
Toluene *p*-sulphonyl-*p*-anisidine	114°	Hexacetyl-mannitol*	120°

SERIES III	
Benzamide	M.p. 130°
Phthalic anhydride	130°
β-Pentacetyl-glucose†	130°
Urea	132°

Corrected Melting-points. In all the above determinations of melting-points, the values obtained are described as "uncorrected," since no allowance has been made for the fact that the column of mercury in the thermometer is at a lower temperature than that in the bulb. For most purposes it is sufficient to record this uncorrected value, which is usually only slightly lower than the corrected value.

Criteria of Purity. Liquid Compounds.

A pure liquid (which distils without decomposition) will have similarly a sharp boiling-point which will remain constant until

* Preparation, p. 114.   † Preparation, p. 113.

the whole of the liquid has boiled off, leaving no residue. Unlike the melting-point, however, this boiling-point, whilst remaining sharp, may vary in value over a range of several degrees, owing to fluctuations in the barometric pressure. The boiling-point of an impure liquid will depend largely on the physical nature of the impurities. If all the impurities are non-volatile, the liquid will have a sharp boiling-point, and the solid impurities will remain behind when the liquid has evaporated. If the impurities are themselves volatile, then the boiling-point of the liquid may (a) remain constant (see below), or (b) rise steadily as the liquid boils, or (c) rise in a series of definite steps, according to the nature and quantity of the impurities present.

Although a pure liquid has a sharp boiling-point, the converse is not necessarily true: a sharp boiling-point does not always indicate a pure liquid, but may be caused by a constant-boiling mixture of two or more liquids. Such mixtures are common in both inorganic and organic chemistry: thus a mixture of 20·2% HCl and 79·8% of water boils steadily at 110°/760 mm.; a mixture of 60·5% benzene and 39·5% methyl alcohol has boiling-point 58·3°/760 mm.; a mixture of 14% of ethyl alcohol and 76% ethyl iodide has boiling-point 63·0°/760 mm. The difference between a pure liquid and a constant-boiling mixture can easily be detected by redistilling at a different pressure. A pure liquid under these conditions will change its boiling-point, but the composition of the distillate will necessarily remain unchanged: a constant-boiling mixture will however change both in boiling-point and in the composition of the distillate. This change in composition can then be detected by analysis, density determinations, *etc.*

As a guide to the probable occurrence of a constant-boiling mixture, it should be noted that such mixtures most frequently occur when one of the components contains an hydroxyl ($-$OH) group. Only aqueous and alcoholic mixtures therefore are likely to have a constant boiling-point.

Experimental Determination of Boiling-point. Unless only minute quantities of the liquid are available, the boiling-point is usually determined by simple distillation. For this purpose, the apparatus shown in Fig. 2 is assembled. A distillation flask **A** of suitable size is fitted to a water-condenser **B**, the water supply of which is arranged as shown. An adaptor **C** is sometimes fitted in turn to the condenser, so that the distillate may be collected directly into a suitable flask **D**, but the use of an adaptor in this way is seldom necessary. The liquid is then placed in the flask **A** (which should not be more than three-fifths filled), some small fragments of unglazed porcelain added, the thermometer **E** placed in position, and the flask then heated—either on a water-bath if the liquid has a low boiling-point, or else on a sand-bath, or directly over a wire gauze. The following important points with regard to simple distillation should be noted:—

FIG. 2.

(1) *The fragments of unglazed porcelain should always be added whenever a liquid is boiled*, in order to provide nuclei for the formation of bubbles of the vapour, and thus ensure steady, gentle boiling. If the porcelain is omitted, the liquid may become superheated, and then suddenly boil with great violence. Fires are often caused by students omitting this precaution when distilling inflammable solvents, which then "bump" so violently that the liquid either pushes the thermometer out of position and boils over, or else shatters the distilling-flask. *Throughout this book, therefore, it is assumed that porcelain is added whenever a distillation is described, and the use of porcelain is mentioned only when it is particularly necessary.*

(2) The thermometer should be so arranged that the top of the bulb is just level with the centre of the side-arm of the distilling-flask.

(3) A water-condenser can be used for any liquid the boiling-point of which does not exceed 130°. Above this temperature, an air-condenser (*i.e.*, a straight glass tube having no jacket) should be used. If a water-condenser is used above 130°, there is always a risk of the condenser cracking at the point where the hot vapour first meets the water-cooled portion.

(4) Low-boiling, inflammable liquids are usually distilled from a water-bath for additional safety. Whether a liquid can thus be distilled from a boiling water-bath will depend chiefly on its boiling-point and also on its latent heat, but as a general rule most liquids of boiling-point below 80° may be distilled readily in this way: for liquids of higher boiling-point a sand-bath or direct

heating on a gauze is necessary. Thus alcohol (boiling-point 78°) can be distilled from a water-bath: benzene (boiling-point 81°) will boil gently when heated on a water-bath, but not sufficiently vigorously to distil over at an appreciable rate.

The water-condenser **B** shown in Fig. 2 represents the simplest and cheapest kind, which because of its limited efficiency should be at least 2 feet long. In Fig. 3(A) is shown a bulb condenser, which, although also cheap, is much more efficient. In Fig. 3(B) is shown the usual double-surface condenser, which, although more costly than the two former condensers, is far more efficient, and need be only one-third to one-half as long as the others. It should therefore be available for reasonably careful students.

Modifications of the simple distillation are described on p. 26 under Purification of Liquid Substances.

FIG. 3.

Experiment 3. Determination of Boiling-point.

Most students will be familiar with simple distillation from their practical inorganic chemistry. Other students should determine the boiling-point of acetone (56°), using a water-bath and water-condenser, or of benzene (81°), using a sand-bath and water-condenser, and finally of either aniline (184°) or nitro-benzene (210°), using for both these liquids a sand-bath and air-condenser.

Filtration. Before discussing the practical details of the purification of solid substances by recrystallisation, it is convenient to describe here the general methods of filtration. The two principal occasions in organic chemistry when filtration is necessary are:

(A) A solid substance has crystallised from a solution, and it is necessary to separate the crystals (*i.e.*, the solute) from the cold mother-liquor by filtration.

(B) A hot solution has to be filtered to remove traces of insoluble impurities, and kept hot meanwhile to prevent crystallisation of the main solute, which would otherwise choke up the filter.

(A) **Filtration of crystals from the cold mother-liquor.** This type of filtration is almost invariably performed with the

B*

aid of a Buchner flask and funnel, by means of which a rapid and almost complete separation can be obtained. The Buchner flask **A** (Fig. 4) consists of a simple thick-walled conical flask with a short side-arm for connection to a water-pump. Into the neck of the flask is fitted the Buchner funnel **B** which consists usually of a cylindrical porcelain funnel, the bed of which is pierced by a number of small holes giving direct access through the stem of the funnel to the flask. Before filtration, two* layers of well-fitting filter-paper are placed in the funnel **B**, and moistened with a few drops of the liquid to be filtered, so that when the suction of the pump is applied the filter-papers adhere firmly to the perforated bed of the funnel, and thus subsequently prevent any solid matter from passing round and under the edge of the paper into the flask and so avoiding filtration. The mixture of crystals and solution is then filtered through the funnel under gentle suction of the pump: when all the mother-liquor has been filtered, some is returned to the vessel which originally contained the mixture, and well stirred to remove any crystals adhering to the sides of the vessel. This portion is then again filtered, and the process is repeated until all the solid material has been trans-ferred to the funnel **B**, and the whole of the mother-liquor has collected in the flask **A**. The action of the pump is then con-tinued until the crystals in **B** are thoroughly drained from traces of the mother-liquor. Students should remember that the speed of filtration is not necessarily proportional to the suction force of the pump. A gentle suction will often cause rapid filtration, whereas increased suction may drag the finer particles of the solute into the pores of the filter-paper, and thus cause filtration to become very slow.

Fig. 4.

When only a small quantity of solid material has to be filtered from a liquid, the small conical Buchner funnel **C** is used in order to collect and drain the material on a very small filter-paper (see p. 44).

One disadvantage of porcelain Buchner funnels (particularly when used in large classes) is the difficulty in detecting and removing solid material which, owing to evaporation of the filtrate, may have collected immediately below the perforated

---

* Two layers of filter-paper are desirable for aqueous solutions: for organic solvents, however, one layer is usually sufficient.

plate. This difficulty is removed in the newer types of funnel which are made of glass, and which have either a transparent glass plate perforated by holes or fine slots, or a plate of fine porous sintered glass. Although the glass funnels are more fragile than the porcelain ones, they will undoubtedly replace the porcelain funnels as they become cheaper.

More advanced students, who may frequently have occasion to filter a very *small* quantity of crystals from a correspondingly small volume of solution, are strongly recommended to use the Irvine filter-cylinder (Fig. 5), which is invaluable for the clean, rapid and complete separation of small crops of crystals. It consists of a glass cylinder **A**, having at the base a simple tap **B**, and at the side a two-way tap **C**, by means of which the cylinder can either be connected directly through to the pump, or alternatively connected through the bottom of **C** to the open air, the pump being simultaneously cut off. A series of Buchner funnels, of various sizes and shapes, fit the top of the cylinder as shown. A mixture of crystals and mother-liquor in a beaker can therefore be filtered as usual through the funnel **D** under suction of the pump. Rotation of the tap **C** then cuts off the suction and relieves the partial vacuum within the cylinder. The mother-liquor can then be run through the tap **B** back into the beaker, the tap **B** closed and **C** opened, thus restarting the suction, and the beaker can then be rinsed out with the mother-liquor, which is filtered again into the cylinder. The process is repeated until all crystalline material has been transferred to **D**, where it is gently pressed down with the spatula and thoroughly drained. If necessary, the filtrate can be run out of **A**, and the crystals then washed with some other liquid while still under suction on the filter.

FIG. 5.

(B) **Filtration of hot solutions.** The quickest method of removing traces of insoluble impurities from a hot solution is to filter it in the usual way through a Buchner funnel. The disadvantage of this method is that the heavy porcelain funnel may so chill the solution that crystallisation occurs before filtration is complete and the funnel may become choked with crystals, both above the filter and below in the stem. The disadvantage may be often overcome by boiling a quantity of the pure solvent (particularly if the latter is water) and, immediately before filtration of the solution, placing the filter-papers in the funnel and filtering a moderate quantity of the pure boiling solvent through the funnel into the flask. The solvent is then poured out, and the hot solution at once filtered through the hot apparatus. This pre-heating of both funnel and flask will often enable a hot solution to be filtered and the clear filtrate transferred into a beaker before any separation of solid matter occurs.

A "hot-water funnel" is a slower and less efficient apparatus for filtering hot solutions. It consists (Fig. 6(A)) of a double-walled metal funnel **C** having a small water reservoir **D**, and an

FIG. 6.

outlet **E**. A glass filter funnel of the usual type fits snugly into the hot-water funnel. The water in **D** is then vigorously boiled in order to keep the inner glass funnel (and its contents) hot during filtration. A much more satisfactory form of the apparatus is shown in Fig. 6(B), in which the double-walled funnel is heated by blowing steam through the apparatus as shown. This type has the greater advantage that, during the filtration of a hot inflammable liquid, the steam generator (and therefore the heating apparatus) can be removed to a safe distance. It should be noted that in both forms of apparatus the inner glass funnel used should have a stem so short that it projects only just below the outer metal funnel. If the stem is longer it serves merely to cool the filtered solution, which may then crystallise and completely stop the filtration.

For the filtration of small quantities of dilute solution, it is often possible to dispense with the outer heater, and use the ordinary glass funnel which has been heated above a flame immediately before use.

The filtration of any solution through the ordinary conical funnel may be hastened considerably by the use of a "fluted" filter-paper, instead of one folded into quarters in the usual way. The folding of a fluted paper may be learnt far more readily by a demonstration in the laboratory than by any written description.

The following is one of the simplest ways of fluting a filter-paper. First make four folds in the paper so that the latter is divided into eight equal sectors (Fig. 7(A)), the two halves of the paper on each occasion being folded *forwards*, so that all the folds tend to be concave. Now take each segment in turn (*e.g.*, **aOb**, Fig. 7(B)) and fold the points **a** and **b** *backwards* until they meet, so that a new convex fold **Ox** is made between them: continue in this way making new folds **Oy**, **Oz**, *etc.*, around the paper. When the complete fluted paper (Fig. 7(C)) is placed in the ordinary conical funnel, it will possess a series of regular corrugations, and only the edges of the folds **Oa, Ob, Oc,** *etc.*, will be in contact with the funnel.

(A)   (B)   (C)

FIG. 7.

Purification of Solid Substances.

Recrystallisation. The process of purification by recrystallisation is undoubtedly the most frequent operation in practical organic chemistry, and it is one which, when cleanly and efficiently performed, should give great pleasure to the chemist, particularly if the original crude material is in a very impure and filthy condition. Yet no operation is carried out so badly, wastefully (and thoughtlessly) by students in general, not only by elementary students, but often by research students of several years' experience. The student who intends later to do advanced work must master the process, for unless he can choose a suitable solvent and then successfully recrystallise often minute quantities of material, he will frequently find his work completely arrested.

Students are familiar with the general process of recrystallisation from their more elementary inorganic work. Briefly, it consists in first finding a solvent which will dissolve the crude material readily when hot, but only to a small extent when cold. The crude substance is then dissolved in a minimum of the boiling solvent, the solution filtered if necessary to remove any insoluble impurities, and then cooled, when the solute will crystallise out, leaving the greater part of the impurities in solution. The crop of crystals is then filtered off, and the process repeated until the crystals are pure, and all impurities remain in the mother-liquor.

Students are sometimes puzzled at the extraordinarily general application of the process of recrystallisation, since it may appear to them to depend on the *assumption* that the impurities are more soluble than the main product, and therefore will always eventually be left in the mother-liquor. Consideration will show that this assumption is not necessarily made: the assumption actually made is that the impurities are either more soluble than the main product, or, if less soluble, are present in such small proportion that in spite of the comparative solubilities they will be eliminated by recrystallisation. The two cases may be exemplified thus. Suppose the crude mixture contains 97% of the required compound **A**, and 3% of an impurity **B**. Then if

(1) **A** is less soluble in a given solvent than **B**.

It is clear that repeated recrystallisation will rapidly leave **B** entirely in the mother-liquors, and thus provide a pure sample of **A**.

(2) **A** is more soluble in the solvent than **B**.

Suppose that a given volume of the solvent *when cold* can dissolve 15 gms. of **A** and 5 gms. of **B**. If 100 gms. of the crude product are dissolved in this volume of the hot solvent, and the solution allowed to cool, then (ignoring the small mutual effect on the solubility of each compound caused by the presence of the other) it is clear that 82 gms. of **A** will crystallise, whilst the whole of **B** will remain in solution, since the latter is not saturated with respect to **B**.

The choice of a solvent is of course determined primarily by its suitability for the actual recrystallisation of the given crude product. If two or more solvents appear to be almost equally suitable for the recrystallisation, the final choice should depend on the inflammability (and therefore risk in use) of the solvent, and also on its cost. It is assumed that a solvent which might have any chemical action on the compound has already been debarred. The chief solvents normally available are:

Solvent.	B.P.	Inflammability.	Remarks.
Water (distilled)	100°	Non-inflammable	To be used whenever suitable.
Ether	35°	Inflammable	Avoid when possible (see below).
Acetone	56°	,,	Should preferably be dried before use.
Methylated (or "Industrial") Spirit	77–82°	Inflammable	
Rectified Spirit	78°	,,	
Absolute Alcohol	78°	,,	Hygroscopic.
Benzene	81°	,,	
Petrol	Available in fractions of b.p. 40–60°, 60–80°, 80–100°, 100–120°		Frequently called "light petroleum" or "petrol ether." Unless specially purified, contains sulphur derivatives, *etc.*, as impurities.

Solvent.	B.P.	Inflammability.	Remarks.
Acetic acid (glacial)	118°	Not readily inflammable	Hygroscopic. Hot liquid gives pungent fumes. Frequently used to dissolve strong oxidising agents (p. 204).
Chloroform	61°	Non-inflammable	Liable to contain traces of HCl, due to oxidation or hydrolysis.
Carbon tetrachloride	77°	,,	

Carbon disulphide should never be used if any alternative solvent is available, as it has a dangerously low flash-point, and its vapours form exceedingly explosive mixtures with air. Ether as a solvent for recrystallisation is much safer than carbon disulphide, but again should be avoided whenever possible, partly on account of the danger of fires, and partly because the filtered solution tends to creep up the walls of the containing vessel and there deposit solid matter by complete evaporation instead of preferential crystallisation.

Homologous mono-alkyl ethers of ethylene glycol, such as mono-ethyl glycol, $HOC_2H_4OC_2H_5$, form excellent solvents as they combine to a large extent the solvent properties of alcohols and ethers. Dioxan (or diethylene dioxide) $O{<}^{CH_2CH_2}_{CH_2CH_2}{>}O$, also possesses exceptional solvent properties. Both alkyl-glycols and dioxan should be used with caution, however, as their hot vapours are poisonous.

Experimental Directions for Recrystallisation. The complete process consists of the following stages, each of which is discussed in full:

(1) *Choice of a Solvent.* No theoretical considerations are of any real use for this purpose, except the very rough generalisation that a solvent will dissolve most readily compounds similar in constitution to itself: thus alcohol will usually dissolve other hydroxy compounds, benzene will dissolve hydrocarbons, *etc.*, but there are many exceptions to this rule. Therefore the experimental determination is alone of value.

Place about 0·2 gm. of the crude powdered compound in a clean dry test-tube, and add sufficient of the possible solvent just to cover the compound. If the compound dissolves readily in the cold, the solvent is obviously unsuitable. If it does not dissolve, warm the mixture *gently* over a very small Bunsen flame until the liquid boils: it is advantageous at this stage to hold the forefinger loosely over the mouth of the tube to prevent undue loss of vapour. Continue adding the liquid if necessary until almost all the substance has dissolved. If a large amount of the solvent is required (*e.g.*, one-half to two-thirds of the tube) then the low solubility renders the solvent unsuitable. If an almost clear solution is obtained, cool by immersing the tube preferably in a mixture of ice and water, or alternatively in cold water. (If benzene is the solvent, cold water alone must be used, as benzene will itself crystallise in ice-water.) Shake the mixture gently in the tube. If crystallisation does not rapidly start, the failure may be due to lack of suitable nuclei for crystal-growth. Therefore scratch the tube below the surface of the solution with a glass rod: the fine scratches on the walls form excellent sites for crystal-growth, and crystals often form rapidly after scratching. Repeat this process with various other possible solvents (using a fresh clean tube for each test) until the best solvent has been selected, and then note carefully the approximate proportions of the solute and the solvent for efficient recrystallisation.

Sometimes the crude substance may contain an insoluble impurity, and on cooling the solution it may be difficult to judge how much of the solid matter is merely undissolved impurity and how much is solute which has subsequently crystallised from solution. To avoid this difficulty, the hot solution should be filtered, and should thus always be absolutely clear before cooling is attempted. Therefore filter the hot solution into a clean tube through a *very small* fluted filter-paper contained in a correspondingly small glass funnel, which should have had its stem cut off as those shown in Fig. 6, p. 12 (and for the same reason). Unless the upper part of the filter is cut away to reduce its size to a minimum, a large proportion of the solution will remain held mechanically in the pores of the paper itself and only a few drops of clear filtrate will be obtained.

(2) *Repetition of Recrystallisation on Larger Scale.* Having now determined both the best solvent and also the approximate proportions of solute and solvent for recrystallisation, the main bulk of the crude material may be recrystallised. If the solvent is water, the material is placed in a beaker or (better) in a conical flask, and a volume of water which is judged to be just insufficient for the purpose is then added, and the mixture gently heated (with the usual addition of fragments of unglazed porcelain) to boiling. More water is then cautiously added until either a clear solution is obtained or until the undissolved material is recognised

from the experience gained in (1) as being insoluble impurity. In either case, the boiling solution is then filtered. For this purpose steps must be taken to prevent undue cooling of the solution during filtration, otherwise crystallisation will occur prematurely and choke the filter. This applies more particularly of course if the preliminary test in (1) has shown that crystallisation starts very rapidly on cooling the hot solution. Therefore if a Buchner funnel and flask are used, this apparatus must usually be preheated by the filtration of some pure boiling water, as described on p. 11, or alternatively a heated funnel must be used.

If an organic solvent is used, boiling in an open vessel is obviously not permissible, as the operation would be wasteful in all cases, and dangerous with an inflammable solvent. The crude material is therefore placed either in a round-bottomed bolt-head flask (Fig. 8) or in a conical flask, the solvent added (again in slight deficiency) and a reflux water-condenser fitted to the flask as shown. The mixture is boiled either on a water-bath or over a gauze, and then more solvent added cautiously down the condenser until a clear solution (apart from insoluble impurities) is again obtained. It is then filtered hot as described above.

Water

The hot filtered solution is then without delay poured into a lipped beaker or a conical flask (*not into an evaporating-basin*, since it is crystallisation and not evaporation which is now required), the beaker covered with a watch-glass, and then cooled in ice-water. As cooling proceeds, the solution should be stirred from time to time to facilitate crystallisation, and when crystallisation appears complete, the cooling should be continued for *at least* another 15 minutes.

Fig. 8.

Occasionally the solute may separate (particularly if strong external cooling is rapidly applied) as a metastable oil or syrup, which solidifies on standing although a considerable interval may elapse before crystallisation occurs. This should be avoided, for even if the oil subsequently crystallises well, it will probably occlude a moderate quantity of crude mother-liquor, and its purity will therefore not be high. In such cases it is best to re-heat the mixture until a clear hot solution is obtained, and then allow it to cool spontaneously, stirring and scratching with a glass rod from time to time. It is thus often possible to induce crystallisation to start, and it will then proceed without the production of the less stable oil. During the cooling and scratching, a *minute* quantity of the crude material may occasionally be added to " seed " the solution and thus facilitate initial crystallisation. Formation of an oil or a syrup on attempted recrystallisation is most likely to occur when an entirely new preparation is carried out in the laboratory. When successful recrystallisation is once accomplished, the laboratory becomes " inoculated " with nuclei of the crystals, and subsequent recrystallisation usually proceeds readily. Hence this difficulty is far more likely to occur in a research laboratory than in one in which routine preparations are repeated at regular intervals.

When an organic substance is found to be freely soluble in one solvent and insoluble in another, a mixture of these solvents (if miscible) will often prove excellent for recrystallisation, the best proportion of the two solvents in the mixture being found by small-scale tests. It sometimes happens, however, that the solute (particularly if it possesses a rather low melting-point) separates from such a mixture as a fine emulsion, which solidifies on further cooling. In such cases, a hot concentrated solution of the crude substance should be prepared in the liquid (e.g., alcohol) in which it is freely soluble, and then the other liquid in which it is almost insoluble (e.g., water) should be added drop by drop with stirring until an emulsion or a cloudiness *just* appears. A clear solution is now again obtained either by warming momentarily, or by adding a few drops of the first solvent, and it is then allowed to cool spontaneously: if the cloudiness should reappear, a few more drops of the first solvent are added. A clear solution can thus be maintained until the temperature has fallen so low that crystallisation starts: the solution can then be stirred and cooled without further risk of emulsion-formation. Examples of this process are described for o-nitrophenol (p. 132) and amino-azobenzene (p. 163).

When crystallisation is complete, the mixture of crystals and crude mother-liquor is filtered at the pump, again using a Buchner funnel and flask as described on p. 10, and the crystals remaining in the funnel are then pressed well down with a spatula whilst continual suction of the pump is applied, in order to drain the mother-liquor from the crystals as effectively as possible. If it has been found in the preliminary tests that the crystalline material is almost insoluble in the *cold* solvent, the crystals in the funnel, after a short preliminary draining from the mother-liquor, may be quickly washed on the filter with a small quantity of the pure solvent, and the draining continued without interruption. An efficient removal of traces of the mother-liquor can thus be effected.

(3) *Drying of Recrystallised Material.* It is now required to obtain the recrystallised material in a thoroughly dry condition and this can seldom be achieved solely by draining on the filter. One rapid method of drying the thoroughly drained material is to transfer it with the aid of a spatula on to a pad of several thicknesses of drying paper (*i.e.*, coarse-grained, smooth-surfaced

filter-paper), place a similar pad on top and then press the material strongly, occasionally transferring it to fresh paper as the earlier sheets become too soiled by the mother-liquor absorbed. The final traces of mother-liquor can then be rapidly removed (if the material is physically and chemically stable up to 100°) by drying in a steam or electric oven. The chief disadvantage of this method however is that the recrystallised material is always apt to become contaminated with filter-paper fibre, and moreover a well-crystallised material may be crushed by the pressure to a fine powder. If time permits, therefore, the drained material should always be finally dried in a desiccator. For this purpose the simple and inexpensive atmospheric desiccator (Fig. 9(A)) is frequently used: the drying agent employed is usually calcium chloride, or small uniform fragments of silica gel. The latter are coloured blue with a cobalt salt, and their colour changes to red as the material becomes spent: it can be regenerated by heating. Far more rapid and efficient drying is, however, obtained with a vacuum desiccator of the type shown in Fig. 9(B).

(A)   (B)

FIG. 9.

A very effective "universal" filling for vacuum desiccators is obtained by having concentrated sulphuric acid **C** in the bottom of the desiccator, and "flake" sodium hydroxide* **D** in the inverted glass collar supported on the shoulders of the desiccator, the collar then being covered with wire gauze. Very rapid drying is thereby obtained, and any acid or basic vapours which may be evolved are absorbed, the interior of the desiccator thus remaining clean and odourless. This is of particular advantage when drying a substance, e.g., an amine hydrochloride, which has been recrystallised from concentrated hydrochloric acid, and which would otherwise fill the desiccator with hydrogen chloride as drying proceeded.

If a compound has been recrystallised from petrol, benzene, etc., some freshly cut shavings of clean paraffin wax should be added to the calcium chloride in (A) or to the sodium hydroxide in **D**. The surface of the wax absorbs organic solvent vapours (particularly the hydrocarbons) and the last trace of such solvents is thus readily removed from the recrystallised material.

* Supplied as "flake" or "petal" sodium hydroxide by chemical manufacturers.

When using a desiccator, the recrystallised material in the Buchner funnel should be transferred to a piece of clean glazed paper with the aid of a spatula, and the last traces carefully removed from the sides of the funnel and the damp filter by careful use of the spatula, in such a way that the surface of the filter is not torn or scratched, and that filter-paper fibre does not contaminate the crystals. The latter can then be tipped without loss from the glazed paper on to a watch-glass. If the atmospheric desiccator (A) is used, the open watch-glass should be left in the desiccator to facilitate the evaporation of the solvent. If the vacuum desiccator (B) is used, the watch-glass should always be covered with a second inverted glass, otherwise, unless the air is subsequently admitted very carefully, the sudden draught may sweep the finer crystals off the watch-glass: moreover, the inverted watch-glass will protect the crystals if, during the evacuation of the desiccator, the pump should for any reason cease working and so allow a mixture of air and water to rush back into the desiccator. As a further safeguard, a Buchner flask arranged as a trap (as **K** in Fig. 15, p. 33) should always be fitted between the desiccator and the pump.

(4) *Checking the Purification.* The purity of the dry recrystallised material must now be determined, as it is possible that repeated recrystallisation may be necessary to obtain the pure material. The purity is therefore checked by a melting-point determination, and the recrystallisation must be repeated until a sharp melting-point is obtained. Should the compound have no well-defined melting-point (*e.g.*, the salt of an organic acid or base), it must be analysed for one suitable component element, until its analysis agrees closely with that theoretically required.

Experiment 4. Choice of Solvent and Complete Recrystallisation. Students should be supplied with distilled water, methylated spirit, rectified spirit, acetone and benzene, and also with the compounds mentioned below. Taking each compound in turn they should decide, by the methods described in (1) above, which of these six solvents is the best for recrystallisation. They should then recrystallise about 5 gms. of at least two of the compounds, dry the product, and whenever possible take its melting-point.

Naphthalene, oxalic acid (hydrated), cinnamic acid, acetamide, benzamide, *m*-dinitrobenzene, *p*-nitrophenol, toluene *p*-sulphonamide.

Students should appreciate that this is probably the most important experimental work (for their purpose) described in this book, and it should therefore be performed with great care. Moreover, on subsequent occasions in the laboratory when short periods are available, *e.g.*, during the longer stages of a preparation, they can put this time to valuable use by taking *small* quantities of organic reagents from the side-shelves, and practising for themselves the process of selecting (on a test-tube scale) a suitable solvent for recrystallisation.

Decolorisation by Animal Charcoal. It sometimes happens (particularly with aromatic and heterocyclic compounds) that a crude product may contain a coloured impurity, which on recrystallisation dissolves in the boiling solvent, but is then partly occluded by crystals as they form and grow in the cooling solution. Sometimes a very tenacious occlusion may thus occur, and repeated and very wasteful recrystallisation may be necessary to eliminate the impurity. Moreover, the amount of the impurity present may be so small that the melting-point and analytical values of the compound are not sensibly affected, yet the appearance of the sample is ruined. Such impurities can usually be readily removed by boiling the substance in solution with a small quantity of finely powdered animal charcoal for a short time, and then filtering the solution while hot. The animal charcoal adsorbs the coloured impurity, and the filtrate is usually almost free from extraneous colour and deposits therefore pure crystals. This decolorisation by animal charcoal occurs most readily in aqueous solution, but can be performed in almost any organic solvent. Care should be taken not to use an excessive quantity of charcoal, however, as it tends to adsorb some of the solute as well as the coloured impurity.

Students should distinguish carefully between the animal charcoal used for decolorisation, and the wood charcoal which is used for absorbing easily liquefiable gases, and which is therefore used in gas respirators and also, when chilled in liquid air, for obtaining high vacua.

Animal charcoal can usually be used as described above without any serious risk of impurities originally present in the charcoal itself dissolving in the hot solvent, and then separating again with the recrystallised material. To remove such risk entirely, the animal charcoal can be boiled under reflux with dilute hydrochloric acid (1 : 1 by volume) for 3 hours. The mixture is then diluted with hot distilled water, filtered through a Buchner funnel, and washed *repeatedly* with much boiling distilled water until all trace of acid has been removed. It is then well drained and finally dried by heating gently in an evaporating-basin over a sand-bath until a fine dry powder is obtained.

Experiment 5. Decolorisation of Crude Sulphanilic Acid.

"Technical" sulphanilic acid is usually almost black in colour. Place 6 gms. of the crude powdered acid in each of two conical flasks **A** and **B** (of about 200–250 c.c. capacity), add 100 c.c. of distilled water to each, but add 0·5–1 gm. of animal charcoal to the flask **A** alone. Heat the two flasks side by side, so that the contents boil *gently* for 5–10 minutes and the volume of the solutions is thus only slightly reduced. Now filter each solution rapidly. This can be done in two ways: (*a*) At the pump, using Buchner funnels and flasks which have been preheated by the filtration of boiling distilled water. Pour the filtrates into two beakers and allow to cool spontaneously side by side for comparison. (*b*) Through ordinary conical funnels fitted with fluted filter-papers and preheated by the filtration of boiling distilled water. In this case collect the filtrates directly into two conical flasks. Crystallisation occurs rapidly. When the solutions are cold and crystallisation complete, filter through cold Buchner funnels. Compare carefully the colour of (i) the two hot filtrates before crystallisation starts, (ii) the crystals when filtered and drained. The filtrate and crystals obtained from the flask **A** (using charcoal) should be colourless, whereas those from **B** will both retain a deep brown colour.

A similar experiment can be performed with commercial aniline hydrochloride (or "aniline salt").

Animal charcoal has a further use. Occasionally, when recrystallising a crude product, it is found that the hot solution contains a very fine suspension of an insoluble impurity. This suspension may be so fine that, although apparent to the eye, it passes freely through the usual filter-paper (particularly when a Buchner funnel is used), and thus cannot easily be eliminated. Alternatively the suspension may be easily held back by the filter-paper in the Buchner funnel, but then may rapidly block up the pores of the filter and so arrest filtration almost completely, with the result that crystallisation occurs in the cooling solution while it is still in the Buchner funnel, *i.e.*, before filtration is complete. Both these difficulties can usually be overcome by boiling the solution with a small quantity of animal charcoal. The latter readily adsorbs such fine suspensions, and the hot solution can then be filtered clearly and rapidly through the Buchner funnel.

Sublimation.

This process is occasionally used for the purification of solid organic compounds. Its use is necessarily limited to those compounds which on heating pass readily and directly from the solid to the vapour state, with a subsequent ready reversal of this process when the vapour is cooled. A simple form of apparatus which gives good results is shown in Fig. 10. The dry crude material is placed in a small evaporating-basin **A**, which is placed on a wire gauze. **A** is then covered with a filter-paper **B** which is pierced by a number of small holes (about 2 mm. in diameter), made in an upward direction. A glass funnel **C**, the rim of which is rather smaller than the largest diameter of **A**, is then inverted as shown over the paper **B**. The basin **A** is then *gently* heated by a small Bunsen flame, which should be carefully protected from side draughts by screens, so that the material in **A** receives a steady uniform supply of heat. The material vaporises, and the vapour passes up through the holes into the cold funnel **C**. Here it cools and condenses as fine crystals on the upper surface of the

FIG. 10.

paper **B** and on the walls of **C**. When almost the whole of the material in **A** has vaporised, the heating is stopped and the pure sublimed material collected. In using such an apparatus, it is clearly necessary to adjust the supply of heat so that the crude material in **A** is being steadily vaporised, while the funnel **C** does not become more than luke-warm.

For an example of sublimation, see the preparation of anthraquinone, p. 204: for semi-micro sublimation, see p. 45.

Chromatographic Absorption. A mixture can often be separated into its components by utilising their absorption from solution by a suitable substance, such as active alumina: the separation can be readily followed if the components are coloured. The method is particularly valuable when only a very small quantity of material is available, or when the mixture does not lend itself readily to separation by fractional crystallisation.

The method consists essentially in allowing a solution of the substance in a suitable solvent to pass slowly down a long column containing the absorbent material. The tenacity with which this material absorbs the various components of the mixture may vary considerably, with the result that a sharp separation of the components into coloured zones or bands may result. At this stage, the passage of the solvent may be stopped and the individual zones removed either by careful extrusion of the absorbent material or by cutting the tube in sections corresponding with the zones. It is usually more convenient to "elute" the components, *i.e.*, by the further passage of the pure solvent (or of a mixture of solvents) to cause each zone to pass down the tube and ultimately to emerge as a solution of the pure component.

If the components are colourless, their separation can often be followed by working in a quartz (or special glass) tube which is placed in the light of a mercury lamp. The separate zones are then often revealed by their fluorescence.

The process of chromatographic separation is illustrated in the following experiment, in which a wider tube than usual is employed to give a reasonably rapid separation within the time normally available to students. The alumina employed is the usual active alumina as supplied by dealers.

Experiment 6. Chromatographic Separation of a Mixture of o- and p-Nitro-aniline.

FIG. 11.

Prepare a glass tube **A** (Fig. 11) in which the wider portion has a diameter of 3 cm. and a length of *ca*. 30 cm.: the narrow portion at the base has a diameter of 5–7 mm. Wash the tube thoroughly (if necessary, with chromic acid, followed by distilled water and alcohol) and then dry. Insert a *small* plug of cotton-wool **P** as shown just within the narrow neck of the tube: it is essential that this plug does not project into the wider portion of the tube. Clamp the tube in a *vertical* position.

Mix 100 gms. of active alumina with dry benzene until a suspension or slurry of suitable consistency is obtained, and pour this carefully into the tube. Clamp a dropping-funnel just above the top of the tube and allow benzene to run slowly down as the alumina column settles in the tube: the benzene emerging from the bottom of the tube is collected in a conical flask. It is essential that the top of the column should be kept immersed in the solvent, and that the latter passes uniformly down the column without "channelling": a disc of filter-paper can, if desired, be fitted over the top of the column to prevent disturbance of the surface.

Meanwhile dissolve not more than 0·5 gm. of a mixture of crude o- and p-nitro-aniline in 30 c.c. of dry benzene and then allow this solution to enter the tube slowly through the dropping-funnel. Immediately this solution has all entered the tube, continue running in the pure solvent, and develop the chromatogram by collecting the benzene from the bottom of the tube and running it again through the top of the tube. Continue in this way until the two yellow bands have become distinct and separate during their passage to the lower portion of the column. Then continue the washing with fresh benzene until each band has been separately eluted in about 150 c.c. of benzene, that of the o-nitro-aniline emerging first from the tube.*

Carefully evaporate each of the two solutions or eluates. Wash the residue from first eluate with petrol and dry: pure o-nitro-aniline, m.p. 72°, is obtained. Wash the second residue with a small quantity of benzene and dry: pure p-nitro-aniline m.p. 148°, is obtained. Record the yield and m.p. of each component.

NOTE. For more delicate work, highly purified solvents are necessary, but for the above experiment dry technical benzene is suitable.

Purification of Liquid Substances.

The purification of liquids is almost invariably performed by distillation, and the type of distillation employed will depend largely on the nature of the impurities and in particular whether they are volatile or non-volatile. The commonest impurity in liquid compounds, namely water, should however be removed before distillation whenever conveniently possible.

Drying of Liquid Compounds.

Liquids are almost invariably dried by being kept in contact with a suitable powdered solid dehydrating agent, the dehydration being occasionally facilitated by boiling the liquid gently under reflux. When dehydration is complete, the liquid is either decanted or (better) filtered from the dehydrating agent, and can then at once be further purified by distillation. The commonest dehydrating agents, with their practical limitations, are:

Calcium chloride (granular).	Cannot be used for alcohols, phenols or amines, with all of which it combines. Not advisable for acidic liquids, as ordinary calcium chloride always contains some calcium hydroxide owing to partial hydrolysis during preparation.

---

* The chromatographic separation should whenever possible be completed in one operation. If, however, shortage of time necessitates an interruption, this can most conveniently be made immediately after the first band has been completely eluted, whereupon the lower end of the tube is closed by a short piece of rubber tubing carrying a screw-clip. Great care should be taken however not to allow even the top of the column to run dry.

Calcium oxide (quicklime).	Usually used for alcohols (see p. 62). Cannot be used for acidic compounds, nor for esters, which it would hydrolyse.
Potassium hydroxide.	Particularly suitable for amines. Obviously cannot be used for any liquids affected by alkalis, *e.g.*, acids, phenols, esters.
Potassium carbonate.	Sometimes used in place of potassium hydroxide for amines, *etc.*, when a strongly alkaline drying agent is to be avoided.
Sodium sulphate (powdered anhydrous).	Can be used on almost all occasions, but its dehydrating action is rather slow.
Magnesium sulphate (powdered anhydrous).	A neutral drying agent, which, like sodium sulphate, can be used on most occasions. Its drying action is more rapid than that of sodium sulphate.
Calcium sulphate ("Drierite").	Applicable to all liquids.
Metallic sodium (preferably as wire).	Used particularly for ethers. Cannot be used for any compound affected by alkalis, or easily subject to reduction (owing to the hydrogen evolved during dehydration).

Liquids are occasionally purified by removing impurities as constant-boiling mixtures, or by shaking with concentrated sulphuric acid and subsequently separating the dried liquid from the acid: the second method is therefore limited to liquids which are insoluble in, and chemically unaffected by, the strong acid (*e.g.*, anhydrous chloral).

Distillation. If the impurities in a liquid are non-volatile, the liquid may be purified by direct distillation, the impurities remaining in the distilling-flask. This process is therefore essentially the same as a simple distillation for boiling-point determination, and has been already described on pp. 7-9.

If, however, the impurities are themselves volatile liquids, then the separation of these impurities from the main bulk of the required substance is achieved by fractional distillation. If an ordinary distilling-flask, such as that shown in Fig. 2, p. 8, is used for this purpose, however, only a very partial separation of the liquid components of the crude mixture is usually obtained, unless there is a considerable difference in boiling-point between the impurities and the main component. To obtain a much sharper and more complete separation, a fractionating column is employed.

Fractional Distillation. For this type of distillation, the fractionating column is inserted vertically between the flask containing the boiling liquid and the condenser. The principle of a fractionating column is that, as the vapours ascend the column from the boiling mixture below, the higher-boiling components are condensed and returned to the flask, the ascending column of vapour being thus steadily "scrubbed" by the descending column of liquid condensate. The ascending column of vapour becomes therefore steadily richer in the lowest-boiling component, and the descending column of condensate steadily richer in the highest-boiling component. It follows that the prime factor which determines the efficiency of a column is the extent to which the vapour is "scrubbed" by the condensate, and columns are therefore designed to make this "scrubbing" as intimate as possible. Text-books of theoretical organic chemistry frequently illustrate remarkable and weird types of fractionating column which the practical chemist never encounters. For actual use in the laboratory two types of column are recommended. (A) For quick rough separations, or (more particularly) for the separation of two components having a considerable difference in boiling-point, the pear column (Fig. 12(A)) is useful. The increase in cooling surface produced by pear-shaped bulbs causes considerable condensation, and the condensate, steadily dripping down from the lower shoulder of each bulb, comes in moderate contact with the ascending vapour. The efficiency of a column can, of course, be increased by increasing the number of bulbs in the column. (B) For accurate work, the column shown in Fig. 12(B) is probably the most efficient and generally useful type available in most laboratories. It consists of a simple glass column, packed with very short sections of glass tubing, the bore of these sections preferably decreasing steadily up the column. For general purposes, the column itself should be about 11–12 mm. internal diameter, and the glass sections* towards the bottom of the column should be about 5 mm. long and 6 mm. external diameter, and towards the top about 3 mm. long and 5 mm. diameter: the length of the column *actually packed* with the tubes should be about 20 cm., but for low-boiling mixtures this length of the column may be considerably increased, and for high-boiling mixtures correspondingly decreased. To retain the glass tubes in position, it is inadvisable to constrict the column immediately below the tube, as this readily causes "choking" of the column when in use. It is better either to seal across the inside

* These glass sections for fractionating columns may be purchased from Messrs. Townson and Mercer, Ltd., 34 Camomile Street, London, E.C.3, and from Messrs. Quickfit & Quartz, Ltd., Quickfit Works, Stone, Staffs.

of the column a very fine glass rod, on which the tubes may rest, or (more easily) to have one section of glass tubing rather larger than the rest at the bottom of the column and to fix this per-manently in place by fusing it carefully to the wall of the column.

The sections *must* be arranged as irregularly as pos-sible in the column: if they tend to arrange themselves regularly they should be well shaken up, otherwise "chan-nelling" of the condensed liquid will occur and the effici-ency of the column will be de-creased. These sections of glass tubing are preferable to similar sections of metal for two reasons, (*a*) the metal sec-tions, because of their low specific heat, do not condense sufficient of the ascending vapour, and the efficiency of the column falls considerably in consequence; (*b*) if the tube becomes fouled in use, parti-cularly by traces of tarry pro-ducts, it can always be cleaned by pouring acids, dichromate mixture, *etc.*, down the column, or even by being allowed to stand overnight immersed in such cleaning agents. For the fractionation of high-boiling liquids it is advisable to have a lagging of cotton-wool **D** around the column as shown.

FIG. 12.

To use such a column, the crude liquid is placed in a round-bottomed flask **C** having a short wide neck, the usual fragments of unglazed porcelain are added, and the column then fixed in position, great care being taken to ensure that it is mounted absolutely vertically, again in order to avoid channelling. A water-condenser is then fitted in turn to the side-arm of the column, particularly when the components of the mixture have low boiling-points. The mixture is then heated with a *very small* flame, carefully protected from draughts to ensure a uniform supply of heat. It is essential that the initial heating of the liquid in **C** (while it is still mounting the cold column) should not be hurried, as considerable extra condensation occurs while the column is warming up, and the latter may easily choke: when once distillation has started, and a thermal equilibrium has been established between the column and its surroundings, the tendency to choke should disappear. The heating is then adjusted until the distillate is issuing from the side-arm of the column not faster than about 1 *drop every* 4–5 *seconds.* In these circumstances, so efficient a fractionation should be obtained that, when the lowest-boiling fraction has distilled over, distillation completely ceases, as the next lower fraction is refluxing definitely below the side-arm of the column. The heating is then *cautiously* increased, and a sharp rise in boiling-point (and therefore a sharp fractionation) should occur as the second fraction starts to distil. Although in Fig. 12(B) a condenser is shown fitted to the side-arm of the column, this is required only for low-boiling components: for most mixtures, however, the above rate of distillation, necessary for efficient fractionation, will be accompanied by complete condensation in the side-arm of the column, from which the successive fractions may be collected directly.

In using a column of this type, it is essential that the distillation be not hurried. Although the complete fractionation may therefore take a moderate time, yet the fractionation is so efficient that the over-all time for the complete process is very much less than when more rapid columns are used, for in the latter case the fractionation usually has to be repeated several times in order to obtain as complete a result.

Experiment 7. Fractional Distillation of a Mixture of Benzene and Toluene. Fractionally distil about 40 c.c. of a mixture of equal volumes of benzene and toluene, using the type of fractionating column shown in Fig. 12(B), in which about 18–20 cm. of the column are actually filled with glass sections, but in which the cotton-wool lagging is not used. Distil *very slowly*, so that the total distillation occupies about $1\frac{1}{2}$ hours. Shield the apparatus very carefully from draughts. Collect the fractions having the b.p.s (a) 80–90°, (b) 90–107°, (c) 107–111°. A sharp separation should be obtained, e.g., these fractions should have volumes of about 19, 2, and 17 c.c. respectively.

It will be found that the first few drops of the lowest fraction are always cloudy, owing to the fine film of water adsorbed on the glass surfaces within the column: this cloudiness is of course increased if the column is fitted to the flask by a cork instead of a rubber stopper.

Distillation under Reduced Pressure. Occasionally a

liquid, when distillation is attempted under atmospheric pressure, will undergo partial or complete decomposition before its boiling-point is reached. To overcome this difficulty, the liquid is distilled under reduced pressure, so that its boiling-point shall be definitely below its thermal decomposition point.

It has already been pointed out that a liquid even when subjected to simple atmospheric distillation may become superheated and then "bump" violently in consequence: this danger is greatly increased during distillation under reduced pressure and therefore a specially designed flask, known as a Claisen flask, is used to decrease the risk of superheating. In Fig. 13(A) a Claisen flask **D** is shown, fitted up as part of one of the simplest types of vacuum-distillation apparatus.

FIG. 13.

The flask has two necks, the right-hand one carrying a thermometer in the usual way, while the left-hand one carries a stout capillary tube **E**, which is closed at the top by a short piece of pressure tubing and a screw-clip, by which the amount of air passing through the capillary can be regulated. The capillary tube **E** should always be prepared by drawing out a piece of thick-walled capillary tube of about 4–5 mm. external bore, and then adjusting the length of the fine capillary tube below so that it reaches to within 1–2 mm. of the bottom of the flask: it should never be prepared by drawing out an ordinary glass "quill" tube, otherwise the fine capillary so obtained will be too fragile, and will probably snap during the course of the distillation. The side-arm is then fitted to an ordinary distillation-flask **F**, which serves as a receiver for the distillate. Well-bored rubber stoppers should be used throughout the apparatus, and immediately before being inserted in position should be lightly smeared with a solution of good-quality rubber in benzene to ensure an air-tight fit.

When performing a distillation, the flask **D** is filled not more than half-full with the liquid, *some fragments of porcelain added*, and the capillary, thermometer and receiver then placed in position, the side-arm of the receiver **F** being connected through a manometer to an efficient water-pump. As the pressure falls to a steady value, the screw-clip above the capillary **E** is adjusted until a steady stream of fine bubbles is emerging through the lower end of **E**. If it is anticipated that the liquid will boil below about 100°, the whole of the bulb of the receiver **F** is cooled with a stream of water as shown, the waste being collected by a funnel below and run off to the sink. In most cases, however, it is sufficient to have the bulb of **F** dipping into a basin of ice-water. A water-condenser is not necessary with this apparatus if the distillation is carried out slowly. The liquid in **D** is then heated steadily, preferably in an oil-bath, and in these circumstances steady ebullition should occur: the temperature of the vapour and the pressure in the apparatus, indicated by the thermometer and the manometer respectively, should then be read.

Examples of the use of this apparatus (or that shown in Fig. 15, p. 33) will be found in the preparation of phenylhydrazine (p. 156), ethyl acetoacetate (p. 208) and ethyl malonate (p. 215).

The simplest form of manometer for this purpose is an ordinary barometer tube, as shown in Fig. 13(B): this form has the disadvantages, however, that the surface of the mercury in the tube is easily fouled and then difficult to read, and that in any case an accurate measurement of the long column of mercury is not simple. A neater and more accurate type of manometer is shown in Fig. 13(C). The mercury is contained in a fine glass U-tube **G** fused to a horizontal cross-piece, which is sealed on one side, and on the other leads through the tap **I** to a thick-walled U-tube **H**, which contains granular calcium chloride in the left-hand arm, and soda-lime in the right-hand arm, the reagents being kept in position by the three plugs of glass wool **P**. To prevent fouling of the mercury surface, the manometer should be placed not directly in line between the distillation apparatus and the pump as in (B), but as a "side-arm" between these two. With this precaution, and with the additional protection by the reagents in **H**, the mercury surface should with care remain clean for years.

When constructing a manometer of the type shown in Fig. 13(C), it is important to apply a very high vacuum (*e.g.*, with a Hy-Vac pump) to the manometer while the mercury in the left-hand (sealed) limb is heated until it boils: unless this is done, traces of air will remain in this limb and cause inaccurate readings. During a distillation, the tap **I** should be kept closed except when a pressure reading is being taken: if it is left open indefinitely, a sudden default by the distillation apparatus or by the pump may cause the mercury in the sealed limb of **G** to fly back and fracture the top of the limb.

Other similar types of manometer, usually reading over a range of about 10–60 mm., are available in many laboratories.

Fractional Distillation under Reduced Pressure. One great disadvantage of the simple vacuum-distillation apparatus shown in Fig. 13(A) is that, if more than one fraction distils, the whole process has to be stopped after collecting each consecutive fraction, in order to change the receiver **F**. This may be overcome by replacing the simple receiving flask **F** by a "pig" (Fig. 14) which collects consecutive

FIG. 14.

fractions without interruption of the distillation. The "pig" consists of a stout glass receiver **A**, which fits either over the side-arm of the Claisen flask or, in the case of low-boiling liquids, over the end of the condenser which is fitted to this side-arm. It has at the top an outlet tube **B** for connection to the manometer and pump, and at the lower end usually three outlet tubes to which are fitted consecutive receivers **C, D, E**.

When distillation starts, the "pig" is so placed that the first fraction collects in **C**. When the second fraction starts to distil, **A** is rotated slightly to bring the outlet tube leading to **D** in the lowest position, so that the second fraction collects in **D**: further rotation then causes the third fraction to collect in **E**. The apparatus however often gives unsatisfactory results, particularly in the hands of students, who frequently find that if a good vacuum is obtained in the apparatus, the "pig" sticks firmly around the cork **F** and refuses to rotate: conversely, easy rotation around this cork usually means a leaky joint at this point, and an unsatisfactory and varying pressure is recorded by the manometer.

For general work, a very satisfactory apparatus for collecting fractions under reduced pressure is the Perkin triangle **C**,* which is

* G. A. R. Kon (*Jour. Chem. Soc.*, 1930, 182) described a modification of the Perkin triangle having only two taps instead of the three described above. It may be purchased from Quickfit & Quartz, Ltd., Quickfit Works, Stone, Staffs., or from Messrs. Howard Rawson & Co., Devon Works, Farm Lane, London, S.W.6.

shown in Fig. 15, together with the requisite fittings for the complete distillation. **A** is a Claisen flask, fitted up as already described, and heated in a beaker of transparent medicinal paraffin, the temperature of which is carefully controlled throughout the distillation.

The Claisen flask is then fitted to a water-condenser **B**, which leads directly into the main receiver **C** of the triangle. This triangle is connected through the upper tap **D** to the manometer and pump, and by the lower tap **E** to a supplementary (bottle) receiver **F**. The tube leading from **E** to the receiver **F** is double-walled: the inner tube

FIG. 15.

gives direct access from **C** through the tap **E** to the receiver **F**, while the outer (annular) tube provides access from **F** through the small holes **H** to the side-arm **JJ**′ carrying the three-way tap **G**. **G** is made to give *either* direct access through the tube **JJ**′, *or* access from the outside through **J** downwards to **F**, *or* from the outside through **J**′ to the manometer and pump. The triangle is then connected to the manometer (fitted in a "side-chain" as before) and through the trap **K** (a Buchner flask) to the pump. The function of **K** is to "smooth out" slight changes in the pressure, within the apparatus, and also, should the pump default, to prevent water from rushing back into the apparatus.

When distillation starts, the taps **D** and **E** are open, and **G** is turned so as to give direct access from **J** to **J**′. The first fraction therefore runs from **C** through **E**, and collects in **F**. Directly the second fraction starts to distil, **E** is closed, so that this fraction collects in **C**. Meanwhile **G** is turned to allow air to enter through **J** to **F**, which can then be detached and a new receiver **F**′ added. If a pump of good capacity is being used, it is sufficient now to turn **G** so as to give direct access again between **J** and **J**′, thus evacuating the new receiver **F**′, which is then ready to receive the second fraction which has been accumulating in **C**. If a rather weak pump is in use, however, this sudden admission of the air from the new receiver **F**′ into the rest of the apparatus may

C

cause a moderate rise in the pressure, and a temporary cessation in the distillation, and in these circumstances "bumping" frequently starts (and persists) when distillation recommences. To avoid this, the tap **G**, before being turned, should be connected to a supplementary pump, which will evacuate the new receiver **F′**: rotation of **G** as before now serves to cut off the supplementary pump and simultaneously reconnect the two parts of the apparatus through **JJ′**.

When a more delicate fractional vacuum-distillation is required, the flask and column shown in Fig. 12(B), p. 28, may be used, the side-arm of the column being fitted directly into receiver **C** (Fig. 15). A rubber stopper must then be used to fit the flask on to the fractionating column, and it should also carry a capillary tube leading to the bottom of the flask, to provide the usual fine stream of bubbles to prevent bumping.

Steam-distillation. Many water-insoluble compounds, both solid and liquid, may be readily purified by distillation in a current of steam, provided that the compound is volatile, and the impurities non-volatile, under these conditions.

(A)   (B)

FIG. 16.

The apparatus consists of a round-bottomed flask **C** (Fig. 16 (A)), having a glass inlet tube which reaches almost to the bottom of the flask and which is connected to a steam generator **D**: the flask **C** has also a glass outlet tube, connected in turn to the water-condenser **E**. The flask is clamped at an angle as shown to prevent the solution in **C** from being splashed into the entrance of the outlet tube and thus being blown over mechanically into the condenser: this purpose is achieved more completely if in addition a still-head (shown on a larger scale in Fig. 16(B)) is used in place of the outlet tube, since spray will be trapped in the still-head, and returned as a steady stream of liquid to the flask **C**.

The material to be steam-distilled (mixed with some water if a solid compound, but not otherwise) is placed in **C**, and a vigorous current of steam blown in from **D**. The mixture in **C** is thus rapidly heated, and the vapour of the organic compound mixed with steam passes over and is condensed in **E**. For distillations on a small scale it is not necessary to heat **C**: if, however, the flask **C** contains a large volume of material or material which requires prolonged distillation, it should be heated by a Bunsen burner, otherwise the steady condensation of steam in **C** will produce too great a volume of liquid.

If the organic compound which is being steam-distilled is freely soluble in water, an aqueous solution will ultimately collect in the receiver **F**, and the compound must then be isolated by ether extraction, *etc*. Alternatively, a water-insoluble compound, if liquid, will form a separate layer in **F**, or if solid, will probably crystallise in the aqueous distillate. When steam-distilling a solid product, it is sometimes found that the distilled material crystallises in **E**, and may tend to choke up the condenser: in such cases, the water should be run out of the condenser for a few minutes until the solid material has melted and been carried by the steam down into the receiver.

Experiment 8. Steam-distillation.

Students should carry out the purification by steam distillation of (*a*) crude nitrobenzene or chlorobenzene, (*b*) crude naphthalene or *o*-nitrophenol (p. 131) as examples of solid compounds which may also be purified in this way.* When the distillation is complete, disconnect the tubing (Fig. 16) between **C** and **D** *before* removing the flame from under **D**, otherwise the contents of **C** will be sucked back into **D** as the latter cools.

Ether Extraction.
In the course of organic preparations, it frequently happens that an organic compound is obtained either in aqueous solution or (less often) in aqueous suspension; if the organic compound is volatile in steam, or if it is chemically affected by prolonged exposure to hot water, it clearly cannot be isolated by evaporation of the water. If, however, the compound is soluble in an organic solvent which is itself almost completely insoluble in water, then repeated extraction of the aqueous solution with the solvent will eventually transfer the compound

---

* As a further example of a solid compound which can be purified by steam-distillation, see *p*-tolunitrile (p. 152).

almost entirely into the organic solvent. Any water-insoluble solvent may be used for this purpose, but ether is usually the most suitable because (*a*) it is chemically inert and is unlikely to react with the compound, (*b*) owing to its great volatility, it can subsequently be readily removed by distillation without serious risk of simultaneously volatilising the compound.

To extract the substance, the aqueous solution or suspension is placed in a separating-funnel, which may be either cylindrical, Fig. 17(A), or (better) pear-shaped, Fig. 17(B). Ether is then

(A)   (B)

Fig. 17.

added and the mixture *thoroughly* shaken, the stopper at the top of the cylinder being occasionally opened to relieve any pressure of ether vapour caused by the heat of the hands. The mixture is allowed to settle until two well-defined layers have formed, and the lower aqueous layer is then run off and separated as completely as possible. The remaining ethereal layer is run off, preferably by pouring it through the upper neck of the funnel, to avoid contamination with any drops of aqueous solution still remaining in the stem of the funnel below the tap. The aqueous solution is then returned to the funnel, and the extraction repeated, using fresh ether on each occasion, until it is judged that very little of the compound remains in the aqueous layer. It should be borne in mind, however, that if a given volume of ether is to be used for the complete extraction, a far more efficient result will be obtained by a number of consecutive extractions using only a small volume of ether for each extraction, than by one or two extractions using a correspondingly greater volume of ether each time.

The ethereal extracts are then united, dried with a suitable drying agent and filtered. The filtrate is then cautiously distilled, the ether being first distilled and finally the organic compound if volatile: if the compound is solid, the crude residue is purified by recrystallisation. *Very great care must be taken on all occasions when ether is distilled, because of the risk of fire or of an explosion:* full experimental details for this operation are given, both on p. 54 (Preparation of Ether) and on p. 123 (Preparation of Aniline).

Soxhlet Extraction. Occasionally a crude product (often of natural occurrence) is obtained, from which a particular component may be isolated by repeated extraction with a hot solvent. For this purpose, Soxhlet's Extraction Apparatus (Fig. 18) is usually employed.

The extractor consists of a glass cylinder **A**, terminating at the base in the open tube **B**. Fused within the top of **A** as shown is another tube **C**, having a small hole **D** blown in the side: a fine glass tube leads from the base of **C**, rises about two-thirds of the height of the cylinder to **E**, and then returns past **F** into the open tube **B**.

The crude organic material is placed in a porous thimble **G** (made of tough filter-paper), and the latter placed as shown within the inner tube **C**. The apparatus is then fitted below to a bolt-head flask **H** containing the requisite solvent, and above to a reflux water-condenser **J**.

The solvent in **H** is then gently boiled. The vapour passes up **B**, through the annular space between the tubes **C** and **A**, and so through the orifice **D** into the reflux condenser above. The condensed solvent falls down into the thimble **G**, and slowly fills the body of **C**, being meanwhile heated by the ascending mantle of hot vapour in the annular space outside. When this condensed liquid reaches the top **E** of the fine glass tube, it syphons down into the flask **H**, taking down that portion of the organic compound which it has extracted in **G**. The process then repeats itself indefinitely, more of the organic material being extracted from **G** and transferred to the solvent in **H** on each occasion. Eventually complete extraction of the crude product in **G** is effected, and the extracted compound can then be isolated from the solution in **H** by any of the usual methods.

FIG. 18.

NOTE. In the older types of Soxhlet extractor, an external tube ran from **B** up to the top of **C** for conveying the ascending column of hot vapour. This type had the disadvantage not only of being more easily broken, but also that the condensed liquid in **C** received very little heat, and therefore the extraction, being carried out by the lukewarm solvent, was usually very slow.

Stirring. In the course of many organic preparations, a solution or suspension has to be kept continuously agitated either during the addition of a reagent or throughout the main stage of the preparation. For other than small-scale preparations, mechanical stirring is most conveniently employed. For this purpose, a stirrer **S** (Fig. 19) is made of stout glass rod, with the lower end bent at right angles if it is intended to sweep over the flat base of a beaker, or curved (as shown in Fig. 19) if it is to be used inside a round-bottomed flask. Other types can be designed for special purposes, or to allow insertion within a narrow-necked flask. The stirrer may be connected to an electric motor by a pulley **P**, which is particularly useful if a number of stirrers are run off one revolving shaft. It is usually more convenient, however, to secure the stirrer **S** directly to the axis of a small motor, which is therefore clamped perpendicularly above.

FIG. 19.

It is frequently necessary, however, to stir a solution which is boiling under reflux, and the stirrer must therefore be fitted with a seal to prevent the escape of vapour. This can often be done very simply by means of a short glass tube **T** (Fig. 19) which passes through the cork of the flask, and which serves as a collar within which the stirrer **A** fits quite closely. To prevent the escape of vapour, a short length of rubber tubing **R** (about $1\frac{1}{2}$ inches long) is fitted over the top of the tube **T**: the upper portion of this tube is then turned back over the stirrer as shown in order to grip the stirrer securely. A few drops of glycerol or mineral oil placed between the upper portion of this tubing and the stirrer allow the latter to rotate freely with very little friction.

Alternatively a mercury-sealed stirrer may be employed. Here again a short glass tube **C** is inserted through the cork of the flask to act as a collar for the stirrer. The tube **C** carries a short wide tube **B** which is either fused at its lower end to **C**, or is fixed to it by means of a cork as shown. The stirrer **D** carries a precisely similar tube **E**, the top of which however is now fixed to **D**: the bore of the tube **E** allows it to fit easily within the annular space between the collar **C** and the tube **B**. Mercury is then placed in this annular space to act as a seal whilst the stirrer is in operation.

Assembling Apparatus. The following points should be noted.

(1) *Drying Apparatus.* Simple pieces of apparatus such as flasks are best dried by heating in the large luminous flame of a blowpipe, air from the blowpipe bellows being blown through the flask meanwhile to remove the water vapour, which would otherwise merely recondense as the flask cooled. Apparatus such as condensers, *etc.*, which cannot be so treated, should first be rinsed out with methylated spirit, and then with ether (preferably dried beforehand over calcium chloride and filtered): a brisk current of air is then blown through the apparatus from the blow-pipe bellows until the ether has completely evaporated.

(2) *Corks.* Before using an ordinary bark cork, examine it carefully for flaws: many corks have such deep holes that they are useless. Before boring, always roll the cork thoroughly (under the foot, if a cork-roller is not available) in order to soften it. Never bore a cork right through from one end to another, as the cork-borer on emerging will almost invariably tear the surface of the cork. Therefore bore halfway through from one end, and then start again from the opposite end, rotating the cork steadily each time to ensure that the borer goes symmetrically along the long axis of the cork. With care the two borings should meet exactly.

Never use unprotected bark corks for an apparatus in which a carefully dried liquid is to be distilled, *etc.*, as these corks always contain appreciable quantities of water, which is exuded when the cork comes into contact with a hot liquid. Rubber stoppers should therefore be used in these circumstances.

When boring rubber stoppers, lubricate the borer well, either with aqueous glycerine or with vaseline. Then clean well and dry before using.

All-glass Apparatus. In modern research laboratories apparatus containing ground-in joints in place of corks is frequently used. Much time is thus saved in assembling apparatus, and the extraction of impurities from corks and rubber stoppers is avoided. Nevertheless it is essential to the training of a chemist that he should acquire skill in assembling apparatus without complete recourse to all-glass apparatus.

Storage of Specimens. Solid compounds after purification should be stored in bottles or in corked specimen tubes, according to the amount of the compound available. The bottle or tube should at once be labelled, so that the identity of the compound, its melting-point, and any particular details concerning the method of purification employed, are clearly recorded. The label should also record the "tare" (*i.e.*, the weight) of the *empty* bottle or tube, including that of the stopper or cork, so that the total weight of material available can subsequently be determined without removing the substance from the bottle. Stable liquids of high boiling-point can be similarly stored in stoppered bottles or in corked specimen tubes: in the latter case, however, unless the liquid is required again shortly, it is advisable to wax the cork in order to hold it firmly in position and also to prevent the liquid from slowly seeping through the cork itself. For this purpose, the cork should be placed firmly in position, and the inverted tube dipped into some clean paraffin wax which has been heated

FIG. 20.

in an evaporating-basin to about 180°, *i.e.*, until it has become a mobile liquid. After the cork and the extreme end of the tube have been immersed in the wax, the tube is removed and, while still inverted, gently rotated so that the wax solidifies as a layer of uniform thickness.

The only satisfactory method for storing liquids of low boiling-point (*e.g.*, ethyl bromide) or liquids which are affected by the air (*e.g.*, acetic anhydride, benzoyl chloride, benzaldehyde) is to seal them in special glass bottles **A** (Fig. 20) or tubes **B** according to the amount available. The bottles, of various sizes, can be purchased: the tubes should be prepared in the laboratory from moderately thick-walled glass tubing. The bottle or tube should first be cleaned and dried: then, by carefully rotating the neck in a suitable small blowpipe flame, a constriction *a* (Fig. 20) of about 15–20 mm. length should be made so that the wall of the tubing remains uniformly thick at this point. A test-tube is then drawn out at the centre so that the upper part can be broken off and used as the funnel **F**; the liquid can now be easily poured into **A** or **B**. If the liquid is readily volatile, the bottle or tube must now be placed in ice-water or in ice-salt for several minutes. It is then removed, the lower portion wrapped in a duster to protect the liquid from the heat of the hand, and the neck quickly sealed off at *a*. For liquids of high boiling-point, these precautions are not necessary, although in all cases the constriction *a* facilitates the sealing of the neck.

Students frequently attempt to seal liquids in test-tubes: the latter are, however, usually too fragile for this purpose.

Methods and Manipulation on a Semi-micro Scale.

When only very small quantities of organic materials are available their manipulation must necessarily be carried out on a correspondingly small scale. This occurs frequently in research problems, but small-scale preparative work is often of value to the student because considerable economy of materials and of time can be achieved. It is emphasised, however, that the proper training for the organic chemist must rest upon the correct understanding and thorough practice of the manipulations on the macro-scale already described, and that he should consider small-scale work as a sequel to and not as a replacement of the above standard techniques.

Preparative work is sometimes divided into three categories. This division is entirely arbitrary and the categories overlap, but they may conveniently be classified thus:

	Scale	Remarks
(a)	*Macro.*	Usually 0·5 gm. to 200 gms. for solids and 5 gms. to 200 gms. for liquids.
(b)	*Semi-micro.*	50 mgm. to 500 mgm. for solids and 1 gm. to 5 gms. for liquids.
(c)	*Micro.*	Below the above limits.

The difficulties of working with small quantities of liquids are much greater than with small quantities of solids. For example a competent worker can, and does in fact, often work with 100 mgms. of solid without any special apparatus. With liquids this is often not practicable because of the much greater losses entailed, particularly when it is realised that one ordinary-sized drop weighs about 50–100 mgms. The account which follows gives details of modifications of standard apparatus suitable for the semi-micro scale defined above.

General Considerations. With liquids and solutions the most serious losses are due to (a) transference from spherical flasks and difficulties of drainage, (b) retention by filter-papers, (c) absorption by large corks. As containers for small quantities of liquids it is therefore often convenient to use pear-shaped flasks **A** and

FIG. 21.

C*

conical test-tubes or centrifuge-tubes **B** (Fig. 21). (In this and subsequent figures, approximate dimensions are given to indicate a convenient size.)

FIG. 22.   FIG. 23.

The transference of a liquid from one vessel to another is best carried out by means of a dropping pipette **A** (Fig. 22). For measuring out a definite volume of liquid it is obviously an advantage to have a calibrated pipette **B** (Fig. 22) of 2 or 5 ml. total capacity. Alternatively, semi-micro burettes reading to 0·02 ml. are particularly convenient for class work.

For the separation of immiscible liquids a small separating funnel of the conventional type should be used whenever practicable, a pear-shaped funnel (Fig. 17, p. 36) of 5–10 ml. capacity being particularly convenient. For separations on a smaller scale a dropping-pipette should be used: for the removal of an upper layer, the bent pipette (Fig. 23) is recommended.

An ordinary hand centrifuge may be employed to promote a clean line of demarcation between two immiscible liquids which show a tendency to emulsify.

In order to minimise the absorption of liquids by corks, single pieces of apparatus are used wherever possible.

A skilled worker can use a micro-Bunsen burner for most types of heating. Nevertheless, as there is a tendency for a liquid to shoot out of a small test-tube when heated, it is preferable to place the tube in a hot water-bath or in a metal heating block. A small glycerol bath is suitable for distillations and heating under reflux, the glycerol being subsequently easily removed from flasks, *etc.*, by washing with water.

Determination of Boiling-points. The following alternative methods are recommended. (*a*) Draw one drop of the liquid into a capillary tube so that the drop is about 1 cm. from one end. Hold the tube horizontally and quickly seal this end in a micro-burner. Attach the tube (with the open end upwards) to a thermometer in the melting-point apparatus (Fig. 1(C), p. 3) so that the trapped bubble of air in the capillary tube is below the surface of the bath-liquid. Now heat the bath, and take as the b.p. of the liquid that temperature at which the bubble reaches the level of the surface of the bath liquid. (*b*) Prepare a fairly wide capillary tube **A** (*ca.* 4 mm. × 8 cm.) (Fig. 24). Using a very fine pipette insert about 1 cm. of the liquid into the bottom of the tube. Now place in the tube **A** a fine inverted melting-point tube **B** of about 1 mm. diameter, sealed at the upper end. Fasten the capillary tube to the thermometer by means of a rubber band and place in a melting-point apparatus. Heat slowly until a stream of bubbles rises from the liquid, then remove the source of heat and, as the bath cools, take as the b.p. that temperature at which the liquid recedes into the inverted tube **B**.

FIG. 24.

Heating under Reflux. For this purpose, a glass water-condenser of length *ca.* 25 cm. can be used. When refluxing very small volumes of liquid, the "cold finger" **A** is of great value (Fig. 25: for a modified design, see Fig. 28). If provided with a shoulder, it can rest on the rim of a test-tube or flask, or it may be inserted through a cork having the usual groove cut in the side to allow escape of gas.

Distillation. This process is carried out in the apparatus shown in Figs. 26 and 27. The vertical condenser **A** (Fig. 26) provides a considerable degree of fractionation and is fused on to the side-arm condenser **B**. The flask **C** is attached by a cork. Such a distillation-unit can be used for refluxing followed by fractional distillation. The distillation apparatus (Fig. 27) is of general application and is made in one piece.

FIG. 25.

FIG. 26.

FIG. 27.

Distillations on the semi-micro scale can also be carried out in the simple pear-shaped distilling flask **A** (Fig. 28). The distillate is collected in the centrifuge-tube **B** placed in the bottom of the vessel **C**, which is simply a boiling-tube with a side-arm at 45°. This arm is connected to that of the flask by a cork. A "cold finger" **D** serves to condense the vapour issuing from the side-arm of the flask. Distillation in this apparatus must be performed *slowly* to ensure efficient condensation and collection of the distillate in **B**. All thermometers for semi-micro preparatiins must have very small bulbs. They may often be inserted into flasks through a short "collar" of rubber tubing in place of the customary corks.

Steam Distillation. A compact and efficient apparatus is shown in Fig. 29. The liquid to be steam-distilled is placed in the tube **A** and water is placed in the outer flask **B**. On heating **B**, steam passes into the inner tube **A** through the inlet tube

FIG. 28.

C, and steam-volatile compounds are rapidly distilled and collected in the receiver placed at the end of the condenser **D**.

For small quantities of compounds which are readily volatile in steam, it will often suffice to add water to the crude material in the reaction flask (e.g. Fig. 27) and to heat directly with a small flame.

FIG. 29.

FIG. 30.

Crystallisation and Filtration. Crystallisation is carried out in apparatus of conventional type but reduced in size. Glass rods should be about 10 cm. long and 2 mm. in diameter. It is advisable to use solvents in which the solute is sparingly soluble, so that larger volumes of liquid can be employed. Light petroleum and *cyclo*hexane are often satisfactory for this purpose.

The filtration of crystals is carried out using a small conical Buchner funnel (Fig. 4(C), p. 10) or a funnel of similar design but having a sintered filtration plate. Alternatively an ordinary conical funnel in which is placed a circular perforated plate can be used.

The complete filtration apparatus is shown in Fig. 5, p. 11. A simpler and cheaper apparatus is shown in Fig. 30. This consists of a boiling-tube **A** having a side-arm for connection to the pump: the tube **A** is conveniently held in a wooden or cork block **B** or in a clamp. The funnel **F** may be fitted into **A** through a pliable rubber disc **D**: the latter is more useful than a cork since it covers tubes of various diameters. The filtrate is collected in the centrifuge-tube **T**.

For the filtration of very small quantities of crystals, the simple apparatus shown in Fig. 31 is often used. It consists of a fine glass rod (sometimes termed a "filtration nail") which is flattened at one end, the flattened surface being preferably roughened. It fits as shown into a small funnel. A circular piece of filter-paper is cut (*e.g.*, with a *clean* sharp cork-borer) so as to fit completely and snugly over the flat end. After draining, the "nail" is raised and the filter-paper and crystals are removed with forceps and dried.

FIG. 31.

The filtration of hot or boiling liquids requires care, as rapid evaporation is likely to occur. Evaporation is minimised by the use of a cylindrical tube **T** (Fig. 32) furnished with a filter-plate or sinter. The tube **T** can be fitted into an adaptor **B** (Fig. 32), or it may be inserted directly through the disc **D** (Fig. 30) so that the filtrate collects in a suitable tube placed in the receiver **A** (Fig. 30). Adaptors such as **B** (Fig. 32) are of considerable use in many kinds of micro-chemical work.

Sublimation. This is a most useful process for small-scale work as the losses are comparatively small. This can be performed: (*a*) In a long narrow tube sealed at one end. The material is shaken to the closed end of the tube, which is then inserted horizontally in a metal-heating block (Fig. 33); (*b*) In the "cold-finger" device (Fig. 25).

FIG. 32.   FIG. 33.   FIG. 34.

Identification of Gases. The apparatus (Fig. 34) consists of a glass bulb **B** with drawn-out open ends, and fitting snugly on to the rim of a test-tube. Before testing for a gas, a drop of the reagent is drawn into the lower end of the bulb, which is then placed on the tube in which the gas is being evolved. On removing the bulb and examining the reagent against a suitable background, significant colour changes or the formation of a precipitate in the reagent can be detected.

Vapours which can be readily condensed (*e.g.*, aniline, nitrobenzene, *etc.*) are readily detected by the device shown in Fig. 35. It is essentially a "cold finger" with a deep indentation or well at the lower end. In this way two or three drops of liquid can easily be collected and removed by a capillary tube for qualitative tests.

Preparations. The more experienced student should carry out some of the preparations given in Part II, but on a reduced scale, and employing modifications recommended above whenever these seem suitable. The following are suggested: nitrobenzene (p. 118, $\frac{1}{10}$ scale), *m*-dinitrobenzene (p. 121, $\frac{1}{10}$ scale), FIG. 35. *m*-nitro-aniline (p. 128, $\frac{1}{8}$ scale), aniline (p. 125, $\frac{1}{10}$ scale), acetanilide (p. 80, $\frac{1}{20}$ scale), benzanilide (p. 191, $\frac{1}{10}$ scale), phenyl toluene-*p*-sulphonate (p. 195, $\frac{1}{10}$ scale), diphenylnitrosamine (p. 158, $\frac{1}{10}$ scale), chlorobenzene (p. 147 $\frac{1}{10}$ scale), benzene-azo-β-naphthol (p. 165, $\frac{1}{20}$ scale), triphenyl carbinol (p. 222, $\frac{1}{10}$ scale).

The preparations of all the derivatives, and all the hydrolyses of esters, anilides, *etc.*, described in Part III provide excellent practice of semi-micro manipulations.

Ordinary analytical balances are adequate for this work, and small nickel spatulas and forceps of suitable design are now commercially available.

PART II

PREPARATIONS

The Oxidation of Ethyl Alcohol.

Ethyl alcohol, being a typical primary alcohol containing the $-CH_2OH$ group, gives on oxidation first acetaldehyde and then acetic acid. This process, when carried out by an aqueous oxidising agent, probably consists in the direct

$$CH_3CH_2OH \xrightarrow{\text{O}} CH_3CH(OH)_2 \xrightarrow{-2H} CH_3COOH$$

Ethyl Alcohol. $\downarrow -H_2O$ Acetic Acid.

$$CH_3CHO$$

Acetaldehyde.

addition of oxygen to the alcohol to give the dihydroxy-derivative, $CH_3CH(OH)_2$: the latter is unstable and readily loses water, e.g., on warming, to give acetaldehyde, while in the presence of an excess of the oxidising agent it loses two atoms of hydrogen to give acetic acid. It is probable that acetaldehyde, when dissolved in water, reforms the dihydroxy-compound, a process which occurs very readily with chloral or trichloro-acetaldehyde, CCl_3CHO, which forms a stable "hydrate," $CCl_3CH(OH)_2$.

The oxidising agent used for the preparation of both acetaldehyde and acetic acid is a mixture of sodium dichromate and sulphuric acid, but the conditions of the experiment are changed according to the product required. For the preparation of acetaldehyde, a mixture of aqueous sodium dichromate and alcohol is added gradually to hot dilute sulphuric acid: just sufficient of the dichromate-sulphuric acid mixture is thus produced to oxidise the added alcohol to acetaldehyde, which is rapidly distilled off from the reaction mixture. Acetaldehyde is thus produced in moderate yield, although in spite of the above precautions part of the aldehyde undergoes further oxidation to acetic acid. A further loss is occasioned by the condensation of some of the aldehyde with the unchanged alcohol under the influence of the sulphuric acid to give acetal: this loss is small,

$$CH_3CH\underline{O + 2H}OC_2H_5 \rightleftharpoons CH_3CH(OC_2H_5)_2 + H_2O$$

however, as the reaction reaches an equilibrium and much of the regenerated aldehyde escapes by volatilisation.

Pure acetaldehyde is extremely volatile, having b.p. $21°$, and its isolation is therefore difficult: hence only the preparation of an aqueous solution is described below.

To prepare acetic acid, aqueous alcohol is added gradually to a hot mixture of aqueous sodium dichromate and sulphuric acid. The oxidising mixture is now always in excess, and therefore the oxidation proceeds as far as possible; moreover, the reaction is carried out under reflux, so that any acetaldehyde which volatilises is returned to the oxidising mixture. Hence the final product contains only a small amount of acetaldehyde.

47

To prepare pure acetic acid (glacial acetic acid), the crude aqueous product is converted into the sodium salt, the latter dehydrated by fusion and then heated with concentrated sulphuric acid: anhydrous acetic acid, b.p. 118°, distils over. Only the preparation of aqueous acetic acid and of crystalline copper acetate is described below.

Technically, acetaldehyde is prepared (a) from acetylene and dilute sulphuric acid, mercuric sulphate being added as catalyst; (b) by the catalytic dehydrogenation of alcohol. Acetic acid is obtained by the catalytic oxidation of the aldehyde so formed.

Acetaldehyde, CH_3CHO, in Aqueous Solution.

Required: Ethyl alcohol, 40 c.c.; sodium dichromate, 50 gms.; sulphuric acid, 17 c.c.

Fit a 500 c.c. bolt-head flask **F** with a well-fitting cork which is free from flaws, and which carries a dropping-funnel **D** and a delivery tube (or "knee-tube") **T**, the latter being connected to a water-condenser **C** (Fig. 36). Attach an adaptor **A** to the lower end of the condenser.

FIG. 36.

Place 50 c.c. of water in the flask **F**, and then add slowly with shaking 17 c.c. (31·5 gms.) of concentrated sulphuric acid: finally add some fragments of unglazed porcelain, and replace the flask. Dissolve 50 gms. of coarsely crushed sodium dichromate* in 50 c.c. water contained in a small beaker, add 40 c.c. (32·5 gms.) of alcohol, and then place the well-stirred mixture in the dropping-

* Sodium dichromate is used instead of the potassium salt because it is far more soluble in water, and is not precipitated from its aqueous solution by addition of the alcohol. It is also cheaper than the potassium salt, but has the disadvantage of being deliquescent.

funnel. Ensure that a rapid stream of cold water is passing through the condenser and that the adaptor **A** dips into a 75 c.c. conical flask which is surrounded with ice-water. Now heat the dilute acid in the flask until it starts to boil gently, and then remove the flame and run the dichromate solution very slowly into the flask. Directly the alcoholic dichromate solution enters the hot acid, a vigorous reaction occurs, and a mixture of acetaldehyde and water, containing a little acetic acid, begins to distil over: meanwhile the reaction mixture becomes green owing to reduction of the dichromate. The addition of the dichromate solution should take about 20 minutes: towards the end of this time it will be necessary to replace the flame under the flask to maintain *gentle* boiling. When the addition of the dichromate solution is complete, a moderately strong aqueous solution of acetaldehyde will have collected in the conical receiver.

Note cautiously the characteristic odour of acetaldehyde which this solution possesses. Then with the solution carry out the following general tests for aldehydes described on p. 257: Test No. 2 (Schiff's reagent), No. 4 (Action of sodium hydroxide), No. 5 (Reduction of ammoniacal silver nitrate). Finally perform the two special tests for acetaldehyde given on p. 258 (Nitroprusside test and the Iodoform reaction).

Pure acetaldehyde is a colourless volatile liquid, of b.p. 21°: freely soluble in water, alcohol and ether.

It should be emphasised that the above experiment serves solely to illustrate the oxidation of alcohol to acetaldehyde: the yield is never high, although it may be increased by blowing carbon dioxide through the solution during the oxidation in order to remove the acetaldehyde as fast as it is formed. For an efficient production of acetaldehyde from ethyl alcohol the latter is catalytically dehydrogenated by passing it over copper at 250–300° in an apparatus designed so that unchanged alcohol is separated from the aldehyde and circulated again over the catalyst.

Acetic Acid, CH_3COOH, in Aqueous Solution, and crystalline Cupric Acetate, $(CH_3COO)_2Cu,H_2O$.

Required: Sulphuric acid, 33 c.c.; sodium dichromate, 35 gms.; alcohol, 15 c.c.; copper carbonate, 15 gms.

Fit a 500 c.c. bolt-head flask **F** (Fig. 37) with a reflux water-condenser **C**, to the top of which a dropping-funnel **D** is fixed by means of a cork having a vertical V-shaped groove **G** cut or filed in the side to allow subsequent escape of air. Place 50 c.c. of water in the flask and then add 33 c.c. (61 gms.) of concentrated sulphuric acid slowly with shaking: finally add 35 gms. of coarsely crushed sodium dichromate and some fragments of unglazed porcelain. The dichromate rapidly dissolves in the acid, which has become hot during the preliminary dilution. Place in the dropping-funnel a mixture of 15 c.c. (12 gms.) of alcohol and 60 c.c. of water, and allow it to fall slowly drop by drop down the condenser into the oxidation mixture. A vigorous reaction occurs and the mixture becomes green owing to the formation of chromic sulphate, $Cr_2(SO_4)_3$. At *frequent* intervals* during the addition of the alcohol, mix the contents of the flask by vigorous shaking. When the addition is complete and the reaction has subsided, heat the flask on a boiling water-bath for 15 minutes. Then detach and reverse the condenser, and reconnect it to the flask through a knee-tube for direct distillation, as shown in Fig. 43, p. 72. Distil the mixture, by direct heating over a gauze, until about 80 c.c. of distillate have been collected. Acetic acid is volatile in steam and an aqueous solution of the acid, containing, however, some acetaldehyde, is thus obtained. With a small portion of this solution, perform the tests for acetic acid given on p. 262.

Place all but 3 c.c. of the remainder of the distillate in a moderately large evaporating-basin, add about 20 c.c. of water (to keep the copper acetate subsequently in solution) and then heat gently on a sand-bath until the solution *just* begins to boil: then without delay add 15 gms. of powdered copper carbonate cautiously, in small quantities at a time, to the well-stirred hot solution until no further evolution of carbon dioxide occurs. Filter the mixture at the pump, using a Buchner

Fig. 37.

funnel and flask which have been preheated by the filtration of some boiling distilled water: finally wash the residue of excess carbonate on the filter with a few c.c. of hot water, allowing the wash-water to join the clear blue filtrate. Transfer the latter to an evaporating-basin, and add the 3 c.c. of original distillate which have been kept in reserve: this prevents the subsequent formation of basic copper acetate. Now evaporate

* If the contents of the flask are not *thoroughly* mixed at this stage, an explosion may occur during the subsequent distillation.

the solution on a water-bath* until crystals begin to appear on the surface. If the solution is now chilled in ice-water, a crop of small crystals of copper acetate is rapidly obtained: if, however, the solution is allowed to cool slowly (and preferably allowed to stand overnight), a crop of large, well-formed and very beautiful crystals results. In either case, filter off the crystals at the pump, wash rapidly with a *small* quantity of distilled water, drain thoroughly, and dry in an atmospheric calcium chloride desiccator to avoid dehydration of the crystals. By further evaporation of the filtrate, a second but less pure crop of crystals may be obtained.

For reactions of acetic acid and acetates, see p. 262.

The Interaction of Ethyl Alcohol and Sulphuric Acid.

Three compounds may be formed by the interaction of ethyl alcohol and sulphuric acid, according to the experimental conditions:

(1) When concentrated sulphuric acid is added to ethyl alcohol, the mixture becomes hot owing to the formation of ethyl hydrogen sulphate, the yield of which is increased if the mixture is then gently boiled under reflux:

$$C_2H_5|OH + H|HSO_4 = C_2H_5HSO_4 + H_2O$$

(2) If the mixture contains an excess of ethyl alcohol, and is heated to 140°, the ethyl hydrogen sulphate reacts with the ethyl alcohol, giving diethyl ether and regenerating the sulphuric acid:

$$C_2H_5|HSO_4 + H|OC_2H_5 = C_2H_5OC_2H_5 + H_2SO_4$$

(3) If the mixture contains a considerable excess of sulphuric acid and is heated to 160–170°, the ethyl hydrogen sulphate breaks down, giving ethylene and again regenerating the sulphuric acid.

$$C_2H_5HSO_4 = C_2H_4 + H_2SO_4$$

The preparation of each of these three compounds will be considered in turn.

Potassium Ethyl Sulphate. $KC_2H_5SO_4$.

Pure ethyl hydrogen sulphate is difficult to prepare, as it is an oily liquid, very soluble in water, and easily hydrolysed. It is therefore usually isolated as the potassium salt, since potassium ethyl sulphate crystallises well from water, and is not readily hydrolysed in neutral or weakly alkaline solution.

To prepare the potassium salt, the mixture of alcohol and sulphuric acid is boiled under reflux, cooled, and treated with an excess of calcium carbonate.

$$2C_2H_5HSO_4 + CaCO_3 = Ca(C_2H_5SO_4)_2 + CO_2 + H_2O$$

The ethyl hydrogen sulphate is thus converted into the soluble calcium ethyl sulphate, whilst the excess of sulphuric acid is removed as insoluble calcium

* The solution must not be concentrated by direct boiling, since copper acetate in these circumstances undergoes hydrolysis and gives a precipitate of cupric oxide.

sulphate. The aqueous filtrate is then mixed with just sufficient potassium carbonate to give potassium ethyl sulphate, the insoluble calcium carbonate being now filtered off.

$$Ca(C_2H_5SO_4)_2 + K_2CO_3 = 2KC_2H_5SO_4 + CaCO_3.$$

The solution of potassium ethyl sulphate can be concentrated on the water-bath without appreciable hydrolysis, and the sulphate finally crystallised out.

Required: Rectified spirit, 40 c.c.; sulphuric acid, 16 c.c.; calcium carbonate, 23 gms.

Place 40 c.c. (32 gms.) of rectified spirit in a 200 c.c. round-bottomed flask, and slowly add* 16 c.c. (30 gms.) of concentrated sulphuric acid, keeping the liquid in the flask well shaken throughout the addition to ensure thorough mixing. Fit a reflux water-condenser to the flask, and heat the latter on a gauze so that the mixture boils gently for 45 minutes. Then cool the product and pour it into 200 c.c. of cold water contained in a large (8-inch) evaporating-basin or in a shallow earthenware dish. Now add 23 gms. of finely powdered calcium carbonate with stirring to the acid solution. *It is essential to add the calcium carbonate as a fine stream of powder, and to stir the latter immediately into the bulk of the solution:* for this purpose, it is best to sift the carbonate through a fine sieve directly into the liquid, or alternatively to add it from a spatula, tapping the latter gently over the liquid to ensure steady addition of the finely powdered chalk. If the carbonate is added carelessly several grams at a time, it becomes rapidly covered with insoluble calcium sulphate, which protects it from further reaction: in these circumstances, at least 10 times the theoretical quantity of the carbonate may be required and the evolution of carbon dioxide may continue for several hours.

The addition of the calcium carbonate should take about 30 minutes, and the well-stirred mixture should finally be neutral to litmus-paper. Now heat the mixture on a water-bath, using a thermometer as a stirrer, until the temperature reaches 60°, and then filter at the pump through a wide Buchner funnel: at this temperature, filtration should be rapid. Finally wash the residue of calcium sulphate on the filter with a small quantity of hot water, adding the wash-water to the main filtrate. In order to convert the calcium ethyl sulphate to potassium ethyl sulphate, add a concentrated aqueous solution of potassium carbonate

---

* The mixture of alcohol and concentrated sulphuric acid required in this and several subsequent preparations should always be prepared by adding the heavy acid to the alcohol. If the alcohol is added to the acid, it will tend to float on the surface of the acid, and the heat generated at the interface may blow the upper liquid out of the flask.

cautiously *drop by drop* to the well-stirred filtrate until a drop of the latter withdrawn on a glass rod is *just* sufficiently alkaline to turn red litmus-paper blue. Then filter the solution at the pump, and wash the residual calcium carbonate again with a small quantity of water. Evaporate the filtrate on a water-bath until a drop withdrawn on a rod crystallises on cooling: then allow the solution to stand until almost cold, and finally chill it thoroughly in ice-water. (If the ice-water cooling is omitted, large well-developed colourless crystals of potassium ethyl sulphate will finally separate.) Filter off the crystals at the pump, drain, and dry over calcium chloride in a desiccator.

Yield, about 12 gms. To obtain a second (but necessarily less pure) crop of the sulphate, evaporate the filtrate further on the water-bath, and cool as before.

Hydrolysis of Potassium Ethyl Sulphate. Dissolve about 1 gm. of the crystals in about 4 c.c. of cold distilled water, and divide the solution into two portions. (*a*) To one portion, add barium chloride solution. If *pure* potassium ethyl sulphate were used, no precipitate should now form, as barium ethyl sulphate is soluble in water. Actually however, almost all samples of potassium ethyl sulphate contain traces of potassium hydrogen sulphate formed by slight hydrolysis of the ethyl compound during the evaporation of its solution, and barium chloride almost invariably gives a faint precipitate of barium sulphate. (*b*) To the second portion, add 2–3 drops of concentrated hydrochloric acid, and boil the mixture *gently* for about one minute. Cool, add distilled water if necessary until the solution has its former volume, and then add barium chloride as before. A markedly heavier precipitate of barium sulphate separates. The hydrolysis of the potassium ethyl sulphate is hastened considerably by the presence of the free acid: caustic alkalis have a similar, but not quite so rapid an effect.

Diethyl Ether.* $(C_2H_5)_2O$.

Required: Rectified spirit, 95 c.c.; sulphuric acid, 40 c.c.

Assemble the apparatus shown in Fig. 38. Into the neck of the distilling- flask **A** (of about 450 c.c. capacity) are fitted a thistle-funnel **F** and a thermometer **T**, both reaching down to the bottom of **A**. The dropping-funnel **D** is then securely fitted by a cork into the mouth of the thistle-funnel as shown, so that the alcohol subsequently dropping from **D** can be clearly seen. To the flask

---

* The preparation of ether is described here because this is chemically its logical position. It is advisable, however, for students to defer its preparation until they have had some experience in the manipulation, and particularly the distillation, of ether, such as its use for the extraction of aniline (p. 123), where full details and precautions are given.

A is fitted a *double-surface* condenser **C**, and to the latter in turn a Buchner flask **B** to act as receiver. To the side-arm of **B** is fitted a length of rubber tubing leading well below the level of the bench, so that any ether vapour escaping condensation cannot return to the neighbourhood of **A**.

Rubber tubing extends
well below bench

FIG. 38.

First place about 5 gms. of clean *dry* sand in **A**, and then 45 c.c. (36 gms.) of rectified spirit: cool the flask in ice-water and *cautiously* add 40 c.c. (74 gms.) of concentrated sulphuric acid, shaking the mixture thoroughly during the addition to ensure a homogeneous product. Then reassemble the apparatus, taking care that the lower end of the thistle-funnel **F** now reaches down to the bottom of the liquid in the flask and that the bulb of the thermometer is completely immersed. Place 50 c.c. (40 gms.) of rectified spirit in the funnel **D**, and cool the receiver **B** in a pan of ice-water. Heat the flask **A** over a gauze by means of a *small* Bunsen flame until the temperature of the liquid reaches 140–145°: owing to the presence of the sand steady boiling now occurs, and ether begins to distil over. Now allow the alcohol in **D** to fall drop by drop into the thistle-funnel **F** at approximately the same speed as that at which the crude ether distils over: in this way the total addition of the alcohol from **D** should take about

1 hour. Then continue heating **A** (still maintaining the temperature at 140–145°) until no more ether distils over, *i.e.*, for about a further 15 minutes. Turn out the gas, and then pour the distillate into a separating-funnel and shake it with about 25 c.c. of 10% aqueous sodium hydroxide solution: this removes both sulphur dioxide and some of the unchanged alcohol from the ether. Run off and reject the lower aqueous layer, and then repeat the extraction with a fresh quantity of sodium hydroxide solution. Again run off the alkaline layer, transfer the ether to a small conical flask and dry it with an ample quantity of granular calcium chloride for at least 30 minutes. (The calcium chloride removes both water and any residual alcohol.)

Now filter the ether through a fluted filter-paper directly into a 100 c.c. distilling-flask, and then equip the latter with a 100° thermometer and a double-surface condenser: to the end of the latter attach a receiver with a rubber delivery-tube *precisely as before*. Place the flask cautiously in a water-bath, the contents of which have previously been heated to about 60° at some distance from the apparatus: arrange the depth of the flask in the water-bath so that the ether distils slowly over. Collect the fraction boiling between 34–39°. Yield, 25 gms. (35 c.c.). Not more than a very small residue of alcohol should remain in the flask.

Diethyl ether is a mobile, colourless liquid having b.p. 35° and *d*, 0·720. It has a characteristic odour, and a burning taste. It is used chiefly as a solvent, and also as an anaesthetic: owing to its chemical non-reactivity, it is very seldom used actually as a reagent, except in the preparation of Grignard reagents (p. 218) where probably its chemical properties reinforce its solvent action.

Very great care should always be taken when manipulating ether, particularly when it is being distilled. The liquid itself is very readily inflammable, and in addition the vapour forms with air a heavy and highly explosive mixture, which may roll along the laboratory bench for surprising distances, and still be capable of exploding when it comes in contact with a flame, the explosion at once travelling back towards the origin of the vapour.

For Williamson's Method for the preparation of ethers, see p. 172.

Pure Ether. Pure ether (entirely free in particular from water) is frequently required in the laboratory, and especially for the preparation and use of Grignard reagents. It is best prepared in quantity for classes by adding an ample quantity of granular calcium chloride to a "Winchester" bottle of technical ether, and allowing the mixture to stand for at least 24 hours, preferably with occasional shaking. The

greater part of the water and alcohol present in the ether is thus removed. The ether should now be filtered through a large fluted filter-paper into another clean dry Winchester bottle. About 25 gms. of sodium are now pressed as fine wire directly into the ether. For this purpose, a sodium press is used (Fig. 39). This consists essentially of a heavy iron stand **S** carrying a plunger **P**, which can be screwed down so that its end fits snugly into an iron cup **C**, which has a small hole at its base.

FIG. 39.

(A number of cups, having holes of different diameters, is usually available for alternative use.) The cup **C** is nearly filled with lumps of sodium, and the plunger is then screwed steadily down, while (in this case) the Winchester bottle of ether is held immediately below **C**: the sodium is thus forced as fine wire directly into the ether, and exposure to the air reduced to a minimum.

The Winchester bottle should then be closed by a rubber stopper carrying a calcium chloride tube (to allow escape of hydrogen) and the ether allowed to stand for a further 24 hours. It should then be decanted into a large distilling-flask, a few small pieces of freshly cut sodium preferably added, and the flask connected with a double-surface water-condenser having a receiver cooled in ice-water. Ether in these quantities should always be distilled in a fume-cupboard having an efficient draught, so that there is no possibility of any uncondensed vapour escaping into the laboratory. The flask itself should be heated by steam. If steam is not laid on in the fume-cupboard, it should be generated *outside* the cupboard in the usual steam-can (Fig. 16, p. 34) and then led into the cupboard through a length of soft metal "compo" tubing. The flask is supported on the usual concentric metal rings over an empty water-bath: a hole is punched in one of the outer rings, and then the compo tubing is led down throught this hole into the bath, and the extreme end of the tubing turned up so that the jet of steam strikes directly upwards on to the base of the flask. If the fume-cupboard has a vigorous draught induced by an electric motor, large quantities of the ether can thus be safely distilled, and an ordinary bottle can be used as a receiver, the end of the condenser being fitted into the neck of the bottle and held firmly in position by a plug of cotton-wool. If a large Buchner flask is used as a receiver, the rubber delivery tube (as shown in Fig. 38, p. 54) is of course not required.

In very hot weather, the condenser water should first be chilled by passing it through a tall spiral of soft metal "compo" tubing immersed in a bucket of ice-water.

Ether so obtained is anhydrous, and almost entirely free from other impurities. On standing, however, it undergoes slight atmospheric oxidation, with the formation of traces of diethyl peroxide, $(C_2H_5)_2O_2$.* The formation of this peroxide can be largely checked, however, by storing the distilled ether over fresh sodium wire, preferably in the dark.

Ethylene. C_2H_4.

Required : Rectified spirit, 20 c.c.; sulphuric acid, 40 c.c.

Assemble the apparatus shown in Fig. 40. **F** is a 200 c.c. flat-bottomed flask supported on a sand-bath and connected by a glass delivery-tube to the wash-bottle **B**, which is about two-thirds full of 10 % aqueous sodium hydroxide solution. A second

FIG. 40.

delivery-tube leads from **B** into a beehive stand (or between two earthenware tiles placed side by side) in a pneumatic trough **T** containing water.

Place 20 c.c. (16 gms.) of rectified spirit in **F**, and add slowly, with cooling and shaking, 40 c.c. (74 gms.) of concentrated sulphuric acid. Then add about 2–3 gms. of clean dry sand, to ensure a steady evolution of ethylene subsequently. Connect

* Consequently traces of these unstable peroxides are present in samples of all the lower aliphatic ethers unless the samples have been freshly distilled. If these ethers when being distilled are heated on, for example, an electric heater, the final residue of peroxide may become sufficiently hot to explode violently. The use of a water-bath for heating, as described above, decreases considerably both the risk of the ether catching fire and of the peroxide exploding.

Peroxides can usually be completely removed from a sample of ether by thorough shaking with aqueous potassium permanganate solution.

up the apparatus and heat **F** over the sand-bath as shown. The liquid becomes progressively darker in colour, and then effervesces gently as ethylene is evolved. Allow the gas to escape from the delivery-tube in **T** for several minutes in order to sweep out the air in **F** and **B**. Now fill a test-tube with water, close it with the finger, and invert the tube in the water in **T** over the delivery-tube so that a sample of the gas collects in the tube. Close the tube again with the finger, and then light the gas at a Bunsen burner at a safe distance from the apparatus. If the tube contains pure ethylene, the latter burns with a clear pale blue (almost invisible) flame: if the ethylene still contains air, the mixture in the test-tube ignites with a sharp report. Allow the gas to escape from the delivery-tube in **T** until a sample tested in this way proves to be pure ethylene. Then collect 3–4 gas-jars of ethylene, closing each one under water with a slightly greased glass plate. Since appreciable quantities of sulphur dioxide are evolved in **F** during the later stages of the reaction, disconnect the delivery-tube joining **F** to **B**, and *then* turn out the gas. Carry out the following tests with the jars of ethylene.

(1) *Odour.* Smell the contents of one of the jars. The ethylene has a characteristic sweetish odour.

Ethylene when deeply inhaled produces temporary anaesthesia which is almost devoid of unpleasant after-effects; hence it is often used for dental surgery, minor operations, *etc.*

(2) *Bromine.* Slip slightly to one side the glass plate covering one jar of ethylene, add 2–3 c.c. of bromine water (preparation, p. 426), restore the glass plate in position, and then shake the jar vigorously. The colour of the bromine rapidly disappears as ethylene dibromide is formed. Note that owing to the absorption

$$C_2H_4 + Br_2 = C_2H_4Br_2$$

of ethylene, a partial vacuum now exists in the jar.

(3) *Alkaline Potassium Permanganate.* Add similarly to a second jar 1–2 c.c. of *very dilute* aqueous potassium permanganate solution to which an equal volume of sodium carbonate solution has previously been added. On shaking as before the purple colour of the permanganate is replaced by the green colour of potassium manganate, K_2MnO_4; further reduction ultimately causes the green manganate to be replaced by a brown precipitate of manganese dioxide. Note that a partial vacuum again exists owing to the absorption of ethylene.

In this reaction the ethylene is oxidised to ethylene glycol, $C_2H_4(OH)_2$.

$$C_2H_4 + H_2O + O = C_2H_4(OH)_2$$

If a solution of potassium permanganate containing dilute sulphuric acid is used, the purple colour disappears and the solution ultimately becomes

$$2KMnO_4 + 3H_2SO_4 = K_2SO_4 + 2MnSO_4 + 3H_2O + 5O$$

colourless. The use of the sodium carbonate solution, and the consequent change in colour first to the green manganate and then to the brown manganese dioxide, make the reagent more sensitive to observation.

Tests for Unsaturation. The above reactions are used as the standard tests for the presence of double or triple bonds joining carbon atoms in an organic compound.

(1) The bromine test is applied first. The organic compound, if a liquid, is treated with 2–3 drops of liquid bromine or (preferably) a solution of bromine in carbon tetrachloride: if the organic compound is a solid, it should first be dissolved in cold carbon tetrachloride or chloroform. The rapid absorption of the bromine (and consequent disappearance of the red colour) is a strong indication that the compound is unsaturated, and is therefore undergoing direct addition of the bromine.

Since, however, some compounds, such as aniline (p. 125), react very rapidly with bromine *by substitution*, the bromine test should whenever possible be confirmed by the alkaline permanganate test.

(2) If the compound is soluble in cold water, its aqueous solution (after neutralisation, if acidic) is shaken with a dilute solution of potassium permanganate containing sodium carbonate as before. The conversion of the purple permanganate to the green manganate or (more frequently) directly to manganese dioxide confirms the result of the bromine test, since the alkaline permanganate is unaffected by possible substitution reactions.

Acetylene. C_2H_2.

Acetylene can be readily obtained by the action of water on calcium carbide: since, however, commercial calcium carbide contains traces of calcium

$$CaC_2 + 2HOH = Ca(OH)_2 + C_2H_2$$

sulphide, phosphide and nitride, the acetylene should be purified before use. If a specially pure sample of acetylene is required, it should be obtained by the action of alcoholic potassium or sodium hydroxide on ethylene dibromide: this reaction should be compared with that of *aqueous* potassium or sodium hydroxide, which merely hydrolyses ethylene dibromide to ethylene glycol.

$$C_2H_4Br_2 + 2KOH \text{ (alcoholic)} = C_2H_2 + 2KBr + 2H_2O$$
$$C_2H_4Br_2 + 2KOH \text{ (aqueous)} = C_2H_4(OH)_2 + 2KBr$$

If acetylene is required either in large quantities or in a steady regular current for several hours, it should be obtained from a cylinder, in which the acetylene is compressed in acetone solution. The cylinders can be purchased, and when empty can then be exchanged for refilled ones. The acetylene in these cylinders is generated from calcium carbide, but is considerably purified before storage in the cylinder. The acetylene before use should, however, be passed through two wash-bottles containing water to eliminate acetone vapour: acetylene of high purity is then obtained.

(A) FROM CALCIUM CARBIDE. Place some small lumps of calcium carbide (about 15 gms.) in a 150 c.c. distilling-flask (or in a Buchner flask of similar capacity), and fit into the neck of the flask a tall dropping-funnel the stem of which has been drawn off to a fine point: the stem should pass well down below the side-arm of the flask. Connect this side-arm to a wash-bottle containing 10% aqueous copper sulphate solution: the tall dropping-funnel is thus required in order to give a sufficient "head" of water in the funnel to force the acetylene through the wash-bottle. Then fit to the wash-bottle a delivery-tube which passes into a pneumatic trough precisely as that in Fig. 40 (p. 57).

Fill the dropping-funnel with water, and allow the latter to fall drop by drop on to the calcium carbide: acetylene is at once generated, and on passing through the copper sulphate solution is freed from hydrogen sulphide, *etc.* Allow the gas to escape from the delivery-tube in the pneumatic trough until the issuing gas smells markedly of acetylene. Then collect a sample of the gas in a *small* test-tube precisely as described for ethylene (p. 58). Ignite the sample at a burner placed as before at a safe distance from the apparatus. If the air in the apparatus has not yet been completely displaced by air, the sample of gas will explode with a sharp report: if, however, the acetylene is free from air, it will burn quietly with a very smoky flame depositing carbon in the tube, in marked contrast to the clear flame of burning ethylene.

Then collect 5–6 gas-jars filled with the acetylene, and carry out the following tests.

(1) *Odour.* The gas collected in this way has a somewhat onion-like odour, which is much less pronounced than that of the crude gas given off directly from the carbide without subsequent purification. Absolutely pure acetylene, however, is almost odourless.

(2) *Bromine.* Slip the glass cover of a jar momentarily aside, add 2–3 c.c. of bromine water, replace the cover and shake the contents of the jar vigorously. Note that the bromine is absorbed only very slowly, in marked contrast to the rapid absorption by ethylene. This slow reaction with bromine water is also in marked contrast to the action of chlorine water, which unites with

acetylene with explosive violence. (Therefore do not attempt this test with chlorine or chlorine water.)

(3) *Alkaline Permanganate.* To another jar add similarly 2–3 c.c. of very dilute potassium permanganate solution containing sodium carbonate. On shaking the jar the permanganate is reduced to green manganate, although the colour of the latter is only transient and is moreover obscured by the manganese dioxide formed.

(4) *Metallic Derivatives.* (a) *Cuprous Acetylide.* Cu_2C_2. Prepare an ammoniacal solution of cuprous chloride by first adding dilute ammonia to 2–3 c.c. of dilute copper sulphate solution until the initial precipitate just redissolves and a clear deep-blue solution is obtained: now add an aqueous solution of hydroxylamine hydrochloride drop by drop with shaking until the solution becomes first green and then completely colourless, the cupric salt being thus reduced to the cuprous derivative.

Now add this solution to a jar of acetylene as before and shake vigorously. A chocolate-red precipitate of cuprous acetylide is at once formed.

(b) *Silver Acetylide.* Ag_2C_2. Add dilute ammonia drop by drop with shaking to 2–3 c.c. of silver nitrate solution until the initial precipitate of silver oxide just redissolves.

Now add this solution to a jar of acetylene and shake. A yellow-white precipitate of silver acetylide at once forms.

The cuprous and silver acetylides are both explosive when dry. Therefore when these tests are completed, wash out the gas-jars thoroughly with water.

(B) FROM ETHYLENE DIBROMIDE. *Required*: Powdered potassium hydroxide, 25 gms.; rectified spirit, 100 c.c.; ethylene dibromide, 15 c.c.

To prepare pure acetylene, assemble the apparatus shown in Fig. 41. F is a wide-

FIG. 41.

necked 300 c.c. bolt-head flask, to which is fitted a double-surface reflux water-condenser **C** and the dropping-funnel **D**. From the top of **C**, a delivery-tube leads down to the pneumatic trough **T**, where the gas can be collected in jars in the usual way. Place 100 c.c. of rectified spirit and 25 gms. of powdered potassium hydroxide in **F**, and boil the mixture gently under reflux until the potash is almost entirely dissolved. Then place 15 c.c. (33 gms.) of ethylene dibromide in **D**, and allow the dibromide to fall drop by drop into the boiling solution in **F**. A rapid reaction occurs, acetylene being generated and potassium bromide precipitated. Test the gas issuing from the delivery-tube in the usual way to ensure that all air has been displaced by acetylene. Then collect the pure acetylene in gas-jars. Note that this acetylene is almost odourless.

Ethylene can be similarly prepared by the action of alcoholic potash on ethyl bromide, but the yield is usually very low.

Absolute Ethyl Alcohol. Supplies of absolute ethyl alcohol, which is frequently required in organic chemical work, are now freely available commercially as a result of azeotropic distillation methods. If however it should be necessary to dehydrate rectified spirit, the process can be carried out with the greatest certainty by the use of quick-lime. The quick-lime should preferably be prepared in the laboratory by heating lumps of marble *strongly* in a good muffle-furnace for about 3 hours; the product, directly it cools, must be stored in a tightly stoppered tin or bottle, although whenever possible it should be used for dehydration immediately after its preparation. If the lime is obtained from a local lime-burner, supplies should be obtained directly they leave the kiln, and preferably reheated immediately before use.

The preparation of absolute alcohol in moderate quantity for classes may be carried out as follows. Pour 3 Winchester bottles (*i.e.*, 7–8 litres) of rectified spirit into a 3-gallon (14–15 litre) can **C** (Fig. 42), add about 600 gms. of the

FIG. 42.

quick-lime, and fit a double-surface reflux condenser by means of a rubber stopper, the top of the condenser being closed with a calcium chloride tube. Place the can in a large galvanised iron bath **G** about half-full of water, supporting the can in the bath on some earthenware tiles. Heat the water-bath over a gas-ring so that the alcohol boils gently under reflux for 6 hours. Now (preferably) allow the apparatus to cool and stand overnight. Next day, add a further 100 gms. of quick-lime to the alcohol, and fit to the can a still-head **S** as shown (Fig. 42). Reverse the condenser for distillation, and connect it to an adaptor **A**, which fits directly into the bottle **B** in which the absolute alcohol will subsequently be stored. Rubber stoppers must be used throughout the apparatus: that which fits into the receiving bottle **B** carries a calcium chloride tube **T** as shown. Now reheat the water-bath so that the alcohol distils over steadily: no "bumping" should occur in the can. Stop the distillation when about 500 c.c. of alcohol still remain in the can.

The absolute alcohol obtained in this way should have $d^{15°}_{4°}$, 0·794. It is very hygroscopic, and the bottle in which it is stored should preferably have a well-fitting ground-glass stopper: alternatively, the bottle can be closed with a tightly fitting rubber stopper but *not* with a cork, as corks contain appreciable quantities of water.

Absolute methyl alcohol can be similarly prepared, and then has $d^{15°}_{4°}$, 0·796.

Chloroform. $CHCl_3$.

When chlorine is passed into boiling alcohol, both chlorination of the methyl group and oxidation of the primary alcohol group to an aldehyde occur, giving trichloro-acetaldehyde or chloral:

$$CH_3CH_2OH + 4Cl_2 = CCl_3CHO + 5HCl$$

When chloral is treated with caustic alkali, fission of the C–C linkage occurs, giving chloroform and a formate:

$$CCl_3 CHO + KO H = CHCl_3 + HCOOK$$

Acetaldehyde and also many ketones, such as acetone, containing the CH_3CO- group behave similarly when treated with bleaching powder, chlorination of the CH_3CO- group being immediately followed by fission of the molecule by the alkali present in the bleaching powder:

$$CH_3COCH_3 + 3Cl_2 = CCl_3COCH_3 + HCl$$

$$2CCl_3 COCH_3 + Ca(O H)_2 = 2CHCl_3 + (CH_3COO)_2Ca$$

The acetone method clearly gives a much cheaper product than the alcohol method.

Required: Bleaching powder, 100 gms.; acetone, 44 c.c.

Place 100 gms. of bleaching powder in a mortar and add 250 c.c. of water in small quantities at a time: between each addition grind the mixture of bleaching powder and water well together and decant the cream-like suspension through a funnel into a 1-litre flat-bottomed flask. Finally, when all the water has thus been used, only a gritty residue remains in the mortar. Fit the flask with an efficient reflux water-condenser, pour 44 c.c. (35 gms.) of acetone in small quantities, at a time, down the condenser and mix by thorough shaking after each addition. The reaction usually starts spontaneously after a few minutes, and a bath of cold water should be available into which the flask may be dipped if necessary to moderate the reaction. Should the reaction show no signs of starting within 5 minutes of the addition of the acetone, warm the flask *cautiously* on a boiling water-bath until the reaction starts, and then remove it immediately. When the vigorous boiling has subsided, heat the flask on a boiling water-bath for a further 5–10 minutes (not more) to complete the reaction. Cool the flask in cold water (to prevent loss of chloroform vapour whilst the apparatus is being rearranged) and then fit the flask with a fairly wide delivery-tube and reverse the water-condenser for distillation (as in Fig. 43, p. 72). Heat the flask on a water-bath until distillation of the chloroform is complete.

The chloroform thus obtained is usually acidic. Therefore shake it thoroughly with *dilute* sodium hydroxide solution in a separating-funnel. (If the chloroform tends to float on the alkaline solution, it still contains appreciable quantities of acetone: in this case the soda should be run out of the funnel and the chloroform shaken with water to extract the acetone. The extraction with the soda can then be performed after the water has been removed.) Carefully run off the heavy lower layer of chloroform into a small conical flask, dry it over calcium chloride for 15–20 minutes, and then filter it directly into a 75 c.c. distilling-flask fitted with a clean dry water-condenser. Distil the chloroform, collecting the fraction of b.p. 60–63°. Yield, 30 gms. (20 c.c.)

Chloroform is a colourless liquid, of b.p. 61° and d, 1·50. It has a characteristic sweetish smell, and is frequently used as a solvent in organic chemistry.

For reactions of chloroform, see pp. 297–299.

Chloroform is widely used in medicine as an anaesthetic. One disadvantage for this purpose is the ready oxidation which chloroform undergoes on exposure to light and air, generating the poisonous phosgene, or carbonyl chloride, $OCCl_2$. This is counteracted by

$$CHCl_3 + O = OCCl_2 + HCl.$$

storing the liquid in dark amber-coloured bottles, and also by the addition of about 2% of alcohol: the latter converts the phosgene into harmless diethyl carbonate:

$$2C_2H_5OH + Cl_2CO = (C_2H_5O)_2CO + 2HCl$$

In addition to chloroform, many other compounds containing the trichloro-methyl group, Cl_3C-, show marked physiological action. Thus trichloro-acetaldehyde or *chloral hydrate*, $Cl_3C \cdot CH(OH)_2$ (p. 256), and trichloro-tertiary-butyl alcohol or *chloretone*, $Cl_3C \cdot C(CH_3)_2OH$, are both hypnotics. Similarly, tribromo-ethyl alcohol or *avertin*, $Br_3C \cdot CH_2OH$, has strong anaesthetic properties.

Iodoform. CHI_3.

The preparation of iodoform is similar to that of chloroform, of which it is the iodine analogue. Many substances which contain either the $CH_3CH(OH)-$ group or the CH_3CO-C group when treated with potassium iodide and sodium hypochlorite readily yield iodoform, and its formation can thus frequently be used as a test for these groups.* Among the compounds which contain the $CH_3CH(OH)-$ group and give iodoform are ethyl alcohol, CH_3CH_2OH, *iso*-propyl alcohol, $CH_3CH(OH)CH_3$, lactic acid, $CH_3CH(OH)COOH$, and also acetaldehyde, which exists in aqueous solution partly as the hydrated form, $CH_3CH(OH)_2$: similar compounds containing the CH_3CO-C group are acetone, CH_3CO-CH_3, pyruvic acid, $CH_3CO-COOH$, and acetophenone, $CH_3CO-C_6H_5$. Methyl alcohol does not give iodoform in these circumstances and can thus be distinguished from ethyl alcohol.

The reactions involved are similar in both cases, and closely parallel to those which give rise to chloroform. The sodium hypochlorite probably first oxidises the potassium iodide to potassium hypoiodite, which then oxidises the ethyl alcohol to acetaldehyde and then iodinates the latter to tri-iodo-

$$CH_3CH_2OH \longrightarrow CH_3CHO \longrightarrow CI_3CHO$$

acetaldehyde or iodal. Aqueous sodium hypochlorite always contains sodium hydroxide, which converts the tri-iodo-acetaldehyde to iodoform and sodium formate.

$$CI_3CHO + NaOH = CHI_3 + HCOONa$$

If acetone is used there is no initial oxidation: tri-iodo-acetone is first formed and is then converted by the sodium hydroxide to iodoform and

$$CI_3COCH_3 + NaOH = CHI_3 + CH_3COONa$$

sodium acetate. Iodoform is obtained more readily and in greater yield from acetone and acetaldehyde than from ethyl alcohol, possibly because no initial oxidation is required.

Iodoform is used in medicine as a disinfectant and as an external antiseptic.

IODOFORM FROM ACETONE. *Required:* Acetone, 2 c.c.; 10% potassium iodide solution, 80 c.c.; 10% sodium hydroxide solution, 30 c.c.; $2N$ sodium hypochlorite solution, 70 c.c.

Place 2 c.c. of acetone, 80 c.c. of 10% aqueous potassium iodide solution and 30 c.c. of 10% aqueous sodium hydroxide solution in a 200 c.c. conical flask, and then add 70 c.c. of a

---

* For other types of compounds which give the iodoform reaction, see H. Booth and B. C. Saunders, *Chem. and Industry*, 1950, 824.

D

freshly prepared molar (*i.e.*, 2*N*) solution* of sodium hypochlorite. Well mix the contents of the flask, when the yellow iodoform will begin to separate almost immediately: allow the mixture to stand at room temperature for 10 minutes, and then filter at the pump, wash with cold water, and drain thoroughly. Yield of crude material, 6 gms. Recrystallise the crude iodoform from methylated spirit. For this purpose, place the crude material in a 150 c.c. round-bottomed flask fitted with a reflux water-condenser, add a small quantity of methylated spirit, and heat to boiling on a water-bath: then add more methylated spirit cautiously down the condenser until all the iodoform has dissolved. Filter the hot solution through a fluted filter-paper directly into a small beaker or conical flask, and then cool in ice-water. The iodoform rapidly crystallises. Filter at the pump, drain thoroughly and dry.

Iodoform forms yellow crystals, of m.p. 120°, and has a characteristic odour.

For reactions of iodoform, see pp. 297–299.

Oximes.

Both aldehydes and ketones usually condense readily with free hydroxylamine, $HONH_2$, to give crystalline *oximes*:

$$CH_3CH[O + H_2]NOH \quad = \quad CH_3CH{:}NOH + H_2O$$
Acetaldehyde   Acetaldoxime

$$(CH_3)_2C[O + H_2]NOH \quad = \quad (CH_3)_2C{:}NOH + H_2O$$
Acetone   Acetoxime

Since hydroxylamine is usually available only in the form of its salts, *e.g.*, the hydrochloride or sulphate, the aqueous solution of these salts is treated with sodium acetate or hydroxide to liberate the base before treatment with the aldehyde or ketone.

Oximes have three important uses:

(1) Being crystalline compounds which usually have sharp melting-points, they are used to characterise the parent aldehydes and ketones.

(2) Impure aldehydes and ketones are sometimes purified by conversion to the corresponding oximes, and the latter after recrystallisation are then hydrolysed by boiling with dilute sulphuric acid:

$$(CH_3)_2C{:}NOH + H_2O + H_2SO_4 = (CH_3)_2CO + H_2NOH,H_2SO_4$$

The acid, by neutralising the hydroxylamine, prevents the reverse reaction and thus causes rapid and complete hydrolysis: distillation of the final solution then drives over the aldehyde or ketone, the hydroxylamine sulphate remaining behind.

* For preparation of 2*N* sodium hypochlorite solution, see p. 426.

(3) Reduction gives pure primary amines:

$$CH_3CH{:}NOH + 4H \quad = \quad CH_3CH_2NH_2 + H_2O$$
Monoethylamine

$$(CH_3)_2C{:}NOH + 4H \quad = \quad (CH_3)_2CHNH_2 + H_2O$$
Iso-propylamine

For the further identification of aldehydes and ketones by phenylhydrazone formation, see pp. 257, 260; by 2:4-dinitrophenylhydrazone formation, see pp. 257, 261; by semicarbazone formation, see p. 203.

Acetoxime. $(CH_3)_2C{:}NOH.$

Required: Hydroxylamine hydrochloride, 12·5 gms.; sodium hydroxide, 7 gms.; acetone, 12 c.c.

Prepare a solution of 12·5 gms. of hydroxylamine hydrochloride in 20 c.c. of water contained in a 100 c.c. conical flask. Dissolve 7 gms. of powdered sodium hydroxide in 20 c.c. of water, cool the solution in ice-water, and then add it to that of the hydroxylamine hydrochloride. Place a thermometer in the mixed solution, and chill the flask in ice-water until the temperature of the solution is between 5° and 10°. Now add 12 c.c. (9·5 gms.) of acetone (preferably from a burette to ensure accuracy) in small quantities so that, when the mixture is gently shaken in the ice-water during the addition, the temperature does not rise above 15°. The acetoxime usually starts to crystallise when about half the acetone has been added. When the addition is complete, allow the mixture to stand in ice-water for 15 minutes, and then filter off the crude acetoxime at the pump, drain well and finally dry by pressing repeatedly between several layers of drying-paper. The acetoxime so obtained contains sodium chloride, but is otherwise almost pure. Yield of crude dry material, 12–13 gms.

The oxime is freely soluble in water and in most organic liquids. Recrystallise the crude *dry* product from a minimum of 60–80° petrol or (less suitably) cyclohexane: for this purpose first determine approximately, by means of a small-scale test-tube experiment, the minimum proportion of the hot solvent required to dissolve the oxime from about 0·5 gm. of the crude material. Then place the bulk of the crude product in a small (100 c.c.) round-bottomed or conical flask fitted with a reflux water-condenser, add the required amount of the solvent and boil the mixture on a water-bath. Then turn out the gas, and quickly filter the hot mixture through a fluted filter-paper into a conical flask: the sodium chloride remains on the filter, whilst the filtrate on cooling in ice-water deposits the acetoxime as colourless crystals. These, when filtered and dried (either by pressing between drying-paper or by placing in an *atmospheric* desiccator) have m.p. 60°. Acetoxime sublimes rather readily when exposed to the air, and rapidly when warmed or when placed in a vacuum. Hence the necessity for an atmospheric desiccator for drying purposes.

Hydrolysis of Acetoxime. Place about 3 gms. of the recrystallised oxime in a small distilling-flask (100 c.c.), add 30 c.c. of dilute H_2SO_4, and heat *gently* until about half the solution has distilled over. Test (*a*) the aqueous distillate for acetone by the iodoform reaction (p. 261), (*b*) the residual solution in the distilling-flask for hydroxylamine by cooling, making strongly alkaline, and treating with Fehling's solution. A deep yellow precipitate of cuprous oxide results:

$$2H_2NOH + 4CuO = 2Cu_2O + N_2O + 3H_2O$$

Esters.

Esters may be prepared by the following methods:

(1) Directly from the corresponding acid and alcohol, in the presence of a dehydrating agent. Thus when ethyl alcohol and acetic acid are mixed, ethyl acetate and water are formed, but in addition an equilibrium is established.

$$CH_3CO|OH + H|OC_2H_5 \rightleftharpoons CH_3COOC_2H_5 + H_2O$$

If, however, concentrated sulphuric acid is present, the water is absorbed, the back reaction prevented, and a high yield of ethyl acetate is obtained. In practice the reaction is not so simple, since the sulphuric acid is usually added to the alcohol, thus giving ethyl hydrogen sulphate and water, the latter being absorbed by the excess of sulphuric acid. A mixture of alcohol and acetic acid

$$C_2H_5|OH + H|HSO_4 = C_2H_5HSO_4 + H_2O$$

is then added to the ethyl hydrogen sulphate, whereupon the latter reacts with the organic acid to give the required ester, liberating the sulphuric acid which

$$C_2H_5HSO_4 + CH_3COOH = CH_3COOC_2H_5 + H_2SO_4$$

at once reacts with the free alcohol, the cycle of operations then recurring. The process can thus continue until the sulphuric acid becomes too dilute to furnish more ethyl hydrogen sulphate.

This method has the disadvantage that the corresponding ether is usually

$$C_2H_5|HSO_4 + H|OC_2H_5 = (C_2H_5)_2O + H_2SO_4$$

formed as a by-product by the interaction of the alkyl hydrogen sulphate and unchanged alcohol.

(2) *The Fischer-Speier Method.* In certain cases of esterification sulphuric acid cannot be used. Thus if the alcohol or the organic acid is unsaturated, the sulphuric acid may add on at the unsaturated group. If the alcohol or the acid is aromatic in type, considerable sulphonation of the benzene ring may result. Finally, if an amino-acid, such as glycine or amino-acetic acid, NH_2CH_2COOH, is to be esterified, the amino group would also

undergo salt formation, and thus the hydrogen sulphate of aminoacetic ethyl ester, $H_2SO_4,NH_2CH_2COOC_2H_5$, would result, and would be very difficult to isolate from the excess of sulphuric acid. These difficulties are overcome by the *Fischer-Speier* method, in which a mixture of the alcohol and the organic acid is gently boiled under reflux whilst a stream of dry hydrogen chloride gas is passed in, a high yield of the ester being thus obtained. The function of the hydrogen chloride is undoubtedly to absorb the water formed: it is also definitely catalytic, since Fischer found that 5% of hydrogen chloride in the reaction mixture would cause efficient esterification. The advantages of the Fischer-Speier method are that the hydrogen chloride does not usually add on to unsaturated groupings, it does not affect aromatic groups, and finally with amino-acids gives the hydrochloride of the ester, from which excess of hydrogen chloride can be readily removed by direct evaporation. A further advantage is that the corresponding ether is not formed as a by-product. The method is also suitable for the preparation of esters of hydroxy-acids, *e.g.*, lactic acid.

(3) Esters can also be prepared by the action of alcohols on acid chlorides and anhydrides.

$$CH_3CO|Cl + H|OC_2H_5 = CH_3COOC_2H_5 + HCl$$
Acetyl chloride

$$CH_3CO|O \cdot COCH_3 + H|OC_2H_5 = CH_3COOC_2H_5 + CH_3COOH$$
Acetic anhydride

(4) By the action of alkyl halides on the silver salt of the acid.

$$CH_3COO|Ag + I|C_2H_5 = CH_3COOC_2H_5 + AgI$$

This method is to be recommended when only a small quantity of the acid is available, since both the conversion of the acid to its silver salt (p. 350) and of the latter to the ester give almost quantitative yields.

(5) Esters of the binary halogen acids (HCl, *etc.*) can be prepared by the action of the corresponding phosphorus tri- or penta-halide. The reaction is often indicated by the equation:

$$3C_2H_5OH + PCl_3 = 3C_2H_5Cl + P(OH)_3$$
Ethyl chloride   Phosphorous acid

It is however more complicated, esters of phosphorous acid* being also formed. Iodides are usually prepared by a modification of this method, the alcohol being mixed with red phosphorus, and iodine added. The phosphorus iodide is thus formed *in situ*, and at once reacts with the alcohol to give the corresponding iodide.

For reactions of esters, see p. 268.

Ethyl Acetate. $CH_3COOC_2H_5$. (Method 1.)

Required: Alcohol, 50 c.c.; sulphuric acid, 10 c.c.; acetic acid, 50 c.c.; calcium chloride, 25 gms.

Mix 50 c.c. (40 gms.) of alcohol and 50 c.c. (52 gms.) of glacial acetic acid thoroughly in a 250 c.c. round-bottomed flask, and

* See Saunders *et al.*, *J. Chem. Soc.*, 1945, 380.

add slowly, with cooling and shaking, 10 c.c. (18·5 gms.) of concentrated sulphuric acid. Ensure that the liquid is homogeneous, then fit the flask with a reflux water-condenser (Fig. 8, p. 17) and boil the mixture gently over a wire gauze for 10 minutes. Now alter the position of the condenser (Fig. 43, p. 72) and distil off about two-thirds of the mixture and then transfer the distillate to a separating-funnel.* Add about 25 c.c. of 30% sodium carbonate solution, cork the funnel and shake carefully in order to neutralise and remove the free acetic and sulphurous acids present in the crude ethyl acetate: much carbon dioxide is evolved during the shaking, therefore release the pressure in the funnel at frequent intervals by cautiously removing the cork, or alternatively by inverting the securely corked funnel and momentarily opening the tap. Now allow the two layers to separate, and carefully run off and reject the lower aqueous layer, ensuring that the sodium carbonate solution is removed as completely as possible. Then prepare a solution of 25 gms. of anhydrous calcium chloride in 25 c.c. of water, add it to the ethyl acetate in the funnel, and again shake vigorously. The calcium chloride solution removes any unchanged alcohol present in the ethyl acetate. Allow the mixture to separate, and again run off the lower aqueous layer as completely as possible. Then run the ethyl acetate into a small conical flask, add a few lumps of granular calcium chloride, and shake occasionally.

After about 20 minutes, when the liquid should be dry, filter it through a small fluted filter-paper into a 100 c.c. distilling-flask attached to a water-condenser. Add some fragments of unglazed porcelain to the ethyl acetate, fit a 100° thermometer to the flask, and place the latter on a cold water-bath, which is then brought to the boil. Some ether is always formed as a by-product with the ethyl acetate, and by these means is carefully distilled off as a preliminary and separate fraction, boiling at 35–40°: if the distilling-flask is rapidly heated on a previously boiling water-bath, however, the ether does not distil as a definite fraction, and the boiling-point of the distillate steadily rises without a perceptible break to that of the ethyl acetate itself. Collect the portion of the distillate boiling between 74° and 79°, rejecting a small fraction boiling immediately below this range. Yield 50 gms. Ethyl acetate is a colourless liquid having b.p. 77° and d, 0·92; it has a pleasant apple-like odour, and is only slightly soluble in water.

* If a separating-funnel of only 100 c.c. capacity is available, divide the distillate into two portions, and work up each separately as far as the drying stage.

Calculation of Yield. The yield of a compound obtained in an organic preparation, in addition to being stated in grams, should also be calculated as a percentage of the yield theoretically possible from the weight of the original compounds taken. Thus in the preparation of ethyl acetate, the equation shows that 60 gms. of acetic acid and 46 gms. of alcohol react to give 88 gms.

$$CH_3COOH + C_2H_5OH = CH_3COOC_2H_5 + H_2O$$
$$60 \qquad\qquad 46 \qquad\qquad 88$$

of ethyl acetate. If equimolecular quantities of acid and alcohol had been taken in the preparation, the percentage yield of the ethyl acetate would clearly be the same if calculated on the basis of either reagent. Actually, however, an excess of alcohol was used and the yield can therefore be calculated on the basis either of the alcohol or of the acid. Thus

46 gms. of alcohol should give 88 gms. of ethyl acetate

∴ 40 gms. ,,　　,,　　　,,　　,,　76 gms. ,, ,, ,,

Actually 50 gms. of ester were obtained. Hence yield of ethyl acetate

$$= \frac{50 \times 100}{76} = 66\%.$$

Similarly, since 60 gms. of acetic acid should theoretically give 88 gms. of ethyl acetate, 52 gms. should give 77 gms. of the ester, and hence the yield,

calculated on the acetic acid, is $\dfrac{50 \times 100}{77} = 65\%.$

(The yield of ester based on the alcohol taken is actually higher than the above value, as the rectified spirit used contains only 96% of alcohol.)

Hydrolysis of Ethyl Acetate.

When esters such as ethyl acetate are shaken with water, hydrolysis slowly occurs, and ultimately an equilibrium is attained:

$$CH_3COOC_2H_5 + HOH \rightleftharpoons CH_3COOH + C_2H_5OH$$

Complete hydrolysis can be rapidly obtained, however, if the ester is boiled under reflux with a dilute aqueous solution of either a caustic alkali, such as sodium hydroxide, or of a strong inorganic acid, such as sulphuric or hydro-chloric acid. In the former case, the sodium hydroxide neutralises the acetic acid as fast as it is formed, and so promotes the hydrolysis: in the latter case, the dilute inorganic acid catalyses the hydrolysis, which in the presence of a large excess of water goes practically to completion. Since the sodium salts of some of the higher fatty acids are soaps, the general process of alkaline hydrolysis of esters (by which the soaps are obtained) is frequently called *saponification*.

Place 5 c.c. of ethyl acetate in a 100 c.c. round-bottomed flask, and add about 50 c.c. of 10% sodium hydroxide solution, together with some fragments of unglazed porcelain. Fit the flask with a reflux water-condenser, and boil the mixture gently over a wire gauze for 30 minutes. Now disconnect the condenser, and fit it by means of a bent delivery-tube (or "knee-tube") to the flask for direct distillation (Fig. 43). Reheat the liquid, and collect the first 10 c.c. of distillate, which will consist of a dilute aqueous solution of ethyl alcohol. Confirm the presence of ethyl alcohol by the iodoform test (Test 3, p. 252).

FIG. 43.

The residual liquid in the flask is a dilute alkaline solution of sodium acetate. To liberate the acetic acid, add dilute sulphuric acid until the solution is definitely acid to litmus, and then distil off about 20 c.c. Perform on this aqueous distillate the tests for acetic acid given on p. 262.

Ethyl Bromide. C_2H_5Br. (Method 1, p. 68.)

Ethyl bromide is an example of an ester formed from an alcohol and an inorganic acid. Since hydrogen bromide is a gas, it is generated actually in the reaction mixture, where it is rapidly esterified without appreciable loss. For this purpose, a solution of ethyl hydrogen sulphate is prepared by adding sulphuric acid to an excess of alcohol. Sodium bromide is then added, and the liberated hydrogen bromide reacts with the ethyl hydrogen sulphate, giving

$$C_2H_5 \vert HSO_4 + H \vert Br = C_2H_5Br + H_2SO_4$$

ethyl bromide. The excess of alcohol ensures that the sulphuric acid liberated in this reaction is reconverted into ethyl hydrogen sulphate, and that the excess of the latter in turn effects maximum conversion of the costly hydrogen bromide to ethyl bromide.

Required: Ethyl alcohol, 37 c.c.; sulphuric acid, 40 c.c.; sodium bromide ($NaBr, 2H_2O$), 35 gms.

Assemble the apparatus shown in Fig. 44. **A** is a 500 c.c. bolt-head flask connected by a "knee-tube" **B** to a water-condenser **C**, to the lower end of which is fitted the adaptor **D**. In view of the low boiling-point of the ethyl bromide, it is essential that the various portions of the apparatus are connected together by well-bored, tightly fitting corks.

Arrange the adaptor **D** so that the end dips below the surface of about 50 c.c. of water contained in a small conical flask, or beaker, which is in turn surrounded by a mixture of ice and water. Place 37 c.c. (30 gms.) of alcohol and 25 c.c. of water in the flask **A**, and then add slowly 40 c.c. (74 gms.) of concentrated sulphuric acid, shaking the mixture gently around and cooling meanwhile. Now add 35 gms. of coarsely powdered sodium bromide ($2H_2O$), reconnect the flask to the tube **B** without delay, and then heat the flask gently on a sand-bath, at the same time ensuring that an ample supply of cold water is passing through the condenser **C**.

FIG. 44.

Ethyl bromide soon distils over, and collects as heavy oily drops under the water in the receiving flask, evaporation of the very volatile distillate being thus prevented. If the mixture in the flask **A** froths badly, moderate the heating of the sand-bath. When no more oily drops of ethyl bromide come over, pour the contents of the receiving flask into a separating-funnel, and carefully run off the heavy lower layer of ethyl bromide. Discard the upper aqueous layer, and return the ethyl bromide to the funnel. Add an equal volume of 10% sodium carbonate solution, cork the funnel securely and shake cautiously. Owing to the presence of hydrobromic and sulphurous acids in the crude ethyl bromide, a brisk evolution of carbon dioxide occurs: therefore release the pressure in the funnel at frequent intervals (as in the preparation of ethyl acetate, p. 70). Allow the two liquids to separate, and again run off the lower layer of ethyl bromide. Discard the upper layer, return the ethyl bromide to the funnel, and shake it with an equal volume of water to remove traces of sodium carbonate. Allow the two liquids to separate, and finally run the lower layer of ethyl bromide carefully into a small conical flask: add a few pieces of calcium chloride, securely cork the flask and then occa-

D*

sionally shake the mixture gently, protecting the liquid as much as possible from the heat of the hand. The liquid should become quite clear (and therefore dry) in about 20 minutes. Then filter the ethyl bromide through a *small* fluted filter-paper directly into a 60 c.c. distilling-flask. Fit the flask with a 100° thermometer, and a water-condenser having as before an ample supply of cold water: then arrange the condenser so that its lower end enters the neck of a small dry weighed conical flask, supporting the latter in line with the condenser, and chilling it externally by a mixture of ice and water. Distil the ethyl bromide slowly from a water-bath, and collect the fraction boiling between 35° and 40°. Yield 33 gms. In view of the low boiling-point of the ethyl bromide, it should be preserved in a sealed glass specimen tube (see Fig. 20, p. 40).

Ethyl bromide is a colourless liquid, of b.p. 38° and d, 1·45, insoluble in water: as prepared above, it always contains some diethyl ether.

Hydrolysis of Ethyl Bromide. Add a few drops of pure freshly distilled ethyl bromide to 2–3 c.c. of aqueous silver nitrate solution in a test-tube and shake. Only a faint opalescence of silver bromide should be formed. Now *carefully* warm the mixture in a small Bunsen flame, with gentle shaking: silver bromide soon appears as a white suspension which rapidly increases in quantity and becomes a heavy precipitate. The ethyl bromide is thus moderately stable in cold water, but rapidly hydrolysed by hot water.

n-Butyl Bromide. C_4H_9Br. (Method 1, p. 68.)

The preparation of *n*-butyl bromide as an example of ester formation by Method 1 (p. 68) has certain advantages over the above preparation of ethyl bromide. *n*-Butyl alcohol is free from Customs restrictions, and the *n*-butyl bromide is of course less volatile and therefore more readily manipulated without loss than ethyl bromide: furthermore, the *n*-butyl bromide boils *ca*. 40° below *n*-butyl ether, and traces of the latter formed in the reaction can therefore be readily eliminated by fractional distillation.

Required: Sodium bromide, 35 gms.; *n*-butyl alcohol, 25 c.c.

Place 30 c.c. of water, 35 gms. of powdered sodium bromide and 25 c.c. (20 gms.) of *n*-butyl alcohol in a 250 c.c. round-bottomed flask, and then fit a dropping-funnel to the flask through a cork which has a groove cut or filed in the side (as **F** in Fig. 1(B), p. 3) to allow escape of air. Place 25 c.c. of concentrated sulphuric acid in the funnel, and then allow the acid to fall slowly dropwise into the flask, keeping the contents well shaken meanwhile and cooled occasionally in an ice-water bath. When the addition is complete, replace the funnel with a reflux water-condenser, and then gently boil the mixture over a sand-bath for *ca*. 45 minutes, shaking the flask gently from time to time. Then remove the reflux condenser, and fit a "knee-tube" and condenser to the flask as shown in Fig. 43 (p. 72), and distil off the crude n-butyl bromide (ca. 30 c.c.). Purify the distillate by first shaking it with water in a separating-funnel: run off the lower layer of bromide, reject the aqueous layer, and then return the bromide to the funnel and shake it with about half its volume of concentrated sulphuric acid; now run off the lower layer of acid, and shake the bromide layer in the funnel cautiously with dilute sodium carbonate solution, taking care to release the pressure in the funnel at frequent intervals.

Run off the lower layer of bromide, dry it with calcium chloride (as in the above preparation of ethyl bromide) and finally distil the filtered bromide from a small flask, preferably through a short column. Collect the n-butyl bromide as a colourless liquid of b.p. 99–102°. Yield, 30 gms.

A small residue of di-n-butyl ether, b.p. 142°, remains in the flask.

The Alkyl Halides. Ethyl bromide and iodide (see below) are typical alkyl halides. Compounds of this class are of very great importance in synthetic work, owing to the reactivity of the halogen atom. This is illustrated by the following *general* reactions:

(1) Reduction gives the corresponding hydrocarbon.

$$C_2H_5{:}Br + H{:}H = HBr + C_2H_6 \text{ (ethane).}$$

(2) Elimination of halogen by sodium (Wurtz's reaction) gives a higher hydrocarbon.

$$C_2H_5{:}Br + 2Na + Br{:}C_2H_5 = 2NaBr + C_4H_{10} \text{ (normal butane).}$$

(3) (a) *Aqueous* potassium hydroxide gives the alcohol.

$$C_2H_5{:}Br + K{:}OH = KBr + C_2H_5OH \text{ (ethyl alcohol).}$$

(b) *Alcoholic* potassium hydroxide gives an unsaturated hydrocarbon, often however in only low yield with the earlier members of the series.

$$C_2H_5{:}Br + K{:}OH = H_2O + KBr + C_2H_4 \text{ (ethylene).}$$

(4) Sodium ethoxide gives an ether (Williamson's reaction).

$$C_2H_5{:}Br + Na{:}OC_2H_5 = NaBr + C_2H_5OC_2H_5 \text{ (diethyl ether).}$$

(5) (a) Potassium cyanide gives an alkyl cyanide or nitrile.

$$C_2H_5{:}Br + K{:}CN = KBr + C_2H_5CN \text{ (ethyl cyanide or propionitrile).}$$

(b) Silver cyanide gives an alkyl *iso*cyanide or *iso*nitrile.

$$C_2H_5{:}Br + Ag{:}CN = AgBr + C_2H_5NC \text{ (ethyl \textit{iso}cyanide).}$$

(6) Silver nitrite gives a mixture of ethyl nitrite and nitro-ethane (p. 102).

$$C_2H_5{:}Br + Ag{:}NO_2 \begin{cases} C_2H_5{\cdot}O{\cdot}NO \text{ (ethyl nitrite)} \\ C_2H_5NO_2 \text{ (nitro-ethane).} \end{cases}$$

(7) Ammonia gives the corresponding amine (see however p. 98).

$$C_2H_5{:}Br + H{:}NH_2 = HBr + C_2H_5NH_2 \text{ (mono-ethylamine).}$$

(8) The alkyl halides are also of great importance in synthetic operations using Grignard reagents (p. 220), acetoacetic ester (p. 210) and malonic ester (p. 216).

Ethyl Benzoate. $C_6H_5COOC_2H_5$. (Method 2; The Fischer-Speier Method, p. 68.)

As a general rule esterification by the Fischer-Speier method should be carried out using absolute alcohol: in the following preparation of ethyl benzoate, however, the yield is not sensibly affected by the use of the cheaper rectified spirit.

Required: Benzoic acid, 20 gms.; rectified spirit, 20 c.c.

Assemble in a fume-cupboard the apparatus shown in Fig. 45. **A** is a wide-necked round-bottomed 100 c.c. flask to which the reflux water-condenser **B** is fitted by means of a *rubber* stopper.

FIG. 45.

The latter carries also an inlet tube **C** (which should not be too narrow in diameter), by means of which a current of hydrogen chloride, dried by passage through the sulphuric acid wash-bottle **D**, can be passed down to the bottom of **A**. The hydrogen chloride is best generated by means of a Kipp's apparatus ₊charged with solid ammonium chloride and concentrated sulphuric acid. The top of the condenser **B** is fitted with a calcium chloride tube* **R**, preferably bent downwards as shown: drops of water tend to collect in the end of **E** as hydrogen chloride steadily escapes during the experiment, and are thus prevented from running back and so fouling the calcium chloride.

Place 20 gms. of benzoic acid and 20 c.c. (16 gms.) of rectified spirit

* In all experiments in which an apparatus is closed by means of a calcium chloride tube, great care should be taken to ensure before the experiment that there is a free air-passage through the tube. This applies particularly when the tube has not been freshly charged, or in experiments where the heating has to be stopped during the night and started again next day: in both cases an airtight crust of hydrated calcium chloride may have formed on the surface of the anhydrous material. The small uniformly sized pellets of the calcium chloride are best held in position by loose plugs of glass wool at each end of the tube.

in **A**, connect up the apparatus, and then heat the flask on a sand-bath so that the solution in the flask boils gently. At the same time, pass a brisk current of hydrogen chloride into the reaction mixture. The speed with which the hydrogen chloride enters the flask **A** must be carefully watched during the first few minutes of the experiment, and any tendency of the solution to suck back along the tube **C** (owing to the high solubility of hydrogen chloride in alcohol) should be checked by increasing the current: when once the boiling solution is saturated, however, the current of hydrogen chloride can be cut down until only a gentle stream of bubbles is passing through **D**.

When the solution has been boiling for $1\frac{1}{2}$ hours, remove **A**, cool the contents, and then pour the alcoholic solution of the ester into a separating-funnel containing about 200 c.c. of water, finally rinsing out the flask with a few c.c. of water which are also poured into the funnel. Since the density of ethyl benzoate is only slightly greater than that of water, a sharp separation of the ester is not usually obtained. It is advisable at this stage therefore to add about 10 c.c. of carbon tetrachloride, and then to shake the mixture in the funnel vigorously: on standing, the heavy solution of the ethyl benzoate in the carbon tetrachloride separates sharply and rapidly at the bottom of the funnel. Run off the ethyl benzoate solution carefully, reject the upper aqueous layer, and then return the ethyl benzoate to the flask and shake it with a very dilute solution of sodium carbonate until all free acid is removed and no further evolution of carbon dioxide occurs. Run off the lower layer into a small conical flask, and dry by the addition of a few pieces of granular calcium chloride. Cork the flask and allow to stand for about 20 minutes with occasional shaking. Then filter the ethyl benzoate solution through a small fluted filter-paper directly into a 50 c.c. distilling-flask containing a few pieces of unglazed porcelain. Fit the flask with a 360° thermometer and an air-condenser: in view of the small quantity of carbon tetrachloride present, a water-condenser during the early stages of the distillation is not necessary. By direct heating over a gauze, distil first the carbon tetrachloride *slowly*, and then the ethyl benzoate, collecting the latter as a fraction of b.p. 210–214°. Yield, 19–20 gms.

Ethyl benzoate is a colourless liquid, of b.p. 213° and *d*, 1·05; almost insoluble in water: it has a characteristic odour.

For a further example of the Fischer-Speier method, see Ethyl cinnamate, p. 185.

Ethyl Iodide. C_2H_5I. (Method 5, p. 69.)

This is a modification of Method 5, iodine being added to a mixture of red phosphorus and ethyl alcohol: phosphorus tri-iodide is thus formed *in situ*, and readily reacts with the alcohol, giving ethyl iodide and phosphorous acid (p. 69).

Required: Red phosphorus, 2·5 gms.; alcohol, 25 c.c.; iodine, 25 gms.

Fit a 250 c.c. round-bottomed flask securely by means of a tightly fitting, well-bored cork to a reflux condenser capable of taking an ample supply of water. Place in the flask 2·5 gms. of *red* phosphorus, and then 25 c.c. (20 gms.) of alcohol. Well powder 25 gms. of iodine, and add it to the contents of the flask in small quantities of about 3–4 gms. at a time, allowing about two minutes between consecutive additions: for this purpose, the flask should be detached from the condenser *immediately* before each addition, the iodine rapidly dropped into the flask and the latter at once returned to the condenser. A moderate evolution of heat occurs, but if the addition of the powdered iodine is carefully performed, the contents of the flask should not actually boil. When all the iodine has been added, allow the product to stand for 10 minutes, and then heat on a boiling water-bath for 1 hour. Then change the position of the condenser for direct distillation, attaching it by means of a knee-tube to the flask, as shown in Fig. 43, p. 72. Reheat the flask on a boiling water-bath, and collect the distillate, which consists of ethyl iodide and unchanged ethyl alcohol, usually coloured by traces of free iodine. When the distillation ceases, transfer the distillate to a separating-funnel, and shake with an equal volume of 10 % aqueous sodium carbonate solution. Run off the lower layer of ethyl iodide, and discard the upper aqueous layer. Return the ethyl iodide to the separating-funnel, and shake it with an equal volume of water to remove traces of sodium carbonate solution. Run off the lower layer of ethyl iodide into a small conical flask, making the separation of the iodide from the upper aqueous layer as sharp and complete as possible. Add some pieces of granular calcium chloride, cork the flask and allow to stand for 15–20 minutes, occasionally shaking the contents gently. Then filter the ethyl iodide through a *small* fluted filter-paper directly into a 60 c.c. distilling-flask. Fit the flask with a 100° thermometer and a water-condenser, and distil the ethyl iodide carefully from a water-bath, collecting the fraction which distils between 68° and 73°. Yield, about 24 gms.

Ethyl iodide is a heavy liquid, of b.p. 72° and of d, 1·94; insoluble in water. When freshly distilled it is colourless, but on prolonged exposure to light it darkens in colour owing to the liberation of free iodine. Its chemical properties are almost identical with those of ethyl bromide given above.

Acetylation.

Compounds of the type ROH (alcohols and phenols), and also compounds of the type RNH_2 and R_2NH (primary and secondary amines) can be directly acetylated, the reactive H atom being replaced by the acetyl radical, $-COCH_3$. The acetylation of alcohols and phenols is really a special case of esterification, since the acetyl derivative, $ROCOCH_3$, is clearly an ester of acetic acid. Primary and secondary amines similarly give acetyl derivatives of the type $RNHCOCH_3$ and R_2NCOCH_3 respectively, which can be regarded as mono-and di-substituted derivatives of acetamide, H_2NCOCH_3.

The two chief methods of acetylation are:

(1) *Heating with a mixture of acetic anhydride and acetic acid.*

If a primary or secondary amine is heated with glacial acetic acid, the

$$RNH|H + HO|OCCH_3 = RNHCOCH_3 + H_2O$$

corresponding acetyl derivative is produced, but the process is often extremely slow. If, however, the acetic acid is mixed with acetic anhydride, rapid acetylation usually results.

$$RNH|H + CH_3CO \cdot O|COCH_3 = RNHCOCH_3 + CH_3COOH$$

One disadvantage of using acetic anhydride is that with primary amines, traces of the diacetyl compound, $RN(COCH_3)_2$, may be formed: the chances of this secondary acetylation are, however, usually remote, and recrystallation from an aqueous solvent will generally hydrolyse the diacetyl derivative rapidly back to the mono-acetyl compound.

For complete acetylation of polyhydric compounds, such as glucose (p. 112) and mannitol (p. 114), even undiluted acetic anhydride is insufficient, and a catalyst must also be employed. In such cases, the addition of zinc chloride or anhydrous sodium acetate to the acetic anhydride usually induces complete acetylation.*

(2) *Treatment with acetyl chloride.*

Acetylation will proceed particularly smoothly with acetyl chloride if pyridine is present to absorb the hydrogen chloride as fast as it is formed.

$$RO|H + Cl|COCH_3 = ROCOCH_3 + HCl$$

Acetylation has two chief uses: (1) to characterise and identify hydroxy compounds and primary and secondary amines, by obtaining crystalline acetyl derivatives. This applies particularly to aromatic compounds, since aliphatic compounds are often liquid, and frequently soluble in water; (2) to protect a

---

* Some amines, e.g., aniline, can on the other hand be readily acetylated by dissolving them in cold dil. acetic acid and adding acetic anhydride: the method is not however general.

primary or secondary amino group during a chemical reaction, as in the preparation of p-nitro-aniline by the nitration of acetanilide, followed by hydrolysis (p. 127), and in the preparation of sulphanilamide (p. 138).

Acetanilide. $C_6H_5NHCOCH_3$. (Method 1.)

Required: Acetic acid/anhydride mixture, 20 c.c.; aniline, 10 c.c.

Add 20 c.c. of a mixture of equal volumes of acetic anhydride and glacial acetic acid to 10 c.c. (10·3 gms.) of aniline contained in a 150 c.c. conical flask. Fit a reflux water-condenser to the flask, and boil the mixture gently for 30 minutes. Then pour the hot liquid into 200 c.c. of cold water, stirring the latter well

$$C_6H_5NH_2 + O(OCCH_3)_2 = C_6H_5NHCOCH_3 + CH_3COOH$$

during the addition. The acetanilide rapidly crystallises. Filter at the pump, and wash the crude acetanilide well with water. Recrystallise from about 60 c.c. of a mixture of one volume of acetic acid and two volumes of water: filter off the colourless crystals at the pump, again wash thoroughly with water, drain, and dry. M.p. 113°; yield, 10 gms. Alternatively, the crude acetanilide may be recrystallised from boiling water, but in this case a much greater volume (about 300 c.c.) of the solvent will be required.

Acetanilide (Semi-Micro Scale) (1/20 of above scale).

Run into a test-tube from a micro-burette 0·5 c.c. of aniline and 1 c.c. of the 1:1 acetic acid-acetic anhydride mixture. Insert a "cold finger" (Fig. 25, p. 43) into the lip of the test-tube, without using a cork. Circulate the water through the finger and gently boil the mixture for 5 minutes. Cool, add about 10 c.c. of cold water, stir well with a thin glass rod and filter off the precipitated acetanilide using the apparatus shown in Figs. 30 or 31 (p. 44). Use the filtrate to effect the *complete* transfer of all the solid from the test-tube to the filter funnel, and then wash the solid with about 1 c.c. of ice-cold water and drain thoroughly. Recrystallise from boiling water (about 15 c.c.). Filter if necessary while hot through a very small fluted filter paper (or using the apparatus shown in Fig. 32, p. 45) into a small conical flask or test-tube. When quite cold filter off the purified acetanilide, again using the apparatus shown in Figs. 30 or 31. Yield, 0·4 gm.

Hydrolysis of Acetanilide.
Anilides in general, such as acetanilide and benzanilide (p. 192) may be hydrolysed by caustic alkalis or by acids. Alkaline hydrolysis, however, is usually very slow, and therefore acid hydrolysis should always be used for anilides. For this purpose, a 70% solution of sulphuric acid, prepared by adding 40 c.c. (74 gms.) of the concentrated acid *cautiously* to 30 c.c. of water with cooling and stirring, gives the most satisfactory results.

Place 4 gms. of acetanilide and 40 c.c. of the 70% sulphuric acid in a small flask fitted with a reflux water-condenser, and boil the mixture gently for 20 minutes, when the hot solution will smell perceptibly of free acetic acid. Dilute the solution with about 20 c.c. of water,

$$C_6H_5NHCOCH_3 + H_2O + H_2SO_4 = C_6H_5NH_2,H_2SO_4 + CH_3COOH$$

transfer it to a small distilling-flask, and distil off about 5–10 c.c. Acetic acid is volatile in steam: therefore apply to this distillate the tests for free acetic acid given on p. 262. Cool the residual liquid, which contains aniline sulphate dissolved in excess of dilute sulphuric acid, and apply the tests for aniline given on p. 283.

Phenyl Acetate. $CH_3COOC_6H_5$. (Method 1 modified.)

Although the acetylation of alcohols and amines by acetic anhydride is almost invariably carried out under anhydrous conditions owing to the ready hydrolysis of the anhydride, it has been shown by Chattaway (1931) that phenols, when dissolved in aqueous sodium hydroxide solution and shaken with acetic anhydride, undergo rapid and almost quantitative acetylation if ice is present to keep the temperature low throughout the reaction. The success of this method is due primarily to the acidic nature of the phenols, which enables them to form soluble sodium derivatives, capable of reacting with the acetic

$$CH_3CO\!\cdot\!O\!\cdot\!COCH_3 + Na\,OC_6H_5 = CH_3COOC_6H_5 + CH_3COONa$$

anhydride before the latter undergoes appreciable hydrolysis. The general conditions of the acetylation are thus similar to those used in the Schotten-Baumann method for benzoylation (p. 189).

When the phenol contains a carboxylic acid group, e.g., m- or p-hydroxy-benzoic acid, the acetylated derivative will of course remain in solution as the sodium salt, but is precipitated when the solution is subsequently acidified. Salicylic acid, however, cannot be acetylated under these conditions. Some amino-acids, e.g., glycine, can also be acetylated by this method.

Required : Phenol, 20 gms.; acetic anhydride, 30 c.c.

Dissolve 20 gms. of phenol in 140 c.c. (1·6 mols.) of 10% aqueous sodium hydroxide solution contained in a stout-walled bottle, and add about 150 gms. of crushed ice. Then add 30 c.c. (32 gms., 1·5 mols.) of acetic anhydride, cork the bottle securely, and shake the contents vigorously for about 5 minutes, by which time the reaction will be complete and an emulsion of phenyl acetate obtained. Pour the mixture into a separating-funnel. Owing to the density of the acetate being only slightly greater than that of water, a sharp separation is usually not rapidly obtained. It is advisable therefore to add about 10 c.c. of carbon tetrachloride, when, after shaking, a sharp and rapid separation of the heavy solution of the phenyl acetate in the tetrachloride is obtained. Run off this solution, reject the upper aqueous layer, return the solution to the funnel, and shake again with about 100 c.c. of very dilute sodium carbonate solution in order to remove traces of acetic acid or anhydride. Run off the lower layer into a small conical flask, dry over granular calcium chloride for 20–30 minutes and then filter through a small fluted filter-paper directly into a 50 c.c. distilling-flask. Fit the latter with a 360° thermometer and an air-condenser and distil the contents *slowly* by heating over a gauze. (The quantity of carbon tetrachloride present is too small to make the preliminary use of a water-condenser necessary.) The boiling-point of the mixture rises slowly but steadily to about 170° before the distillation of the carbon tetrachloride is complete, and then rises rapidly to about 193°. Collect the phenyl acetate as the fraction of b.p. 193–197°. Yield, 27 gms.

Phenyl acetate is a colourless liquid, of b.p. 196° and d, 1·08, almost insoluble in water and almost odourless.

β-**Naphthyl Acetate.** $CH_3COOC_{10}H_7$. Dissolve 5 gms. of pure β-naphthol in 25 c.c. (1·8 mols.) of 10% sodium hydroxide solution as before, add 50 gms. of crushed ice, and 5·5 c.c. (5·7 gms., 1·5 mols.) of acetic anhydride. Shake the mixture vigorously for about 10–15 minutes; the β-naphthyl acetate separates as colourless crystals. Filter at the pump, wash with water, drain, and dry thoroughly. Yield of crude material, 7 gms. (theoretical). Recrystallise from 60–80° petrol, from which, on cooling and scratching, the β-naphthyl acetate separates as colourless crystals, m.p. 71°: yield, 6·5 gms.

Acetyl-salicylic Acid (Aspirin). $C_6H_4\begin{smallmatrix}O·COCH_3·\\COOH.\end{smallmatrix}$ (Method 2.)

Required: Salicylic acid, 10 gms.; pyridine, 7 c.c.; acetyl chloride, 7·5 c.c.

Dissolve 10 gms. of salicylic acid (*o*-hydroxy-benzoic acid) in 7 c.c. of *dry* pyridine contained in a 100 c.c. conical flask. Then without delay (since this solution if allowed to stand tends to become a semi-solid mass) run in 7·5 c.c. (8·3 gms.) of acetyl chloride, adding about 1 c.c. of the chloride at a time, and shaking the mixture continuously during the addition. The heat of the reaction causes the temperature of the mixture to rise rapidly: therefore maintain the latter between 50° and 60° throughout the addition, cooling the flask occasionally in cold water if necessary. Finally heat the mixture on a boiling water-bath for 5 minutes,

$$CH_3COCl + HOC_6H_4COOH = CH_3COOC_6H_4COOH + HCl$$
$$\text{Salicylic Acid} \qquad\qquad \text{Aspirin}$$

and then, after cooling in cold water, pour it in a thin stream into about 300 c.c. of cold water, stirring the mixture vigorously meanwhile. The crude acetyl-salicylic acid either solidifies at once, or separates as an oil which rapidly crystallises as the stirring proceeds. Filter the solid product at the pump, wash thoroughly with water and drain. Recrystallise from a mixture of equal volumes of water and acetic acid: yield, 11 gms. (Alternatively, press the crude product between several sheets of drying-paper until *quite dry*, and then recrystallise from benzene: a sticky product will result, however, if traces of water still remain.) The acetyl-salicylic acid is obtained as colourless crystals, m.p. 136–137°.

It should be emphasised that salicylic acid can be readily acetylated by Method 1, and that the above preparation of acetyl-salicylic acid is given solely as an illustration of Method 2. To employ Method 1, add 10 gms. of salicylic acid to 20 c.c. of a mixture of equal volumes of acetic anhydride and acetic acid, and boil gently under reflux for 30 minutes. Then pour into about 200 c.c. of cold water in order to precipitate the acetyl salicylic-acid (11 gms) and finally recrystallise as above. Method 2, however, gives the purer product.

Acetyl-salicylic acid is largely used in medicine as an analgesic (*i.e.*, for removing pain) and as an antipyretic (*i.e.*, for reducing the body temperature).

Reactions of Aspirin. (1) *Distinction from Salicylic acid.* Shake up with water in two clean test-tubes a few crystals of (*a*) salicylic acid, (*b*) aspirin, a very dilute aqueous solution of each substance being thus obtained. Note that the addition of 1 drop of ferric chloride solution to (*a*) gives an immediate purple coloration, due to the free $-OH$ group, whereas (*b*) gives no coloration if the aspirin is pure.

(2) *Hydrolysis of Aspirin.* Gently boil a mixture of 3 gms. of aspirin and 50 c.c. of 10% sodium hydroxide solution in a 100 c.c. conical flask under reflux for 20 minutes. Then cool the solution thoroughly and add dilute sulphuric acid until the precipitation of the

$$CH_3COOC_6H_4COOH + 2NaOH = CH_3COONa + HOC_6H_4COONa + H_2O$$

salicylic acid is complete. Filter off the salicylic acid, recrystallise it from hot water, and confirm its identity by reaction (1) above. M.p. 156°.

The original filtrate still contains the acetic acid which is the other product of the hydrolysis. Therefore place this filtrate (which must be distinctly acid to litmus-paper) in a distilling-flask and distil off about 20 c.c. through a water-condenser. Then apply to the filtrate the tests for acetic acid given on p. 262.

Oxalic Acid. $\begin{array}{c} \text{COOH} \\ | \\ \text{COOH} \end{array}$, $2H_2O$.

Many aliphatic compounds are oxidised by concentrated nitric acid, the carbon atoms being split off in pairs, with the formation of oxalic acid. This disruptive oxidation is shown by many carbohydrates, *e.g.*, cane sugar, where the chains of secondary alcohol groups, $-CH(OH)\cdot CH(OH)\cdot CH(OH)\cdot CH(OH)-$, present in the molecule break down particularly readily to give oxalic acid.

It should be noted that aliphatic compounds (except the paraffins) are *usually* oxidised by concentrated nitric acid, whereas aromatic compounds (including the hydrocarbons) are usually nitrated by the concentrated acid and oxidised by the dilute acid. As an example of the latter, benzaldehyde, C_6H_5CHO, when treated with concentrated nitric acid gives *m*-nitrobenzaldehyde, $NO_2C_6H_4CHO$, but with dilute nitric acid gives benzoic acid, C_6H_4COOH.

Required : Cane sugar, 30 gms.; nitric acid, 150 c.c.

Owing to the copious evolution of nitrous fumes, this preparation must be carried out in a fume-cupboard having an *efficient draught*. Place 30 gms. of coarsely powdered cane sugar (sucrose) in a 750 c.c. flat-bottomed flask, add 150 c.c. of concentrated nitric acid and heat the flask on a boiling water-bath. As the mixture becomes warm, the greater part of the sugar dissolves and a vigorous but harmless reaction, accompanied by a tremendous evolution of nitrous fumes, takes place. Immediately the evolution of gas starts, remove the flask from the water-bath and place it on a wooden block or some similar non-conducting surface. When the reaction subsides (after about 15 minutes) pour the hot solution into an evaporating-basin, wash out the flask with about 20 c.c. of concentrated nitric acid, and then evaporate the acid solution on the water-bath until it has a volume of about 25 c.c. Some oxidation continues in the solution during the evaporation, which is comparatively rapid. Now add about 50 c.c. of water to the solution, and again evaporate to about 25 c.c. Cool the solution thoroughly in ice-water; oxalic acid rapidly crystallises. When crystallisation is complete, filter at the pump, and then recrystallise from a small quantity of hot water. Dry by pressing between pads of drying-paper, or in an atmospheric desiccator, but not in an oven where partial loss of water of crystallisation may occur. Yield, 10–11 gms. The hydrated acid has m.p. 101°; the anhydrous acid decomposes on heating.

For reactions of oxalic acid, see p. 264.

Formic Acid, HCOOH (in aqueous solution), and Lead Formate, $(HCOO)_2Pb$.

When a mixture of anhydrous glycerol and crystalline oxalic acid,

$(COOH)_2,2H_2O$, is heated the glycerol undergoes esterification, giving first glyceryl monoxalate (A): the latter, however, decomposes as the temperature

$$CH_2(OH){\cdot}CH(OH){\cdot}CH_2(OH) + (COOH)_2$$
$$= H_2O + CH_2(OH){\cdot}CH(OH){\cdot}CH_2OOC{\cdot}COOH \ (A)$$
$$CH_2(OH){\cdot}CH(OH){\cdot}CH_2OOC{\cdot}COOH$$
$$= CO_2 + CH_2(OH){\cdot}CH(OH){\cdot}CH_2OOCH \ (B)$$
$$CH_2(OH){\cdot}CH(OH){\cdot}CH_2OOCH + H_2O$$
$$= CH_2(OH){\cdot}CH(OH){\cdot}CH_2(OH) + HCOOH$$

reaches about 100°, losing carbon dioxide and giving glyceryl monoformate (B). On further heating, particularly if more oxalic acid is added, the mono-formate is hydrolysed (the necessary water being provided both by the oxalic acid and by the first reaction), and consequently a distillate of aqueous formic acid is obtained.

Required: Glycerol, 70 c.c.; oxalic acid, 40 gms.; lead carbonate.

Since glycerol is a very hygroscopic substance, it is necessary first to ensure that the sample used is anhydrous. For this purpose, place about 70 c.c. in a porcelain evaporating-basin, and heat it carefully over a gauze (preferably in a fume-cupboard), stirring it steadily with a thermometer until the temperature is 175–180°: then maintain this temperature for a further 5 minutes. Allow the glycerol to cool, but while it is still warm (*i.e.*, before it becomes viscous) pour 50 c.c. (63 gms.) into a 250 c.c. distilling-flask containing 40 gms. of powdered crystalline oxalic acid. Fit a thermometer in the flask so that the bulb is completely immersed in the glycerol mixture, and then fit a water-condenser to the flask. Heat the mixture carefully over a gauze so that the temperature rises to 110–120°, and then adjust the heating so that the temperature remains within these limits. A vigorous effervescence of carbon dioxide occurs, and the aqueous formic acid begins slowly to distil over. When the effervescence tends to subside, remove the Bunsen flame and allow the temperature to fall to 70–80°: then add a further 40 gms. of powdered oxalic acid, and continue the heating as before. Ultimately 25–30 c.c. of distillate are obtained, the total period of heating being about 1 hour. While the distillation is proceeding, withdraw a few c.c. of the distillate and apply Tests 2, 3 and 4 for formic acid given on p. 264.

To obtain lead formate, add about 100 c.c. of water to the distillate and then stir powdered lead carbonate into the gently heated solution until no further effervescence of carbon dioxide occurs. Then boil the mixture vigorously and filter at the pump, using a Buchner funnel. Evaporate the clear filtrate by direct boiling in a beaker until crystals appear on the surface, and then

86   PRACTICAL ORGANIC CHEMISTRY

allow to cool, finally chilling in ice-water. The lead formate separates as colourless crystals; filter off, wash with a small quantity of cold water, and dry. Yield, about 6 gms.

A considerable amount of the formic acid, however, still remains behind in the distilling-flask as the unhydrolysed monoformate. Therefore, if time allows, dilute the residue in the flask with about an equal volume of water, and then steam-distil, the monoformate ester being thus completely hydrolysed and the formic acid then driven over in the steam. Collect about 400 c.c. of distillate. Add this distillate to that obtained by direct heating of the reaction mixture and then treat with lead carbonate as described above. Total yield of lead formate is now about 40 gms.

Lead formate is only slightly soluble in cold water, and insoluble in hot absolute alcohol: it can therefore be readily distinguished from lead acetate or "sugar of lead" because, quite apart from chemical tests, the acetate is readily soluble in cold water and moderately soluble in alcohol.

Lead formate separates from aqueous solution without water of crystallisation. It is therefore frequently used for the preparation of anhydrous formic acid. For this purpose, the powdered lead formate is placed in the inner tube of an ordinary jacketed condenser, and there held loosely in position by plugs of glass-wool. The condenser is then clamped in an oblique position and the lower end fitted into a receiver closed with a calcium chloride tube. A current of dry hydrogen sulphide is passed down the inner tube of the condenser, whilst steam is passed through the jacket. The formic acid which is liberated

$$(HCOO)_2Pb + H_2S = 2HCOOH + PbS.$$

collects in the receiver, and is then purified from dissolved hydrogen sulphide by redistillation over a further quantity of lead formate.

For reactions of formic acid and formates, see p. 264.

If the reaction mixture used in the above preparation of formic acid is heated to 190–200°, the glyceryl monoformate which has escaped hydrolysis undergoes decomposition, with the loss of carbon dioxide and water, and the

$$CH_2(OH) \cdot CH(OH) \cdot CH_2OOCH = CH_2 : CH \cdot CH_2OH + CO_2 + H_2O$$

formation of allyl alcohol.

The neutral glyceryl oxalate (C), which is also formed in the reaction mixture, loses carbon dioxide at the higher temperature and thus also gives allyl alcohol.

$$\begin{array}{ccc} CH_2OH \cdot CH & - & CH_2 \\ (C) \quad | & & | \\ OOC.COO \end{array}$$

Potassium Antimonyl Tartrate (Tartar Emetic).
$C_4H_4O_6KSbO, \frac{1}{2}H_2O.$

Tartaric acid is noteworthy for (a) the excellent way in which the majority of its salts crystallise, and (b) the frequent occurrence of salts having mixed metallic (or electropositive) radicals. Examples of the latter are sodium potassium tartrate (or Rochelle salt), $C_4H_4O_6NaK$, used for the preparation of Fehling's solution (p. 426), sodium ammonium tartrate, $C_4H_4O_6NaNH_4$, used by Pasteur for his early optical resolution experiments, and potassium anti-monyl tartrate (or Tartar Emetic), $C_4H_4O_6K(SbO)$. The latter is prepared by boiling a solution of potassium hydrogen tartrate (or "cream of tartar") with antimony trioxide, when the acidic hydrogen atom is replaced by the mono-

$$2\ \begin{matrix} CH(OH)COOK \\ | \\ CH(OH)COOH \end{matrix} + Sb_2O_3 = 2\ \begin{matrix} CH(OH)COOK \\ | \\ CH(OH)COO(SbO) \end{matrix} + H_2O$$

valent antimonyl (–Sb:O) radical.

Required: Potassium hydrogen tartrate, 10 gms.; antimony trioxide, 10 gms.

Add 10 gms. of potassium hydrogen tartrate and 10 gms. of antimony trioxide (each being finely powdered) to 50 c.c. of water contained in a small flask, and boil the mixture under a reflux water-condenser for 15 minutes. Then filter hot, using a Buchner funnel and flask which have been preheated by the filtration of some boiling distilled water. Pour the clear filtrate into a beaker and allow to cool. Potassium antimonyl tartrate separates as colourless crystals. Filter, drain and dry. Yield, 10 gms. The product can be recrystallised from hot water, but this is usually not necessary.

Tartar emetic, as its name indicates, is used medicinally to cause vomiting. For the preparation of tartar emetic intended for medicinal use, pure antimony trioxide, free (in particular) from traces of arsenic, must of course be employed.

Acetic Anhydride. $CH_3CO \cdot O \cdot COCH_3$

Although some dibasic acids, *e.g.*, succinic acid and phthalic acid, readily lose water on heating with the formation of cyclic anhydrides, most monobasic

$$\begin{matrix} CH_2COOH \\ | \\ CH_2COOH \end{matrix} \xrightarrow[\longrightarrow]{Heat} \begin{matrix} CH_2CO \\ | \quad\ \rangle O + H_2O \\ CH_2CO \end{matrix}$$

Succinic acid.　　　　Succinic anhydride.

carboxylic acids when heated merely distil unchanged. Their anhydrides can however be prepared by the interaction of the acid chloride with a metallic salt of the acid itself. Thus acetyl chloride and sodium acetate readily interact with

$$CH_3CO\ |Cl + Na|\ OOCCH_3 = CH_3CO \cdot O \cdot COCH_3 + NaCl$$

the formation of acetic anhydride.

Required: Anhydrous sodium acetate, 21 gms.; acetyl chloride, 15 c.c.

Place 21 gms. (a 20% excess) of powdered anhydrous sodium

acetate* in a 100 c.c. round-bottomed flask fitted with a reflux water-condenser, and cool the flask in ice-water. Place 15 c.c. (16·5 gms.) of acetyl chloride in a dropping-funnel fitted into the top of the condenser by means of a grooved cork (cf. Fig. 37, p. 50). Now allow the acetyl chloride to run slowly down into the chilled sodium acetate, thoroughly mixing the contents by shaking as soon as the product becomes sufficiently liquid. Then heat the flask on a boiling water-bath for 10 minutes to complete the reaction. Next disconnect the condenser and fit it by means of a "knee-tube" (Fig. 43, p. 72) to the flask for distillation. Heat the flask with a luminous smoky Bunsen flame (without a gauze), waving the flame around the base of the flask to ensure uniform heating and to minimise risk of cracking: continue heating until no more distillate passes over. Now fractionally distil the crude acetic anhydride *slowly* from a 40 c.c. distilling-flask, preferably using an air-condenser. A small quantity passes over at 130–135° (due to traces of free acetic acid) and the major fraction at 135–140°. Yield, 18 gms.

Add a few drops of the distillate to an aqueous silver nitrate solution containing some dilute nitric acid and warm gently: no silver chloride should be precipitated, indicating the complete absence of unchanged acetyl chloride.

Acetic anhydride is a colourless liquid, having b.p. 138° and *d*, 1·08: it has a sharp pungent odour resembling that of acetic acid. It is used in organic chemistry chiefly as an acetylating agent, for which purpose it is frequently mixed with acetic acid, sodium acetate, *etc.*: for examples of such acetylations see pp. 79, 112–114.

For reactions of acetic anhydride, see p. 274.

Acid Amides.

Acid amides may be prepared by the following methods:

(1) *Dehydration of the corresponding ammonium salt.* Thus ammonium acetate on heating loses water giving acetamide. An excess of acetic acid is

$$CH_3COONH_4 = CH_3CONH_2 + H_2O$$

* For this preparation, it is particularly necessary that the sodium acetate should be free from traces of water. The anhydrous material can be prepared by gently heating the hydrated salt ($CH_3COONa,3H_2O$) in an evaporating-basin. The salt dissolves in its water of crystallisation and resolidifies as this water is driven off: further heating then causes the anhydrous material to melt. Stir the molten anhydrous material to avoid charring, and then allow it to cool in a desiccator. Powder the cold material rapidly in a mortar, and bottle without delay.

If a sample of the anhydrous salt is taken from stock, it should preferably be melted, allowed to cool, and then pulverised.

usually added before heating, in order to suppress thermal dissociation of the ammonium acetate into ammonia and acetic acid.

(2) *By the action of Concentrated Aqueous Ammonia on:*

(*a*) *Esters*

$$\begin{array}{c}\text{CO} \vert \text{OC}_2\text{H}_5 \quad \text{H} \vert \text{NH}_2 \\ \vert \qquad\qquad + \qquad = \\ \text{CO} \vert \text{OC}_2\text{H}_5 \quad \text{H} \vert \text{NH}_2 \end{array} \qquad \begin{array}{c}\text{CONH}_2 \\ \vert \qquad\qquad + \ 2\text{C}_2\text{H}_5\text{OH} \\ \text{CONH}_2 \end{array}$$

Ethyl oxalate   Oxamide

(*b*) *Acid Chlorides* $\text{C}_6\text{H}_5\text{CO}\vert\text{Cl} + \text{H}\vert\text{NH}_2 = \text{C}_6\text{H}_5\text{CONH}_2 + \text{HCl}$

     Benzoyl Chloride   Benzamide

(*c*) *Acid Anhydrides*

$$\text{CH}_3\text{CO}\vert\text{O}\cdot\text{OCCH}_3 + \text{H}\vert\text{NH}_2 = \text{CH}_3\text{CONH}_2 + \text{CH}_3\text{COOH}$$

  Acetic anhydride   Acetamide

In reactions (*b*) and (*c*) the hydrochloric and acetic acids formed are of course at once neutralised by the excess of ammonia.

Method (1) is most frequently used for aliphatic acid amides, while Methods (2*a*), (2*b*) and (2*c*) are used most frequently for aromatic acid amides. Of the last three methods, the Acid Chloride Method (2*b*) is the most rapid and certain. The Ester Method (2*a*) is practicable only when the amide is insoluble in water, and even then is often very slow unless the ester itself is appreciably soluble in the aqueous ammonia solution.

For reactions of acid amides, see p. 271.

Acetamide. CH_3CONH_2. (Method 1.)

Required: Ammonium carbonate, 15 gms.; acetic acid, 50 c.c.

Add 15 gms. of finely powdered ammonium carbonate gradually to 50 c.c. of glacial acetic acid contained in a 150 c.c. round-bottomed flask, shaking the mixture during the addition to ensure a steady evolution of carbon dioxide. When all the carbonate has dissolved and the evolution of carbon dioxide has ceased, fit a reflux air-condenser to the flask and boil the solution *gently* for 30 minutes, when the dehydration of the ammonium acetate will be complete. Now remove the condenser and fit a fractionating column to the flask: for this purpose a 4-pear column may be used, but far better results are obtained if a column of the type shown in Fig. 12(B) (p. 28), in which the glass sections themselves occupy a height of about 12 cm., is used. Fit a 360° thermometer in the column, and fit the air-condenser to the side-arm for distillation. Now distil the liquid through the column *very slowly* (to give about 1 drop of distillate every 3 seconds) until the temperature reaches 170°: it is very important that this operation should be carried out slowly in order to distil over as much water and excess acetic acid as possible, and thus to leave almost pure acetamide in the flask. Without delay, pour the hot molten acetamide into a small (50 c.c.) distilling-flask, and attach the side-arm of the flask to a short glass tube (about 30 cms. long and 12 mm. internal diameter) to act as an air-condenser. Distil the acetamide carefully at such a rate that none escapes condensation, and that none crystallises while still in the condenser. Collect the fraction boiling between 215° and 225° directly into a weighed specimen-tube, where it should crystallise readily on cooling. Yield, 15 gms.

Acetamide is thus obtained as a colourless crystalline solid, which has a characteristic odour of mice, stated to be due to the presence of small quantities of methyl-acetamide, $CH_3CONHCH_3$. The acetamide can be purified and rendered odourless by recrystallisation from acetone, and then has m.p. 82°, b.p. 223°. If this recrystallisation is contemplated, the distilled material should be collected directly into a small weighed beaker or conical flask, so that the solidified acetamide can be readily broken up and removed.

Oxamide. $NH_2CO \cdot CONH_2$. (Method 2(a), p. 89.)

Required: Concentrated ammonia, 50 c.c.; ethyl oxalate, 10 c.c.

Oxamide differs from most aliphatic acid amides in being almost insoluble in water, and therefore can be readily prepared from the diethyl ester by Method 2(*a*). Place a mixture of 50 c.c. of concentrated (*d*, 0·880) ammonia solution and 50 c.c. of water in a 200 c.c. conical flask, for which a well-fitting cork is available. (The large excess of ammonia solution is employed chiefly to prevent too great a rise in temperature during the reaction.) Now add 10 c.c. (10·9 gms.) of ethyl oxalate, cork the flask *securely* and shake vigorously: the mixture becomes perceptibly warm, and therefore throughout the shaking hold the cork tightly in position, with the flask pointing *away* from the operator (and from neighbouring students!). At intervals, release the pressure by cautiously removing the cork. The oxamide rapidly separates as a white powder and after 15 minutes' shaking the reaction is complete. Filter off the oxamide at the pump, wash it well with water and drain thoroughly. Dry by pressing between sheets of drying-paper, or in a desiccator. Yield, 5·5–6·0 gms. The low solubility of oxamide in most liquids makes recrystallisation very difficult: the product obtained in this preparation when dried is pure, however, and recrystallisation is therefore not necessary. Oxamide has no definite melting-point, as on heating it partly sublimes and partly decomposes.

Succinamide. NH$_2$COCH$_2$·CH$_2$CONH$_2$. (Method 2(a)). Add 5 c.c. (5·8 gms.) of dimethyl succinate to a mixture of 50 c.c. of water and 25 c.c. of concentrated (d, 0·880) aqueous ammonia solution in a 150 c.c. conical flask. Cork the flask and shake the contents: the dimethyl succinate rapidly dissolves to give a clear solution. Allow the solution to stand; after about 1 hour the succinamide starts to crystallise, and then continues to separate for some time. Next day, filter off the succinamide at the pump, wash with cold water, and drain. Recrystallise from water, from which the succinamide separates as colourless crystals: the latter soften at 240° and melt at 254–255° with

$$\begin{matrix} CH_2CONH_2 \\ | \\ CH_2CONH_2 \end{matrix} = \begin{matrix} CH_2CO \\ | \quad >NH + NH_3 \\ CH_2CO \end{matrix}$$

considerable effervescence, as ammonia is liberated and succinimide formed by ring closure. Yield, 2·5 gms.

Benzamide. C$_6$H$_5$CONH$_2$. (Method 2(b), p. 89.)

Required: Concentrated ammonia, 50 c.c.; benzoyl chloride, 10 c.c.

Carry out this preparation in precisely the same way as the above preparation of oxamide, using 10 c.c. (12·1 gms.) of benzoyl chloride instead of the ethyl oxalate, and *observing the same precautions.* Considerably more heat is generated in this reaction; therefore hold the cork very securely in position during the shaking. After vigorous shaking for 15 minutes, no trace of oily benzoyl chloride remains. Filter off the fine flakes of benzamide, wash with cold water, and then recrystallise from hot water: yield, 7·5 gms. Colourless crystals, m.p. 130°.

Hydrolysis of Benzamide. When acid amides are hydrolysed, the corresponding acid and ammonia are formed. Consequently the hydrolysis, which is extremely slow with water alone, is hastened con-

$$C_6H_5CO\;NH_2 + H\;OH = C_6H_5COOH + NH_3$$

siderably by the addition of either caustic alkalis (which give the alkali salt of the acid and liberate ammonia) or mineral acids (which neutralise the ammonia and liberate the organic acid). Caustic alkalis usually effect the more rapid hydrolysis, and their use is to be preferred.

Place 3 gms. of benzamide and 50 c.c. of 10% aqueous sodium hydroxide solution in a 150 c.c. conical flask fitted with a reflux water-condenser, and boil the mixture gently for 30 minutes, during which period ammonia is freely evolved. Then detach the condenser and continue the boiling in the open flask for 2–3 minutes to drive off residual ammonia. Now cool the solution in ice-water, and add concentrated hydrochloric acid until the mixture is strongly acid. Benzoic acid immediately separates. Allow the mixture to stand in the ice-water for a few minutes, and then filter off the benzoic acid at the pump, wash with cold water, and drain. Recrystallise from hot water. The benzoic acid is obtained as colourless crystals, m.p. 121°, almost insoluble in cold water: yield, 2·7 gms. (almost theoretical). Confirm the identity of the benzoic acid by the tests given on p. 261.

Mercury Benzamide. $(C_6H_5CONH)_2Hg$.

Acid amides have weakly amphoteric properties, and thus give salts such as $C_6H_5CONH_2,HCl$ with strong acids, and salts of the type $C_6H_5CONHNa$ with strong bases. These compounds have to be prepared at low temperatures to avoid hydrolysis, and are difficult to isolate. The *mercury* derivatives can, however, usually be readily prepared, because mercuric oxide is too feebly basic to cause hydrolysis of the amide, and the heavy mercuric derivatives crystallise well.

Required: Mercuric oxide, 5 gms.; benzamide, 4 gms.; alcohol, 50 c.c.

Add 5 gms. of *finely powdered* mercuric oxide and 4 gms. of benzamide to 50 c.c. of alcohol, and boil the mixture under a reflux water-condenser for 30 minutes. Now filter the hot solution through

$$2C_6H_5CONH_2 + HgO = (C_6H_5CONH)_2Hg + H_2O$$

a fluted filter-paper to remove unchanged mercuric oxide: if a fine suspension of the oxide passes through with the first portion of the filtrate, return the latter to the filter, when the remainder of the alcoholic solution will pass through as a clear filtrate. Cool the latter in ice-water, whereupon colourless crystals of mercury benzamide will separate. Finally filter the crystals at the pump, wash with a small quantity of alcohol, and then drain and dry. M.p. 222–223°: yield, 1·5 gms. The mercury benzamide so obtained may be recrystallised from hot alcohol, but this is not necessary.

Nitriles (or Cyanides).

Aliphatic nitriles (or alkyl cyanides) can be prepared by the following methods:

(1) Dehydration of the corresponding acid amides. This process usually requires phosphorus pentoxide (correctly termed phosphoric anhydride) as a dehydrating agent.

$$CH_3CONH_2 - H_2O = CH_3CN$$
$$\text{Acetamide} \qquad \text{Acetonitrile}$$

(2) By the action of potassium cyanide on the corresponding alkyl halide.

$$CH_3 I + K CN = CH_3CN + KI$$

NOTE.—*Silver* cyanide in these circumstances gives the *iso*-cyanide, CH_3NC.

(3) By the direct addition of hydrogen cyanide to aldehydes and ketones, giving cyanhydrins:

$$CH_3CHO + HCN = CH_3CH(OH)CN$$
$$\text{Acetaldehyde cyanhydrin (Lactonitrile)}$$
$$(CH_3)_2CO + HCN = (CH_3)_2C(OH)CN$$
$$\text{Acetone cyanhydrin (α-Hydroxy-}iso\text{-butyronitrile)}$$

By this method, the nitrile of an α-hydroxy acid is necessarily obtained.

Aromatic nitriles (or aryl cyanides) can be obtained by methods (1) and (3), but not by method (2). In addition, aromatic nitriles can be prepared by two other methods, (a) from the corresponding diazo compound by Sandmeyer's Reaction (p. 149), (b) by fusing the corresponding sulphonic acid (or its salts)

$$C_6H_5|SO_3K + K|CN = C_6H_5CN + K_2SO_3$$

with potassium cyanide.

Acetonitrile (Methyl Cyanide). CH_3CN. (Method 1.)

Required: Acetamide, 20 gms.; phosphorus pentoxide, 35 gms.

In view of the great avidity of phosphorus pentoxide for water, the apparatus used in this experiment should be assembled before the pentoxide is weighed out. Fit a 500 c.c. bolt-head flask to a water-condenser (see Fig. 43, p. 72). Disconnect the flask, then twist some glazed paper into the form of a cone, and push the narrow end of the latter (slightly opened) into the neck of the flask. Using a rough balance, weigh out on pieces of glazed paper first 20 gms. of dry acetamide, and then (as quickly as possible) 35 gms. of phosphorus pentoxide. With the aid of a spatula, tip the pentoxide without delay down the paper cylinder into the flask, then add the acetamide similarly, remove the paper, and at once cork the flask and mix the contents by gentle shaking. (Before throwing away the paper used for weighing the pentoxide, wet it thoroughly, otherwise residual pentoxide may cause it to smoulder and possibly inflame.) Now heat the flask by direct application of a Bunsen burner, using however a luminous smoky flame, and applying it uniformly over the bottom of the flask. The acetamide melts and then the mixture starts to effervesce gently. Adjust the heating so that the acetonitrile distils slowly over; use a small conical flask as a receiver, and continue heating until no more distillate can be readily obtained.

The crude acetonitrile contains as impurity chiefly acetic acid, arising from the action of phosphoric acid on the acetamide. Therefore add to the nitrile about half its volume of water, and then add powdered dry potassium carbonate until the well-shaken mixture is saturated. The potassium carbonate neutralises any acetic acid present, and at the same time "salts out" the otherwise water-soluble nitrile as a separate upper layer. Allow to stand for 20 minutes with further occasional shaking. Now decant the mixed liquids into a separating-funnel, run off the lower carbonate layer as completely as possible, and then pour off the acetonitrile into a 25 c.c. distilling-flask into which about 3–4 gms. of phosphorus pentoxide have been placed *immediately* before. Fit a thermometer and water-condenser to the flask and distil the acetonitrile slowly, collecting the fraction of b.p. 79–82°. Yield 9·5 gms. (12 c.c.).

Acetonitrile is a colourless liquid, of b.p. 82° and *d*, 0·790. It has a faint but pleasant odour: if a sample has a faint odour of mice, it indicates the presence of unchanged acetamide.

For reactions of acetonitrile, see p. 271.

Hydrolysis of Acetonitrile. Nitriles, like acid amides, undergo hydrolysis to give the corresponding carboxylic acid and ammonia. Consequently

$$CH_3CN + 2H_2O = CH_3COOH + NH_3$$

the hydrolysis (which is *extremely* slow with hot water alone) is hastened considerably by the presence of caustic alkalis or of mineral acids. The aliphatic nitriles, being soluble in water, are readily hydrolysed by sodium hydroxide or by hydrochloric acid. The aromatic nitriles (such as benzonitrile, C_6H_5CN) are almost insoluble in water and, although usually readily hydrolysed by alkalis, are only very slowly hydrolysed by hydrochloric acid: concentrated sulphuric acid (70%) causes rapid hydrolysis but there are practical objections to its use (p. 151). Consequently students are recommended to use 10% aqueous sodium hydroxide for hydrolysing nitriles generally, increasing the concentration of the hydroxide to 15 or 20% for very stable nitriles.

Boil a mixture of 5 c.c. (4 gms.) of acetonitrile and 75 c.c. of 10% aqueous sodium hydroxide solution in a 200 c.c. flask under a reflux water-condenser for 30 minutes, when hydrolysis will be complete. Detach the condenser and boil the solution in the open flask for a few minutes to drive off all free ammonia. Then cool the solution, and add dilute sulphuric acid (1 volume of concentrated acid: 2 volumes of water) until the solution is distinctly acid to litmus-paper. Fit the flask to a water-condenser by means of a bent delivery (or "knee") tube, and distil off about 10–15 c.c. of the liquid. Confirm the presence of acetic acid in this distillate by the tests given on p. 262.

Urea (or Carbamide). $CO(NH_2)_2$.

Urea (the diamide of carbonic acid) can be prepared by the historic method of Wöhler. When an aqueous solution of ammonium cyanate is allowed to stand, the cyanate undergoes molecular rearrangement to urea, and an equilibrium mixture containing about 93% of urea is thus formed. Urea is

$$NH_4CNO \rightleftharpoons NH_2CONH_2$$

less soluble in water than ammonium cyanate; therefore if the solution is evaporated, urea begins to separate, and consequently the ammonium cyanate undergoes steady conversion to urea in order to maintain the above equilibrium. Ultimately, if the solution is evaporated to dryness, the conversion to urea becomes complete.

Ammonium cyanate, because of its instability in solution, is usually prepared

$$(NH_4)_2SO_4 + 2KCNO = 2NH_4CNO + K_2SO_4$$

by mixing aqueous solutions of ammonium sulphate and potassium cyanate. Complete evaporation then gives a mixture of potassium sulphate and urea, from which the urea may be extracted with hot absolute alcohol, in which potassium sulphate is insoluble.

Required: Ammonium sulphate, 10 gms.; potassium cyanate, 12 gms.

Add 10 gms. of ammonium sulphate and 12 gms. of potassium cyanate to 75 c.c. of water contained in an evaporating-basin. Evaporate the mixed solution to dryness on a water-bath. During the evaporation, a crust of potassium sulphate crystals forms on the surface of the solution, and must be repeatedly broken by stirring with a glass rod, otherwise the evaporation, which even in favourable circumstances takes 4–5 hours, becomes extremely slow: the stirring also prevents any solid material from creeping over the edge of the basin. It is essential that the evaporation be continued until the solid residue is *completely* dry. Now transfer the residue to a 100 c.c. flask fitted with a reflux water-condenser, add 40 c.c. of absolute alcohol, and boil gently for 5–10 minutes in order to extract the urea. Filter the boiling solution through a small fluted filter-paper, and cool the filtrate in ice-water. Urea separates in colourless crystals, which when filtered at the pump, drained and dried, have m.p. 132°: yield, 4 gms. A small second crop may be obtained by evaporating the alcoholic filtrate to about 10 c.c., and again cooling in ice-water.

Urea is a monacidic base, and forms a characteristic nitrate, $CO(NH_2)_2, HNO_3$, and oxalate, $2CO(NH_2)_2, (COOH)_2, 2H_2O$. To prepare the nitrate, dissolve 1 gm. of urea in about 5 c.c. of water, and add 2 c.c. of concentrated nitric acid. White crystals of the nitrate separate almost immediately. Filter at the pump, drain thoroughly, and then wash with a few c.c. of alcohol and ether in turn.

The oxalate is prepared in a similar way, using a solution of 1·2 gms. of oxalic acid in about 15 c.c. of water. On stirring the mixed solutions with a rod, the oxalate crystallises out.

The chief disadvantage of the above preparation of urea is the long time required for the complete evaporation of the mixed solutions, particularly as occasional stirring is required throughout this operation. A more rapid evaporation is obtained if ammonium chloride is used instead of the sulphate, as the potassium chloride formed is more soluble in water than potassium sulphate: the chloride is, however, slightly soluble in alcohol, and an impure sample of urea is thus obtained. The following preparation of monophenyl-urea (Method 1) may well be substituted for that of urea, as the reaction involved (molecular rearrangement of the cyanate of an amino compound) is the same, but since the monophenyl-urea is insoluble in cold water, the long evaporation is avoided.

For reactions of urea, see p. 273; for estimation, pp. 363, 419.

When the potassium cyanate used in the above preparation is replaced by potassium thiocyanate (or sulphocyanide), the ammonium thiocyanate formed undergoes partial rearrangement to thio-urea (or sulpho-urea). Even above

$$NH_4CNS \rightleftharpoons NH_2CSNH_2$$

100°, however, the conversion to thio-urea is incomplete, and the method does not readily give a satisfactory preparation of thio-urea.

Monophenyl-urea. $C_6H_5NH \cdot CO \cdot NH_2$. (First Method.)

Mono-substituted and unsymmetrical di-substituted ureas may be prepared by a modification of Wöhler's urea synthesis, salts of primary or secondary amines being used instead of the ammonium salt for interaction with potassium cyanate. Thus when an aqueous solution containing both aniline hydrochloride and potassium cyanate is heated, aniline cyanate is first formed, and then

$$C_6H_5NH_2,HCl + KCNO = C_6H_5NH_2,HCNO + KCl$$
$$C_6H_5NH_2,HCNO = C_6H_5NHCONH_2$$

by the usual molecular rearrangement is converted into monophenyl-urea.

Required: Aniline hydrochloride, 5 gms.; potassium cyanate, 4 gms.

Dissolve 5 gms. of aniline hydrochloride in 120 c.c. of hot water contained in a 200 c.c. conical flask and then add 4 gms. of potassium cyanate. Heat the solution on a water-bath for 30 minutes, adding about 1–2 gms. of animal charcoal towards the end of the heating if a slight turbidity has developed. Now bring the solution quickly to the boil over a gauze, and filter it at the pump, using a Buchner funnel and flask which have been pre-heated by the filtration of some boiling distilled water. The clear filtrate on cooling deposits fine colourless crystals of monophenyl-urea. Filter off at the pump and then recrystallise from hot water: slow cooling of the hot aqueous solution causes the monophenyl-urea to separate in large crystals. Yield, 3·0–3·5 gms.; m.p. 147°.

Monophenyl- and Diphenyl-urea. (Second Method.)

These substances, having the formula $C_6H_5NHCONH_2$ and $OC(NHC_6H_5)_2$ respectively, are both formed when an aqueous solution of urea and aniline hydrochloride is heated. Their subsequent separation is based on the fact that diphenyl-urea is insoluble in boiling water, whereas monophenyl-urea is readily soluble. The formation of these compounds can be explained as follows.

When urea is dissolved in water, a small proportion of it undergoes molecular rearrangement back to ammonium cyanate, an equilibrium thus being formed.

$$NH_2CONH_2 \rightleftharpoons NH_4CNO$$

The ammonium cyanate then reacts with the aniline hydrochloride giving aniline cyanate which, as in the previous preparation, gives in turn monophenyl-urea.

$$NH_4CNO + C_6H_5NH_2,HCl = NH_4Cl + C_6H_5NH_2,HCNO$$
$$C_6H_5NH_2,HCNO = C_6H_5NHCONH_2$$

A portion of the monophenyl-urea then reacts with the aniline (formed by the hydrolysis of the aniline hydrochloride or cyanate) to give diphenyl-urea and ammonia, a reaction which probably proceeds through the

$$C_6H_5NH\cdot CO\cdot NH_2 + H_2NC_6H_5 = C_6H_5NH\cdot CO\cdot NHC_6H_5 + NH_3$$

intermediate formation of an unstable addition product of the formula $C_6H_5NHC(OH)(NH_2)NHC_6H_5$. The relative amounts of the monophenyl- and the diphenyl-urea formed will therefore depend chiefly on the time during which the aqueous solution is heated.

Required : Aniline hydrochloride, 12 gms.; urea, 6 gms.

Dissolve 12 gms. of aniline hydrochloride and 6 gms. of urea in 50 c.c. of warm water, and then filter the solution through a fluted filter to remove any suspended impurities which may have been introduced with the aniline hydrochloride. Transfer the clear filtrate to a 200 c.c. conical flask, fit the latter with a reflux water-condenser, and boil the solution *gently* over a gauze for about 1½ hours. Crystals of diphenyl-urea usually start to separate after about 30–40 minutes' boiling. Occasionally however, the solution becomes supersaturated with the diphenyl-urea and therefore remains clear: in this case, if the solution is vigorously shaken after about 40 minutes' heating, a sudden separation of the crystalline diphenyl compound will usually occur. The further deposition of the crystals during the re-mainder of the heating may cause the solution to "bump": if this bumping becomes too vigorous, remove the flame for a few minutes to allow the solution to cool slightly and thus to ensure it is not superheated, then add some fragments of unglazed porcelain down the condenser, and continue the heating.

When the 1½ hours' boiling is complete, preheat a Buchner funnel and flask by pouring some boiling water through the funnel with the filter-paper already in position, and then quickly filter the boiling solution. Transfer the filtrate to a beaker to cool, and then wash the insoluble residue of diphenyl-urea on the filter twice with hot water, and drain thoroughly. Cool the filtrate in ice-water; the monophenyl-urea separates as colourless needles. Filter at the pump and drain well. Recrystallise the

E

crude product from boiling water, as in the previous preparation. Yield of monophenyl-urea, 2·5–3 gms.; m.p. 147°.

The insoluble residue of diphenyl-urea from the original filtration is chemically almost pure. It may be recrystallised from hot methylated spirit or alcohol, a process which will be necessary if the material contains fragments of porcelain. When using either of these solvents, however, the hot solution should be filtered* at the pump using a *small* Buchner funnel and flask which again have been preheated by the filtration of some of the hot solvent, as the solution when cooled rapidly deposits the diphenyl-urea. *Sym*-Diphenyl-urea (or carbanilide) is thus obtained as fine colourless crystals, m.p. 237°; yield, 1–1·5 gms.

Hofmann's Primary Amine Synthesis.

The preparation of pure primary amines by the interaction of alkyl halides and ammonia is very difficult, because the primary amine which is formed reacts with unchanged alkyl halide to give the secondary amine: the latter

$$C_2H_5I + HNH_2 = C_2H_5NH_2 + HI$$
$$C_2H_5I + HNC_2H_5 = (C_2H_5)_2NH + HI$$
$$C_2H_5I + HN(C_2H_5)_2 = (C_2H_5)_3N + HI$$
$$C_2H_5I + (C_2H_5)_3N = (C_2H_5)_4NI$$

similarly gives the tertiary amine, which unites with unchanged alkyl halide to give the quaternary ammonium halide. The preparation of pure primary amines is carried out therefore by special methods, such as the reduction of oximes (p. 67) and of nitro-compounds (pp. 104, 121). A third method due to Hofmann is based on the action of bromine on acid amides, with subsequent alkaline hydrolysis. The reactions involved probably proceed as follows. When acetamide is treated with bromine, acet-bromoamide (A) is produced.

$$CH_3CONH_2 + Br_2 = HBr + CH_3CONHBr (A)$$

This is soluble in sodium hydroxide giving the sodium acet-bromoamide (B), which exists in the ionised state in the alkaline solution. Warming with an

$$CH_3CONHBr + NaOH = H_2O + CH_3CONNaBr (B)$$

excess of sodium hydroxide now causes sodium bromide to break off, and the organic residue undergoes rearrangement to give methyl *iso*cyanate (C), which then by the usual alkaline hydrolysis gives monomethylamine (D) and sodium carbonate.

$$CH_3CONNaBr = NaBr + CH_3NCO (C)$$
$$CH_3NCO + 2NaOH = Na_2CO_3 + CH_3NH_2 (D)$$

A certain amount of hydrolysis of the original acetamide to acid and ammonia always occurs, and the final amine always contains traces of ammonia. This

---

* Alternatively a preheated conical funnel and fluted filter may be used, and the filtrate collected directly in a conical flask.

is separated by extracting the mixed anhydrous hydrochlorides with absolute alcohol, which dissolves the amine hydrochloride but not the ammonium chloride: filtration of the hot alcoholic extract removes the ammonium chloride, whilst the amine hydrochloride crystallises readily from the filtrate on cooling.

Hofmann's amine synthesis can be applied to both aliphatic and aromatic carboxylic acid amides, benzamide, $C_6H_5CONH_2$, thus giving aniline, $C_6H_5NH_2$.

METHYLAMINE HYDROCHLORIDE. CH_3NH_2,HCl.

Required: Acetamide, 12 gms.; bromine, 10·8 c.c.; sodium hydroxide, 26 gms.

Place 12 gms. of acetamide in a 200 c.c. conical flask, and run in 10·8 c.c. (32·4 gms.) of bromine: the mixture forms a deep red liquid (*exercise care in manipulating liquid bromine!*). Cool by immersing the flask in cold water,* and add 10% aqueous sodium hydroxide solution (about 100 c.c.) until the mixture becomes pale yellow in colour: shake the contents of the flask well throughout the addition of the soda. At this stage the sodium bromo-acetamide is present in the alkaline solution.

FIG. 46.

Now assemble the apparatus shown in Fig. 46. Fit a 500 c.c. bolt-head flask **F** with a three-holed cork. Into one hole fit a thermometer **T** so that it reaches nearly to the bottom of the flask; into the second hole place a dropping-funnel **D**; finally

* Do not cool in ice-water at this stage, as the acet-bromoamide may crystallise out, and is then usually difficult to redissolve.

into the third fix a bent delivery-tube and connect the latter to a
water-condenser **C**. It is essential that well-fitting corks free
from flaws are used throughout, and that the holes are carefully
and accurately bored to ensure absence of leaks: otherwise much
methylamine vapour may subsequently escape. Fit the lower end
of the condenser by means of a short piece of rubber tubing to a
small inverted funnel. Arrange the latter so that its lip is just
below the surface of 100 c.c. of dilute hydrochloric acid (1 volume
of concentrated acid diluted with 3 volumes of water) contained
in a beaker **B**: the hydrochloric acid is thereby prevented from
being sucked back into the condenser during the subsequent
distillation.

Place a solution of 26 gms. of sodium hydroxide in 60 c.c.
of water in the flask **F** (together with a few fragments of unglazed
porcelain) and warm gently until the thermometer in the liquid
registers 60–70°. Place the acet-bromoamide solution in the
funnel **D**, and allow the solution to run *slowly* into the flask at
such a speed that the temperature *does not rise above* 70°. After
all the acet-bromoamide solution has been added, maintain the
temperature of the mixture in the flask at 60–70° for 10 minutes.
Then gently boil the solution, the methylamine vapour being thus
driven over and absorbed in the dilute hydrochloric acid. Keep
the solution boiling smoothly and uniformly so that no methylamine vapour escapes absorption in the hydrochloric acid, and at
the same time so that the acid shows no marked tendency to rise
in the funnel.

After boiling for 30 minutes, the distillation of the amine may
be considered complete. Concentrate the hydrochloric acid
solution by placing it in a 250 c.c. distilling-flask connected with a
water-condenser, and distilling carefully until about 30 c.c. remain. Then transfer this residual solution to a small evaporating-
basin, and evaporate to dryness on a boiling water-bath. (Yield
of crude dry material, about 11 gms.) Break up the *dry* solid
(which consists of methylamine hydrochloride together with a
small amount of ammonium chloride), and transfer it without
delay to a 150 c.c. round-bottomed flask fitted with a reflux
water-condenser. Add about 60–70 c.c. of *absolute* alcohol (in
which ammonium chloride is insoluble), and boil the mixture for
5 minutes. Then pour the hot supernatant liquid quickly through
a small fluted filter-paper into a conical flask. Again extract the
undissolved residue with a further 20 c.c. of absolute alcohol, and
cool the united alcoholic filtrates: colourless crystals of methylamine hydrochloride separate out. Filter off the crystals at the

pump, and, since they are deliquescent, transfer quickly to a weighed specimen-tube: the methylamine hydrochloride may be finally dried by placing the tube in a desiccator. The yield of the recrystallised material should be about 5 gms.; evaporation of the alcoholic filtrate from this first crop gives a second crop of methylamine hydrochloride, weighing about 3 gms.

NOTE.—If the alcohol used to extract the methylamine hydrochloride is not "absolute," *i.e.*, if it contains traces of water, considerably less than the above suggested quantity will be required for the extraction, because the solubility of the hydrochloride will be markedly increased by the water present. The recrystallised material will now, however, contain traces of ammonium chloride.

Glycine (Amino-acetic Acid). $NH_2 \cdot CH_2COOH$.

Glycine is the simplest member of a large and very important class of compounds, the α-amino-carboxylic acids. There are many different methods available for the synthesis of amino-acids, but glycine can be readily prepared by the action of an excess of ammonia on chloro-acetic acid:

$$ClCH_2COOH + 2NH_3 = NH_2 \cdot CH_2COOH + NH_4Cl$$

(Note that although glycine is conveniently written as above, it is actually a zwitter-ion, $\overset{+}{NH_3} \cdot CH_2\overset{-}{COO}$: consequently although the ammonium salt of glycine may be initially formed in the above reaction, it readily dissociates during the subsequent concentration of the solution to give the free glycine).

The glycine so formed has to be separated from the ammonium chloride, and

the salt-like nature of the zwitter-ion precludes the use of most organic solvents for this purpose. The mixture can be treated with copper hydroxide (cf. p. 290) and the glycine precipitated as the insoluble non-ionic cupric complex (annexed formula): the latter can then be filtered off, washed and decomposed in aqueous suspension by hydrogen sulphide. The following more convenient method is based on the fact that glycine is much less soluble than ammonium chloride in methyl alcohol.

Note that the amino-acids, because of their salt-like nature, usually decompose on heating, and therefore seldom have sharp melting-points. Furthermore, all naturally occurring amino-acids are α-amino-acids, and consequently, with the exception of glycine, can exist in optically active forms.

Required: Chloro-acetic acid, 15 gms.; ammonia solution (0·880), 300 c.c.

Add 15 gms. of chloro-acetic acid to 300 c.c. of aqueous ammonia solution (*d*, 0·880) contained in a 750 c.c. conical flask. (The manipulation of the concentrated ammonia should preferably be carried out in a fume-cupboard, and great care taken to avoid ammonia fumes.) Cork the flask *loosely* and set aside overnight at room temperature. Now concentrate the solution to about 30 c.c. by distillation under reduced pressure. For this purpose, place the solution in a suitable distilling-flask with some fragments of unglazed porcelain, fit a capillary tube to the neck of the flask, and connect the flask through a water-condenser and receiver to a water-pump: then heat the flask carefully on a water-bath. Make the concentrated solution up to 40 c.c. by the addition of water, filter, and then add 250 c.c. of methyl alcohol. Cool the solution in ice-water, stir well, and set aside for *ca.* 1 hour, when the precipitation of the glycine will be complete.

Filter off the glycine through a Buchner funnel, and then transfer it to a beaker, add 80 c.c. of methyl alcohol and stir the mixture well. Then filter again, wash the glycine on the filter with a small quantity of ether, drain and dry.

The glycine so obtained is almost pure. To remove traces of ammonium chloride, however, dissolve the glycine in 30 c.c. of water, and then reprecipitate by the addition of 200 c.c. of methyl alcohol. Cool the product in ice-water with stirring, and then filter again through a Buchner funnel. The glycine is obtained as a fine colourless crystalline powder, which has m.p. 230–231° (with decomposition) if it is placed in a bath pre-heated to *ca.* 210° and the temperature then increased fairly rapidly. Yield, 7·5–8·0 gms.

Aliphatic Nitro-compounds.

Since aliphatic hydrocarbons (unlike aromatic hydrocarbons, p. 117) can be directly nitrated only under very special conditions, indirect methods are usually employed for the preparation of compounds such as nitro-ethane, $C_2H_2NO_2$. When ethyl iodide is heated with silver nitrite, two isomeric compounds are formed, and can be easily separated by fractional distillation. The first is the true ester, ethyl nitrite, C_2H_5ONO, of b.p. 17°: its identity is shown by the action of hot sodium hydroxide solution, which hydrolyses it, giving ethyl alcohol and

$$C_2H_5|ONO + Na|OH = C_2H_5OH + NaNO_2$$

sodium nitrite. The second compound is nitro-ethane, $C_2H_5NO_2$, of b.p. 114°: its identity is clearly shown by the action of reducing agents, which convert it into ethylamine, $C_2H_5NH_2$, thus proving the presence of a nitrogen-carbon

$$C_2H_5NO_2 + 6H = C_2H_5NH_2 + 2H_2O$$

link in the nitro-ethane. This formation of the isomeric nitrite ester and nitro-paraffin occurs when the lower alkyl halides react with silver nitrite.

Nitromethane, CH_3NO_2, the first member of the homologous series, can, however, be readily prepared by a special reaction.* When equimolecular amounts of sodium nitrite and sodium monochloro-acetate are heated together in aqueous solution, the chlorine in the monochloro-acetate is replaced by the nitro group, and the sodium nitroacetate thus formed undergoes hydrolysis followed by decarboxylation:

$$NaNO_2 + ClCH_2COONa = NaCl + NO_2CH_2COONa$$
$$2NO_2CH_2COONa + H_2O = 2NO_2CH_3 + Na_2CO_3 + CO_2$$

The characteristic property of aliphatic nitro-compounds is that they are *pseudo-acids*, *i.e.*, whereas they are neutral in the normal form (A), they are able by tautomeric change under the influence of alkali to give the acidic hydroxy form (B) which thus in turn gives the sodium salt (C). When this sodium salt is treated with one equivalent of hydrochloric acid, the *acid* form (B) is at once

$$CH_3CH_2 \cdot N{<}{\overset{O}{\underset{O}{}}} \quad\rightleftharpoons\quad CH_3CH{:}N{<}{\overset{OH}{\underset{O}{}}} \quad\underset{HCl}{\overset{NaOH}{\rightleftharpoons}}\quad CH_3CH{:}N{<}{\overset{ONa}{\underset{O}{}}}$$

$$\text{(A)} \qquad\qquad \text{(B)} \qquad\qquad\qquad \text{(C)}$$

regenerated, and then more slowly reverts to the more stable normal form (A).

Nitromethane. CH_3NO_2.

Required: Monochloro-acetic acid, 50 gms.; anhydrous sodium carbonate, 30 gms.; sodium nitrite, 36·5 gms.

Dissolve 50 gms. of monochloro-acetic acid in 100 c.c. of water contained in a 500 c.c. round-bottomed bolt-head flask, and then neutralise the solution by the cautious addition of 30 gms. of *finely powdered* anhydrous sodium carbonate. For this purpose, add the sodium carbonate in small quantities (about 1 gm.) at a time, preferably with the aid of a spatula, and shake the solution gently around after each addition to facilitate the evolution of carbon dioxide: a clear solution is thus maintained throughout, whereas the rapid addition of large quantities of the carbonate produces lumps of material which are subsequently difficult to dissolve. Now dissolve 36·5 gms. of sodium nitrite in 50 c.c. of water with gentle heating, cool the solution thoroughly in ice-water, and then add it with shaking to that of the sodium mono-chloro-acetate. Add some fragments of unglazed porcelain, and then fit the flask with a delivery-tube of moderately wide bore connected in turn to a water-condenser (as in Fig. 43, p. 72). Support the flask over a gauze, and then heat it *gently* with a small Bunsen flame. The solution slowly becomes yellow in colour, then greenish and finally a yellowish-brown, when a

* This reaction is general for α-chloro-carboxylic acids: of these, however, only monochloro-acetic acid is readily and cheaply obtainable, and it also gives the highest yield of the nitro-hydrocarbon.

vigorous effervescence starts: *at once* remove the Bunsen flame, and allow the reaction to proceed spontaneously, carbon dioxide being evolved and the solution boiling vigorously. When the reaction subsides, replace the Bunsen flame and maintain a steady boiling. Nitromethane distils over in the steam and separates as a colourless oil at the bottom of the distillate: since nitromethane is slightly soluble in water, stop the distillation as soon as drops of nitromethane can no longer be detected in the distillate leaving the condenser. Transfer the distillate to a separating-funnel, and carefully run off the lower layer of nitromethane and then dry it over anhydrous sodium sulphate for 30 minutes. Filter the dry nitromethane (preferably through a *small* dry Buchner funnel), transfer it to a 30 c.c. distilling-flask fitted with a water-condenser, and then slowly distil, collecting the fraction of b.p. 100–102°.

In view of the small volume of nitromethane to be manipulated, if a small Buchner funnel is not available, it is advisable to extract the crude nitromethane from the aqueous distillate with ether (30–40 c.c.). Dry the ethereal extract over sodium sulphate, filter through a fluted filter-paper, and then distil off the ether on a water-bath with the usual precautions (pp. 54, 123): finally distil the residual nitromethane.

Nitromethane is obtained as a colourless liquid, of b.p. 101° and d, 1·16: yield, 10 gms.

Reactions of Nitromethane. (1) Nitromethane, although only slightly soluble in cold water, is freely soluble in sodium hydroxide solution, the alkaline solution slowly becoming yellow in colour.

(2) Place a few drops of nitromethane in a test-tube, add about 3 times as much concentrated hydrochloric acid, and then a piece of granulated tin. The tin dissolves in the acid and the nascent hydrogen produced reduces the nitromethane to monomethylamine:

$$CH_3NO_2 + 6H = CH_3NH_2 + 2H_2O$$

Moderate the reaction if necessary by dipping the tube in cold water. When the tin has completely dissolved, cool the solution thoroughly, and make alkaline by the addition of concentrated (30%) sodium hydroxide solution. A strong ammoniacal smell of monomethylamine is produced, and white fumes form when the open end of the tube is placed near an open bottle of concentrated hydrochloric acid. This formation of methylamine proves that in the original nitromethane the nitrogen atom is joined directly to the carbon.

(3) Dissolve 0·5 gm. of sodium in 10 c.c. of anhydrous methyl alcohol contained in a small conical flask: check the reaction at first by cooling the flask in water to prevent evaporation of the alcohol, but finally warm the mixture gently to hasten the dissolution of the last traces of sodium. Cool this solution of sodium methoxide, and then add 1 c.c. of nitromethane, and mix thoroughly. A gelatinous

precipitate of sodium nitromethane rapidly appears. Cool the mixture in ice-water for 5 minutes, and then filter off the sodium derivative at the pump, using a *small* dry Buchner funnel; drain quickly, and then wash with a *few drops* of methyl alcohol, to remove traces of excess sodium methoxide, again draining the white sodium derivative as quickly as possible. Perform the following tests with this sodium derivative whilst it is still damp with methyl alcohol:

(*a*) Dissolve a small portion of the sodium derivative in a few c.c. of water in a test-tube, and add one drop of ferric chloride solution. A deep red coloration is produced, but rapidly disappears as the iron is precipitated as ferric hydroxide. The sodium derivative (A) of the nitromethane when dissolved in water undergoes partial hydrolysis,

$$CH_2:N \overset{ONa}{\underset{O}{\diagdown}} + HOH \rightleftharpoons CH_2:N \overset{OH}{\underset{O}{\diagdown}} + NaOH$$

(A)· (B)

giving sodium hydroxide and the free acid (B): the latter, like many hydroxy compounds (compare phenols, p. 254), gives a marked coloration with ferric chloride.

(*b*) Dissolve the remainder of the sodium derivative in about 50 c.c. of cold water in a clean beaker. Add a drop of phenolphthalein solution. A deep pink coloration is produced, owing to the free sodium hydroxide formed in the above hydrolysis. Now by means of a small pipette or a fine glass tube, add *very* dilute sulphuric acid *drop by drop* until the pink coloration is *just* discharged. In a few seconds the pink coloration becomes again perceptible, and rapidly deepens in tint. The sulphuric acid may again be added, and the process repeated several times. The addition of the sulphuric acid first neutralises the sodium hydroxide, and then gives a weakly acidic and therefore colourless solution. The sodium derivative (A) then undergoes further partial hydrolysis in order to re-establish the original equilibrium, and the sodium hydroxide thus formed again produces the pink coloration, which increases in depth as the hydrolysis proceeds.

When the above tests have been completed, wash thoroughly with water all apparatus contaminated with the sodium derivative, since the latter, if allowed to dry, becomes very explosive.

(4) Dissolve a few drops of nitromethane in 10% sodium hydroxide solution. Add a few crystals of sodium nitrite and shake. Now add dilute sulphuric acid drop by drop. A brownish-red coloration develops, but fades again when an excess of acid is added. The sulphuric acid has thus liberated nitrous acid, which has in turn reacted with the nitromethane to give a *nitrolic acid*, the sodium salt of which is

$$CH_3NO_2 + ONOH = CH(NO_2):NOH + H_2O$$

reddish-brown. An excess of sulphuric acid then converts the coloured sodium salt back to the almost colourless nitrolic acid.

E*

NOTE.—A secondary nitro-paraffin, such as 2-nitro-propane, $(CH_3)_2CHNO_2$, when similarly treated gives a *pseudo-nitrol*, which dissolves in chloroform,

$$(CH_3)_2CHNO_2 + HONO = (CH_3)_2C(NO)NO_2 + H_2O$$

producing a blue solution.

A tertiary nitro-paraffin, such as trimethyl-nitromethane, $(CH_3)_3CNO_2$, gives no reaction with nitrous acid. These reactions may therefore be used to distinguish between primary, secondary and tertiary alcohols (Victor Meyer's test). The alcohol is converted into the corresponding iodide, and the latter into the nitro-compound, which is then treated as above. A primary alcohol would thus give a reddish-brown coloration, a secondary alcohol a blue coloration, and a tertiary alcohol no reaction or coloration.

The Sugars (or Carbohydrates).

The only sugars which the student is likely to meet in the course of ordinary laboratory work are the two isomeric *monosaccharides* glucose (sometimes called dextrose or grape sugar) and fructose (laevulose or fruit sugar) of formula $C_6H_{12}O_6$, and the three isomeric *disaccharides* sucrose (cane sugar), lactose (milk sugar) and maltose (malt sugar) of formula $C_{12}H_{22}O_{11}$. It has been established that sugars possess ring structures (I, II, IV), but nevertheless under certain conditions the ring opens out to give a straight chain compound which may possess either a free – CHO group (aldoses, such as glucose, III) or a free >CO group (ketoses, such as fructose, V). Many of the characteristic reactions of sugars, particularly those of reduction and of osazone formation, are due to these groups.

It will be seen that the ring form of glucose can exist in two isomeric forms, α and β, which differ only with regard to the disposition of the H and the OH groups around carbon atom 1, since if the ring is regarded as being in the plane of the paper, α-glucose (I) may have this H atom above, and the OH group below, the plane of the paper, whilst β-glucose (II) will have the H atom below, and the OH group above this plane. These ring structures for α and β-glucose can alternatively of course be represented by (VI) and (VII). α and β-glucose, when dissolved in water, have different optical rotatory powers (although they are not of course optical enantiomorphs, as the above formulae show): the optical rotation of each solution changes slowly on standing, and the final value attained is identical in each case, *i.e.*. a mixture of both forms in equilibrium is ultimately obtained from either α or β-glucose. The difference between α- and β-glucose disappears in the straight chain form (III), and since it is in this form that glucose often appears to react, this difference between the α and β forms can frequently be ignored in practical work.

$$CH_2OH \qquad\qquad CH_2OH$$

(VI)   (VII)

Fructose exists similarly in two forms, determined by the disposition of the OH and the CH_2OH groups around carbon atom 2, this difference again disappearing in the straight chain form (V). It will be noted that carbon atom 1 in glucose is concerned with the formation of the ring, and that when the latter opens out, the free aldehyde group appears at this point. The grouping on carbon atom 1 may conveniently be called the "potential aldehyde group," and that on carbon atom 2 in the fructose molecule similarly the "potential ketone group."

For an elementary study of the sugars, it is not suggested that the student should remember the structure of the disaccharides: their chief and characteristic reactions will, however, be readily understood if the following facts are borne in mind.

Sucrose on hydrolysis with dilute acids, or with the enzyme *invertase* (or "*sucrase*," p. 412,) gives rise to one molecule of glucose and one molecule of fructose:

$$C_{12}H_{22}O_{11} + H_2O = C_6H_{12}O_6 + C_6H_{12}O_6$$
$$\text{sucrose} \qquad\qquad \text{glucose} \quad \text{fructose}$$

In the sucrose molecule, union takes place through carbon atom 1 of the glucose molecule and carbon atom 2 of the fructose molecule: hence sucrose is a non-reducing sugar, since neither the potential aldehyde nor the potential ketone grouping is now available for reaction. If glucose is represented as G-r, where r is the potential aldehyde group, and fructose as F-r, where r is the potential ketone group, then the sucrose molecule may be conveniently remembered as G-r-r-F, indicating clearly that the reducing groups are concerned in the union of the two monosaccharide residues.

Maltose on hydrolysis with dilute acids or with the enzyme *maltase* gives rise to two molecules of glucose: only one of the potential aldehyde groups is concerned in the union of the glucose molecules, and the structure of maltose may therefore be represented as G-r-G-r. Maltose has thus one free potential aldehyde group, and is therefore a reducing sugar, differing in this respect from sucrose.

Lactose on hydrolysis gives glucose and an isomeric monosaccharide galactose, which may be given the symbol Ga-r. The lactose molecule may be represented as G-r-Ga-r, and it has therefore also a free potential aldehyde group and is a reducing sugar like maltose.

A very important method of identifying reducing sugars is by means of the *osazones* which they form with phenylhydrazine, $C_6H_5NHNH_2$. These osazones are bright yellow compounds, which exhibit characteristic crystalline forms under the microscope. To explain the formation of the osazones of glucose and fructose, the latter sugars are represented for simplicity by the straight chain formulae (III) and (V) respectively. When glucose is treated with an excess of phenylhydrazine (preferably in the presence of acetic acid), a soluble *phenylhydrazone* (IIIA) is first formed by the condensation of one molecule of phenylhydrazine with the $-CHO$ group of the glucose. This is strictly analogous to the formation of benzaldehyde phenylhydrazone from benzaldehyde (p. 177). Now phenylhydrazine will readily act as an oxidising agent, since it can accept two hydrogen atoms from another compound, being itself reduced to aniline

1 CH$\vert$O + H$_2\vert$NNHC$_6$H$_5$ CH:NNHC$_6$H$_5$ CH:NNHC$_6$H$_5$ CH:NNHC$_6$H$_5$

     | | | |

2 CHOH   CHOH   C$\vert$O + H$_2\vert$NNHC$_6$H$_5$ C:NNHC$_6$H$_5$

    | | $-2H$ | |

(CHOH)$_3$ $\longrightarrow$ (CHOH)$_3$ $\longrightarrow$ (CHOH)$_3$ $\longrightarrow$ (CHOH)$_3$

    | | | |

CH$_2$OH   CH$_2$OH   CH$_2$OH   CH$_2$OH

(III)   (IIIA)   (IIIB)   (IIIC)

and ammonia, $C_6H_5NHNH_2 + 2H = C_6H_5NH_2 + NH_3$. The second molecule of phenylhydrazine therefore oxidises the secondary alcohol group ($>$CHOH) of carbon atom 2 to a ketone ($>$C:O) group by removal of two hydrogen atoms, giving the compound (IIIB). The free $>$C:O group of the latter compound now condenses with a third molecule of phenylhydrazine, giving the osazone of glucose, or *phenyl glucosazone* (IIIC).

Fructose (V) under similar conditions gives first the *phenylhydrazone* (VA) by the direct condensation of the $>$C:O group of carbon atom 2 with one molecule of phenylhydrazine. The second molecule of phenylhydrazine then oxidises the primary alcohol group of carbon atom 1 to the $-CHO$ group by

1 CH$_2$OH   CH$_2$OH   CH$\vert$O+H$_2\vert$NNHC$_6$H$_5$ CH:NNHC$_6$H$_5$

    | | | |

2 C$\vert$O+H$_2\vert$NNHC$_6$H$_5$ C:NNHC$_6$H$_5$ C:NNHC$_6$H$_5$ C:NNHC$_6$H$_5$

    | | $-2H$ | |

(CHOH)$_3$ $\longrightarrow$ (CHOH)$_3$ $\longrightarrow$ (CHOH)$_3$ $\longrightarrow$ (CHOH)$_3$

    | | | |

CH$_2$OH   CH$_2$OH   CH$_2$OH   CH$_2$OH

(V)   (VA)   (VB)   (VC)

removal of two atoms of hydrogen, which as before serve to reduce the phenyl-hydrazine to aniline and ammonia. The compound (VB) which is thus produced then undergoes direct condensation with the third molecule of phenyl-hydrazine, giving the osazone of fructose, or *fructosazone* (Vc).

Now since the configuration of carbon atoms 3, 4 and 5 of glucose and fructose are identical, it follows that glucosazone and fructosazone are identical in all respects. The osazone is formed however more rapidly from fructose than from glucose, and this difference in rate of formation may be used to distinguish the two sugars, provided the reactions are carried out under strictly parallel conditions (pp. 110, 279).

Both maltose and lactose, being reducing sugars, give osazones which differ from one another and from glucosazone in crystalline form. Sucrose (G-r-r-F), having no potential aldehyde or ketone grouping, does not form an osazone.

Glucosazone (Phenyl-glucosazone). $C_6H_{10}O_4(N \cdot NHC_6H_5)_2$.

In the preparation of osazones (as in the preparation of phenylhydrazones, p. 177) the free phenylhydrazine base may be used directly. Condensation occurs more readily and a cleaner product is obtained, however, if the reaction is carried out in weakly acidic solution—preferably at about pH 5 (see foot-note, p. 407). The phenylhydrazine base should therefore always be dissolved in acetic acid for this purpose.

Phenylhydrazine is, however, frequently supplied in the form of its hydro-chloride or sulphate, since these salts on exposure to light darken less rapidly than the free base. If these salts are used, however, osazone formation is unsatisfactory, partly because the mineral acid formed by hydrolysis of

$$C_6H_5NHNH_2,HCl \rightleftharpoons C_6H_5NHNH_2 + HCl$$

the salt hydrolyses the glucosazone to glucosone, $CHO \cdot CO \cdot (CHOH)_3CH_2OH$. Therefore if these salts are used, they should be mixed in solution with a small excess of sodium acetate, whereby the pH of the solution is raised to approxi-mately the required value. On the other hand, care should be taken not to add too large an excess of sodium acetate, which by hydrolysis would make the solution too alkaline: this can if necessary be corrected by the addition of a few drops of acetic acid.

Required: Glucose, 2 gms.; acetic acid, 4 c.c.; phenylhydrazine, 4 c.c.

Dissolve 2 gms. of glucose (or fructose) in 10 c.c. of water in a boiling-tube. In another tube dissolve 4 c.c. of glacial acetic acid in 10 c.c. of water, add 4 c.c. of phenylhydrazine,* and shake until a solution of phenylhydrazine acetate is obtained. Add this solution (which is often opalescent) to the sugar solution, stir gently with a glass rod, and then place the tube in a boiling water-bath. The yellow osazone usually begins to crystallise out

* If only the hydrochloride or sulphate of the base is available, dissolve 6 gms. of crystalline sodium acetate (or 4 gms. of the anhydrous acetate) in 25 c.c. of water, add 6 gms. of the phenylhydrazine salt, warm *gently* until dissolved, filter the solution if necessary, and then add to the sugar solution.

after about 20 minutes' heating. Continue the heating (with occasional stirring) for a total period of 45 minutes, then remove the tube and cool by immersion in cold water. Filter the product through a Buchner funnel, and wash it first with water and then with a few c.c. of methylated spirit, and drain thoroughly. Yield of osazone from glucose, 3 gms.* If fructose is used, only 30 minutes' heating is necessary, and the yield of osazone is 3·7 gms., *i.e.*, almost theoretical.

Glucosazone is only slightly soluble in boiling alcohol or methylated spirit: for recrystallisation therefore it is sufficient to place about 0·5 gm. of the crude material in a 150 c.c. flask fitted with a reflux condenser, then to add about 75 c.c. of methylated spirit, and boil gently. The osazone dissolves slowly; filter the hot solution through a fluted filter-paper (or a preheated Buchner funnel), and allow the filtrate to cool slowly in order to ensure good crystal formation.

| (A) | (B) | (C) |
| Glucosazone (Fructosazone) | Maltosazone | Lactosazone |

FIG. 47.

If it is desired to observe the crystalline form of the osazone, draw up in a glass tube a few drops of the cold filtrate containing the fine crystals, and transfer to a microscope slide. Cover the drops with a slip and examine under the microscope: unless the filtrate has been cooled very slowly and thus given moderately-sized crystals, the high power of the microscope will probably be required. Note the fine yellow needles aggregated in the form of sheaves. Compare with Fig. 47(A).

Then filter the remainder of the product at the pump, drain and dry. The glucosazone is thus obtained as bright yellow crystals, m.p. 204° with decomposition.

---

* If the reaction mixture is heated for 1½ hours, this yield is slightly increased. The increase is too small, however, to warrant the extra time expended.

Maltosazone (Phenyl-maltosazone).
$C_{12}H_{20}O_9(N \cdot NHC_6H_5)_2$.

Required: Maltose, 2 gms.; acetic acid, 2 c.c.; phenylhydrazine, 2 c.c.

Proceed as in the preparation of glucosazone, using for the first solution 2 gms. of maltose in 10 c.c. of water, but for the second solution 2 c.c. of phenylhydrazine dissolved in a mixture of 2 c.c. of glacial acetic acid and 5 c.c. of water. Heat in a boiling water-bath for 30 minutes. Maltosazone is much more soluble than glucosazone in hot water, and therefore does not separate whilst the boiling-tube is still in the boiling water-bath. When the heating is complete, either turn out the gas and allow the tube to cool slowly while still in the bath, or alternatively transfer the tube to a small beaker of boiling water and there let it cool: the maltosazone crystallises as the solution cools. (If the solution is cooled rapidly, the osazone separates as minute crystals, and subsequent filtration at the pump will be very slow.) Finally complete the cooling by immersing the boiling-tube in cold water, and then filter off the maltosazone at the pump, wash with a few c.c. of cold water, and drain. (Yield, 1·2 gms.). Recrystallise the osazone from a small quantity of boiling water. Allow the solution to cool very slowly as before, and examine the crystals as directed in the previous preparation. Note the long narrow plates, and compare them with Fig. 47(B). Filter off the remainder of the recrystallised material, drain and dry. The maltosazone is obtained as yellow crystals, m.p. 206°* with decomposition.

Lactosazone (Phenyl-lactosazone).
$C_{12}H_{20}O_9(N \cdot NHC_6H_5)_2$.

Proceed exactly as for maltosazone. When the heating is complete, however, remove the boiling-tube from the water-bath,

---

* This is the value originally given by Fischer for the m.p. of maltosazone: it is a value obtained, however, only if the capillary tube containing the material is placed in a bath previously heated to about 180° and the temperature then rapidly increased. The m.p. of most samples of maltosazone, when determined in the usual way, is 190–192°.

The m.p. of lactosazone used to be given as 200°, but the pure samples of lactose now available give an osazone having the higher m.p. of 208° given above. In view of these variations in the m.p., and also of the fact that the m.p.s of all osazones of the commoner sugars lie very close together, the identification of an osazone should be based primarily on its crystal form: for this purpose it is frequently unnecessary to recrystallise the osazone, as the crystal form can often be observed excellently if a few drops of the original solution are used.

and allow it to cool spontaneously in the air. (Lactosazone does not require the extremely slow cooling used for maltosazone in order to ensure rapid subsequent filtration.) Finally complete the cooling in cold water, and then filter at the pump, wash with cold water, and drain thoroughly. (Yield, 2 gms.). Lactosazone is not so soluble as maltosazone in boiling water: for recrystallisation, therefore, boil a portion of the lactosazone with water, and then add alcohol drop by drop until a clear solution is obtained. Allow to cool slowly. Examine the crystals as before, and note the dense yellow clusters of very fine needles (sometimes referred to as "hedgehog" crystals): compare with Fig. 47(C). Filter off the remainder of the lactosazone, drain and dry. The pure lactosazone is obtained as yellow crystals, m.p. 208° with decomposition, the material darkening in colour immediately before melting.

α- and β-Pentacetyl-glucose. $C_6H_7O(O \cdot COCH_3)_5$.

When glucose is heated with an excess of acetic anhydride in the presence of a catalyst, all five hydroxyl groups are acetylated, and the resulting pentacetyl-glucose can clearly exist in two isomeric forms, corresponding to the α and β forms of glucose itself (see Formulae I and II, p. 106). When zinc chloride is used as a catalyst, the α-pentacetyl-glucose is formed, and when sodium acetate is used, the β-pentacetyl-glucose is produced. It is probable that the product in each case contains traces of the other isomeride, which however can be readily eliminated by recrystallisation.

(A) α-PENTACETYL-GLUCOSE. *Required:* Zinc chloride, *ca.* 1 gm.; acetic anhydride, 25 c.c.; glucose, 5 gms.

From a clean, dry stick of zinc chloride, break off a piece weighing roughly 1 gm., crush it quickly into coarse fragments in a mortar, and then add it to 25 c.c. of acetic anhydride contained in a 100 c.c. round-bottomed or conical flask. (Owing to the very deliquescent nature of zinc chloride, this manipulation must be carried out *as rapidly as possible*: hence have both the acetic anhydride in the flask, and the mortar available near the balance, before the zinc chloride stick is withdrawn from the stock bottle.) Fit the flask with a reflux water-condenser and heat the mixture of zinc chloride and acetic anhydride on a vigorously boiling water-bath for about 5 minutes until the maximum temperature is reached and nearly all the chloride has dissolved. Now remove the condenser and add 5 gms. of powdered glucose (anhydrous or monohydrate) cautiously to the acetic anhydride, shaking the mixture around occasionally during the addition, in order to control the vigorous reaction which follows. Finally replace the condenser and heat the mixture for 1 hour on the water-bath, and then pour the liquid into about 250 c.c. of cold water. The latter should preferably be cooled externally with ice-water, and be stirred vigorously during the addition of the acetylated product. A viscous oil separates at the bottom of the beaker, and if occasionally stirred will crystallise within about 10 minutes. After solidification of the oil, allow the mixture to stand for a further 15 minutes, and then filter at the pump. If any large lumps of the crude acetyl compound have formed, transfer them to a mortar, pulverise, and then wash them back into the Buchner funnel. Finally wash the product on the filter thoroughly with water, and drain. (Yield of crude material, 7·5–8·0 gms.). Recrystallise the product from methylated spirit until the α-pentacetyl-glucose is obtained as colourless crystals melting sharply at 110–111°. Two recrystallisations are usually sufficient for this purpose.

(B) β-PENTACETYL-GLUCOSE. *Required:* Anhydrous sodium acetate, 2·5 gms.; acetic anhydride, 25 c.c.; glucose, 5 gms.

Carry out this preparation precisely as described for the α-compound, but instead of zinc chloride add 2·5 gms. of anhydrous powdered sodium acetate (preparation, p. 88) to the acetic anhydride. When this mixture has been heated on the water-bath for 5 minutes, and the greater part of the acetate has dissolved, add the 5 gms. of powdered glucose. After heating for 1 hour, pour into cold water as before. The viscous oil crystallises more readily than that obtained in the preparation of the α-compound. Filter the solid material at the pump, breaking up any lumps as before, wash thoroughly with water and drain. (Yield of crude product, 10·0–10·5 gms.). Recrystallise from methylated spirit until the pure β-pentacetyl-glucose is obtained as colourless crystals, m.p. 130–131°: again two recrystallisations are usually sufficient for this purpose.

Conversion of β- to α-pentacetyl-glucose. The β-pentacetyl-glucose is readily converted into the α-isomeride by heating in acetic anhydride solution with zinc chloride. Add 0·5 gm. of zinc chloride (rapidly crushed to coarse fragments as before) to 25 c.c. of acetic anhydride and heat on a boiling water-bath for about 5 minutes in order to dissolve the zinc chloride. Then add 5 gms. of pure β-pentacetyl-glucose, which will dissolve rapidly in the hot solution. Continue heating on the water-bath for 30 minutes, and then pour the hot solution, which will have acquired a pale brown colour, into 250 c.c. of cold water, stirring vigorously. The oily drops rapidly solidify. Filter the solid product at the pump, wash, drain and recrystallise from methylated spirit. One recrystallisation is usually sufficient to give pure α-pentacetyl-glucose, m.p. 110–111.°

For the determination of the number of acetyl groups in pentacetyl-glucose, see p. 360.

Hexacetyl-mannitol.
$$CH_2(O \cdot COCH_3)(CH \cdot O \cdot COCH_3)_4 CH_2(O \cdot COCH_3).$$

Mannitol, $CH_2OH(CHOH)_4CH_2OH$, is a hexahydric alcohol obtained by the reduction of mannose. Since ring formation does not occur in mannitol, the hexacetyl derivative can exist in only one form, and therefore either zinc chloride or sodium acetate can be used as a catalyst for the acetylation.

Required: Mannitol, 5 gms.; acetic anhydride, 30 c.c.; zinc chloride, *ca.* 0·5 gm.

Add 5 gms. of finely powdered mannitol to 30 c.c. of acetic anhydride contained in a 100 c.c. round-bottomed or conical flask. Now break off a *small* fragment (not exceeding 0·5 gm.) from a clean dry stick of zinc chloride, crush it quickly into coarse fragments in a mortar, and then add it to the acetic anhydride: this manipulation of the zinc chloride—as in the above preparation of α-pentacetyl-glucose—should be performed as rapidly as possible. (Alternatively, 4 gms. of powdered anhydrous sodium acetate may be added in place of the zinc chloride.) Boil the mixture gently on a sand-bath under a reflux water-condenser for 30 minutes, a clear solution being rapidly obtained. Then pour the solution into 250 c.c. of cold water, stirring the mixture vigorously for a few minutes until the oil which separates at first has solidified to a mass of fine colourless crystals. Allow to stand for 15 minutes, and then filter at the pump, wash thoroughly with water, and drain. Recrystallise the well-drained material (without drying) from a small quantity of methylated spirit, when the hexacetyl-mannitol will separate in colourless crystals, m.p. 120°: yield, 11·5 gms. (almost theoretical).

For the determination of the number of acetyl groups in hexacetyl-mannitol, see p. 360.

α-Methylglucoside. $C_6H_7O(OH)_4(OCH_3)$.

When anhydrous glucose is boiled in methyl alcohol solution containing a small quantity of hydrogen chloride, condensation occurs between the methyl alcohol and the terminal (aldehydic) hydroxyl group of the glucose molecule, and a mixture of the isomeric α- and β-methylglucosides (A and B) is obtained: these correspond to α- and β-glucose respectively (compare formulae I and II, p. 106).

It should be noted that, since the hydroxyl group concerned in this condensation is derived from the terminal aldehydic group, the glucosides are similar in chemical nature to the acetals, e.g., $CH_3CH(OC_2H_5)_2$, which are also formed by the condensation of an aldehyde with an alcohol. Consequently the methylglucosides can be readily hydrolysed back to methyl alcohol and glucose: if, on the other hand, the remaining hydroxyl groups in the glucose molecule are methylated, true ethers are obtained and these methyl groups cannot be readily hydrolysed.

The following preparation works excellently if it is carried out in a laboratory which has become "inoculated" by the methylglucoside from previous preparations, or alternatively if some of the glucoside is available for "seeding" the solution of the crude material: otherwise there may be a considerable delay before crystallisation starts.

Required: Anhydrous glucose, 40 gms.; methyl alcohol, 80 c.c.

Add 40 gms. of pure powdered anhydrous glucose to 80 c.c. of anhydrous methyl alcohol (preparation, p. 62) contained in a flask fitted by means of a rubber stopper to a reflux water-condenser: close the top of the condenser with a calcium chloride tube. It is now required to add about 5 % of dry hydrogen chloride to the methyl alcohol in the flask. For this purpose, fit a corked boiling-tube with two narrow delivery-tubes so that it can act as a wash-bottle: fit the inlet tube to a hydrogen chloride Kipp's apparatus (p. 76) through a concentrated sulphuric acid wash-bottle to ensure thorough drying of the gas, and fit the outlet tube with a calcium chloride tube. Place 5 c.c. of anhydrous methyl alcohol in the boiling-tube, stand the latter in ice-water, and bubble hydrogen chloride through the chilled methyl alcohol until the latter is saturated. (The gas should be passed briskly through the alcohol at first, to prevent the latter from "sucking back" through the inlet tube.) Then add this saturated alcohol without delay to the contents of the flask, and mix well.

Boil the mixture *gently* on a sand-bath for 4 hours and then decant into a conical flask and cool. Seed the cold solution if necessary with a trace of α-methylglucoside. The glucoside separates as colourless crystals. When crystallisation ceases, filter the glucoside at the pump, drain, wash quickly with a *small* quantity of methyl alcohol, and then recrystallise from a minimum of methyl alcohol. For this purpose methyl alcohol of good quality, but not necessarily anhydrous, should be used. The α-methylglucoside is obtained as colourless crystals, m.p. 165°. Yield, 13–14 gms.

If the mother-liquor from the crude product (together with the washings) is concentrated to nearly half its original volume by gentle distillation, and is then cooled and seeded with a trace of the first crop, a second and less pure crop of the α-methylglucoside is obtained. This should be purified by recrystallisation from the mother-liquor obtained from the recrystallisation of the first crop, and then if necessary recrystallised a second time from a small quantity of fresh methyl alcohol. Yield of second crop, about 5 gms.

The crude concentrated mother-liquor still contains some α-methylglucoside, together with the more soluble β-methylglucoside: the amount of the latter is too small, however, to warrant attempted isolation.

If difficulty is experienced in inducing the first crude crop of the α-glucoside to crystallise, place a few drops of the solution on a watch-glass and expose freely to the air, with occasional scratching: meanwhile keep the main volume of the solution securely corked in the conical flask. After an interval of varying length (possibly several days), partial crystallisation occurs in the material on the watch-glass. Then seed the solution with this material: crystallisation of the first main crop will rapidly follow.

α-Methylglucoside responds to General Tests 1 and 2 for carbohydrates given on p. 277 (blackening with sulphuric acid, and Molisch's test). Since, however, the glucoside does not contain a free aldehydic hydroxyl group, it does not possess the reducing properties of glucose itself. Confirm this by applying to pure α-methylglucoside Tests 1 and 2 for glucose (p. 277), *i.e.*, the reduction of ammoniacal silver nitrate and of Fehling's solution respectively. No reduction is obtained in either case, although prolonged warming in Test 1 and (in particular) prolonged boiling in Test 2 causes partial hydrolysis of the glucoside with consequent slight reduction.

Nitration.

One of the chief differences between aliphatic and aromatic hydrocarbons is that the latter when treated with nitric acid undergo direct *nitration*, benzene being thus converted to nitrobenzene:

$$C_6H_5|H + HO|NO_2 = C_6H_5NO_2 + H_2O.$$

A similar reaction occurs only very rarely with aliphatic hydrocarbons.

It is found experimentally, however, that if benzene is treated with concentrated nitric acid alone, the yield of nitrobenzene is small, since numerous by-products are simultaneously formed. If, however, the nitric acid is first mixed with concentrated sulphuric acid, a high yield of nitrobenzene results. The sulphuric acid here undoubtedly has a dehydrating function, as in the formation of esters (p. 68), but the *necessity* for the dehydration is, however, quite distinct in the two processes. Esterification involves a reaction in which the ester and water are simultaneously formed, and unless this water were removed from the sphere of reaction, it would in turn hydrolyse the ester, and an equilibrium mixture would result. This consideration does not arise in nitration, since nitrobenzene does not react with water, and no back reaction can occur.

Ingold and co-workers have shown that nitration is caused by the nitronium ion, $\overset{+}{N}O_2$. The overall reaction is: $C_6H_6 + \overset{+}{N}O_2 \longrightarrow C_6H_5NO_2 + \overset{+}{H}$

It is considered that the $\overset{+}{N}O_2$ is produced in the mixture of nitric and sulphuric acids by changes such as:

$$H_2SO_4 + HNO_3 \longrightarrow H\overset{-}{S}O_4 + H_2\overset{+}{N}O_3$$
$$H_2\overset{+}{N}O_3 + H_2SO_4 \longrightarrow H\overset{-}{S}O_4 + H_3\overset{+}{O} + \overset{+}{N}O_2$$

Nitrobenzene. $C_6H_5NO_2$.

Required: Nitric acid, 35 c.c.; sulphuric acid, 40 c.c.; benzene, 29 c.c.

The conversion of benzene to nitrobenzene has to be performed with care in order to avoid the further nitration of the nitrobenzene to *m*-dinitrobenzene. Place 35 c.c. of concentrated nitric acid in a 500 c.c. flask, and add slowly 40 c.c. (74 gms.) of concentrated sulphuric acid, keeping the mixture cool during the addition by immersing the flask in cold water. Place a thermometer in this nitrating mixture, and then add *very slowly* 29 c.c. (25 gms.) of benzene. The benzene should be added about 3 c.c. at a time, and the contents of the flask *thoroughly* mixed after each addition: the temperature of the mixture must not be allowed to rise above 50°, and should be kept under control if necessary by cooling the flask in cold water. When all the benzene has been added, fit a reflux water-condenser to the flask, and place the latter *in a* water-bath, which is then maintained at 60° for 45 minutes. During this period the flask should be withdrawn from the bath from time to time and vigorously shaken in order to break up the nitrobenzene layer which would otherwise float on the dense acid layer below. After the 45 minutes' heating, pour the contents of the flask into a large excess of cold water (about 300 c.c.), in which the nitrobenzene, being heavier than water, sinks to the bottom. Stir the mixture vigorously in order to wash out as much acid as possible from the nitrobenzene. Decant off as much as possible of the supernatant aqueous layer,* and then transfer the residual liquid to a separating-funnel. Run off the lower layer of nitrobenzene, rejecting the upper aqueous layer, and then return the nitrobenzene to the separating-funnel, and shake it vigorously with an equal volume of cold water. Allow the nitrobenzene to separate again, and then run it off and repeat the washing using dilute sodium carbonate solution. The nitrobenzene should be shaken with increasing quantities of the carbonate solution until the cessation of evolution of carbon dioxide shows that all free acid has been neutralised. The nitrobenzene ought now to be separated and again washed with water to remove traces of sodium carbonate solution: washing with water at this stage, however, frequently gives an emulsion of nitrobenzene and water which takes a very long time to separate again into two well-defined layers. It is best therefore to omit this final washing with water, and to separate the nitrobenzene *as completely as possible* from the sodium carbonate solution. Then transfer the nitrobenzene to a small flask, add some granular calcium chloride, and shake the mixture occasionally until the liquid is quite clear (usually about 20 minutes). Filter the nitrobenzene through a small fluted filter-paper directly into a 60 c.c. distilling-flask fitted to an air-condenser. Distil the nitrobenzene carefully, collecting the fraction which boils between 207° and 211°. Yield, 35 gms.

Nitrobenzene is a pale yellow liquid, having a b.p. 210°, and *d*, 1·20. It has an odour which is similar to that of almonds, and which is therefore often confused with that of benzaldehyde. Nitrobenzene is used chiefly for the preparation of aniline.

Nitrobenzene (semi-micro scale) (1/10 of above scale).

Place 3·5 c.c. conc. HNO_3 in a 50 c.c. round-bottomed flask and add slowly with cooling 4 c.c. of conc. H_2SO_4. (Measure the acids from a burette or 5 c.c. measuring cylinder.) Add slowly from a burette 2·9 c.c. of benzene, shaking the mixture well during the addition: the temperature must be kept below 50°. Fit a small reflux water-condenser to the flask and heat in a water-bath maintained

---

* This is done so that a small separating-funnel of about 100 c.c. capacity may be used for the subsequent washing of the nitrobenzene.

at 60° for 10 minutes. During this period, shake the flask vigorously from time to time, and then pour the mixture into 30 c.c. of cold water. Proceed as in the larger-scale experiment above as far as the drying stage. Use only 2–3 small pieces of granular calcium chloride, and dry for 10 minutes. If a clear liquid is obtained, omit the filtration, and decant carefully into the flask shown in Fig. 27 (p. 43). Distil without water in the condenser. Keep the hot vapour of the nitrobenzene around the bulb of the thermometer (which has a considerable heat-capacity) for one minute without actually distilling, so that the true temperature can be recorded, and then collect the fraction of b.p. 207–211°. Yield, 3·5 gms.

For reactions of nitrobenzene, see pp. 292, 293.

Aromatic Substitution.

The student when preparing disubstituted benzenes should bear in mind Vorländer's Rules of aromatic substitution, which form the most convenient modification of Crum Brown's earlier rules. Vorländer stated that if a substance C_6H_5P be converted into a substance C_6H_4PQ, where P and Q are any substituents, then

(1) The nature of C_6H_4PQ depends solely on P, and is independent of Q.

(2) The product C_6H_4PQ is either

    (a) the *meta* isomeride,

    or (b) a mixture of the *ortho* and *para* isomerides.

(3) If the group P contains a double or triple bond, then C_6H_4PQ will be the *meta* isomeride: otherwise, C_6H_4PQ will be a mixture of *ortho* and *para* isomerides.

The chief *meta* directing groups are therefore:

$$- CHO, \ - COOH, \ - CONH_2, \ - CN, \ - NO_2, \ - SO_3H,$$

and the chief *ortho* and *para* directing groups are:

$$- Cl, \ - Br, \ - I, \ - OH, \ - OCH_3, \ - NH_2, \ - CH_3 \ \text{and other alkyl groups}.$$

It must be emphasised that the above are empirical rules, and not scientific laws, and are not always accurate. The only common exceptions are the $- NHCOCH_3$ group, which, like the parent $- NH_2$ group, directs *ortho* and *para*, the $- CH:CHCOOH$ group (as in cinnamic acid) which also directs *ortho* and *para*, and the $- CCl_3$ group, which directs *meta*. Moreover, many reactions which give the *meta* isomeride (e.g., m-dinitrobenzene, p. 121) also give traces of the *ortho* and *para* isomerides, and *vice-versa*.

It is also to be noted that *ortho* and *para* substitution often occur together in the same molecule, so that the group Q enters the *para* and also both the *ortho* positions: thus both aniline and phenol on bromination readily give symmetric (2:4:6) tribromo-compounds (p. 125), while both toluene and phenol on nitration readily give the symmetric trinitro-derivatives (p. 133).

The course of aromatic substitution has been placed on a more scientific basis by the following rules of Hammick and Illingworth (*Jour. Chem. Soc.*, 1930, 2358). If a monosubstituted benzene derivative has the formula C_6H_5XY, where X is the atom joined to the benzene ring and Y is an atom or group of atoms attached to X, then

XY is *meta* directing:
> (*a*) if Y is in a higher group in the Periodic Classification than X,
> (*b*) if Y is in the same group as X, but is of lower atomic weight.

XY is *ortho* and *para* directing:
> (*c*) if Y is in a lower group than X,
> (*d*) if X and Y are atoms of the same element,
> (*e*) if the group XY consists of 1 atom alone.

To apply those rules, only the elements given in the accompanying Table need usually be considered. Hydrogen is considered as being in Group I: if Y consists solely of hydrogen atoms, the latter obey the above rule; if, however, Y consists partly of hydrogen and partly of another element, both attached to X (as in $-CHO$), then the influence of the hydrogen can usually be ignored and the rules applied to the remaining element alone.

Group I	IV	V	VI	VII
H	C	N	O	F
			S	Cl
				Br
				I

Examples of the above classes are:

Meta directing:
> (*a*) $-CHO$, $-COOH$, $-CN$, $-CCl_3$, $-NO_2$.
> (*b*) $-SO_2OH$.

Ortho and *para* directing:
> (*c*) $-CH_3$, $-OH$, $-OCH_3$, $-NH_2$, $-NHCOCH_3$, $-SCN$.
> (*d*) $-CH_2.CH_3$ (X and Y being the C.C atoms).
> $-CH:CHCOOH$ (X and Y being the C:C atoms).
> $-N:N-$ (X and Y being the N:N atoms).
> (*e*) $-Cl$, $-Br$, $-I$.

The student should remember that *para* compounds have almost invariably higher melting-points than the corresponding *ortho* and *meta* isomerides, as the following examples show:

Melting-points of Disubstituted Benzenes

		Ortho	Meta	Para
Dichloro-benzene	$C_6H_4Cl_2$	-17	-25	53
Chloro-bromo-benzene	C_6H_4ClBr	12	-21	67
Dibromo-benzene	$C_6H_4Br_2$	6	-7	89
Chloro-aniline	$C_6H_4ClNH_2$	-2	-10	70
Bromo-aniline	$C_6H_4BrNH_2$	31	18	66
Nitro-aniline	$C_6H_4(NO_2)NH_2$	72	114	148
Bromo-phenol	$C_6H_4Br(OH)$	5	32	63
Nitro-phenol	$C_6H_4(NO_2)OH$	46	97	114
Bromo-toluene	$C_6H_4BrCH_3$	-26	-40	28
Nitro-toluene	$C_6H_4(CH_3)NO_2$	-4	16	52
Toluene sulphonylchloride	$C_6H_4(CH_3)SO_2Cl$	10	12	66

It will be seen that the *para* compound is frequently the only isomeride which is solid at room temperature, a fact which should be borne in mind when identifying organic compounds.

m-Dinitrobenzene. $C_6H_4(NO_2)_2$.

Required: Fuming nitric acid, 15 c.c.; sulphuric acid, 20 c.c.; nitrobenzene, 12 c.c.

This preparation must be performed in a fume-cupboard, because nitrous fumes are evolved during the nitration.

Place 15 c.c. of fuming nitric acid (*d*, 1·5) in a 150 c.c. flask and add carefully with shaking 20 c.c. (37 gms.) of concentrated sulphuric acid and then *some fragments of unglazed porcelain.* Fit a reflux air-condenser securely to the flask, and then add slowly down the condenser 12 c.c. (14·5 gms.) of nitrobenzene: do not add more than 3 c.c. of the nitrobenzene at a time, and after each addition *shake the flask to ensure thorough mixing of the contents.* Now heat the flask on a boiling water-bath for 1 hour, both the flask and the condenser being securely clamped in position, as the acid fumes which are evolved may attack and weaken the cork. Shake the flask vigorously from time to time throughout this period of heating. Finally pour the mixture carefully with stirring into an excess of cold water (about 300 c.c.), whereupon the heavy oily dinitrobenzene will rapidly solidify. Filter the crystalline material at the pump, wash *thoroughly* with water to remove all acid, and then drain as completely as possible.

To purify the crude dinitrobenzene, transfer it to a 200 c.c. conical flask fitted with a reflux water-condenser, add about 100 c.c. of methylated spirit, and heat on a water-bath until the crystalline material dissolves completely. If the solution so obtained is not quite clear, filter it through a Buchner funnel which has been preheated by the filtration of some boiling solvent. The solution on cooling deposits *m*-dinitrobenzene as colourless crystals: yield, 14–15 gms. A second recrystallisation is, however, usually necessary in order to eliminate traces of *o*- and *p*-dinitrobenzene, and thus obtain pure *m*-dinitrobenzene, m.p. 90°.

For reactions of *m*-dinitrobenzene, see p. 292, 293.

Aniline. $C_6H_5NH_2$.

Both aliphatic and aromatic nitro-compounds can be readily reduced in acid solution to the corresponding primary amine. Thus when a mixture of nitrobenzene and tin is treated with hydrochloric acid, the tin dissolves to give stannous chloride, $SnCl_2$, which in these circumstances then reacts with more acid to give stannic chloride, $SnCl_4$, and the nascent hydrogen produced from

$$Sn + 2HCl = SnCl_2 + 2H \qquad SnCl_2 + 2HCl = SnCl_4 + 2H$$
$$C_6H_5NO_2 + 6H = C_6H_5NH_2 + 2H_2O$$

these sources reduces the nitrobenzene to aniline. The stannic chloride combines with the excess of hydrochloric acid to give the complex chlorostannic acid, H_2SnCl_6, with which the aniline forms a salt, aniline chlorostannate $(C_6H_5NH_2)_2,H_2SnCl_6$, similar in type to aniline chloroplatinate (p. 353). The crude product is therefore made strongly alkaline with sodium hydroxide, which liberates the base with the formation of sodium stannate, and the aniline can

$$(C_6H_5NH_2)_2H_2SnCl_6 + 8NaOH = 2C_6H_5NH_2 + Na_2SnO_3 + 6NaCl + 5H_2O$$

then be removed by steam-distillation.

NOTE. *In view of the price and scarcity of tin, it may be replaced in the following preparation by the same weight of iron, the directions being otherwise unchanged. To obtain successful reduction with iron, however, it is essential to use fine turnings of pig- or cast-iron (or of "soft mottled" iron): the use of very fine filings, or—more particularly—of a hard iron or steel may cause incomplete reduction.*

Required: Nitrobenzene, 21 c.c.; tin, 50 gms.; hydrochloric acid, 100 c.c.; sodium hydroxide, 75 gms.; common salt, *ca.* 30 gms.

Place 21 c.c. (25 gms.) of nitrobenzene and 50 gms. of granulated tin in a 600 c.c. bolt-head flask fitted with a reflux water-condenser. Now pour about 20 c.c. of concentrated hydrochloric acid down the condenser, and shake the contents of the flask steadily. If the heat of the reaction causes the mixture to boil too vigorously, moderate the action by immersing the flask temporarily in cold water. Then as the reaction slackens, pour another 20 c.c. of hydrochloric acid down the condenser, and shake the flask to ensure good mixing, again cooling the flask if the action becomes too violent. Continue in this way until a total of 100 c.c. of hydrochloric acid has been added. Then heat the flask on a briskly boiling water-bath for 20 minutes. By these means the reduction is completed by the stannous chloride present: at the end of this time, therefore, the odour of the nitrobenzene should be barely perceptible. Now cool the flask in water, and slowly add a solution of 75 gms. of sodium hydroxide in 100 c.c. of water, thus making the solution strongly alkaline and liberating the aniline. Equip the flask for steam-distillation as shown in Fig. 16, p. 34, and steam-distil the mixture until about 175 c.c. of distillate have been collected. The aniline is only moderately soluble in cold water (giving an approximately 3% solution), and the greater part therefore separates as oily drops in the aqueous distillate: in order to reduce further the solubility of the aniline in the water, add about 30 gms. of powdered salt to the entire distillate and shake thoroughly until all the salt has dis-

solved. In spite of the decreased solubility of the aniline in the
aqueous distillate, an ether extraction is still advisable to ensure
efficient isolation of the aniline. Therefore transfer the distillate
to a separating-funnel,* add about 40 c.c. of ether, and shake
vigorously, occasionally relieving the pressure of the ether vapour
within the funnel by momentarily lifting the stopper. Allow the
two layers to separate, and then run off the lower aqueous layer,
finally pouring off the remaining ethereal layer through the mouth
of the funnel into a 200 c.c. conical flask. Replace the aqueous
solution in the funnel, and again extract with a further 40 c.c. of
ether. Proceed as before, and transfer the ethereal layer to the
conical flask. Now add some coarsely powdered potassium
hydroxide to the combined ethereal extracts, and allow the
securely corked flask to stand (preferably overnight) until the
ethereal solution is clear and dry.

*Tubing extends
well below bench*

FIG. 48.

Owing to the volatility of ether, and the explosive inflammability
of its vapour when mixed with air, special precautions must be
taken when distilling off this solvent. Fit up the apparatus as
shown in Fig. 48. **A** is a 60 c.c. distilling-flask fitted with a

---

* If only 100 c.c. separating-funnels are available, the distillate must be
divided into two portions and each extracted with ether as described, the final
ether extracts being united for drying with potassium hydroxide.

dropping-funnel **B**, so that the bottom of the stem of the funnel passes well below the side-arm of the flask. The latter is then connected to a water-condenser **C**, through which an ample supply of water can be passed. The lower end of **C** is then securely fitted into a Buchner flask **D** of about 300 c.c. capacity. A long piece of rubber tubing is attached to the side-arm of **D** as shown, so that the rubber tubing reaches well below the level of the bench: should any of the heavy ether vapour escape condensation during distillation, it will thus be carried away well below the apparatus. Place some fragments of unglazed porcelain in **A**, and extinguish all flames near the apparatus. Now decant the dried ethereal solution carefully into a small fluted filter-paper, so that it filters directly into the funnel **B**. It is probable that the water extracted from the ether during drying will have dissolved some of the potassium hydroxide, and that a mixture of solid potash and saturated aqueous potash solution will have collected at the bottom of the ether. If some of this aqueous potash solution should pass into the filter during the decantation of the ether, it will not pass through the filter-paper whilst the latter is saturated with the non-miscible ether, but will merely collect at the bottom of the fluted paper. When the filtration is complete, run about 25 c.c. of the ether solution into **A**, and place under the latter a water-bath which has been brought to the boil at some considerable distance from the apparatus. (With large classes, or in crowded laboratories, the water-baths may well be heated in fume-cupboards, which are usually at a safe distance for this purpose from the working benches.) As the ether distils off from **A**, run in more of the solution from **B**, and thus continue until it appears that all the ether has been distilled off, and only aniline remains in **A**. To complete the latter stages of the distillation, it may be necessary to reheat the water-bath: this should be done as before at a safe distance from the apparatus. Now detach the Buchner flask **D**, pour the contents into an ether residue bottle, and then replace **C** by an air-condenser: finally replace the funnel **B** by a thermometer reading to at least 200°. Distil the residual aniline carefully by direct heating over a gauze, and collect the fraction boiling at 180–185°. During the early part of distillation, a small quantity of ether may come over although the recorded temperature may be well above its boiling-point: hence ensure that the flame is kept well away from the open end of the condenser. Yield, 17 gms.

Aniline when freshly distilled is a colourless liquid of b.p. 184° and d, 1·025: on exposure to air and light, it develops a deep

brown colour. It is an extremely important substance technically, being the starting point of many azo and other dyes.

Aniline Semi-Micro Scale (1/10 of above scale).

Place 2·1 c.c. (measured from a micro-burette) of nitro-benzene and 5 gms.
of granulated tin in a 100 c.c. round-bottomed flask fitted with a small reflux
water-condenser. Pour 10 c.c. of conc. HCl down the condenser: on this scale
the reaction is not sufficiently vigorous to get out of control. Heat over a gauze
for 15 minutes. Cool the flask and add a solution of 7·5 gms. of NaOH in
10 c.c. of water to redissolve the initial precipitate. Add about 15 c.c. of water
and fit the flask with a small knee-tube and water-condenser (Fig. 43, p. 72).
Heat over a gauze and collect the distillate in a small flask: the aniline distils
rapidly in the steam, and the distillate suddenly becomes clear when about
18 c.c. have been collected. Add 3 gms. of powdered salt, shake to dissolve
and extract twice with about 4 c.c. of ether each time. Dry the ethereal extracts
in a 20 c.c. conical flask with a few small pieces of solid KOH: the solution will
be dry in about 15 minutes. Carefully decant the ethereal solution into the
flask shown in Fig. 27 (p. 43), taking care that no adhering moisture or solid
falls into the flask; add a small piece of unglazed porcelain or a few granules of
carborundum (which does not absorb the liquid) and place the flask in a beaker
containing hot water. Distil off *all* the ether with water running through the
condenser, and away from all flames. Then run the water out of the condenser
and heat the flask with a small flame. Attempt to keep the vapour of the hot
aniline around the bulb of the thermometer for about one minute before actually
distilling over the aniline. This is done in order to allow the bulb to reach the
true temperature of the vapour. Collect the fraction of b.p. 180–185°. Using
the pear-shaped flask shown in Fig. 27, it is usually possible to distil almost to
the last drop. Yield, 1·5 gm.

For reactions of aniline, see p. 282–284.

Sym-Tribromo-aniline. $C_6H_2(NH_2)Br_3$.

Aniline undergoes very ready nuclear substitution by bromine even in the
cold, the bromine atoms entering the two *ortho* positions and the *para* position
with the formation of symmetric or 2:4:6-tribromo-aniline. The presence

$$C_6H_5NH_2 + 3Br_2 = C_6H_2(NH_2)Br_3 + 3HBr$$

of the bromine atoms in tribromo-aniline reduces considerably the basic
properties of the amino group, and salts even with strong acids are almost
completely hydrolysed in the presence of water, although they can be prepared
in the presence of solvents such as benzene (p. 158).

It should be noted that phenol also reacts very readily with bromine to give
the corresponding *sym*-tribromophenol, $C_6H_2(OH)Br_3$.

Required: Aniline, 4 c.c.; bromine, 6·4 .cc.

Assemble the apparatus shown in Fig. 49. A 500 c.c. Buchner
flask **A** is fitted with a cork through which passes a glass delivery-
tube **B** reaching nearly to the bottom of **A**. **B** is then connected

by a short piece of rubber tubing to the side-arm of a 150 c.c. distilling-flask **C**, care being taken to ensure that the two glass tubes touch one another inside the rubber connection. A narrow glass tube **D** is then fitted as shown so that it reaches within 2–3 cm. of the bottom of **C**.

Dissolve 4 c.c. of aniline in 10 c.c. of dilute hydrochloric acid in **A**, and then dilute the solution with 200 c.c. of water. Now

place 6·4 c.c. (20·5 gms.) of bromine (*care!*) in **C**, and cover it with about 40 c.c. of cold water. Adjust the position of the tube **D** until it nearly touches the surface of the bromine layer. Connect **A** to a suction water-pump, so that a steady stream of bromine vapour is carried over from **C** into **A**, where the greyish-white tribromo-aniline soon begins to separate. Shake the contents of **A** from time to time to ensure an even distribution of the tribromo-aniline. When the evap-

FIG. 49.

oration of the bromine has caused the water in **C** to become almost colourless (about 40 minutes), stop the current of air, and filter off the tribromo-aniline at the pump, wash well with water and drain. Recrystallise from methylated spirit, using animal charcoal: the tribromo-aniline is obtained as colourless crystals, m.p. 120°. Yield, 8·5 gms.

For the elimination of the amino group from tribromo-aniline, see p. 157.

p-Bromo-acetanilide. $BrC_6H_4NHCOCH_3$.

Acetanilide also undergoes ready bromination, with the formation of a mixture of *o*- and *p*-bromo-acetanilide. The *ortho* compound is formed in only

$$C_6H_5NHCOCH_3 + Br_2 = BrC_6H_4NHCOCH_3 + HBr$$

small amount, however, and being more soluble in alcohol than the *para* compound, can be readily eliminated by recrystallisation.

Required: Acetanilide, 5 gms.; bromine, 2·1 c.c.; acetic acid 30 c.c.

Dissolve 5 gms. of finely powdered acetanilide in 25 c.c. of cold glacial acetic acid contained in a 200 c.c. conical flask. Then in another small flask prepare a solution of 2·1 c.c. (6·7 gms.) of bromine (*care!*) in 30 c.c. of glacial acetic acid, and add this solution *slowly* to the acetanilide solution, shaking the latter throughout the addition to ensure thorough mixing. Allow the final mixture to stand at room temperature for 15 minutes. Then pour the pale reddish-orange solution, which may already contain some crystals of *p*-bromo-acetanilide, into a large excess (about 300 c.c.) of cold water, whereupon the *p*-bromo-acetanilide will rapidly crystallise out. Stir these crystals thoroughly with the water to eliminate acetic acid, unchanged bromine, *etc.*, and then filter at the pump, wash well with cold water, drain, and finally recrystallise from methylated spirit. The *p*-bromo-acetanilide is obtained as colourless crystals, m.p. 167°. Yield, 7 gms.

p-Nitro-acetanilide, $NO_2C_6H_4NHCOCH_3$, and *p*-Nitro-aniline, $NO_2C_6H_4NH_2$.

Aniline cannot be directly nitrated with the usual nitrating mixture of nitric and sulphuric acid, because considerable charring and oxidation of the aniline occurs. The difficulty may be overcome either by using a very large excess of sulphuric acid, or (better) by protecting the reactive amino group by acetylation, since the acetylamino group, CH_3CONH-, has the same *ortho* and *para* directing influence as the NH_2- group itself. Acetanilide undergoes ready nitration, giving chiefly the colourless *p*-nitro-acetanilide, mixed, however, with a much smaller proportion of the yellow *o*-nitro-acetanilide. Recrystallisation from alcohol readily removes the more soluble *ortho* compound, and the pure *p*-nitro-acetanilide which separates can then be hydrolysed to *p*-nitro-aniline.

Required: Acetanilide, 10 gms.; acetic acid, 10 c.c.; sulphuric acid, 20 c.c.; fuming nitric acid, 4 c.c.

Add 10 gms. of powdered acetanilide to 10 c.c. (10·6 gms.) of glacial acetic acid contained in a 100 c.c. beaker, and then to the well-stirred mixture add 20 c.c. (37 gms.) of concentrated sulphuric acid. The mixture becomes hot and a clear solution is rapidly obtained. Place the beaker in an intimate mixture of salt and crushed ice until the temperature of the mixture falls to about 0–5°. Now, whilst stirring the viscous mixture continuously with the thermometer, add 4 c.c. of ordinary fuming nitric acid (*d.* 1·5) cautiously drop by drop from a burette (preferably in a fume-cupboard), so that the temperature of the mixture does not rise above 25°: this operation should take 10–15 minutes. Then remove the beaker from the freezing mixture, allow it to stand for 30 minutes at room temperature, and pour the contents on to about 100 gms. of crushed ice, whereby the crude nitro-acetanilide is at once precipitated: finally rinse out the beaker with 50 c.c. of water containing a few fragments of ice, adding the solution to the main bulk of the product. Allow the mixture to stand for about 20 minutes, and then filter at the pump, wash *thoroughly* with cold water to remove acid, and drain. Yield of crude product, 14 gms., the high value being due to traces of polynitro-derivatives.

Recrystallise the crude pale yellow product from methylated spirit, filter at the pump, wash quickly with a few c.c. of fresh spirit, and then drain and dry. The yellow *o*-nitro-acetanilide remains in the filtrate, whilst the *p*-nitro-acetanilide is obtained as colourless crystals, m.p. 212°. A second recrystallisation of the *para* compound should not be necessary. Yield of pure product, 8 gms.

Hydrolysis to *p*-Nitro-aniline. For this purpose use 70% sulphuric acid, the usual reagent employed for the hydrolysis of anilides (p. 80). Add 5 gms. of the recrystallised *p*-nitro-acetanilide to 30 c.c. of 70% sulphuric acid, and boil the mixture gently under a reflux water-condenser for 20 minutes. Then pour the clear hot solution into about 150 c.c. of cold water, and finally add an excess of sodium hydroxide solution until precipitation of the yellow *p*-nitro-aniline is complete. Cool the mixture in ice-water if necessary, and then filter at the pump, wash well with water, and drain thoroughly. The *p*-nitro-aniline is thus obtained as a dark yellow powder, which has m.p. 147–148° and therefore, in spite of the dark colour, is practically pure. Yield, 3·5 gms. (almost theoretical). Recrystallise from a mixture of equal volumes of methylated spirit and water, boiling the solution gently with a small quantity of animal charcoal for 3–4 minutes, and then filtering the hot solution through a Buchner funnel preheated by the filtration of some boiling solvent. The *p*-nitro-aniline separates in bright yellow crystals, m.p. 148°.

For reactions of *p*-nitro-aniline, see p. 294.

***m*-Nitro-aniline. $C_6H_4(NO_2)NH_2$.**

m-Nitro-aniline, unlike *o*- and *p*-nitro-aniline, clearly cannot be prepared by the direct nitration of aniline or of acetanilide. It has therefore to be prepared by reducing only one of the nitro groups in the readily accessible *m*-dinitrobenzene. The earlier method for this purpose consists in boiling an alcoholic solution of the dinitrobenzene with ammonium sulphide. The latter undergoes dissociation giving hydrogen sulphide, which reduces the dinitrobenzene to

$$C_6H_4(NO_2)_2 + 3H_2S = C_6H_4(NO_2)NH_2 + 2H_2O + 3S$$

m-nitro-aniline with liberation of sulphur. The method however is long and tedious, primarily because the hot alcoholic solution has to be repeatedly cooled and resaturated with hydrogen sulphide to ensure efficient reduction. Very much better results are obtained by boiling an aqueous suspension of *m*-dinitrobenzene with sodium disulphide solution, prepared by the direct addition of sulphur to sodium sulphide. In these circumstances the dinitrobenzene is

$$Na_2S + S = Na_2S_2$$
$$C_6H_4(NO_2)_2 + Na_2S_2 + H_2O = C_6H_4(NO_2)NH_2 + Na_2S_2O_3$$

readily reduced to *m*-nitro-aniline, the sodium disulphide being mainly oxidised to sodium thiosulphate.

Required: Sulphur, 4·2 gms.; sodium sulphide, 16 gms.; *m*-dinitrobenzene, 10 gms.

The crystalline sodium sulphide ($Na_2S,9H_2O$) used to prepare the disulphide is very deliquescent, and only a sample which has been kept in a well-stoppered bottle and therefore reasonably dry should be used. A sample from a badly-stoppered bottle may contain, in addition to the crystals, a certain amount of aqueous solution, in which hydrolysis and partial decomposition will have occurred: such a sample should therefore be rejected. Add 4·2 gms. of finely powdered sulphur to a solution of 16 gms. of the crystalline sodium sulphide in 60 c.c. of water, and boil the mixture gently for a few minutes until a clear solution of the disulphide is obtained.

Heat a mixture of 10 gms. of pure *m*-dinitrobenzene and 450 c.c. of water in a 750 c.c. beaker on a sand-bath until the water boils gently. Transfer the sodium disulphide solution to a small dropping-funnel, and clamp the funnel in position so that the end of the stem is immediately above the beaker. Now allow the disulphide solution to fall drop by drop into the boiling water at such a rate that the total addition takes 10–15 minutes: *throughout this period* keep the molten *m*-dinitrobenzene vigorously stirred by means of a glass rod (having the lower end covered by a short length of rubber tubing) so that the dinitrobenzene is kept continuously dispersed as fine drops and not allowed to settle to the bottom. (On a larger scale a mechanical stirrer can be advantageously used at this stage, but with the above quantities hand-stirring gives excellent results.) When the addition of the disulphide is complete, boil the solution gently for a further 20 minutes. Then add sufficient hot water to restore the total volume to at least 500 c.c., boil vigorously for a few moments and quickly filter the solution, using a Buchner funnel and flask which have been preheated by the filtration of much boiling water: a small quantity of elementary sulphur remains on the filter. The pale brown filtrate rapidly deposits yellow crystals of the *m*-nitro-aniline. Chill in ice-water, and then filter at the pump, wash

F

with cold water, and drain. (Yield, 6·5–7·0 gms.) Recrystallise from much hot water (about 80 c.c. per gm. of nitraniline, to allow filtration through a preheated funnel without premature crystallisation). *m*-Nitro-aniline is thus obtained as bright yellow crystals, m.p. 114°.

If an impure and discoloured sample of *m*-dinitrobenzene is used in the above preparation, add some animal charcoal to the solution immediately prior to the 20 minutes' boiling: the use of charcoal is to be avoided when possible, however, as it is liable to absorb an appreciable quantity of the *m*-nitro-aniline.

For reactions of *m*-nitro-aniline, see p. 294.

The Nitration of Phenol.

One of the characteristic properties of phenol is the ease with which it gives substitution products, this property being particularly well shown by the ready nitration, sulphonation and bromination which the benzene ring in the phenol molecule undergoes.

If phenol is treated even with dilute nitric acid at room temperature, nitration readily occurs with the simultaneous formation of the yellow *o*-nitrophenol and the white *p*-nitrophenol. These compounds can be readily separated, because the former is volatile, and the latter non-volatile, in steam.

If phenol is heated with more concentrated nitric acid, nitration occurs ultimately at the *para* and at both the *ortho* positions, giving picric acid or 2:4:6-trinitrophenol. To prepare picric acid, however, it is more convenient first to heat the phenol with sulphuric acid, whereby a mixture of *o*- and *p*-phenol sulphonic acids is readily obtained. If this mixture is now heated

$$HOC_6H_4 | H + HO | SO_3H = HOC_6H_4SO_3H + H_2O$$

with concentrated nitric acid, nitration occurs at the two positions *meta* to the – SO$_3$H group in each compound, and finally the – SO$_3$H group in each of the

$$HOC_6H_4SO_3H + 2HONO_2 = HOC_6H_2(NO_2)_2SO_3H + 2H_2O$$
$$HOC_6H_2(NO_2)_2SO_3H + HONO_2 = HOC_6H_2(NO_2)_3 + H_2SO_4$$

dinitrophenol sulphonic acids is replaced by a third nitro group, giving picric acid in both cases.

o- and *p*-Nitrophenols. NO$_2$C$_6$H$_4$OH.

Required: Nitric acid, 25 c.c.; phenol, 20 gms.

Prepare a mixture of 25 c.c. of concentrated nitric acid and 80 c.c. of water in a 750 c.c. flat-bottomed flask for which a steam-distillation fitting is available for subsequent use. Warm a mixture of 20 gms. of phenol and 15 c.c. of water *gently* in a small conical flask until the phenol is molten: on shaking the mixture vigorously an emulsion of the phenol in the water is thus obtained. Now place a thermometer in the dilute nitric acid, cool the latter in ice-water, and add the phenol emulsion in small quantities at a time so that the temperature of the well-shaken mixture does not rise above 30°. When the addition of the phenol is complete, remove the flask from the ice-water and allow the mixture to stand for at least 2 hours—and preferably overnight. During the first hour of this period of standing, retain the thermometer in the liquid and occasionally shake the latter vigorously to ensure thorough mixing: the temperature will spontaneously rise slowly to 50–55° but should not be allowed to rise above this upper limit. If the mixture is allowed to stand for only 2 hours, chill it thoroughly in ice-water at the *end* of this period in order to coagulate and partly harden the black syrupy insoluble residue and so obtain a sharp separation between this heavy residue and the aqueous layer above. (If the mixture is allowed to stand overnight, a complete separation will occur spontaneously.)

Then add 100 c.c. of water, shake well to extract excess of acid, and allow the black oily drops to settle. Then decant the clear reddish-brown aqueous solution from the heavy black residual oil: this can readily be done if the nitration mixture has been set aside overnight, as the oily drops then rapidly sink and collect at the bottom of the aqueous layer, but if the mixture has been allowed to stand for only 2 hours, care must be taken that any oily drops still floating on the surface of the solution are not poured away with the aqueous solution. Now add 200 c.c. of water, repeat the shaking, when the heavy oil will become semi-solid and the aqueous layer can readily be poured off. Add 300 c.c. of water to the residue in the flask, fit the latter with the steam-distillation inlet and outlet tubes, and assemble the complete apparatus for steam-distillation (Fig. 16, p. 34), using a single-surface glass-jacketed condenser of wide bore. Steam-distil the mixture until about 250 c.c. of distillate have been collected, the receiver being meanwhile cooled in ice-water. The o-nitrophenol readily passes over in the steam and crystallises in the cold distillate. If the nitrophenol crystallises in the condenser, run out the con-denser-water for a few moments: the nitrophenol will then soon melt and pass on into the distillate. When the distillation is complete (*i.e.*, when a few c.c. of the distillate collected in a test-tube give no crystalline deposit on thorough cooling), cool the distillate in ice-water for a further few minutes to ensure complete solidification of the o-nitrophenol, and then filter the latter at the pump, and drain thoroughly. Yield, 7 gms. The o-nitrophenol so obtained is practically pure. It may be further purified if desired either by steam-distilling a second time, or by recrystallisation.

For the latter purpose, dissolve the crystals in hot methylated spirit, and then add water drop by drop to the well-stirred solution until a fine emulsion *just* appears: then add more spirit, also drop by drop, until the emulsion just redissolves. Now allow the solution to cool spontaneously: if the emulsion reappears, add a few drops of methylated spirit from time to time in order to keep the solution clear. Finally the o-nitrophenol separates in crystals, and the well-stirred mixture may now be cooled in ice-water until crystallisation is complete. Filter, drain and dry either in an atmospheric desiccator, or by pressing between drying-paper.

The o-nitrophenol is obtained as bright yellow crystals, m.p. 46°, possessing an odour which resembles both that of phenol and of nitrobenzene.

Meanwhile to obtain the p-nitrophenol, chill the crude residue in the steam-distillation flask thoroughly in ice-water for about 20 minutes.* The black tar becomes almost solid, and crystals of crude p-nitrophenol separate. Filter off the complete solid product at the pump, wash it with water, and transfer it to a beaker. Extract the p-nitrophenol by boiling this residue with about 150 c.c. of water, finally decanting off the aqueous solution and filtering it through a fluted filter-paper directly into a 800 c.c. beaker. Repeat the extraction with a further 150 c.c. of boiling water, and finally a third time with a boiling mixture of 150 c.c. of water and 50 c.c. of concentrated hydrochloric acid. Finally add about 3 gms. of animal charcoal to the united filtrate, and then boil the latter in the open beaker until the volume is reduced to about 100 c.c. Then filter through a small Buchner funnel which has been preheated by the filtration of some boiling distilled water. The filtrate on cooling, and finally chilling in ice-water, deposits the p-nitrophenol as pale brownish-white crystals: filter at the pump, wash with a *small* quantity of water and drain. Yield, 4 gms. The p-nitrophenol can be recrystallised with very little loss from a mixture of equal volumes of water and concentrated hydrochloric acid, and is thus obtained as colourless odourless crystals, m.p. 114°. (If the p-nitrophenol is recrystallised from hot water alone, it almost invariably separates first as a fine emulsion, which subsequently crystallises.)

For properties and reactions of o- and p-nitrophenols, see pp. 293, 294.

---

* The preparation can be shortened by omitting this stage and extracting the black residue by boiling it first with the water already present in the flask. In this case the yield of p-nitrophenol is increased somewhat, but the product is usually very dark in colour.

$$\text{OH}$$
$$NO_2 \bigcirc NO_2$$
$$NO_2$$

Picric Acid (2:4:6-Trinitrophenol).

Required: Phenol, 8 gms.; sulphuric acid, 10 c.c.; nitric acid, 30 c.c.

Weigh out 8 gms. of phenol into a *dry* 750 c.c. flat-bottomed flask, add 10 c.c. (18·5 gms.) of concentrated sulphuric acid, and shake the mixture, which becomes warm. Now heat the flask on a briskly boiling water-bath for 30 minutes to complete the formation of the phenol-sulphonic acid, and then chill the flask thoroughly in an ice-water mixture. Place the flask on a wooden block (or on some similar non-conducting surface) in an efficient fume-cupboard, and without delay, *i.e.*, whilst the phenol-sulphonic acid is still a cold viscous syrup, add 30 c.c. of concentrated nitric acid and *at once* thoroughly mix the liquids by shaking for a few seconds. Then allow the mixture to stand undisturbed. Usually within one minute a vigorous (but harmless) reaction occurs, and red fumes pour out of the flask. When the action subsides, heat the flask on a boiling water-bath for 1½ hours, with occasional shaking. During this period the heavy oil, which is present at the beginning, ultimately forms a mass of crystals. When the heating is complete, add 100 c.c. of cold water, mix well and then chill thoroughly in ice-water. Filter the yellow crystals at the pump, wash *thoroughly* with water to eliminate all inorganic acid and drain. Recrystallise from a mixture of 1 volume of alcohol and 2 volumes of water, about 90 c.c. of the mixed solvent being required. Picric acid is obtained in beautiful yellow leaflets, m.p. 122°. Dry by pressing between sheets of drying-paper, or in a desiccator. Yield of recrystallised material, 13 gms.

Picric acid if stored in bulk should, for safety, first be damped. Smaller quantities may be safely kept whilst dry, but should be stored in bottles having cork or rubber stoppers: glass stoppers should never be used for potentially explosive substances, because on replacing the stopper some of the material may be ground between the neck of the flask and the stopper, and so caused to explode.

REACTIONS OF PICRIC ACID. (1) The presence of the three nitro groups in picric acid considerably increases the acidic properties of the phenolic group and therefore picric acid, unlike most phenols, will evolve carbon dioxide from sodium carbonate solution. Show this by boiling picric acid with sodium carbonate solution, using the method described in Section 5, p. 248. The reaction is not readily shown by a cold saturated aqueous solution of picric acid, because the latter is so dilute that the sodium carbonate is largely converted into sodium bicarbonate without loss of carbon dioxide.

(2) To a cold aqueous solution of picric acid, add about an equal volume of dilute potassium cyanide solution. An orange coloration develops and rapidly darkens to a deep red.

USES OF PICRIC ACID. The following further reactions of picric acid are used for analytical purposes in the laboratory.

(3) *Identification of Aromatic Hydrocarbons.* Picric acid combines with many aromatic hydrocarbons, giving addition products of definite m.p. Thus with naphthalene it gives yellow naphthalene picrate, $C_{10}H_8,(NO_2)_3C_6H_2OH$, m.p. 152°, and with anthracene it gives red anthracene picrate, $C_{14}H_{10},(NO_2)_3C_6H_2OH$, m.p. 138°. For practical details, see p. 301.

(4) *Identification of Amines.* Picric acid combines with many amines to give crystalline picrates, of general formula $B,(NO_2)_3C_6H_2OH$, where B is a molecule of a monacidic base. These picrates have usually sharp melting- or decomposition-points, and serve to characterise the amines concerned. They may be formed either by (*a*) direct union of the acid and the base in a suitable solvent, or (*b*) by the interaction of sodium picrate and a salt of the amine in aqueous solution.

(*a*) Dissolve 3–4 drops of pyridine in about 3 c.c. of alcohol, and add a cold alcoholic solution of picric acid. A yellow precipitate of pyridine picrate, $C_5H_5N,(NO_2)_3C_6H_2OH$, at once separates. It may be filtered off, and recrystallised from alcohol: m.p. 167°. Quinoline similarly gives quinoline picrate, $C_9H_7N,(NO_2)_3C_6H_2OH$, m.p. 203°.

(*b*) If an alcoholic solution of picric acid is similarly added to one of aniline, no precipitation occurs, owing to the high solubility of aniline picrate in alcohol. If, however, a cold aqueous solution of aniline hydrochloride is added to a similar solution of sodium picrate and the mixture shaken, yellow crystals of aniline picrate, m.p. 165°, soon separate.

(5) *Detection of Potassium in the presence of Sodium.* Add a cold saturated aqueous solution of sodium picrate to a solution of potassium chloride. A rapid precipitation of the less soluble potassium picrate occurs, even from a 1% solution of potassium chloride.

Picric acid is used on a large scale as a high explosive, but for this purpose requires a detonator. If a *few small* crystals of the pure acid are heated on a crucible lid, they first melt, and ultimately burn harmlessly with a smoky flame. Metallic salts of picric acid are much less stable than the free acid, and should always be stored damp. Aqueous solutions of picric acid are sometimes used in medicine for the treatment of burns (p. 428).

Bromobenzene. C_6H_5Br.

If cold benzene is treated with bromine in the absence of sunlight, very little reaction occurs; if, however, a "halogen carrier," such as iron, iodine, pyridine, *etc.*, is also present, a rapid reaction by substitution occurs, forming first

$$C_6H_6 + Br_2 = C_6H_5Br + HBr$$

bromobenzene, and then mainly *p*-dibromobenzene.

The reaction must be carried out in the absence of direct sunlight, since sunlight causes the bromine to add directly on to benzene, particularly if the

$$C_6H_6 + 3Br_2 = C_6H_6Br_6$$

latter is warm, to give benzene hexabromide.

Required: Purified benzene, 34 c.c.; pyridine, 0·5 c.c.; bromine, 24 c.c.

The benzene used in this preparation should be reasonably free from toluene: therefore use a sample of benzene supplied by dealers as "crystallisable benzene," *i.e.*, one which crystallises readily when cooled in ice-water. It should preferably be dried over calcium chloride and, immediately before use, filtered through a fluted filter-paper. The pyridine should also preferably be dried over solid potassium hydroxide and redistilled.

Place 0·5 c.c. of the pyridine in a 200 c.c. round- or flat-bottomed flask and add 34 c.c. (30 gms.) of benzene. Fit the flask with a reflux water-condenser, and then place it *in* a cold water-bath. If the experiment is conducted in a fume-cupboard, the top of the condenser can be closed with a calcium chloride tube bent downwards (as in Fig. 45, p. 76) and the hydrogen bromide subsequently allowed to escape: if, however, the experiment is performed in the open laboratory, fit to the top of the condenser a glass delivery-tube which leads through a piece of rubber tubing to an inverted glass funnel, the rim of which dips just below the surface of some water in a beaker, so that the hydrogen bromide may be absorbed without risk of "sucking back." Ensure that the apparatus is not standing in the direct rays of the sun. Now pour 24 c.c. (76 gms.) of bromine (*care in manipulation!*) down the condenser, and *at once* replace the calcium chloride tube or the delivery-tube, as a vigorous reaction occurs when the bromine dissolves in the benzene. When the initial evolution of hydrogen bromide slackens, heat the water-bath to 25–30° for one hour, occasionally shaking the contents of the flask: finally raise the temperature of the bath to 65–70° for a further 45 minutes. Now transfer the dark-coloured liquid to a separating-funnel and shake with an *excess* of 10% aqueous sodium hydroxide solution: the heavy lower layer of crude bromobenzene becomes almost colourless at this stage. Run off the bromobenzene, shake it again with water to ensure absence of alkali, and then dry with calcium chloride for 20–30 minutes. Filter through a small fluted filter-paper directly into a 50 c.c. distilling-flask fitted with an air-condenser. Now distil the crude bromobenzene *slowly*, rejecting the fraction boiling up to 150°, and collecting that of b.p. 150–160°. Yield, 28–29 gms. (about 19 c.c.). A small quantity of crude *p*-dibromobenzene remains in the flask.

Carefully refractionate the liquid of b.p. 150–160°, either by direct distillation from a small distilling-flask or (preferably) by using a short fractionating column, of the type shown in Fig. 12(B), p. 28. Almost pure bromobenzene is thus obtained, usually of b.p. 154–156° if distilled directly, and of b.p. 155–156° if a column is used. Yield in either case, about 22 gms. (14–15 c.c.).

Bromobenzene is a colourless liquid of b.p. 156°, and d, 1·50: it has a faint agreeable odour. The bromine atom, being directly joined to the benzene ring, is very inert, and the only common reactions in which it is split off from the ring are the Fittig reaction (p. 225) and the Grignard reaction (pp. 218–221).

For reactions of bromobenzene, see p. 297.

The *p*-dibromobenzene formed as a by-product in the above reaction usually solidifies when the undistilled residue obtained in the first distillation is chilled. It may be isolated by adding about 10 c.c. of methylated spirit and some animal charcoal to the flask, boiling for a few minutes, and filtering hot. On cooling the filtrate in ice-water, crystals of *p*-dibromobenzene, m.p. 89°, separate: recrystallise a second time if necessary to obtain colourless crystals.

Sulphonation.

A further difference between aliphatic and aromatic hydrocarbons is that only the latter are capable of direct *sulphonation*. Thus benzene when heated with concentrated sulphuric acid gives benzene sulphonic acid, a reaction which proceeds more readily, however, if chlorosulphonic acid is used instead of sulphuric acid.

$$C_6H_5 | H + HO | SO_3H = C_6H_5SO_3H + H_2O$$

$$C_6H_5 | H + Cl | SO_3H = C_6H_5SO_3H + HCl$$

Aromatic sulphonic acids are frequently difficult to obtain pure, since they almost invariably decompose on attempted distillation, and many are very soluble in water: such aqueous solutions on being concentrated often give syrupy solutions from which the sulphonic acid crystallises with difficulty. A more suitable preparation to illustrate sulphonation is that of sulphanilic acid, $NH_2C_6H_4SO_3H$, a highly crystalline substance of low solubility in cold water.

If aniline is treated with an excess of concentrated sulphuric acid, aniline hydrogen sulphate is first formed, and then on heating is converted into sulphanilic acid. This conversion to the sulphanilic acid is, however, very slow

$$C_6H_5NH_2 + H_2SO_4 = C_6H_5NH_2,H_2SO_4$$
$$C_6H_5NH_2,H_2SO_4 = NH_2C_6H_4SO_3H + H_2O$$

with concentrated sulphuric acid: if fuming sulphuric acid is used, the sulphonation proceeds much more rapidly, but the aniline undergoes a certain amount of charring and decomposition on the addition of the stronger acid. It is best, therefore, first to add concentrated sulphuric acid to the aniline, and then to add fuming sulphuric acid to the more resistant aniline hydrogen sulphate so formed: under these conditions little decomposition occurs, and sulphonation proceeds readily on heating.

Sulphanilic Acid (*p*-Amino-benzene Sulphonic Acid). $NH_2C_6H_4SO_3H,2H_2O.$

Required: Aniline, 10 c.c.; sulphuric acid, 20 c.c.; fuming sulphuric acid (10%), 20 c.c.

Place 10 c.c. (10·3 gms.) of aniline in a 150 c.c. conical flask, and add slowly 20 c.c. (37 gms.) of concentrated sulphuric acid; shake the mixture gently during the addition, and keep it cool by immersing the flask occasionally in cold water. White lumps of aniline hydrogen sulphate separate. Add cautiously 20 c.c. of 10% fuming sulphuric acid (*i.e.*, concentrated sulphuric acid containing 10% of dissolved sulphur trioxide), and then heat the mixture in an oil-bath at 180–190° for 1 hour, preferably in a fume-cupboard. Allow the product to cool, and pour carefully into about 200 c.c. of cold water, stirring the mixture vigorously during the addition. Allow to stand for about 5 minutes, and then filter off at the pump the sulphanilic acid which has crystallised out, wash it well with water, and drain. The crystals so obtained should be almost colourless. Purify by recrystallising from about 250 c.c. of boiling water: filter the hot solution through a Buchner funnel and flask which have been preheated by the filtration of boiling distilled water. If, however, the temperature of the reaction mixture has been allowed to rise above 190°, the crude sulphanilic acid may be greyish-brown in colour: in this case, boil the aqueous solution obtained during the recrystallisation with about 2 gms. of animal charcoal for 10–15 minutes (see p. 22), and then filter the hot solution through the preheated Buchner funnel. The sulphanilic acid rapidly separates from the filtrate in colourless crystals: when the filtrate is quite cold, filter off the crystals at the pump, wash with a small quantity of cold water and drain thoroughly. Dry

F*

the crystals by pressing between sheets of drying-paper, or by placing in an atmospheric calcium chloride desiccator. In a vacuum desiccator the sulphanilic acid loses its water of crystallisation, and hence its crystalline form. Yield, about 10 gms.

Sulphanilic acid has no melting-point, as it decomposes on being heated. It is only slightly soluble in cold water, but easily soluble in boiling water. The strongly acid sulphonic group suppresses considerably the basic properties of the amino-group: consequently although the substance will act as an acid, forming salts with alkalis, it will not usually act as a base to form salts with acids. It is probable that in aqueous solution sulphanilic acid exists as a doubly charged ion, $H_3\overset{+}{N}C_6H_4S\bar{O}_3$.

For reactions of sulphanilic acid, see p. 291.

One of the chief uses of sulphanilic acid is in the preparation of coloured derivatives of the methyl-orange type (p. 169).

Sulphanilamide (p-Amino-benzene Sulphonamide). $NH_2 \cdot C_6H_4 \cdot SO_2NH_2$.

Sulphanilamide, the simplest member of a large series of bacteriostatic drugs, can readily be prepared by the following reactions. Acetanilide, when treated with an excess of chlorosulphonic acid, gives p-acetamido-benzene sulphonyl chloride (Reaction A), which readily reacts with ammonia to give p-acetamido-benzene sulphonamide (Reaction B). The acetamido-group in the latter

$$CH_3CO \cdot NHC_6H_5 + HOSO_2Cl = CH_3CO \cdot NH \cdot C_6H_4 \cdot SO_2Cl + H_2O \quad (A)$$
$$CH_3CO \cdot NH \cdot C_6H_4 \cdot SO_2Cl + 2NH_3 = CH_3CO \cdot NH \cdot C_6H_4 \cdot SO_2NH_2 + NH_4Cl \quad (B)$$
$$CH_3CO \cdot NH \cdot C_6H_4 \cdot SO_2NH_2 + H_2O = NH_2 \cdot C_6H_4 \cdot SO_2NH_2 + CH_3COOH \quad (C)$$

compound can be readily hydrolysed under conditions which leave the sulphonamido group unaffected, and sulphanilamide can thus be obtained (Reaction C).

Note that p-acetamido-benzene sulphonyl chloride will similarly react with primary and secondary amines, and the products, after hydrolysis of the acetyl group, may furnish notable drugs: e.g., the condensation products with 2-amino-pyridine and 2-aminothiazole, after removal of the acetyl groups, provide the drugs commonly known as sulphapyridine (M & B 693) and sulphathiazole respectively.

Required: Acetanilide, 25 gms.; chlorosulphonic acid, 63 c.c.; aqueous ammonia (0·880), 120 c.c.

p-ACETAMIDO-BENZENE SULPHONYL CHLORIDE. (Reaction A.) Carefully add 25 gms. of dry powdered acetanilide, with occasional shaking, to 63 c.c. (110 gms., *i.e.*, 5 molecular equivalents) of chlorosulphonic acid* contained in a 250 c.c.

* The chlorosulphonic acid should be handled *with great care*, and always in a fume-cupboard. The technical acid is usually pure enough for the above preparation. If it is dark in colour, it can be further purified *by careful* distillation (preferably in an all-glass apparatus) and the fraction of b.p. 149–152° collected for use.

conical flask (fume-cupboard), and then heat the solution to 60–70° for 2 hours. Cool the mixture and pour it *carefully* on to about 500 gms. of crushed ice, whereupon the sulphonyl chloride separates as a white solid. Filter off the sulphonyl chloride at the pump, wash it thoroughly with water, and drain. This crude product (weight when dry, *ca.* 38 gms.) is sufficiently pure to use directly in the next stage. A small sample may be dried and recrystallised from chloroform, and is finally obtained as colourless crystals, m.p. 149–150°.

p-ACETAMIDO-BENZENE SULPHONAMIDE. (Reaction B.) Place the above crude damp sulphonyl chloride in a 500 c.c. conical flask and *cautiously* add 120 c.c. of concentrated ammonia solution (*d*, 0·880) (fume-cupboard): a vigorous reaction with evolution of heat will follow. Stir the mixture until a smooth thin paste is obtained, and then heat at 70° for 30 minutes with occasional stirring. Cool the mixture and make it *just* acid with dilute sulphuric acid. Filter off the precipitated *p*-acetamido-benzene sulphonamide at the pump, wash it well with cold water, and drain it thoroughly. (Yield almost theoretical.) Again, this material is pure enough for the next stage: a sample may be recrystallised from hot water and the pure sulphonamide obtained as colourless crystals, m.p. 219°.

SULPHANILAMIDE. (Reaction C.) Add 15 gms. of the above thoroughly drained sulphonamide to 10 c.c. of concentrated hydrochloric acid diluted with 20 c.c. water, and boil the mixture gently under reflux for 1 hour. Then add 30 c.c. of water and heat the mixture again to boiling, with the addition of a small quantity of animal charcoal. Filter the boiling solution, and add powdered sodium carbonate in small quantities to the filtrate with stirring until all effervescence ceases and the sulphanilamide is precipitated as a white powder. Cool the mixture thoroughly and filter off the sulphanilamide at the pump, wash with water and dry. Yield, *ca.* 10 gms.

Purify by recrystallisation from hot water: the sulphanilamide is obtained as colourless crystals, m.p. 163°.

Diazotisation.

Aromatic primary amines differ markedly from aliphatic amines in their reaction with nitrous acid. Thus a cold aqueous solution of mono-ethylamine hydrochloride reacts with nitrous acid to give the corresponding primary alcohol:

$$C_2H_5NH_2,HCl + HONO = C_2H_5OH + H_2O + N_2 + HCl$$

Aniline hydrochloride under similar conditions gives, however, phenyl diazonium chloride, sometimes called diazo-benzene chloride:

$$C_6H_5NH_2,HCl + HONO = C_6H_5 \overset{+}{N}\overset{-}{Cl} + 2H_2O$$
$$\underset{N}{|||}$$

Diazonium compounds are usually very soluble in water, and cannot be readily isolated, since on warming their aqueous solutions, decomposition occurs with the formation of a phenol:

$$C_6H_5 \overset{+}{N}\overset{-}{Cl} + HOH = C_6H_5OH + N_2 + HCl$$
$$\underset{N}{|||}$$

When an aqueous solution of phenyl diazonium chloride is added to a cold concentrated solution of potassium hydroxide, the unstable potassium diazotate, C_6H_5N:NOK, is formed, and this when heated with alkali to 130° changes to the isomeric but far more stable potassium isodiazotate: it is probable that these compounds have the structures (A) and (B) respectively, although the precise allocation of these structures to each of the compounds remains uncertain.

$$\begin{array}{ccc} & C_6H_5N & C_6H_5N \\ (A) & \| \longrightarrow & \| \quad (B) \\ & KON & NOK \end{array}$$

In preparing an aqueous solution of a diazonium salt, such as diazobenzene chloride, it is usual to dissolve the amine in a slight excess (about 2·2 molecular equivalents) of dilute hydrochloric acid (or alternatively to dissolve the crystalline amine hydrochloride in 1·2 equivalents of the acid) and then add an aqueous solution of a metallic nitrite. Nitrous acid is thus generated *in situ*, and reacts with the amine salt to give the diazonium compound. For a successful preparation of an aqueous solution of the diazonium salt, however, two conditions must always be observed:

(1) The solution of the aniline hydrochloride should be cooled to 5°C., and this temperature maintained throughout the addition of the sodium nitrite solution. External cooling has to be maintained, otherwise the heat of the reaction would cause the temperature to rise, with the consequent decomposition of the diazonium chloride and the production of phenol. If, on the other hand, the temperature is reduced to about 0°, diazotisation becomes extremely slow and unchanged nitrous acid may remain in the solution for an impracticably long time.

(2) Sufficient sodium nitrite must be added to diazotise all the aniline present, otherwise the unchanged aniline will react with the diazonium chloride to give diazo-aminobenzene (p. 161):

$$C_6H_5N_2|Cl + H|NHC_6H_5 = C_6H_5N_2NHC_6H_5 + HCl$$

To ensure the presence of a slight excess of nitrous acid, potassium iodide-starch paper is sometimes used as an external indicator, a drop of the solution being removed from time to time during the addition of the sodium nitrite, and then dropped on to the paper. When an excess of nitrous acid is present, iodine is liberated, and gives the familiar

$$2HNO_2 + 2HCl + 2KI = 2NO + 2KCl + I_2 + 2H_2O$$

blue colour with starch. In actual practice, however, it is found that long before the addition of the theoretical quantity of sodium nitrite is complete, the solution will give a blue coloration (presumably by atmospheric oxidation) within a few seconds of being placed on the KI-starch paper. If this indicator is used, therefore, it should be noted that an excess of nitrous acid is not present until an *immediate* blue colour is obtained when a drop of the solution is placed on the paper.

The use of KI-starch paper is definitely not recommended, however: it is better to use sodium nitrite* of good quality and to add an amount which is about 10% in excess of that theoretically required.

The student is recommended to carry out the preparation of iodo-benzene in order to gain experience in the preparation of aqueous solutions of diazonium compounds, and then to prepare phenyl diazon-ium hydrogen sulphate (either solid or in solution) with which to carry out the chief reactions that diazonium compounds undergo.

Iodobenzene. C_6H_5I.

When potassium iodide or hydrogen iodide is added to an aqueous solution of a diazo-compound, nitrogen is readily evolved (no catalyst being necessary) and the corresponding iodo-compound is formed. Iodo-compounds can thus

$$C_6H_5N_2Cl + KI = C_6H_5I + N_2 + KCl$$

be readily obtained from aromatic primary amines.

Required: Aniline, 15 c.c.; hydrochloric acid, 40 c.c.; sodium nitrite, 12·5 gms.; potassium iodide, 35 gms.

Dissolve 15 c.c. (15·4 gms.) of aniline in a mixture of 40 c.c. of concentrated hydrochloric acid and 40 c.c. of water contained in a 250 c.c. conical flask. Place a thermometer in the solution, immerse the flask in a mixture of ice and water, and cool until the temperature of the stirred solution reaches 5°. Dissolve 12·5 gms. of powdered sodium nitrite in 30 c.c. of water, and add this solution in small quantities (about 2–3 c.c. at a time) to the cold aniline hydrochloride solution, meanwhile keeping the latter well stirred by means of a thermometer. Heat is evolved by the reaction, and therefore a short interval should be allowed

---

* Hence all the following preparations involving diazotisation are based on the use of "Sodium Nitrite Recryst." and not "Sodium Nitrite Technical" or "Commercial."

between consecutive additions of the sodium nitrite, partly to allow the temperature to fall again to 5°, and partly to ensure that the nitrous acid formed reacts as completely as possible with the aniline. The temperature must not be allowed to rise above 10°, otherwise appreciable decomposition of the diazonium compound to phenol will occur: on the other hand, the temperature should not be allowed to fall as low as 0°, as at this temperature diazotisation becomes very slow, and free nitrous acid may remain in the solution for a considerable time.

When all the sodium nitrite has been added and diazotisation is complete, transfer the cold solution to a 600 c.c. round-bottomed bolt-head flask. Dissolve 35 gms. of potassium iodide in 50 c.c. of water, and add this solution slowly with shaking to the cold diazo solution. A vigorous reaction occurs, nitrogen being freely evolved, and some iodine being liberated owing to the slight excess of nitrous acid present. Allow the complete mixture to stand for 10 minutes with occasional shaking, and then heat it on a boiling water-bath for a further 20 minutes to complete the reaction: the crude iodobenzene separates as a heavy dark oil at the bottom of the flask. Add 10% sodium hydroxide solution to the mixture until the latter is definitely alkaline, i.e., until a drop withdrawn on a glass rod imparts a definite blue colour to red litmus-paper: this converts any phenol which may have been formed into sodium phenoxide which (unlike phenol itself) is not volatile in steam. Now equip the flask for steam-distillation (Fig. 16, p. 34), and steam-distil the mixture until no more oily drops of iodobenzene come over with the aqueous distillate. Transfer the distillate to a separating-funnel, and carefully run off the heavy lower layer of iodobenzene into a small conical flask, rejecting the upper aqueous layer. (The iodobenzene should now have a pale yellow colour. If it is dark in colour, return it to the funnel, and shake it vigorously with a dilute aqueous solution of sodium thiosulphate until a pale yellow colour is obtained: then run off the heavy lower layer as before.) Add a few pieces of granular calcium chloride to the liquid in the conical flask, and shake for about 10 minutes until the liquid is clear and dry. Filter through a small fluted filter-paper directly into a 60 c.c. distilling-flask. Fit the flask with a thermometer reading up to at least 200°, and with a short air-condenser about 12 inches long. Distil the liquid slowly, and collect the fraction boiling at 185–190°. Yield, about 28 gms. (15–16 c.c.).

Iodobenzene, as usually prepared, is a very pale yellow liquid of b.p. 188°, and d, 1·83. The freshly distilled pure liquid is colourless, but soon redevelops the yellow colour on exposure to light. Iodobenzene is insoluble in water.

The iodine atom in iodobenzene (unlike that in the corresponding aliphatic compounds) is very resistant to the action of alkalis, potassium cyanide, silver nitrite, *etc.* This firm attachment of the iodine atom to the benzene ring is typical of aromatic halides generally, although in suitably substituted nitro-compounds, such as 2:4-dinitro-chloro-benzene, the halogen atom does possess an increased reactivity.

Iodobenzene Dichloride, $C_6H_5ICl_2$, Iodoso-benzene, C_6H_5IO, and Iodoxy-benzene, $C_6H_5IO_2$.

When iodobenzene in chloroform solution is treated with chlorine, the iodine becomes trivalent by the addition of chlorine, and iodobenzene dichloride is formed. The latter can be regarded as a salt of the basic iodoso-benzene, which can be readily obtained by treating the dichloride with sodium hydroxide.

$$C_6H_5ICl_2 + 2NaOH = C_6H_5IO + 2NaCl + H_2O$$

Iodoso-benzene forms similar salts with other acids; dilute nitric acid gives the dinitrate, $C_6H_5I(NO_3)_2$, and acetic acid the diacetate, $C_6H_5I(OOCCH_3)_2$.

When iodoso-benzene is boiled with water, interaction occurs with the formation of one equivalent of iodobenzene and one of iodoxy-benzene:

$$2C_6H_5IO = C_6H_5I + C_6H_5IO_2$$

the iodobenzene steam-distils off, whilst the iodoxy-benzene dissolves in the hot water and rapidly crystallises on cooling.

IODOBENZENE-DICHLORIDE. If a cylinder of chlorine is not available for this preparation, generate the chlorine by allowing concentrated hydrochloric acid to fall from a dropping-funnel which is fitted into the neck of a Buchner flask containing coarsely powdered potassium permanganate, aiding the reaction when necessary by gentle warming on a water-bath: purify the chlorine by passing it through wash-bottles containing water and sulphuric acid respectively. Chlorine from a cylinder may be used directly without washing.

Dissolve 5 c.c. (9·2 gms.) of iodobenzene in 35 c.c. of chloroform contained in a wide boiling-tube or in a conical flask. Cool the latter in ice-water and then pass a steady stream of chlorine through the solution until no further precipitation of the yellow crystals of iodobenzene dichloride occurs. Then filter the latter at the pump, and wash with a small quantity of chloroform. Yield, 11–12 gms. The dichloride slowly decomposes on standing, giving chiefly *p*-chloro-iodobenzene and hydrogen chloride: $C_6H_5ICl_2 = ClC_6H_4I + HCl$. Its melting-point is therefore uncertain, but a freshly prepared dry sample usually melts at 101–103° with decomposition.

IODOSO-BENZENE. The hydrolysis of the dichloride may be carried out using either sodium hydroxide or pyridine: the former gives the better product.

(*a*) Add 4 gms of the *finely powdered* dichloride to 40 c.c. of 10%

sodium hydroxide solution contained in a conical flask and shake the mixture vigorously. A rapid reaction follows, and the yellow colour of the dichloride fades. Shake at intervals over a period of 20 minutes, and then filter at the pump, wash with 10% sodium hydroxide solution, then repeatedly with water, drain thoroughly and dry. Yield, theoretical (2·9 gms.).

(*b*) Dissolve 4 gms. of the dichloride in 12 c.c. of pyridine, and then dilute the mixture by slowly adding 150 c.c. of water, stirring vigorously throughout the addition. The iodoso-benzene separates at first as a fine emulsion, which rapidly crystallises. Filter, wash with water, and dry. Yield, 2 gms.

Melting-point determinations should not be attempted with iodoso-benzene, as it explodes violently at about 220°.

IODOBENZENE DIACETATE. Add 2 gms. of iodoso-benzene to 6 c.c. of glacial acetic acid, boil gently until a clear solution is obtained, and then cool. The diacetate is freely soluble in acetic acid, but not in ether. Therefore add ether (about 50 c.c.) in order to precipitate the iodobenzene diacetate, which rapidly separates in colourless crystals, particularly on scratching with a rod. Filter, wash with ether, and dry. M.p. 157°. Yield, 2 gms. The diacetate so obtained is pure, but may if desired be recrystallized from benzene. Unlike the dichloride, it is stable on being kept.

IODOXYBENZENE. Add 3 gms. of iodoso-benzene to about 100 c.c. of water contained in a small flask, and steam-distil the mixture until iodobenzene ceases to come over and the distillate leaving the condenser is no longer turbid (usually about 20 minutes). The residual solution in the flask should now be clear: pour it quickly into a beaker and cool. (If the residual solution is not clear, it should be filtered rapidly, using a Buchner funnel and flask preheated by the filtration of boiling distilled water, as the iodoxy-benzene begins to separate very rapidly on cooling.) Filter off the colourless crystals of iodoxy-benzene, wash with water, and dry. Yield, 1 gm.

Alternatively, if it is not desired to collect the iodobenzene, the iodoso-benzene can be added to about 150 c.c. of water contained in an open beaker or conical flask, and the mixture *gently* boiled until a clear solution is obtained and the pale yellow colour has disappeared. On cooling the iodoxybenzene rapidly separates.

Iodoxybenzene on being heated explodes at 236–237°, and a m.p. determination should not be attempted.

Crystalline Phenyl Diazonium Hydrogen Sulphate (Diazo-benzene Hydrogen Sulphate). $C_6H_5N_2HSO_4$.

Although diazonium compounds are almost invariably prepared and used in aqueous solution, without any attempt to isolate the diazo-compound itself, the student should prepare one solid diazonium salt in order to gain some practical experience in handling this class of compound.

To isolate a crystalline diazonium derivative of one of the simpler primary amines, two factors must be considered:

(1) Diazonium compounds are usually extremely soluble in water and therefore will not crystallise out: moreover, their instability renders concentration of such solutions impracticable. A solvent such as alcohol is therefore used instead of water, and the diazonium compound prepared as one of the salts least soluble in alcohol, *i.e.*, as the hydrogen sulphate rather than as the chloride.

(2) The nitrous acid used in the diazotisation cannot be introduced as a metallic nitrite, otherwise metallic salts (*e.g.*, $NaHSO_4$) would crystallise out with the diazonium sulphate, and could not easily be subsequently removed. The nitrous acid is therefore introduced as an ester, usually as amyl nitrite, which is the cheapest and most readily accessible nitrous ester. In these circumstances the sulphuric acid reacts with the amyl nitrite, giving amyl hydrogen sulphate and nitrous acid: the latter then diazotises the aniline, giving phenyl diazonium hydrogen sulphate, which crystallises out.

$$C_5H_{11}ONO + H_2SO_4 = C_5H_{11}HSO_4 + HONO$$
$$C_6H_5NH_2,H_2SO_4 + HONO = C_6H_5N_2HSO_4 + 2H_2O$$

A higher temperature ($30-35°$) is employed than for an aqueous diazotisation in order to keep the sparingly soluble aniline hydrogen sulphate in alcoholic solution until diazotisation is complete: no appreciable decomposition of the diazonium compound occurs at the higher temperature, however, as the only water present is that formed by the reaction, and it is very considerably diluted by the alcohol used as a solvent.

Required : Aniline, 5 c.c.; absolute alcohol, 50 c.c.; sulphuric acid, 5·5 c.c.; amyl nitrite, 7 c.c.

Dissolve 5 c.c. (5 gms.) of aniline in 50 c.c. of absolute alcohol contained in a 100 c.c. conical flask. Add 5·5 c.c. (10 gms.) of concentrated sulphuric acid very slowly with continuous shaking: aniline sulphate may crystallise out at first, but will redissolve later as the heat of neutralisation increases the temperature of the mixture. Then place a thermometer in the solution, and by immersing the flask in cold water reduce the temperature to 30–35°. Add 7 c.c. (6·5 gms.) of amyl nitrite *very slowly* drop by drop; throughout the addition of the amyl nitrite, keep the mixture well stirred with the thermometer, and ensure (by occasional gentle heating in a *warm* water-bath, if necessary) that the temperature is maintained between 25° and 35°. When all the amyl nitrite has been added, allow the solution to stand for 10 minutes to complete the reaction, and then cool in ice-water for at least a further 20 minutes. The minute greenish-white crystals of the phenyl diazonium hydrogen sulphate rapidly separate and increase in size during the cooling in ice-water, so that they may subsequently be readily filtered. Finally filter off the sulphate at the pump, using a small Buchner funnel, and wash the crystals with a few c.c. of absolute alcohol to remove all traces of the brown filtrate. The phenyl diazonium hydrogen sulphate thus produced is highly reactive and soon becomes dark green in colour.

Dissolve some of the solid in cold water and note its great solubility: filter the solution if necessary to remove any undissolved particles of impurity, and then with the clear filtrate carry out the following typical reactions of diazonium salts. Use about 5 c.c. of the solution in a test-tube for each of the reactions (1) to (5) below. Since dry diazonium salts are explosive, dissolve in cold water any of the phenyl diazonium sulphate remaining from the tests, and pour the solution down the sink.

Phenyl Diazonium Hydrogen Sulphate, $C_6H_5N_2HSO_4$, in aqueous solution.

Required: Aniline, 5 c.c.; sodium nitrite, 4·5 gms.

Dissolve 5 gms. (5 c.c.) of aniline in 50 c.c. of dilute sulphuric acid in a conical flask and add 50 c.c. of water. Place a thermometer in the solution, immerse the flask in a mixture of ice and water, and cool until the temperature of the stirred solution falls to 5°. Dissolve 4·5 gms. of powdered sodium nitrite in 20 c.c. of water, and add this solution in small quantities (about 2–3 c.c. at a time) to the cold aniline sulphate solution. Keep the latter well shaken and maintain the temperature at about 5° (see p. 140). When all the sodium nitrite solution has been added, transfer about 5 c.c. of the cold solution to a test-tube for each of the following reactions. The remainder of the diazonium hydrogen sulphate solution must be kept in ice-water until required, and then when all the reactions have been carried out, the solution should be poured down the sink.

(1) Boil the solution gently for 1–2 minutes. Nitrogen is rapidly evolved, and phenol is formed in solution. Cool the solution (which

$$C_6H_5N_2 \overline{|HSO_4 + H|}OH = C_6H_5OH + N_2 + H_2SO_4$$

should smell of phenol) and test for phenol by adding bromine water. A brownish-white precipitate of tribromophenol is produced (p. 254).

(2) To the cold solution, add about 2 c.c. of 10% potassium iodide solution. A brisk effervescence of nitrogen occurs, and iodobenzene separates, usually as drops so small that in spite of their density they float on the surface.

$$C_6H_5N_2 \overline{|HSO_4 + K|}I = C_6H_5I + N_2 + KHSO_4$$

(3) (a) Dissolve about 0·5 gm. of phenol in a considerable excess of sodium hydroxide solution and cool in ice-water. Pour the diazonium solution into this sodium phenoxide solution and note the formation of an orange-yellow solution of the sodium derivative of benzene-azophenol.

$$C_6H_5N_2 \overline{|HSO_4 + H|}C_6H_4ONa = C_6H_5N:NC_6H_4ONa + H_2SO_4$$

The sulphuric acid is of course neutralised at once by the alkaline solution.

(b) Repeat, using 0·5 gm. of β-naphthol instead of the phenol. A scarlet precipitate of benzene-azo-β-naphthol is similarly produced.

$$C_6H_5N_2\!\mid\!HSO_4 + H\!\mid\!C_{10}H_6OH = C_6H_5N{:}NC_{10}H_6OH + H_2SO_4$$

The above condensations occur only in alkaline solution, hence the need of an excess of sodium hydroxide in the phenol solutions.

(4) (a) To 1 c.c. of the diazonium solution, add 0·5 c.c. of aniline, and shake vigorously. Diazo-aminobenzene separates as a finely-divided yellow solid.

$$C_6H_5N_2\!\mid\!HSO_4 + H\!\mid\!NHC_6H_5 = C_6H_5N{:}NNHC_6H_5 + H_2SO_4$$

(b) Repeat, using 0·5 c.c. of dimethylaniline in place of aniline. A red solution of benzene-azo-p-dimethylaniline hydrochloride is produced on adding dil. hydrochloric acid. Add an excess of sodium

$$C_6H_5N_2\!\mid\!HSO_4 + H\!\mid\!C_6H_4N(CH_3)_2,HCl = C_6H_5N_2C_6H_4N(CH_3)_2,HCl + H_2SO_4$$

hydroxide solution in order to liberate the free base, which is yellow.

(5) Add 2 c.c. of alcohol to the solution, shake the mixture and warm gently. Phenetole (phenyl ethyl ether) is the main product.

$$C_6H_5N_2\!\mid\!HSO_4 + H\!\mid\!OC_2H_5 = C_6H_5OC_2H_5 + N_2 + H_2SO_4$$

At the same time, the alcohol reduces some of the diazonium compound to benzene, the alcohol itself being oxidised to acetaldehyde, the odour

$$C_2H_5OH = CH_3CHO + 2H$$
$$C_6H_5N_2HSO_4 + 2H = C_6H_6 + N_2 + H_2SO_4$$

of which can sometimes be detected.

Chlorobenzene. C_6H_5Cl. (Sandmeyer's Method.)

Chlorobenzene may be obtained from an aqueous solution of phenyl diazonium chloride by two methods:

(a) *Gattermann's Method.* The addition of finely divided copper powder to the diazo-benzene chloride solution has a catalytic action even at room tempera-

$$C_6H_5N_2Cl = C_6H_5Cl + N_2$$

ture, causing the evolution of nitrogen and the formation of chlorobenzene.

(b) *Sandmeyer's Method.* If the aqueous solution of phenyl diazonium chloride is added to a solution of cuprous chloride in hydrochloric acid and the mixture then warmed, a similar decomposition occurs, nitrogen and chlorobenzene being formed.

Required: Copper sulphate, 28 gms.; sodium chloride, 9·5 gms.; sodium sulphite, 14 gms.; hydrochloric acid, 70 c.c.; aniline, 20 c.c.; sodium nitrite, 17 gms.

To prepare the solution of cuprous chloride, add 28 gms. of crystalline copper sulphate and 9·5 gms. of sodium chloride in turn to 100 c.c. of water in a 250 c.c. beaker, and warm the mixture to 55–60°, stirring it with a thermometer until a clear solution is obtained at this temperature. Now reduce this solution *either* by adding a solution of 14 gms. of sodium bisulphite in 25 c.c. of water, whereupon the mixed solutions will rapidly become green in colour, *or*, if a syphon of liquid sulphur dioxide is available, by passing a brisk current of sulphur dioxide into the solution. By either method, the cupric chloride formed by the interaction of the cupric sulphate and the sodium chloride is reduced to cuprous chloride, which separates as a white powder as the solution cools. Now place the beaker in cold water containing a *small quantity* of ice in order to cool the solution to about 10–15°, and thus to complete the separation of the cuprous chloride: it is important that the solution is not cooled below this temperature, otherwise crystals of sodium sulphate, *etc.*, may separate and contaminate the cuprous chloride. Allow the solution to stand in the cold water whilst the diazotisation of the aniline is being performed; then filter off the cuprous chloride rapidly through a Buchner funnel at the pump, wash it once with a few c.c. of distilled water, and then, immediately it is well drained, transfer it to a mixture of 20 c.c. of concentrated hydrochloric acid and 20 c.c. of water in a 600 c.c. round-bottomed flask. During the draining of the cuprous chloride on the filter, slight atmospheric oxidation may give the surface of the chloride a blue colour: the cuprous chloride will, however, dissolve in the hydrochloric acid to give a clear brownish-coloured solution. Attach a reflux water-condenser to the flask, and in the top of the condenser fit a dropping-funnel securely by a cork which has a shallow groove cut or filed vertically down the side, in order to allow the subsequent escape of nitrogen.

Meanwhile, during the cooling of the cuprous chloride solution, prepare a solution of phenyl diazonium chloride by dissolving 20 c.c. (20·5 gms.) of aniline in a mixture of 50 c.c. of concentrated hydrochloric acid and 50 c.c. of water, and after cooling to 5°, adding slowly a solution of 17 gms. of sodium nitrite in 40 c.c. of water. Observe carefully the general conditions for diazotisation given in the preparation of iodobenzene (p. 141).

When the preparation of the cuprous chloride is complete, place the diazonium solution in the dropping-funnel at the top of the reflux condenser, and then heat the flask containing the cuprous chloride on a boiling water-bath. When the cuprous chloride solution has been thoroughly heated, remove the water-bath, support the flask on a stand, and allow the diazonium solution to run *slowly* drop by drop down the condenser, meanwhile shaking the flask gently to ensure thorough mixing. As each drop of the diazo solution enters the liquid in the flask, a momentary separation of a yellow addition product, $C_6H_5N_2Cl,Cu_2Cl_2$, occurs: this compound then breaks down, giving nitrogen and chlorobenzene, and the heat of the reaction maintains the temperature of the solution well above 60°. When all the diazonium solution has been added, allow the mixture to stand for 10 minutes, and then replace the flask on the boiling water-bath for a further 15 minutes in order to complete the reaction. Then detach the flask, equip it for steam-distillation (Fig. 16, p. 34) and steam-distil the contents until no more oily drops of chlorobenzene pass over. Place the distillate in a separating-funnel, and run off the lower layer of chlorobenzene into a small conical flask: add a few pieces of granular calcium chloride, allow to stand for 15–20 minutes, and then filter the dry chlorobenzene directly into a 60 c.c. distilling-flask. Fit the flask with an air-condenser, and distil the chlorobenzene, collecting the fraction which boils at 130–135°. Yield, 18–19 gms.

Chlorobenzene is a stable colourless liquid having b.p. 132° and *d*, 1·11; it is insoluble in water.

For reactions of chlorobenzene, see p. 297.

Benzonitrile (Phenyl Cyanide). C_6H_5CN. (Sandmeyer's Method.)

Sandmeyer's method for the preparation of chlorobenzene can similarly be extended to the preparation of bromobenzene and of cyanobenzene or benzonitrile. Thus an aqueous solution of phenyl diazonium chloride on treatment with a solution of cuprous bromide in hydrobromic acid gives nitrogen and bromobenzene: alternatively, on treatment with a solution of potassium cuprocyanide, $K_3[Cu(CN)_4]$, it gives nitrogen and cyanobenzene, C_6H_5CN. No similar catalyst is required for the preparation of iodobenzene (p. 141).

Potassium cupro-cyanide is the most convenient form in which cuprous cyanide can be used in Sandmeyer's Reaction. It is prepared by adding an excess of potassium cyanide to copper sulphate solution, whereby the cupric cyanide which is formed immediately breaks down to give cuprous cyanide and cyanogen, and the cuprous cyanide then dissolves in the excess of potassium

$$CuSO_4 + 2KCN = Cu(CN)_2 + K_2SO_4 \qquad 2Cu(CN)_2 = Cu_2(CN)_2 + C_2N_2$$
$$6KCN + Cu_2(CN)_2 = 2K_3[Cu(CN)_4]$$

cyanide to give potassium cupro-cyanide.

Required: Aniline, 20 c.c.; hydrochloric acid, 50 c.c.; sodium nitrite, 17 gms.; copper sulphate, 55 gms.; potassium cyanide, 60 gms.

Apart from the diazotisation, *the whole of the following preparation up to the completion of the steam-distillation must be carried out in a fume-cupboard having a vigorous draught.*

Prepare a solution of phenyl diazonium chloride from 20 c.c. (20·5 gms.) of aniline precisely as in the preparation of chlorobenzene (p. 148), *i.e.*, by dissolving the aniline in a mixture of 50 c.c. of concentrated hydrochloric acid and 50 c.c. of water, cooling to 5°, and then cautiously adding a solution of 17 gms. of sodium nitrite in 40 c.c. of water to the well-cooled and stirred aniline hydrochloride solution so that the temperature of the mixture remains between 5° and 10°.

Then, while the diazonium solution is standing in ice-water, dissolve 55 gms. of powdered copper sulphate ($CuSO_4, 5H_2O$) in 200 c.c. of water contained in a 1500 c.c. flat-bottomed flask, for which a steam-distillation fitting is available for subsequent use. Place a thermometer in the copper sulphate solution and warm the latter to 60–65°. Now cautiously add a solution of 60 gms. of powdered potassium cyanide* in 100 c.c. of water to the copper sulphate solution, shaking the flask during the addition to facilitate the evolution and escape of the cyanogen—*take great care to avoid inhaling traces of the cyanogen.* During the addition of the cyanide solution the temperature of the mixture rises a few degrees (usually to about 75°), and finally a clear pale-brown solution of potassium cupro-cyanide is obtained.

Now add the diazonium solution to the potassium cupro-cyanide in small quantities at a time so that the temperature of the mixture remains between 60° and 70°: shake the mixture vigorously after each addition of the diazo solution. Then fit an air- or water-condenser to the flask, and heat the latter on a boiling water-bath for 15 minutes to complete the reaction. Finally steam-distil the solution until no more oily benzonitrile passes over (usually until about 600 c.c. of distillate have been collected).

Place the distillate in a separating-funnel and extract the benzonitrile twice, using about 30 c.c. of ether for each extraction. Return the united ethereal extracts to the funnel and shake with 10% sodium hydroxide solution to eliminate traces of phenol

---

* The "double salt," *i.e.*, potassium cyanide mixed with sodium cyanide, is best and cheapest for this purpose, and can be obtained already powdered, in which form, however, storage in an air-tight receptacle is particularly necessary. If only fused or lump cyanide is available, great care should be taken when powdering the material in a mortar, in order to prevent small fragments from flying up and adhering to the lips, nostrils, or eyes. This is best achieved by draping a duster tent-wise around the pestle and over the mortar, so that the cyanide is completely covered while it is being crushed.

formed by decomposition of the phenyl diazonium chloride. Then run off the lower aqueous layer, and shake the ethereal solution with about an equal volume of dilute sulphuric acid to remove traces of foul-smelling phenyl *iso*-cyanide (C_6H_5NC) which are always present. Finally separate the sulphuric acid as completely as possible, and shake the ether with water to ensure absence of acid. Run off the water and dry the benzonitrile solution over granular calcium chloride for about 20 minutes.

Filter the dried ethereal solution, and then distil off the ether from a small flask, using precisely similar apparatus and the same method as those described in the preparation of aniline (Fig. 48, p. 123) and observing the same precautions. When the ether has been removed, fit the distilling-flask to a short air-condenser, and distil the benzonitrile, collecting the fraction boiling between 187° and 191°. Yield, 16·5 gms. (16 c.c.).

Benzonitrile is a colourless liquid, having b.p. 190° and *d*, 1·02: it is almost insoluble in water, and has an odour resembling that of nitrobenzene and of benzaldehyde.

Hydrolysis of Benzonitrile. Benzonitrile is moderately readily hydrolysed by 10% aqueous sodium hydroxide, but only slowly by hydrochloric acid (*cf.* p. 94). Ready hydrolysis is obtained by boiling the nitrile under reflux

$$C_6H_5CN + 2H_2O = C_6H_5COOH + NH_3$$

with 70% sulphuric acid (preparation, p. 80), but the benzoic acid volatilises in the steam and crystallises again in the reflux condenser, which may become choked with a hard deposit of the acid: moreover some aromatic nitriles are liable to undergo sulphonation as well as hydrolysis when boiled with such concentrated sulphuric acid. These disadvantages do not apply to hydrolysis by sodium hydroxide, as the benzoic acid remains in solution as sodium benzoate: furthermore, the completion of the hydrolysis is readily detected by the complete disappearance of oily drops of the insoluble nitrile.

Boil 5 c.c. (5·1 gms.) of benzonitrile and 75 c.c. of 10% aqueous sodium hydroxide in a 200 c.c. flask under a reflux water-condenser until no more oily drops of unchanged nitrile run down from the condenser (usually about 40 minutes). Then detach the condenser and boil the solution in the open flask for a few minutes to remove free ammonia. Cool the liquid, and add concentrated hydrochloric acid cautiously until precipitation of benzoic acid is complete. Cool the mixture again thoroughly, filter off the benzoic acid at the pump, and wash well with cold water. Yield, 5·8 gms. (almost theoretical). Confirm the identity of the benzoic acid by the tests given on p. 261. The benzoic acid obtained in this way should be pure and have m.p. 121°: a portion may if desired be recrystallised from hot water.

p-Tolunitrile (*p*-Tolyl Cyanide).   CH₃C₆H₄CN.   (Sandmeyer's Method.)

Required: *p*-Toluidine, 24 gms.; hydrochloric acid, 55 c.c.; sodium nitrite, 17 gms.

The preparation of *p*-tolunitrile illustrates the method employed for the diazotisation of amines the hydrochlorides of which are only moderately soluble in cold water. Dissolve 24 gms. of powdered *p*-toluidine in a warm mixture of 55 c.c. of concentrated hydrochloric acid and 180 c.c. of water, and then chill the solution thoroughly in ice-water: during the cooling, stir the mixture continuously in order to ensure that the *p*-toluidine hydrochloride crystallises out as small feathery crystals which will subsequently redissolve readily during the diazotisation. Now continue precisely as in the above preparation of benzonitrile, *observing the same precautions against inhaling cyanogen,* and using the same quantities of all the reagents, *i.e.,* diazotising with a solution of 17 gms. of sodium nitrite in 40 c.c. of water, and pouring the diazotised solution into the potassium cupro-cyanide solution prepared as before. During the addition of the diazotised solution, however, the potassium cupro-cyanide mixture must be occasionally warmed on a water-bath in the fume-cupboard in order to keep the temperature between 60° and 70°.

If during the steam-distillation the *p*-tolunitrile tends to crystallise in the condenser, it is usually sufficient to increase the amount of steam momentarily in order to melt and dislodge the nitrile: alternatively the condenser-water can be turned off for a few moments. Collect about 500 c.c. of distillate to ensure complete distillation of the nitrile, and cool the receiver in ice-water during the distillation. The oily nitrile in the distillate readily solidifies, particularly on stirring. Then filter at the pump, and press and drain the solid nitrile thoroughly on the filter to remove liquid impurities. Dry in a desiccator, or by pressing between layers of drying-paper: in the latter case, take care that the nitrile does not melt under the warmth of the hand. *p*-Tolunitrile is thus obtained as a pale brown solid: yield, 19 gms. Purify the dry material by direct distillation, preferably after mixing it with 1–2 gms. of animal charcoal: use a *short* air-condenser, which will require gentle warming at the beginning of the distillation to prevent premature crystallisation. Collect the fraction having b.p. 214–218°. The distilled nitrile solidifies as colourless crystals, m.p. 29°, b.p. 218°.

Hydrolysis of *p*-Tolunitrile. As in the case of benzonitrile, alkaline hydrolysis is preferable to hydrolysis by 70% sulphuric acid. Boil a mixture of 5 gms. of *p*-tolunitrile, 75 c.c. of 10% aqueous sodium hydroxide solution and 15 c.c. of alcohol under a reflux water-condenser. The alcohol is added partly to increase the speed of the hydrolysis, but in particular to prevent the nitrile (which volatilises in the steam) from actually crystallising in the condenser. The solution becomes clear after about 1 hour's heating, but the boiling should be continued for a

total period of 1·5 hours to ensure complete hydrolysis. Then precipitate and isolate the p-toluic acid, $CH_3C_6H_4COOH$, in precisely the
same way as the benzoic acid in the above hydrolysis of benzonitrile.
Yield 5·5 gms. (almost theoretical). The p-toluic acid has m.p. 178°,
and may be recrystallised from a mixture of equal volumes of water and
methylated spirit.

The methyl group in p-toluic acid may be oxidised to a $-COOH$ group
forming p-phthalic (or tere-phthalic) acid, $C_6H_4(COOH)_2$, but the oxidation is
usually very slow.

Phenol. C_6H_5OH.

When a diazonium salt in aqueous solution is gently warmed, it reacts with
the water, liberating nitrogen and forming the corresponding phenol:

$$C_6H_5N_2|HSO_4 + H|OH = C_6H_5OH + N_2 + H_2SO_4$$

The diazonium hydrogen sulphate is used for this reaction in preference to the
diazonium chloride since the latter by direct decomposition always forms small
quantities of the chloro-hydrocarbon as a by-product:

$$C_6H_5N_2Cl = C_6H_5Cl + N_2$$

For the preparation of phenol, the aqueous solution should be heated carefully
to 50–55°, at which temperature the reaction proceeds smoothly: above this
temperature, however, the reaction may rapidly become very vigorous, and
the heat of reaction will then cause a marked rise in the temperature and the
production of a large amount of tarry by-products.

Required: Sulphuric acid, 27·5 c.c.; aniline, 24 c.c.; sodium
nitrite, 20 gms.; potassium carbonate, 3–4 gms.

Add 27·5 c.c. (50·5 gms.) of concentrated sulphuric acid cautiously with shaking to 150 c.c. of water, and to the hot solution so
obtained, add 24 c.c. (24·5 gms.) of aniline. If all the aniline
sulphate thus formed does not dissolve, warm the mixture gently
until a clear solution is obtained. Now pour the solution into
200 c.c. of cold water contained in a 600 c.c. flask, and cool the
mixture in ice-water until the temperature falls to 5°. (Some
aniline sulphate may crystallise out again at this stage. This
does not interfere with the reaction, however, because the sulphate separates as very fine crystals which rapidly redissolve
as the reaction proceeds.) Dissolve 20 gms. of sodium nitrite in
50 c.c. of water, and add this cautiously to the aniline sulphate
solution, carrying out the diazotisation with the precautions
described in the preparation of iodobenzene (p. 141). When all
the sodium nitrite solution has been added, allow the solution to
stand at room temperature for 15 minutes to ensure complete
diazotisation, and then place the flask *in* a water-bath and heat the
latter until the temperature of the diazotised solution (recorded by

a thermometer in the solution itself) reaches 50–55°. Continue the heating for a further 30 minutes, taking particular care that the temperature of the well-stirred solution does not rise above 55°. A vigorous evolution of nitrogen occurs meanwhile, and the liquid becomes dark in colour. Pour the contents of the flask into a 1-litre round-bottomed flask, and steam-distil, collecting about 500 c.c. of distillate: the solution is apt to foam during the steam distillation, hence the necessity for the large flask.

Now transfer the cold distillate to a separating-funnel,* and shake vigorously with about 50–60 c.c. of ether: run off the lower aqueous layer and then decant† the ethereal solution through the mouth of the funnel into a 200 c.c. conical flask. Replace the aqueous layer in the funnel, and extract similarly twice more with ether, combining the ethereal extracts in the conical flask. Add 3–4 gms. of *dry* powdered potassium carbonate to the ethereal solution, securely cork the flask and shake the contents gently. The ethereal solution of the phenol should now be allowed to remain in contact with the potassium carbonate for at least one hour, and preferably overnight.

Then fit up the apparatus for ether distillation as shown in Fig. 48 (p. 123). Filter the dry ethereal solution through a small fluted filter-paper directly into the dropping-funnel, run about 30 c.c. into the distilling-flask, and finally continue running in the solution as fast as the ether distils over (as described in the preparation of aniline, p. 123). When all the ether has apparently distilled off, disconnect the flask, and fit it with a thermometer reading up to at least 200°, and also with an air-condenser about 12–14 inches long. Now heat the flask very cautiously, as some residual ether always comes over at first, although the temperature may rise rapidly above the boiling-point of ether itself: therefore keep flames away from the open end of the condenser, particularly during the early stages of the distillation. Distil the phenol at such a rate that none escapes condensation, and none crystallises in the condenser. Finally collect the fraction boiling at 178–184°

---

* If only small separating-funnels are available, divide the distillate into portions, and extract each thoroughly with ether, uniting the ethereal extracts subsequently.

† The ethereal solution is decanted through the mouth of the funnel to prevent contamination by traces of water which, after running off the heavier aqueous layer, will always be present in the tap and the stem of the funnel. Traces of water will similarly still be present also in the body of the separating-funnel, but will remain adhering to the sides when the ethereal solution is carefully decanted through the mouth. This process should be generally adopted for removing a light liquid from a separating-funnel after a heavier liquid has been run off.

directly into a small weighed specimen-tube, where it should crystallise on cooling. The phenol so obtained sometimes remains as a super-cooled liquid which does not readily crystallise: in such a case, chill the liquid in ice-water, and either scratch it with a glass rod, or seed it with a crystal of pure phenol, when crystallisation should rapidly occur. Yield, 14 gms.

Pure phenol is a colourless crystalline substance, having m.p. 43°, and b.p. 182°: on exposure to air, it slowly sublimes, and on exposure to light, develops a pink colour. It has a characteristic odour, and a limited solubility in water. Phenol in dilute aqueous solution has strongly antiseptic properties, but the crystalline substance should not be allowed to come in contact with the skin, as it may cause severe blistering.

For reactions of phenol, see p. 253.

Phenylhydrazine. $C_6H_5NH \cdot NH_2$.

Phenyl diazonium chloride reacts in solution with sodium sulphite to give phenyl diazonium sodium sulphonate, which when treated with sulphurous

$$C_6H_5N_2Cl + Na_2SO_3 = C_6H_5N_2SO_3Na + NaCl$$
$$C_6H_5N_2SO_3Na + 2H = C_6H_5NH \cdot NH \cdot SO_3Na$$
$$C_6H_5NH \cdot NH \cdot SO_3Na + HCl + H_2O = C_6H_5NH \cdot NH_2,HCl + NaHSO_4$$

acid undergoes reduction to phenylhydrazine sodium sulphonate. The latter readily hydrolyses in the presence of concentrated hydrochloric acid to give phenylhydrazine hydrochloride, from which the free base can be isolated by the action of caustic alkalis.

Phenyl diazonium chloride also undergoes direct reduction to phenylhydrazine

$$C_6H_5N_2Cl + 2SnCl_2 + 4HCl = C_6H_5NH \cdot NH_2,HCl + 2SnCl_4$$

when treated with an *acid* solution of stannous chloride (*e.g.*, a solution in hydrochloric acid) but the yields are not so high as those obtained by the above sulphonate method.

Required: Aniline, 20 c.c.; hydrochloric acid, 50 c.c.; sodium nitrite, 17 gms.; sodium carbonate (anhydrous) 17 gms.; sodium sulphite ($7H_2O$), 115 gms.

First prepare a solution of phenyl diazonium chloride from 20 c.c. (20·5 gms.) of aniline precisely as described in the preparation of chlorobenzene (p. 148), adding a solution of 17 gms. of sodium nitrite in 40 c.c. of water to a solution of the aniline in 50 c.c. of concentrated hydrochloric acid and 50 c.c. of water, the temperature of the mixture being kept between 5° and 10°.

While this solution is standing, dissolve 17 gms. of anhydrous sodium carbonate in 70 c.c. of warm water in a 800 c.c. beaker, and then add 115 gms. of finely powdered crystalline sodium sulphite

($Na_2SO_3,7H_2O$) and continue warming the solution at 40–50° for a few minutes, so that the greater part of the sulphite dissolves. Then cool the solution in ice-water until the temperature is between 5° and 10°, some of the sulphite meanwhile crystallising out again. Now add the diazonium solution *slowly* to the well-stirred sulphite solution: the mixture becomes red in colour, and a deep red oil separates and later solidifies as orange-coloured crystals (sometimes the orange crystals separate without the intermediate formation of the oil). When the addition of the diazo solution is complete, continue stirring the mixture for 5–10 minutes, and then warm it to 30° on a water-bath (in a fume-cupboard) and pass in a stream of sulphur dioxide from a syphon until the solution is saturated and no more gas is absorbed: the excess of sodium sulphite and the orange crystals dissolve up at this stage. Now heat the solution to 70° and add 150 c.c. of concentrated hydrochloric acid with stirring. Within a few minutes, crystals of phenylhydrazine hydrochloride separate out: cool the mixture in ice-water for 30 minutes with occasional stirring and then filter at the pump and drain thoroughly.

Suspend the crude hydrochloride in some water in a separating-funnel and add 20% sodium hydroxide solution until the mixture is definitely alkaline and the crude phenylhydrazine base floats as a deep red oil on the surface. Now extract the phenylhydrazine twice with benzene (using about 30 c.c. of benzene on each occasion) and dry the united benzene extracts with powdered anhydrous potassium carbonate. After the mixture has been allowed to stand for 20–30 minutes, filter at the pump, and wash the residual carbonate with a small quantity of dry benzene.

The benzene has now to be distilled off at atmospheric pressure and the residual phenylhydrazine at reduced pressure. For this purpose, fit a small dropping-funnel to the main neck of a 60 c.c. Claisen flask, cork the other neck, and fit a water-condenser to the side-arm. Run about 30 c.c. of the benzene solution into the flask, and heat the latter in an oil-bath, controlling the temperature of the bath so that the benzene distils gently over. Allow the remainder of the solution to run in from the dropping-funnel as fast as the benzene itself distils over. When the benzene has been almost entirely removed, fit a capillary tube and a thermometer into the necks of the flask, and then assemble the complete apparatus for vacuum distillation, using either the simple apparatus shown in Fig. 13(A) (p. 30) or a water-condenser and Perkin triangle (Fig. 15, p. 33). Distil the phenylhydrazine carefully from an oil-bath and collect a fraction boiling over a range of about $3°$, *e.g.*, at $127-130°/22$ mm. The phenylhydrazine is thus obtained as a very pale yellow (almost colourless) oil, of d, $1·10$: it has a characteristic odour and is only slightly soluble in water. Yield, $16-17$ gms. Pure phenylhydrazine has m.p. $23°$; it boils at $242-243°$ at atmospheric pressure with partial decomposition.

Phenylhydrazine on exposure to light slowly darkens and eventually becomes deep red in colour: salts of the base share this property but to a lesser degree, the sulphate and acetate (of the common salts) being most stable to light. Phenylhydrazine is largely used in organic chemistry to characterise aldehydes and ketones as their phenyl-hydrazones (pp. 257, 260), and carbohydrates as their osazones (pp. 109–112). It is readily reduced: thus in the process of osazone formation some of the phenylhydrazine is reduced to aniline and ammonia. On the

$$C_6H_5NH·NH_2 + 2H = C_6H_5NH_2 + NH_3$$
$$C_6H_5NH·NH_2 + 2CuO = C_6H_6 + N_2 + Cu_2O + H_2O$$

other hand, Fehling's solution oxidises it to benzene and nitrogen.

Add $2-3$ drops of phenylhydrazine to about 2 c.c. of Fehling's solution in a test-tube and shake the mixture vigorously: nitrogen is evolved and reddish-brown cuprous oxide is precipitated. The reaction proceeds rapidly on gentle warming, more slowly in the cold.

Sym-Tribromobenzene, $C_6H_3Br_3$, from *Sym*-Tribromo-aniline.

When a solution of a diazonium compound in absolute methyl alcohol is boiled, the chief product is the corresponding methyl ether, phenyl diazonium hydrogen sulphate thus giving phenyl methyl ether or anisole:

$$C_6H_5N_2HSO_4 + HOCH_3 = C_6H_5OCH_3 + N_2 + H_2SO_4$$

In absolute ethyl alcohol solution, the ethyl ether and the corresponding hydrocarbon are formed, the latter by reduction of the diazonium compound by the ethyl alcohol, which is itself oxidised to acetaldehyde:

$$CH_3CH_2OH = CH_3CHO + 2H$$
$$C_6H_5N_2HSO_4 + 2H = C_6H_6 + N_2 + H_2SO_4$$

With higher alcohols, the formation of the ether becomes negligible, the reaction being limited almost entirely to reduction to the hydrocarbon.

This elimination of the diazonium group is therefore a very valuable reaction, as it affords almost the only method by which nitro and primary amino groups directly attached to the benzene ring can be eliminated.

A similar reaction occurs when an aqueous solution of a diazonium compound is made strongly alkaline and then warmed with an alkaline solution of stannous chloride. This reaction, however, involves the intermediate formation of

$$C_6H_5N_2Cl \xrightarrow{\text{KOH}} C_6H_5N:NOK \xrightarrow{\text{2H}} C_6H_6 + N_2 + KOH$$

the unstable alkali diazotate, which may explode even in cold aqueous solution.

Sym-Tribromo-aniline (preparation, p. 125) is used to illustrate this elimination of the amino group, because the tribromobenzene so formed is solid, and small quantities can easily be purified by recrystallisation.

Required: Sym-tribromo-aniline, 5 gms.; absolute alcohol, 40 c.c.; dry benzene, 10 c.c.; sodium nitrite, 3 gms.

Dissolve 5 gms. of *sym*-tribromo-aniline in a hot mixture of 40 c.c. of absolute ethyl alcohol and 10 c.c. of dry benzene contained in a 150 c.c. wide-necked bolt-head flask. (The benzene is added to increase the solubility of the tribromo-aniline.) Now add 2 c.c. (3·9 gms.) of concentrated sulphuric acid (preferably from a burette or a small pipette) to the hot solution, shaking the latter gently round. Attach the flask to a reflux water-condenser and heat on a water-bath until the clear solution boils. Now detach the flask, add 3 gms. of dry powdered sodium nitrite, and return the flask to the condenser but not to the water-bath. Shake the flask vigorously: the heat of the reaction causes the solution to continue boiling for several minutes. When the boiling subsides, return the flask to the water-bath and boil the solution for 45 minutes with occasional vigorous shaking. Allow the solution to cool somewhat and then cool it thoroughly in ice-water. A mixture of tribromobenzene and sodium sulphate crystallises out. Filter at the pump, drain, wash once with a small quantity of methylated spirit and then repeatedly with water to remove all sodium sulphate.

Recrystallise from methylated spirit, using animal charcoal: for this purpose, use about twice the minimum quantity of methylated spirit required to obtain a clear solution, and filter through a funnel preheated by the filtration of some boiling solvent, as the tribromobenzene separates very rapidly as the solution cools. The *sym*-tribromobenzene is thus obtained as colourless crystals, m.p. 122°: yield, 3 gms.

The tribromobenzene obtained in this way should be entirely free from unchanged tribromo-aniline. To test its purity, dissolve a small quantity in hot dry benzene and pass in hydrogen chloride gas from a Kipp's apparatus: no trace of crystals of tribromo-aniline hydrochloride should appear. Note also that although the m.p.s of the two compounds are almost identical, that of the recrystallised product from the above preparation is considerably depressed by admixture with tribromo-aniline.

Diphenyl-nitrosamine. $(C_6H_5)_2N\cdot NO$.

Secondary amines of both the aliphatic and the aromatic series react similarly with nitrous acid, giving *nitrosamines*:

$$R_2N|H + HO|NO = R_2N\cdot NO + H_2O$$

The nitrosamines are insoluble in water, and the lower members are liquid at ordinary temperatures. The separation of an oily liquid when an aqueous solution of an amine salt is treated with sodium nitrite is therefore strong evidence that the amine is secondary. Diphenyl-nitrosamine is selected as a preparation because it is a crystalline substance and is thus easier to manipulate on a small scale than one of the lower liquid members. For this preparation, a fairly pure (and therefore almost colourless) sample of diphenylamine should be used. "Technical" diphenylamine, which is almost black in colour, should not be employed.

Required: Diphenylamine, 8 gms.; alcohol, 60 c.c.; sodium nitrite, 4 gms.; hydrochloric acid, 6 c.c.

Prepare two solutions, one containing 8 gms. of diphenylamine in 60 c.c. of warm alcohol, and the other containing 4 gms. of sodium nitrite in 6 c.c. of water, and cool each solution in ice-water until the temperature falls to 5°. Now add 6 c.c. of concentrated hydrochloric acid steadily with stirring to the diphenyl-amine solution, and then *without delay* (otherwise diphenylamine hydrochloride may crystallise out) pour the sodium nitrite solution rapidly into the well-stirred mixture. The temperature rises at once to about 25° and the diphenyl-nitrosamine rapidly crystallises out. Allow the mixture to stand in the ice-water for 15 minutes, and then filter off the crystals at the pump, drain thoroughly, wash with water to remove sodium chloride, and then drain again. Recrystallise from methylated spirit. Diphenyl-nitrosamine is thus obtained as very pale yellow crystals, m.p. 67–68°: yield, 8 gms.

Reaction of Diphenyl-nitrosamine. Carry out Liebermann's Nitroso Reaction as described for phenol (p. 255), but use about 0·05 gm. of the nitrosamine instead of the one crystal of sodium nitrite, and finally add only 3–4 drops of sulphuric acid. The deep greenish-blue colour is obtained, becoming red on dilution and reverting to blue on being made alkaline.

p-Nitroso-dimethylaniline. $(CH_3)_2NC_6H_4NO.$

Nitrous acid does not react with aliphatic tertiary amines, such as triethylamine, $(C_2H_5)_3N$, nor does it usually react with aromatic tertiary amines such as triphenylamine, $(C_6H_5)_3N$, which contain three aryl groups.

If, however, a tertiary amine has two alkyl groups and also an aryl group having the *para* position unsubstituted, then the action of nitrous acid is to insert the nitroso group directly into this *para* position. Dimethylaniline, for example, when treated with nitrous acid readily gives *p*-nitroso-dimethyl-

$$(CH_3)_2NC_6H \vdots H + HO \vdots NO = (CH_3)_2NC_6H_4NO + H_2O$$

aniline. The salts of *p*-nitroso-dimethylaniline, such as the hydrochloride, are yellow, whereas the free base is a beautiful green crystalline compound. This marked difference in colour between a base and its salts is also exemplified in the case of amino-azobenzene (p. 163).

Tertiary amines containing one alkyl and two aryl groups, such as mono-methyl-diphenylamine, $CH_3(C_6H_5)_2N$, are rarely encountered and are unimportant. They usually react with nitrous acid with the insertion of a nitroso group into only one of the two available *para* positions: monomethyl-diphenylamine thus gives monomethyl - mono - p - nitroso - diphenylamine, $CH_3(C_6H_5)NC_6H_4NO$.

Required: Dimethylaniline, 15 c.c.; hydrochloric acid, 50 c.c.; sodium nitrite, 9 gms.

Dissolve 15 c.c. (14·3 gms.) of dimethylaniline in a mixture of 50 c.c. of concentrated hydrochloric acid and 50 c.c. of water contained in a 300 c.c. beaker, and then place the latter in a freezing-mixture consisting of finely crushed ice and salt. Stir the contents of the beaker with a thermometer until the temperature of the solution is between 0° and 2°. Dissolve 9 gms. of sodium nitrite in 20 c.c. of water and add this solution in small quantities (about 2 c.c. at a time) to the dimethylaniline hydrochloride solution, keeping the mixture well stirred and taking care that the temperature recorded by the thermometer in the solution does not rise above 2°. When the addition of the sodium nitrite solution is complete, allow the product to remain in the freezing-mixture for a further 45 minutes, and then filter off the yellow crystalline nitroso-dimethylaniline hydrochloride at the pump, wash it with dilute hydrochloric acid, and then drain thoroughly. Yield of crude hydrochloride, about 18 gms. Recrystallise approximately half the hydrochloride by dissolving it in a minimum amount of boiling water, and adding about 0·5 c.c. of concentrated hydrochloric acid: on cooling the solution, the hydrochloride crystallises out in yellow needles, m.p. 177°.

In order to prepare the free base, place the remaining half of the crude hydrochloride in a 200 c.c. beaker, add 20 c.c. of water, and then stir the mixture with a glass rod until a thin paste of uniform consistency (quite free from lumps) is obtained. Now add 10% aqueous sodium hydroxide solution with stirring until the whole mass has become bright green—the colour of the free base. Pour the contents of the beaker into a separating-funnel, and isolate the free base by one of the following alternative methods.

(*a*) Extract the free base by shaking the mixture in the separating-funnel with about 40 c.c. of benzene, repeating the extraction to ensure that all the base has entered the benzene solution. Dry the combined benzene extracts by shaking with powdered anhydrous potassium carbonate for a few minutes, and then filter through a fluted filter-paper directly into a distilling-flask fitted with a water-condenser. Distil off about half the benzene over a sand-bath, and then pour the residual hot benzene solution into a small beaker. On cooling, the *p*-nitroso-dimethylaniline crystallises out in brilliant deep green leaflets: when these are filtered off and dried, however, they usually decrepitate, giving a fine green crystalline powder, m.p. 85°.

(*b*) Extract the mixture with about 40 c.c. of chloroform, in which the free base is very soluble. Run off the lower chloroform layer, dry it with potassium carbonate as in (*a*), and then add carbon tetrachloride slowly with stirring to the filtered chloroform solution until the base starts to crystallise out. Allow to stand for a short time (*i.e.*, until the deposition of crystals ceases) and then filter at the pump: as the crystals lose the last trace of solvent, they tend as before to break up into a fine powder, the deep green colour becoming paler in consequence.

A small quantity of the base may be recrystallised from hot ether, and magnificent deep green crystals obtained: the base is not sufficiently soluble in cold ether, however, to enable this solvent to be used advantageously in the above extractions.

Reactions. (1) *p*-Nitroso-dimethylaniline does *not* give Liebermann's Nitroso Reaction with phenol and sulphuric acid (see footnote, p. 255).

(2) Place about 1 gm. of the base in a test-tube, and cover with concentrated (about 20%) sodium hydroxide solution. Bring the mixture gently to the boil, keeping the test-tube lightly closed with the finger meanwhile to prevent undue escape of vapour. As the solution boils a strong fishy odour of dimethylamine is detected, and white fumes form when the test-tube is held near an open bottle of concentrated

$$\overline{NaO|H + (CH_3)_2N|}C_6H_4NO = (CH_3)_2NH + NaOC_6H_4NO$$

hydrochloric acid. The sodium hydroxide has hydrolysed the base, giving the volatile dimethylamine, whilst the sodium derivative of *p*-nitrosophenol remains in solution. The reaction affords an excellent method of preparing *pure* aliphatic secondary amines, particularly when required completely free from primary and tertiary amines.

Diazo-aminobenzene. $C_6H_5N_2NHC_6H_5$.

Diazonium salts couple readily with aromatic primary amines, giving diazo-amino compounds. If for instance an aqueous solution of aniline sulphate is diazotised with a deficiency of nitrous acid, only part of it is converted into phenyl diazonium sulphate, and the latter then couples with the unchanged

G

aniline to give diazo-aminobenzene. The reaction is carried out at the opti-

$$C_6H_5NH_2,H_2SO_4 + HONO = C_6H_5N_2HSO_4 + 2H_2O$$

$$C_6H_5N_2HSO_4 + HNHC_6H_5 = C_6H_5N_2NHC_6H_5 + H_2SO_4$$

mum temperature of 30°, for at this temperature coupling takes place readily, and the diazonium sulphate is used up before it has time to decompose.

Dissolve 2 c.c. (3·7 gms.) of concentrated sulphuric acid in 350 c.c. of water contained in a 600 c.c. beaker, and then add with stirring 12 c.c. (12·3 gms.) of aniline. Place the beaker *in* a water-bath and heat the latter gently until a thermometer in the solution records a temperature of 30°. Dissolve 4·5 gms. of sodium nitrite in 15 c.c. of water, and add about 1 c.c. of this solution at half-minute intervals to the solution of aniline sulphate, keeping the mixture well stirred meanwhile. When the addition of the nitrite is complete, keep the mixture at 30° for a further 15 minutes: the diazo-aminobenzene rapidly begins to separate as a yellow crystal-line mass. Then remove the beaker from the bath, and allow it to stand for 30 minutes, with occasional stirring. Filter off the solid material at the pump, using a Buchner funnel, wash re-peatedly with water, and then drain thoroughly. Finally dry the diazo-aminobenzene by pressing between several sheets of thick drying-paper. The sample so obtained is sufficiently pure for the following preparation of amino-azobenzene. Yield of crude material, 11–12 gms. (almost theoretical).

The recrystallisation of diazo-aminobenzene has to be performed with care, as the substance is freely soluble in most liquids and tends moreover to decompose if its solution is not rapidly cooled. Place 2 gms. of the crude, freshly prepared, well-drained material in a boiling-tube, add about 15–20 c.c. of alcohol and 1–2 drops of 10% aqueous sodium hydroxide solution, and then heat *rapidly* until boiling: if the solution should contain insoluble impurities, filter through a *small* fluted paper, and at once cool the filtrate in ice-water. The diazo-aminobenzene should rapidly crystallise out from the cold and stirred solution: filter the crystals rapidly at the pump whilst the solution is still cold, as they tend to redissolve if the solution reaches room temperature. Diazo-aminobenzene is thus obtained as yellow crystals, which melt at 98°, the molten material decomposing vigorously above this temperature: the crystalline material darkens on exposure to light and most specimens are therefore of a yellowish-brown colour.

Amino-azobenzene. $C_6H_5N{:}NC_6H_4NH_2$.

When diazo-aminobenzene is added to a warm aqueous solution of hydro-chloric acid, it tends to break up into its original components, *i.e.*, to phenyl diazonium chloride and aniline, and an equilibrium is thus established. The diazonium chloride and the aniline, however, in addition to recombining to form diazo-aminobenzene, also undergo direct condensation at the *p*-hydro-

$$C_6H_5N_2NHC_6H_5 + HCl \rightleftharpoons C_6H_5N_2Cl + H_2NC_6H_5 \rightarrow C_6H_5N{:}NC_6H_4NH_2 + HCl$$

gen atom of the aniline molecule, giving amino-azobenzene. Since this re-action is irreversible, whilst the former is freely reversible, the final result is the complete conversion of the diazo-aminobenzene to the amino-azobenzene. (The intermediate formation of the phenyl diazonium chloride can be demon-strated by adding dimethylaniline, with which the diazonium chloride couples preferentially, giving dimethylamino-azobenzene $C_6H_5N{:}NC_6H_4N(CH_3)_2$.)

The conversion of the diazo-aminobenzene to amino-azobenzene is promoted by the addition of aniline hydrochloride even more readily than by that of free hydrochloric acid. The aniline hydrochloride dissociates in solution giving hydrochloric acid and aniline: the former promotes the formation of the above equilibrium, and the latter by increasing the active mass of the free aniline further accelerates the condensation to amino-azobenzene.

Amino-azobenzene is a very weak base, and consequently it will not form salts with weak organic acids, such as acetic acid, although it will do so with the strong mineral acids, such as hydrochloric acid. Amino-azobenzene is a yellowish-brown compound, whilst the hydrochloride is steel blue. The colour of the latter is presumably due to resonance of the cation, one form of which is the quinonoid ion, $C_6H_5NH{\cdot}N{:}C_6H_4{:}\overset{+}{N}H_2$.

Required: Aniline hydrochloride, 4 gms.; aniline, 16 c.c.; diazo-aminobenzene, 8 gms.; acetic acid, 20 c.c.

Add 4 gms. of aniline hydrochloride to 16 c.c. of aniline contained in a 100 c.c. conical flask, and then add 8 gms. of diazo-aminobenzene, both the solid components being finely powdered. Place the flask in a water-bath, and heat the latter carefully so that the well-stirred mixture is kept at 40° for 1 hour. Then remove the flask from the water-bath and allow it to stand overnight to ensure that the conversion is complete. Then add about 20 c.c. of glacial acetic acid dissolved in the same volume of water, and stir the mixture well to extract the free aniline in the form of its soluble acetate. Allow the mixture to stand (with occasional stirring) for at least 10 minutes, and then filter at the pump and wash well with water.

Amino-azobenzene is freely soluble in methylated spirit, although insoluble in water. For recrystallisation, therefore, dissolve the crude substance in boiling methylated spirit, remove from the water-bath, and then add water drop by drop until the solution becomes just cloudy owing to the separation of the solute: replace the solution momentarily on the water-bath until the cloudiness disappears, and then at once remove the solution, and allow it to cool slowly. (Alternatively, the crude *dry* material can be recrystallised from carbon tetrachloride in the usual way.) Amino-azobenzene is thus obtained as yellowish-brown crystals, m.p. 126°: yield, 5 gms.

To prepare the hydrochloride, add about 1 gm. of amino-azobenzene to 200 c.c. of dilute hydrochloric acid and boil until nearly all the solid material has dissolved. Filter hot and allow to cool slowly. Amino-azobenzene hydrochloride separates as beautiful steel-blue crystals: filter and dry. If a small quantity of the powdered hydrochloride is moistened with water and a few drops of ammonia added, the blue hydrochloride is converted back to the yellowish-brown base.

Azo-Compounds.

Amino-azobenzene is a member of the large class of azo-compounds, all of which contain the characteristic grouping, $C \cdot N : N \cdot C$. Azo-compounds are of considerable technical importance, as they are all coloured, and the majority possess considerable stability. They may be prepared by the following methods:

(1) By coupling a diazonium salt with:

(a) A primary amine to give the diazo-amino compound, which is then converted to the isomeric amino-azo compound (as in the above preparation of amino-azobenzene).

$$C_6H_5N_2 | HSO_4 + H | NHC_6H_5 \longrightarrow C_6H_5N_2NHC_6H_5 \longrightarrow C_6H_5N:NC_6H_4NH_2$$

(b) A tertiary amine, the azo-compound being directly formed. Thus phenyl diazonium sulphate and dimethylaniline give dimethylamino-azobenzene (p. 147).

$$C_6H_5N_2 | HSO_4 + H | C_6H_4N(CH_3)_2 \longrightarrow C_6H_5N:NC_6H_4N(CH_3)_2$$

(c) A phenol in alkaline solution. β-Naphthol dissolved in sodium hydroxide solution thus gives benzene-azo-β-naphthol, a scarlet dye.

$$C_6H_5N_2 | HSO_4 + H | \overset{HO}{\bigcirc} \longrightarrow C_6H_5N:H\overset{HO}{\bigcirc} + H_2SO_4$$

(2) The alkaline reduction of an aromatic nitro-compound to give the azoxy derivative, which is then further reduced to the azo-compound. Nitrobenzene thus gives first azoxybenzene, and then azobenzene.

$$2C_6H_5NO_2 \longrightarrow C_6H_5NO:NC_6H_5 \longrightarrow C_6H_5N:NC_6H_5$$

(3) By condensing nitroso derivatives with primary amines. Nitrosobenzene

and aniline, for example, readily give azobenzene. This method is seldom used,

$$C_6H_5N\overline{|O + H_2|}NC_6H_5 = C_6H_5N:NC_6H_5 + H_2O$$

but is of importance in that it establishes clearly the constitution of the azo grouping. The most noteworthy reaction of azo-compounds is their behaviour on reduction. Prolonged reduction first saturates the azo group, giving the *hydrazo* derivative (C·NH·NH·C), and then breaks the NH·NH linkage, with the formation of two primary amine molecules. If method (1) has been employed to prepare the azo-compound, these two primary amines will therefore be respectively (*a*) the original amine from which the diazonium salt was prepared, and (*b*) the amino derivative of the amine or phenol with which the diazonium salt was coupled. For example, amino-azobenzene on complete reduction gives one equivalent of aniline, and one of *p*-phenylene diamine, $NH_2C_6H_4NH_2$; benzene-azo-β-naphthol similarly gives one equivalent of aniline and one of

α-amino-β-naphthol, experimental details for this reduction being given below. The constitution of an azo-compound (and particularly the position of the azo group in the molecule) can thus often be determined by identifying the two primary amines formed on complete reduction.

Benzene-azo-β-naphthol.
$C_6H_5N:NC_{10}H_6OH$ [Method 1 (c)].

Required: Aniline, 4·5 c.c.; hydrochloric acid, 10 c.c.; sodium nitrite, 4 gms.; β-naphthol, 7 gms.

Dissolve 4·5 c.c. of aniline in a mixture of 10 c.c. of concentrated hydrochloric acid and 20 c.c. of water: cool the solution to 5°, and diazotise by the addition of 4 gms. of sodium nitrite dissolved in 20 c.c. of water, observing the usual precautions given on page 141. Dissolve 7 gms. of β-naphthol in 60 c.c. of 10% sodium hydroxide solution contained in a 200 c.c. beaker, and cool this solution to 5° by external cooling, aided by the direct addition of about 20–30 gms. of crushed ice. Now add the diazotised solution very slowly to the naphthol solution, keeping the latter well stirred meanwhile: the mixed solutions immediately develop a deep red colour, and the benzene-azo-naphthol should rapidly separate as red crystals. If the diazonium solution is added too rapidly, the azo-compound may separate at first as a thick viscous mass, which, however, will crystallise later and may then be easily broken up with the stirrer. When the addition of the diazo solution is complete, allow the mixture to stand in an ice-salt mixture for 30 minutes, with occasional stirring, and then filter the solution through a Buchner funnel under gentle suction from the pump: if the above directions have been carefully followed, filtration should be rapid. Wash the benzene-azo-β-naphthol well with water, and then drain thoroughly, pressing the crystals well down on to the filter with a spatula. Recrystallise one-third of the product from glacial acetic acid, reserving the remainder for reduction to α-amino-β-naphthol. (The azo-compound when dry is freely soluble in acetic acid, but when moist is only moderately soluble: about 40 c.c. of acetic acid are required for the portion recrystallised as above.) Filter the re-crystallised material at the pump, wash with a few c.c. of alcohol or methylated spirit to eliminate acetic acid, and dry: yield, 3 gms. Benzene-azo-β-naphthol is obtained as deep red crystals, m.p. 131°. Should further recrystallisation of the *dry* compound be required, alcohol is the best solvent.

Hydrochloride of α-amino-β-naphthol (1-amino-2-hydroxynaphthalene). $C_{10}H_6(NH_2)OH,HCl$.

Required: Benzene-azo-naphthol from above experiment; methylated spirit, 100 c.c.; stannous chloride, 22 gms.; hydrochloric acid, 60 c.c.

Add the reserved portion of the unrecrystallised benzene-azo-naphthol to 100 c.c. of methylated spirit contained in a 350 c.c. conical flask and boil gently under reflux until the greater part of the azo-compound has gone into solution. Meanwhile dissolve 22 gms. of stannous chloride in 60 c.c. of concentrated hydrochloric acid (warming gently, if necessary, to obtain a clear solution), add this solution to that of the azo-compound, and continue the boiling under reflux for 30 minutes. The azo-compound rapidly dissolves, and is reduced by the stannous chloride, and after about 20 minutes' boiling the red colour disappears and the solution acquires a permanent very pale brown tint. (If the red colour, instead of disappearing, slowly darkens to a deep reddish-violet, the stannous chloride is at fault, as the violet colour usually develops if a stale sample of stannous chloride, particularly one which has been unduly exposed to the air, is employed.) When the boiling for 30 minutes is complete, decant the solution into a beaker, and cool in ice-water; the amino-naphthol hydrochloride separates as fine greyish-white crystals. Filter off at the pump, and wash the hydrochloride thoroughly with dilute hydrochloric acid, in which it is almost insoluble. Recrystallise from hot water containing a *few drops* of dilute hydrochloric acid; care must be taken that too much water is not used for this purpose, as the hydrochloride usually contains traces of a sparingly soluble stannous impurity which should be left undissolved and removed by filtration from the hot solution. If the hydrochloride does not crystallise readily from the cold filtrate, seed the latter with a minute quantity of the crude material, or add a few more drops of dilute hydrochloric acid. α-Amino-β-naphthol hydrochloride is thus obtained as fine colourless crystals, which darken in colour on exposure to light: yield, 3 gms.

Azoxybenzene, $C_6H_5NO:NC_6H_5$, and Azobenzene, $C_6H_5N:NC_6H_5$. (Method 2, p. 164.)

When a solution of nitrobenzene in methyl alcohol is boiled with sodium hydroxide, the nitrobenzene is reduced to azoxybenzene by the methyl alcohol, which is itself oxidised to formic acid.

$$4C_6H_5NO_2 + 3CH_3OH + 3NaOH = 2C_6H_5NO:NC_6H_5 + 3HCOONa + 6H_2O$$

The azoxybenzene in turn, when heated with iron filings, readily undergoes

$$C_6H_5NO:NC_6H_5 + Fe = C_6H_5N:NC_6H_5 + FeO$$

further reduction to azobenzene.

AZOXYBENZENE. *Required:* Sodium hydroxide,23 gms.; nitrobenzene, 15 c.c.; methyl alcohol, 120 c.c.

Add 23 gms. of powdered (or "flake") sodium hydroxide to a solution of 15 c.c. (18 gms.) of nitrobenzene in 120 c.c. of methyl alcohol contained in a 250 c.c. short-necked bolt-head flask. Fix a reflux water-condenser to the flask and boil the solution on a water-bath for 3 hours, shaking the product vigorously at intervals to ensure thorough mixing. Then fit a bent delivery-tube to the flask, and reverse the condenser for distillation, as in Fig. 43, p. 72). Place the flask *in* the boiling water-bath (since methyl alcohol will not readily distil when heated on a water-bath) and distil off as much alcohol as possible. Then pour the residual product with stirring into about 250 c.c. of cold water: wash out the flask with water, and then acidify the mixture with hydrochloric acid. The crude azoxybenzene separates as a heavy oil, which when thoroughly stirred soon solidifies, particularly if the mixture is cooled in ice-water.

Then filter off the solid azoxybenzene at the pump, wash it thoroughly with water, and drain well. Recrystallise from a minimum of methylated spirit, allowing the hot solution to cool spontaneously (with occasional stirring) until crystallisation starts, and then cool in ice-water. If crystallisation is delayed, "seed" the solution with a trace of the crude product: if on the other hand the azoxybenzene separates at first as an emulsion, add methylated spirit, drop by drop, with stirring until the solution is clear, and then allow the cooling to proceed as before. The azoxybenzene is obtained as very pale yellow crystals, m.p. 36°. Yield of recrystallised material, 11 gms.

The fact that a mixed azoxy-compound, such as *p*-toluene-azoxy-benzene, $CH_3C_6H_4NO:NC_6H_5$, exists in two isomeric forms, disproves the earlier symmetric formula (A) alloted to azoxybenzene, and supports the formula (B), in which the oxygen is joined by a co-ordinate link to one nitrogen atom: this formula (B) receives support also from the parachor values of azoxy-compounds.

$$C_6H_5N\diagdown O \qquad C_6H_5N\to O$$
$$(A)\ C_6H_5N\diagup \qquad C_6H_5N\ (B)$$

AZOBENZENE.   *Required:* Azoxybenzene, 8 gms.; iron filings, 25 gms.

Place 8 gms. of the pure powdered azoxybenzene and 25 gms. of iron filings (both reagents being quite dry) in a 75 c.c. distilling-flask **F** and mix *thoroughly* by shaking. Cork the flask and fit to the side-arm a boiling-tube **B** to act as receiver (Fig. 50):

FIG. 50.

cut or file a groove **G** in the boiling-tube cork to allow escape of air. Now heat the mixture directly with the Bunsen flame, waving the latter around the base of the flask to ensure uniform heating: heat gently at first and later more strongly. The red liquid azobenzene distils over smoothly and eventually solidifies in the receiver. When no more distillate passes over, detach the boiling-tube, and then, in order to eliminate basic impurities which are formed as by-products in the reaction, add 20–30 c.c. of dilute hydrochloric acid (1 vol. of concentrated acid : 2 vols. of water) which have been heated to about 70°: cork the tube securely and shake the mixture, so that impurities in the molten drops of azobenzene are thoroughly extracted by the acid, which usually becomes dark in colour. Now cool in water until the globules of azobenzene solidify, and then filter at the pump. Break up the azobenzene with a spatula on the filter, wash thoroughly with water, and drain. Recrystallise from a minimum of boiling methylated spirit, filtering the hot solution through a small fluted filter-paper. The azobenzene separates as reddish-orange crystals, m.p. 67–68°. Yield, 4 gms. A second recrystallisation from methylated spirit may be necessary to obtain a satisfactory melting-point.

In order to save the cost of the distilling-flask (which after the above treatment is useless for further work), the mixture may be distilled from a small retort made by blowing a suitable bulb on the end of a rather thick-walled tube of about 8–10 mm. internal diameter: the tube is then bent through almost 90° a few cm. above the bulb, cut to a suitable length, and the open end fitted into the boiling-tube as before.

Methyl-orange (Sodium salt).
$NaO_3SC_6H_4N : NC_6H_4N(CH_3)_2$.

When hydrochloric acid is cautiously added to an aqueous solution containing both sodium nitrite and the sodium salt of sulphanilic acid, $NaO_3SC_6H_4NH_2$, the amino group of the latter undergoes normal diazotisation, giving the diazonium chloride (A). The latter, however, ionises in solution, giving sodium and chloride ions and the internal salt (B), which possesses two opposite charges and is therefore neutral: this internal salt is stable under

$$\text{(A)} \quad NaO_3SC_6H_4\overset{+}{N}_2Cl = \overset{+}{Na} + \overset{-}{Cl} + \overset{-}{O}_3SC_6H_4\overset{+}{N}_2 \quad \text{(B)}$$

these conditions, and being only moderately soluble in water, will be largely precipitated unless the solution is very dilute. If now dimethylaniline hydrochloride is added to the solution, coupling will occur between the internal salt and the tertiary amine, with the formation of methyl-orange:

$$\bar{O}_3S\langle\rangle\overset{+}{N}_2 + H\langle\rangle N(CH_3)_2, HCl = HO_3S\langle\rangle N:N\langle\rangle N(CH_3)_2 + HCl$$

On the addition of sodium hydroxide, the sparingly soluble sodium salt of methyl-orange, $NaO_3SC_6H_4N:NC_6H_4N(CH_3)_2$, will crystallise out.

It is important in this preparation to avoid an excess of nitrous acid before coupling occurs, otherwise the excess of nitrous acid will react directly with the dimethylaniline, and the deep green p-nitrosodimethylaniline so formed will contaminate the methyl-orange.

Required: Anhydrous sodium carbonate, 2 gms.; sulphanilic acid, 7 gms.; sodium nitrite, 2·2 gms.; hydrochloric acid, 12 c.c.; dimethylaniline, 4 c.c.

Dissolve 2 gms. of anhydrous sodium carbonate in 50 c.c. of water contained in a 300 c.c. beaker and add 7 gms. of finely powdered crystalline sulphanilic acid ($2H_2O$), warming the mixture gently in order to obtain a clear solution. Add a solution of 2·2 gms. of sodium nitrite in 10 c.c. of water and then cool the mixture in ice-water until the temperature has fallen to 5°. Now add *very slowly* (drop by drop) with continual stirring a solution of 8 c.c. of concentrated hydrochloric acid in 15 c.c. of water: do not allow the temperature to rise above 10°. When all the acid has been added, allow the solution to stand in ice-water for 15 minutes to ensure complete diazotisation: during this period fine crystals of the internal salt separate from the pink solution. Dissolve 4 c.c. of dimethylaniline in a mixture of 4 c.c. of concentrated hydrochloric acid and 10 c.c. of water, cool the solution in ice-water, and add it slowly to the cold well-stirred diazo solution: a pale red coloration is developed. Allow the mixture to stand for 5 minutes and then add *slowly with stirring* aqueous

G*

10% NaOH solution until the mixture attains a uniform orange colour (about 50 c.c. are required).

The sodium salt of methyl-orange separates as very fine particles, and filtration, if attempted directly, may be very slow. Therefore warm the mixture to 50–55°, stirring it meanwhile with a thermometer: when nearly all the methyl-orange has dissolved, add about 10 gms. of finely powdered sodium chloride, and continue warming for a few minutes until the chloride itself has dissolved. Now allow the mixture to cool spontaneously for 10–15 minutes, and then cool in ice-water. Filter off the methyl-orange at the pump: filtration is now rapid, particularly if only gentle suction is employed, so that the particles of the methyl-orange are not dragged into the pores of the filter-paper. Drain thoroughly, and then recrystallise the methyl-orange from about 100 c.c. of boiling water: filter the hot solution (if necessary) through a Buchner funnel which has been preheated by the filtration of some boiling water. The deep reddish-orange crystals of methyl-orange separate rapidly as the solution cools. Yield, 9 gms.

The use of methyl-orange as an indicator is based on the fact that the sodium salt in aqueous solution furnishes a yellow anion, which when treated with acids (except weak acids such as H_2CO_3 and H_2SO_3) apparently gives rise to a red

quinonoid cation, the change being reversed by alkalis. It is possible, however, that there are additional factors governing these colour changes.

Benzidine or pp'-Diamino-diphenyl.
$H_2N \cdot C_6H_4 \cdot C_6H_4 \cdot NH_2$.

When hydrazobenzene, or sym-diphenylhydrazine, is warmed with acids, it undergoes an intramolecular rearrangement, with the formation of benzidine,

or pp'-diamino-diphenyl. This reaction is of wide application and is known as the *Benzidine Transformation*.

Required: Hydrazobenzene, 10 gms.; zinc dust, 10 gms.

HYDRAZOBENZENE. The above preparation of benzidine should be carried out with pure hydrazobenzene. This compound, however, when kept in store undergoes atmospheric oxidation to azobenzene (p. 167), and such samples are therefore usually orange-red in colour due to contamination with azobenzene. If the hydrazobenzene is coloured in this way, it should be purified by the following process, which reduces any azobenzene back to hydrazobenzene.

Add 10 gms. of the crude hydrazobenzene to 80 c.c. of alcohol contained in a flask fitted with a reflux water-condenser. Heat the mixture on a water-bath until the alcohol boils, and then add 10 gms. of zinc dust and 30 c.c. of 30% aqueous sodium hydroxide solution. Remove the flask from the water-bath and shake the contents vigorously from time to time. After about 10 minutes, replace the flask on the water-bath and boil the contents for 3–5 minutes. Filter the mixture at the pump, transfer the filtrate to a beaker and cool in ice-water with stirring. The hydrazobenzene separates as colourless crystals, which are filtered off at the pump and drained. A portion when dried in a desiccator has m.p. 124°.

BENZIDINE. Add 5 gms. of the thoroughly drained (and almost dry) hydrazobenzene to a mixture of 15 c.c. of concentrated hydrochloric acid and 100 c.c. of distilled water contained in a 250 c.c. conical flask. Warm the mixture to 25–30°, and then securely cork the flask and shake the contents vigorously. Occasionally withdraw the cork, and re-warm the mixture before shaking again. After about 15 minutes, heat the mixture carefully to 50° for about 5 minutes. If the original hydrazobenzene were pure, a clear solution should now be obtained. If any undissolved material remains, however, filter the solution, and precipitate the benzidine by the addition of aqueous sodium hydroxide solution to the cooled filtrate. Filter off the precipitated benzidine, and recrystallise from boiling water (in which it is only moderately soluble), adding some animal charcoal to the boiling solution if it is coloured. The benzidine separates from the cooled filtrate as a monohydrate, which when placed in a· vacuum desiccator readily gives the anhydrous benzidine as colourless crystals, m.p. 127°. A second recrystallisation from water is however sometimes necessary. Yield, 2·5 gms. Alternatively, the crude precipitated benzidine can be recrystallised from alcohol, or it may be dried and recrystallised from benzene.

N-Phenyl-anthranilic Acid, $C_6H_5NHC_6H_4 \cdot COOH$.
(The Ullmann Condensation.)

A halogen atom directly attached to a benzene ring is usually unreactive, unless it is activated by the nature and position of certain other substituent groups. It has been shown by Ullmann, however, that halogen atoms normally of low reactivity will condense with aromatic amines in the presence of an alkali carbonate (to absorb the hydrogen halide formed) and a trace of copper powder or oxide to act as a catalyst. This reaction, known as the *Ullmann Condensation*, is frequently used to prepare substituted diphenylamines: it is exemplified

in the following condensation of *o*-chlorobenzoic acid with aniline to give N-phenyl-anthranilic acid.

Required: Aniline, 35 c.c.; *o*-chlorobenzoic acid, 10 gms.; potassium carbonate, 10 gms.; copper oxide, 0·5 gm.

Prepare a mixture of 35 c.c. of aniline, 10 gms. of *o*-chloro-benzoic acid, 10 gms. of anhydrous potassium carbonate and 0·5 gm. of copper oxide in a 500 c.c. round-bottomed flask fitted with an air-condenser, and then boil the mixture under reflux for 1·5 hours: the mixture tends to foam during the earlier part of the heating owing to the evolution of carbon dioxide, and hence the large flask is used. When the heating has been completed, fit the flask with a steam-distillation head, and steam-distil the crude product until all the excess of aniline has been removed. The residual solution now contains the potassium N-phenyl-anthranilate: add *ca.* 2 gms. of animal charcoal to this solution, boil for about 5 minutes, and filter hot. Add dilute hydrochloric acid (1 : 1 by volume) to the filtrate until no further precipitation occurs, and then cool in ice-water with stirring. Filter off the N-phenyl-anthranilic acid at the pump, wash with water, drain and dry. Yield, 10–11 gms. The acid may be recrystallised from aqueous alcohol, and is obtained as colourless crystals, m.p. 179–181° with preliminary shrinking.

Methylation can be carried out by the following methods:

(1) *Williamson's Method*, more particularly for hydroxy- and thiohydroxy-(mercapto) compounds. The substance is treated either directly with sodium or (more usually) with a solution of sodium methoxide in methyl alcohol, to give the sodium derivative. The latter is then boiled with methyl iodide.

$$RO\,|Na + I\,|CH_3 = ROCH_3 + NaI$$

Note that this is only a particular case of Williamson's general method for the preparation of ethers.

(2) *Purdie's Method*, also chiefly for hydroxy-compounds. The substance is mixed with a small excess of dry silver oxide, and then shaken (or, if neces-

sary, heated) with methyl iodide, a smooth methylation usually occurring.

$$2ROH + Ag_2O + 2CH_3I = 2ROCH_3 + 2AgI + H_2O$$

This method is used more particularly for hydroxy-compounds which also contain other groups (such as Cl atoms, *etc.*) which might be affected by the sodium hydroxide used in the following method.

(3) *Dimethyl Sulphate Method*, for hydroxy-compounds and for primary and secondary amines, acid amides, *etc.* The substance is dissolved or suspended in water, a small excess (above the theoretical) of sodium hydroxide added and then the theoretical quantity of dimethyl sulphate, the mixture being finally shaken without external warming. Methylation is usually rapid, the dimethyl sulphate being converted to methyl hydrogen sulphate,

$$ROH + (CH_3)_2SO_4 + NaOH = ROCH_3 + CH_3NaSO_4 + H_2O$$
$$RNH_2 + (CH_3)_2SO_4 + NaOH = RNHCH_3 + CH_3NaSO_4 + H_2O$$

which dissolves in the alkali present. The general conditions are thus very similar to those used for the Schotten-Baumann reaction (p. 189) by which the same classes of compound (hydroxy-derivatives, primary and secondary amines) can be benzoylated, *etc.*

Dimethyl sulphate is poisonous, both when the hot vapour is inhaled and even when the cold liquid is spilt on the hands, and considerable care should be exercised in its use (*cf.* pp. 175, 429).

(4) *Diazo-methane Method.* Diazo-methane readily methylates phenolic hydroxy-compounds, primary and secondary amines, and carboxylic acids,

$$ROH + N_2CH_2 = ROCH_3 + N_2$$

nitrogen being liberated. Since diazo-methane is a gas, it is usually employed in ethereal solution. It is both poisonous and (in the gaseous state) explosive, and requires therefore careful manipulation.

Methods (2) and (3) have been extensively used in the investigation of the structure of sugars.

Anisole (Phenyl Methyl Ether). $C_6H_5OCH_3$. (Method 1.)

Required: Sodium, 3·8 gms.; methyl alcohol, 75 c.c.; phenol, 15 gms.; methyl iodide, 11 c.c.

Weigh out 3·8 gms. of metallic sodium, cut it into small pieces, and add it to 75 c.c. of good-quality (preferably absolute) methyl alcohol contained in a 250 c.c. bolt-head flask: at once attach the flask to an efficient reflux water-condenser. Considerable heat is evolved by the dissolution of the sodium, and the alcohol boils vigorously under reflux: no attempt should be made to cool the alcohol (unless the condenser tends to "choke"), otherwise a considerable time will elapse before the last traces of the sodium dissolve. Then cool the clear solution of sodium methoxide in ice-water, and add 15 gms. of phenol,* which will rapidly dissolve to give sodium phenoxide (or phenate) when the mixture is gently shaken. Now add 11 c.c. (25 gms., 1·1 mols.) of methyl iodide and some fragments of unglazed porcelain, re-attach the flask to the reflux condenser, and boil the solution *gently* on a water-bath for one hour. Then remove the flask from the water-bath, and rearrange the condenser for direct distillation, connecting it through a "knee-tube" to the flask (as in Fig. 43, p. 72). Replace the latter on the water-bath, and distil off the excess of methyl alcohol as completely as possible. Pour the residual liquid in the flask into 100 c.c. of cold water contained in a separating-funnel, and wash out the flask with another 50 c.c. of water, adding these washings also to the liquid in the funnel. Then extract the anisole by shaking with about 40–50 c.c. of ether. Run off the lower aqueous layer, and shake the ethereal solution with an equal volume of 10 % aqueous sodium hydroxide solution: this removes unchanged phenol, and also any traces of free iodine present, leaving the ethereal solution quite colourless. Run off the sodium hydroxide solution as completely as possible, and shake the ethereal solution with an equal volume of water to remove the last traces of the sodium hydroxide. Separate the ethereal solution, dry it with calcium chloride, and then distil off the ether from the filtered solution in a 50 c.c. distilling-flask, using a similar apparatus and observing the same precautions as in the preparation of aniline (see Fig. 48, p. 123). When all the ether has been distilled off, replace the water-condenser by an air-condenser, and distil the residual anisole slowly over a gauze. Collect the fraction distilling at 152°–156°. Yield, 9 gms.

Anisole is a colourless and almost odourless liquid, having b.p. 154°, and *d*, 0·99. Like the aliphatic ethers, it is chemically inert, although of course the phenyl group shows the normal aromatic reactions.

Phenetole. (Phenyl Ethyl Ether.) $C_6H_5OC_2H_5$. (Method 1, p. 172.)

In view of the high cost of methyl iodide in the above preparation of anisole, and the fact that, unless absolute methyl alcohol is used, the ready hydrolysis of the methyl iodide may cause a low yield of the ether, the preparation of anisole may be advantageously replaced by that of phenetole. The reaction is

---

* The phenol should be weighed out *carefully* on a piece of glazed paper on the balance pan. If spilt crystals of phenol are allowed to remain on the balance pans, the latter may become corroded. If phenol is allowed to come in contact with the hands, it should be washed off without delay.

not of course a methylation, but is nevertheless of the same type as that used in the preparation of anisole.

Required: Sodium, 3·8 gms.; rectified spirit, 75 c.c.; phenol, 15 gms.

Dissolve 3·8 gms. of sodium in 75 c.c. of rectified spirit, using otherwise the same conditions as in the preparation of anisole. Then add 15 gms. of phenol, and to the clear solution add 13·2 c.c. (19·1 gms., 1·1 mols.) of ethyl bromide. Continue precisely as in the preparation of anisole, shaking the ethereal extract with sodium hydroxide solution as before in order to eliminate any unchanged phenol. Finally collect the fraction boiling at 168–172°. Yield, 14 gms.

Phenetole is a colourless liquid, having b.p. 171°, and *d*, 0·98.

β-Naphthyl Methyl Ether. (Nerolin.) $C_{10}H_7OCH_3$. (Method 3, p. 173.)

Experiments involving the use of dimethyl sulphate should be carried out by students only under immediate supervision. Not only is the vapour of dimethyl sulphate highly poisonous, but the cold liquid itself is absorbed easily through the skin, with toxic results: individual susceptibility to dimethyl sulphate poisoning varies and may be very high. If the sulphate is splashed on to the hands, wash immediately with plenty of concentrated ammonia solution in order to hydrolyse the methyl sulphate before it can be absorbed through the skin (see p. 429).

Required: β-Naphthol, 10 gms.; dimethyl sulphate, 6·9 c.c.

Dissolve 10 gms. of pure β-naphthol in 30 c.c. of 10% sodium hydroxide solution (1·1 mols.) contained in a stout-walled widenecked bottle of about 200 c.c. capacity, and for which a wellfitting *rubber* stopper is available. Dilute the solution with 30 c.c. of water in order to moderate the subsequent reaction, and then run in from a burette 6·9 c.c. (9·2 gms., 1·05 mols.) of dimethyl sulphate. Cork the bottle securely and shake the contents vigorously. As the reaction proceeds, the mixture becomes warm and the naphthyl methyl ether rapidly separates as a greyish-white powder: finally after about 20 minutes' shaking the reaction is complete and the mixture has again become almost cold. Filter the naphthyl methyl ether at the pump, wash with dilute (10%) sodium hydroxide to remove any traces of unchanged naphthol or methyl sulphate, and then wash thoroughly with water and drain.

Recrystallise from methylated spirit, from which the β-naphthyl methyl ether separates readily as colourless crystals, m.p. 72°: yield, 9 gms.

Nerolin, which has a faint but persistent odour, is used technically for scenting soaps, *etc.*

α-Naphthol, similarly methylated, gives the liquid α-naphthyl methyl ether, b.p. 263°. Phenol gives anisole, the preparation of which by Method 1 has, however, already been described.

Toluene *p*-Sulphon-dimethylamide.
$CH_3C_6H_4SO_2N(CH_3)_2$. (Method 3, p. 173.)

Toluene *p*-sulphonamide can be similarly converted into the dimethylamide, but the methylation now occurs in two definite stages. First the suphonamide dissolves in the sodium hydroxide to form the mono-sodium salt (see p. 198), which then reacts with the dimethyl sulphate to give the mono-

$$CH_3C_6H_4SO_2NHNa + (CH_3)_2SO_4 = CH_3C_6H_4SO_2NH(CH_3) + NaCH_3SO_4$$

methylamide: the latter, being still acidic, remains dissolved in the alkaline solution as the sodium salt, which then reacts with a second equivalent of

$$CH_3C_6H_4SO_2NNa(CH_3) + (CH_3)_2SO_4 = CH_3C_6H_4SO_2N(CH_3)_2 + NaCH_3SO_4$$

dimethyl sulphate to give the dimethylamide. The dimethylamide is neutral and therefore separates from solution.

Required: Toluene *p*-sulphonamide, 10 gms.; dimethyl sulphate, 12·7 c.c.

Dissolve 10 gms. of powdered toluene *p*-sulphonamide in 60 c.c. of 10% aqueous sodium hydroxide (2·5 mols.) diluted with 50 c.c. of water to moderate the reaction. Then, using the same precautions as in the previous preparation, add 12·7 c.c. (17 gms., 2·3 mols.) of dimethyl sulphate and shake the mixture vigorously. The crystalline dimethylamide rapidly separates from the warm solution. After 15–20 minutes' shaking, cool the mixture in ice-water, and filter off the dimethylamide. Wash with sodium hydroxide solution, then with water and drain. The product thus prepared is (when dry) almost pure, but can be readily recrystallised from a mixture of equal volumes of water and glacial acetic acid: filter the recrystallised material at the pump, wash with water, drain and dry. Colourless crystals, m.p. 79°: yield, 8 gms.

The toluene *p*-sulphon-dimethylamide can be readily hydrolysed by boiling under reflux with 70% sulphuric acid (see p. 80). If the

$$CH_3C_6H_4SO_2N(CH_3)_2 + H_2O + H_2SO_4 = CH_3C_6H_4SO_2OH + (CH_3)_2NH,H_2SO_4$$

clear solution so obtained is placed in a distilling-flask and made alkaline, the liberated dimethylamine may be driven over by heating, and then absorbed in hydrochloric acid. Evaporation of the hydrochloric acid solution gives the deliquescent crystalline dimethylamine hydrochloride, $(CH_3)_2NH,HCl$.

Benzaldehyde Phenylhydrazone. $C_6H_5CH:NNHC_6H_5$.

Phenylhydrazine condenses readily with aldehydes and ketones to give *phenylhydrazones*, which, being usually crystalline compounds of sharp

$$C_6H_5CH[O + H_2]NNHC_6H_5 = C_6H_5CH:NNHC_6H_5 + H_2O$$

Benzaldehyde   Phenylhydrazine   Benzaldehyde
                                    Phenylhydrazone

melting-point, can therefore be used to identify the aldehydes and ketones from which they have been formed. For this purpose phenylhydrazones are frequently more suitable than oximes (p. 66) since their greater molecular weight causes a lower solubility in most solvents, and they can therefore often be more easily isolated and recrystallised. The phenylhydrazones of the lower aliphatic aldehydes and ketones, however, often have low melting-points, and are thus not suitable for identification purposes: to overcome this difficulty, substituted phenylhydrazines such as p-nitrophenylhydrazine, $(NO_2C_6H_4NHNH_2)$, 2:4-dinitrophenylhydrazine (pp. 257, 261), and p-bromophenylhydrazine are often used, since the corresponding substituted phenylhydrazones usually crystallise well, and are of low solubility and high melting-point.

Phenylhydrazine is usually dissolved in acetic acid for hydrazone formation: if a salt of phenylhydrazine with an inorganic acid is used, it must be mixed with an excess of sodium acetate (see preparation of osazones, p. 109).

Required: Acetic acid, 3 c.c.; phenylhydrazine, 4 c.c.; benzaldehyde, 2 c.c.

Dissolve 3 c.c. of glacial acetic acid in 20 c.c. of water in a 100 c.c. conical flask, and add 4 c.c. (4·4 gms.) of phenylhydrazine. Mix thoroughly to obtain a clear solution of phenylhydrazine acetate and then add 2 c.c. (2·1 gms.) of benzaldehyde. Cork the flask securely and shake the contents vigorously. A yellow crystalline mass of the hydrazone soon begins to separate. Allow to stand for 15 minutes, with occasional shaking, and then filter the solid product at the pump, wash first with very dilute acetic acid and then with water, and finally drain thoroughly. Recrystallise the material from methylated spirit, the benzaldehyde phenylhydrazone being thus obtained in fine colourless needles, m.p. 157°: yield, 3 gms.

Hydrobenzamide. $(C_6H_5CH)_3N_2$.

Benzaldehyde reacts with ammonia to give hydrobenzamide, in accordance with the equation:

$$3C_6H_5CHO + 2NH_3 = (C_6H_5CH)_3N_2 + 3H_2O$$

This behaviour is in marked contrast to that of the aliphatic aldehydes, which usually give direct addition products with ammonia, although polymerisation

$$CH_3CHO + HNH_2 = CH_3CH(OH)NH_2 \longrightarrow (C_2H_7ON)_3$$

may follow. Formaldehyde is an exception among the aliphatic aldehydes, since it undergoes condensation with ammonia to give hexamethylene tetramine (or

$$6CH_2O + 4NH_3 = (CH_2)_6N_4 + 6H_2O$$

urotropine), a reaction which is similar to that given by benzaldehyde.

Required: Benzaldehyde, 5 c.c.; ammonia, 50 c.c.

Place 5 c.c. of benzaldehyde in a wide-necked stout-walled bottle of about 100 c.c. capacity (a conical flask is too fragile for this purpose) and add 50 c.c. of concentrated (d, 0·880) ammonia solution. Cork the bottle securely, shake vigorously, and then allow to stand for 24 hours, by which time the layer of benzaldehyde at the bottom of the bottle will have been converted into a hard mass of hydrobenzamide. (If after 24 hours the crude hydrobenzamide is still syrupy, shake the mixture vigorously and allow to stand for another hour, when the conversion will be complete.) Break up the solid pellet with a strong spatula, filter at the pump, wash with water and drain thoroughly. Recrystallise from alcohol: methylated spirit should not be used, as it contains sufficient water to cause partial hydrolysis back to benzaldehyde and ammonia. Hydrobenzamide is obtained as colourless crystals, m.p. 101° (and not 110° as frequently quoted): yield, 4 gms.

Hydrobenzamide is readily hydrolysed even by cold dilute acids.

Benzylidene-aniline. $C_6H_5CH{:}NC_6H_5$.

Aldehydes undergo condensation with primary amines with the elimination of water to give substances known as Schiff's Bases, which can also be used to characterise aldehydes. Benzaldehyde for example condenses readily with

$$C_6H_5CH|O + H_2|NC_6H_5 = C_6H_5CH{:}NC_6H_5 + H_2O$$

aniline to give benzylidene-aniline. In other cases in which the condensation is not so rapid, it may be hastened considerably by the addition of a trace of anhydrous zinc chloride.

Required: Benzaldehyde, 4 c.c.; aniline, 4 c.c.

Mix 4 c.c. of benzaldehyde and 4 c.c. of aniline in a small evaporating-basin, place the latter on a boiling water-bath and stir the mixture gently with a glass rod. Globules of water soon appear on the oily layer. After about 20 minutes place the basin in ice-water, and stir the contents well, whereupon solidification should rapidly occur. (If the material does not solidify, replace the basin on the boiling water-bath for a further 10 minutes.) Break up the solid material in the basin, transfer to a conical flask, and recrystallise from methylated spirit. The benzylidene-aniline is obtained as colourless crystals, m.p. 52°: yield, 5 gms.

Dibenzal-acetone. $C_6H_5CH{:}CHCOCH{:}CHC_6H_5$ (Claisen Reaction).

When an alcoholic solution containing both acetone and two equivalents of benzaldehyde is made alkaline with sodium hydroxide, rapid condensation occurs with the formation of dibenzal-acetone, or dibenzylidene-acetone. This

$$2C_6H_5CHO + CH_3COCH_3 = C_6H_5CH{:}CHCOCH{:}CHC_6H_5 + 2H_2O$$
Dibenzal-acetone.

is a particular example of the Claisen Reaction,* for Claisen showed that aldehydes under the influence of sodium hydroxide will condense with (i) another aldehyde, or (ii) a ketone, with the elimination of water. Thus benzaldehyde will condense with (i) acetaldehyde to give cinnamic aldehyde, and with (ii) one equivalent of acetone to give (mono) benzal-acetone. In these

(i) $C_6H_5CHO + HCH_2CHO = C_6H_5CH{:}CH{\cdot}CHO + H_2O$
Cinnamic aldehyde.

(ii) $C_6H_5CHO + HCH_2COCH_3 = C_6H_5CH{:}CHCOCH_3 + H_2O$
Benzylidene-acetone.

reactions it is probable that an intermediate hydroxy-compound is formed ($C_6H_5CH(OH)CH_2CHO$ and $C_6H_5CH(OH)CH_2COCH_3$ respectively) and water is then lost from the unstable $-CH(OH)CH_2-$ group.

Required: Benzaldehyde, 5 c.c.; acetone, 2 c.c.; methylated spirit, 50 c.c.

Dissolve 5 c.c. of benzaldehyde and 2 c.c. of pure acetone in 50 c.c. of methylated spirit contained in a conical flask or wide-mouthed bottle of about 200 c.c. capacity. Dilute 10 c.c. of 10% aqueous sodium hydroxide solution with 40 c.c. of water, and add this dilute alkali solution to the former solution. Shake the mixture vigorously in the securely corked flask for about 10 minutes (releasing the pressure from time to time if necessary) and then allow to stand for 45 minutes, with occasional shaking: finally cool in ice-water for a few minutes. During the shaking, the dibenzal-acetone separates at first as a fine emulsion which then rapidly forms pale yellow crystals. Filter at the pump, wash well with water to eliminate traces of alkali, and then drain thoroughly. Recrystallise from hot methylated spirit. The dibenzal-acetone is obtained as pale yellow crystals, m.p. 112°: yield, 3·5–4.0 gms.

Benzyl Alcohol, $C_6H_5CH_2OH$, and Benzoic Acid, C_6H_5COOH. (Cannizzaro's Reaction).

When benzaldehyde is treated with a concentrated caustic alkali solution, polymerisation occurs with the formation of benzyl benzoate, which then

* This Reaction should be carefully distinguished from the *Claisen Condensation*, which is the condensation of an ester, under the influence of *sodium ethoxide*, with (i) another ester, (ii) a ketone, or (iii) a nitrile, with the elimination of alcohol. For details of this condensation, see Ethyl Acetoacetate, p. 206.

undergoes hydrolysis giving benzyl alcohol and the alkali salt of benzoic acid. The final result is equivalent to the reduction of one molecule of benzaldehyde

$$C_6H_5CHO + OHCC_6H_5 = C_6H_5COOCH_2C_6H_5$$
$$C_6H_5COOCH_2C_6H_5 + KOH = C_6H_5CH_2OH + C_6H_5COOK$$

to the corresponding alcohol, and oxidation of the second molecule to the corresponding acid. The two products can be readily separated by treatment with water, in which the potassium benzoate dissolves, whilst the benzyl alcohol separates as an insoluble oil which can be removed by extraction with ether: acidification of the residual aqueous solution by concentrated hydrochloric acid then precipitates the benzoic acid.

This reaction is given by most aromatic aldehydes having the aldehyde group directly joined to the benzene ring: it is also given by formaldehyde, with the formation of methyl alcohol and formic acid. Other aliphatic aldehydes do not give Cannizzaro's reaction under these conditions.

Required: Potassium hydroxide, 27 gms.; benzaldehyde, 30 c.c.

Dissolve 27 gms. of potassium hydroxide* in 20 c.c. of water contained in a small beaker or conical flask, keeping the latter partly immersed in ice-water to prevent the mixture from boiling as the potash dissolves, and finally to ensure that the complete solution is thoroughly cooled. Pour the cold solution into a stout-walled bottle of about 250 c.c. capacity, and add 30 c.c. (31·5 gms.) of benzaldehyde; *cork* the bottle securely (a glass stopper must not be used because the alkaline solution on standing would cement it firmly in position) and then shake the mixture vigorously until it has been converted into a thick emulsion, which may finally coagulate into a heavy dough-like mass. Allow the product to stand for at least 4 hours (preferably overnight), and then add sufficient water (about 100 c.c.) to dissolve all the solid matter present. Pour the liquid into a separating-funnel, rinse out the bottle with about 20 c.c. of ether, and then add this ether to the solution in the funnel. Shake the solution in order to extract the benzyl alcohol with the ether, separate the lower aqueous solution, and then repeat the extraction twice more, using about 20 c.c. of ether on each occasion. If the original reaction product has been allowed to stand overnight, the ethereal solution of the benzyl alcohol will be free from unchanged benzaldehyde: if it has been allowed to stand for only about 4 hours, shake the united ether extracts with a moderately concentrated solution of sodium bi-

---

* The cost of this preparation (particularly for large classes) can be appreciably reduced by using a solution of 20 gms. of sodium hydroxide in 25 c.c. of water, in place of the potassium hydroxide solution. In this case, however, the product on standing overnight forms a very hard mass, which should be dissolved in *warm* water. The yields of alcohol and acid are unchanged.

sulphite to remove traces of benzaldehyde, and then shake the ethereal solution in turn with dilute sodium hydroxide solution (to ensure complete removal of the bisulphite) and lastly with a small quantity of water. Finally, in either case, dry the ethereal solution by shaking with powdered anhydrous potassium carbonate, and then distil off the ether from the filtered solution, using the usual apparatus for this purpose (p. 123): then replace the water-condenser by an air-condenser and distil the benzyl alcohol over a gauze, collecting the fraction of b.p. 200–207°. Benzyl alcohol is a colourless liquid of b.p. 205° and d, 1·04: it is almost odourless, and is only slightly soluble in water. Yield, 14 gms.

To obtain the benzoic acid, add an excess of concentrated hydrochloric acid carefully with stirring to the aqueous alkaline solution remaining from the original extraction. When no further precipitation of benzoic acid occurs, cool the solution (if perceptibly warm) in ice-water, and then filter at the pump. Wash the benzoic acid thoroughly with cold water, drain, and then recrystallise from a large volume of boiling water. Benzoic acid is obtained as colourless crystals, m.p. 121°: yield, 19–20 gms.

For reactions of benzyl alcohol, see p. 251, and of benzoic acid, p. 261.

Benzoin. $C_6H_5CH(OH)COC_6H_5$.

Many aromatic aldehydes (having the $-CHO$ group joined directly to the benzene ring) undergo polymerisation when heated with a solution of potassium cyanide in aqueous alcohol. Thus benzaldehyde gives benzoin, a compound of double function, since it contains both a secondary alcoholic and a ketonic

$$2C_6H_5CHO = C_6H_5CH(OH)COC_6H_5$$

grouping. The reaction is probably due to the potassium cyanide undergoing partial hydrolysis, generating hydrogen cyanide, which then adds on to the benzaldehyde giving benzaldehyde cyanhydrin: the latter then reacts with

$$C_6H_5CH(OH)\overline{CN + H}COC_6H_5 = C_6H_5CH(OH)COC_6H_5 + HCN$$

unchanged benzaldehyde, giving benzoin and regenerating the hydrogen cyanide.

Required: Potassium cyanide, 5 gms.; alcohol, 50 c.c.; benzaldehyde, 25 c.c.

Add 5 gms. of powdered potassium cyanide* to a mixture of 20 c.c. of water and 50 c.c. of alcohol contained in a 200 c.c. conical flask, and then add 25 c.c. (26 gms.) of freshly distilled benzaldehyde. Fit the flask with a reflux water-condenser, and boil the mixture gently on a water-bath for 30 minutes, a clear

* See footnote, p. 150.

solution being rapidly obtained. Then pour the solution into a beaker and cool; the benzoin separates as a crystalline mass. Filter at the pump, and wash well with water. (Yield, about 20 gms.) Recrystallise a portion from hot methylated spirit, reserving the remainder for the following preparation. Benzoin is a very pale yellow (almost colourless) crystalline substance, m.p. 137°.

Benzil. $C_6H_5CO \cdot COC_6H_5$.

The secondary alcohol group, $-CH(OH)-$, in benzoin is readily oxidised to a ketone group, and thus benzil, a diketone, is obtained.

$$C_6H_5CH(OH)COC_6H_5 + O = C_6H_5CO \cdot COC_6H_5 + H_2O$$

For this purpose, the usual oxidising agent is nitric acid, which in these circumstances (*i.e.*, in the absence of sulphuric acid) does not nitrate the benzene ring. Owing to the nitrous fumes formed by the reduction of the nitric acid, the experiment should be performed in a fume-cupboard.

Required: Benzoin, 10 gms.; nitric acid, 25 c.c.

Place 10 gms. of powdered benzoin and 25 c.c. of concentrated nitric acid in a 150 c.c. flask fitted with a reflux water-condenser, and heat the flask on a boiling water-bath. A flask having a ground-glass neck fitting directly to the condenser is best for this purpose. If this is not available, fit the flask to the condenser by means of a cork (*not* a rubber stopper) and clamp both flask and condenser securely in position during the heating on the water-bath: the nitrous fumes rot the cork during the heating, and if only one clamp is used, the flask may possibly slip away from the condenser, or alternatively the latter may fall sideways under its own weight. Continue the heating for $1\frac{1}{2}$ hours, when the crystalline benzoin will have been completely replaced by the oily benzil. Then pour the mixture into a beaker of cold water, when on vigorous stirring the oil will crystallise into a yellow solid. Filter off the latter at the pump, and wash *thoroughly* with water to ensure complete elimination of acid. Recrystallise from methylated spirit. Benzil separates as clear yellow crystals, m.p. 95°: yield, 9 gms.

Benzil Osazone. $C_6H_5C(:N \cdot NHC_6H_5)C(:N \cdot NHC_6H_5)C_6H_5$.

The ready oxidation of the secondary alcohol group in benzoin to a ketone group is also shown by the action of phenylhydrazine, which when present in excess first gives benzoin phenylhydrazone, $C_6H_5CH(OH)C(:NNHC_6H_5)C_6H_5$, then oxidises the latter to the ketone, $C_6H_5COC(:NNHC_6H_5)C_6H_5$, and finally gives the diphenylhydrazone, *i.e.*, the osazone of benzil, the complete action being similar to the formation of glucosazone (p. 108). Benzil osazone can therefore be prepared either (a) from benzoin or (b) directly from benzil, and its constitution thus placed beyond doubt.

Required: Benzoin, 2 gms.; acetic acid, 30 c.c.; phenylhydrazine, 4 c.c.

(a) Dissolve 2 gms. of powdered benzoin in 30 c.c. of hot glacial acetic acid contained in a boiling-tube, and add 4 c.c. of phenylhydrazine. Heat the tube in a boiling water-bath for 20 minutes. The osazone crystallises out either during the heating or when the tube is removed from the bath and the contents stirred. Cool the tube thoroughly in water, filter off the yellow crystals at the pump through a small Buchner funnel, drain, and then wash thoroughly first with glacial acetic acid and then with alcohol, in order to remove all traces of the original mother-liquor. The benzil osazone is thus obtained as fine yellow crystals, which when dry are pure. M.p. 225°. Yield, 2 gms. The osazone can be recrystallised from acetic acid, or (better) from benzene, although the benzene solution may require seeding or scratching before crystallisation starts.

(b) Repeat the preparation, using 2 gms. of benzil instead of 2 gms. of benzoin. The benzil osazone crystallises out readily in yellow needles, usually after about 5 minutes' heating. Continue heating for 20 minutes, and then isolate as before. Yield, 3·3 gms. Carry out a mixed melting-point determination to show that the two products are identical.

Benzilic Acid. $(C_6H_5)_2C(OH)\cdot COOH.$

When benzil is heated with potassium hydroxide solution, it undergoes a "molecular rearrangement" with the formation of the potassium salt of benzilic acid, or diphenyl-glycollic acid:

$$C_6H_5\cdot CO\cdot CO\cdot C_6H_5 + KOH \longrightarrow (C_6H_5)_2C(OH)\cdot COOK$$

This reaction applies to many 1:2-diketones, and is termed the *Benzilic Acid Rearrangement*. It provides a ready method for the preparation of disubstituted α-hydroxy-carboxylic acids. When applied to a cyclic 1:2-diketone, the ring system is necessarily reduced by one carbon atom: for example, *cyclo*hexa-1:2-

dione gives the potassium salt of 1-hydroxy-*cyclo*pentane-carboxylic acid.

Required: Benzil, 5 gms.; potassium hydroxide, 5 gms.

Dissolve 5 gms. of benzil in 15 c.c. of boiling ethyl alcohol in a conical flask fitted with a reflux water-condenser. Then add a solution of 5 gms. of potassium hydroxide in 10 c.c. of water, and heat the mixture (which rapidly develops a purple colour) on a boiling water-bath for about 15 minutes. Cool and stir the solution, from which the potassium benzilate separates in fine crystals. Filter the product at the pump, using an alkali-resisting filter-paper, or a sintered glass filter-funnel. Wash the crystals on the filter with a small quantity of alcohol to remove the purple colour, and then drain thoroughly.

To obtain the free acid, dissolve the potassium salt in 50 c.c. of cold water, filter the solution if a small undissolved residue remains, and then boil the clear solution *gently* whilst dilute sulphuric acid is added until the separation of the acid is complete. Cool the solution and filter off the pale orange-coloured crystals of the benzilic acid: wash the crystals on the filter with some hot distilled water, drain well, and then dry in a desiccator. Yield of crude acid, 4 gms. Recrystallise from benzene (about 50 c.c.) to which a small quantity of animal charcoal has been added: filter the boiling solution through a preheated funnel, as the benzilic acid readily crystallises as the solution cools.

The benzilic acid is obtained as colourless crystals, m.p. 150°.

Cinnamic Acid. $C_6H_5CH:CHCOOH$. (Perkin's Reaction.)

Cinnamic acid is usually prepared by Perkin's reaction, benzaldehyde being heated with sodium acetate in the presence of acetic anhydride. It is probable that the benzaldehyde and the acetic anhydride combine under the catalytic action of the sodium acetate, and the product then readily loses water to give mono-benzylidene acetic anhydride (A). The latter, when subsequently

$$C_6H_5CH|O + H|CH_2CO \cdot O \cdot OCCH_3 = C_6H_5CH(OH)CH_2CO \cdot O \cdot OCCH_3$$

$$C_6H_5CH(OH)CH_2CO \cdot O \cdot OCCH_3 = H_2O + C_6H_5CH:CHCO \cdot O \cdot OCCH_3 \text{ (A)}$$

heated with sodium carbonate solution, undergoes hydrolysis to sodium cinnamate and acetate.

$$C_6H_5CH:CHCO \cdot O \cdot OCCH_3 + Na_2CO_3 = C_6H_5CH:CHCOONa$$
$$+ CH_3COONa + CO_2$$

Although the *cis-trans* isomerism about the double bond is possible in cinnamic acid, Perkin's reaction gives rise only to the stable *trans* form, of m.p. 133°, the *cis* form (known as *allo*-cinnamic acid) being unstable and easily converted to the *trans* form. In substituted ethylene compounds, it is frequently found that if the two groups joined to either of the double-linked carbon atoms differ considerably in nature or in mass (*e.g.*, in cinnamic acid, the phenyl group and hydrogen atom on one carbon, or the hydrogen atom and the – COOH group on the other carbon), then one isomeride is formed to the almost complete exclusion of the other.

Required: Benzaldehyde, 20 c.c.; acetic anhydride, 30 c.c.; anhydrous sodium acetate, 10 gms.

Place 20 c.c. (21 gms.) of benzaldehyde (freshly distilled to ensure absence of benzoic acid), 30 c.c. of acetic anhydride, and 10 gms. of finely powdered anhydrous sodium acetate in a 100 c.c. round-bottomed flask fitted with an air-condenser closed at the top by means of a calcium chloride tube. Now heat the flask in an oil-bath at 180° for 8 hours: the mixture boils vigorously under reflux and white particles separate in the liquid. Pour the mixture whilst still hot into 100 c.c. of water contained in a round-bottomed flask (of about 1 litre capacity) which has previously been fitted for steam-distillation. Now add with vigorous shaking a saturated aqueous solution of sodium carbonate until a drop of the liquid withdrawn on a rod turns red litmus-paper a distinct blue. (Sodium hydroxide must not be used for this purpose, as it may generate benzoic acid by the Cannizzaro reaction from any unchanged benzaldehyde.) Now steam-distil the solution until unchanged benzaldehyde has been removed and the distillate is no longer turbid. Cool the residual solution until the small quantity of insoluble oily impurity has formed a semi-solid sticky mass, and then filter at the pump. Acidify the clear filtrate by adding concentrated hydrochloric acid *cautiously* with vigorous stirring until the evolution of carbon dioxide ceases and the precipitation of cinnamic acid is complete. Cool if necessary in ice-water, and then filter off the cinnamic acid, wash thoroughly with water, and drain. Recrystallise from a mixture of 3 volumes of water and 1 volume of methylated spirit: yield, 18 gms. Cinnamic acid is thus obtained as colourless crystals, m.p. 133°: it has a faint and pleasant odour and is almost insoluble in cold water.

If in the above preparation 8 hours' continuous heating is impracticable, the heating may be stopped after about 4 hours, the mixture allowed to stand (*e.g.*, overnight) and the heating then continued to make up the total period: in these circumstances the yield usually drops to about 15 gms.

For reactions of cinnamic acid, see p. 267.

Ethyl Cinnamate. $C_6H_5CH:CHCOOC_2H_5$. *Required:* Cinnamic acid, 20 gms.; rectified spirit, 20 c.c.

Cinnamic acid can be readily esterified by the Fischer-Speier method without any risk of the addition of hydrogen chloride at the double bond. Proceed precisely as for the preparation of ethyl benzoate (p. 76), using 20 gms. of cinnamic acid and 20 c.c. of rectified spirit. When the crude product is poured into water, a sharp separation of the ester is not readily obtained, and hence the addition of about 10 c.c. of carbon tetrachloride is particularly desirable. Finally distil off the carbon tetrachloride *slowly* from the dried product and then collect the ester as the fraction boiling at 269–272°. Yield, 17 gms.

Ethyl cinnamate is a colourless liquid of b.p. 271° and *d*, 1·05; it possesses a pleasant and characteristic odour.

Benzoic Acid, C_6H_5COOH, from Benzyl Chloride, $C_6H_5CH_2Cl$.

When an aromatic compound having an aliphatic side chain is subjected to oxidation, fission of the side chain occurs between the first and second carbon atoms from the benzene ring, the first carbon atom thus becoming part of a carboxyl (– COOH) group. For example:

$$C_6H_5CH_3 \longrightarrow C_6H_5COOH \qquad C_6H_5CH_2CH_3 \longrightarrow C_6H_5COOH$$
$$C_6H_5COCH_3 \longrightarrow C_6H_5COOH \qquad C_6H_5CH{:}COOH \longrightarrow C_6H_5COOH$$

Such oxidations are frequently important for determining the position of a side chain relative to other substituents in the benzene ring. The oxidation is usually carried out with a mixture of potassium permanganate and sodium carbonate in aqueous solution, or alternatively with dilute nitric acid (1:1 by volume). These oxidations are, however, often very slow, particularly if the side chain is a simple alkyl group: to overcome this difficulty, the alkyl group is frequently chlorinated in order to increase its susceptibility to oxidation. Thus the side chain in toluene, $C_6H_5CH_3$, is only very slowly oxidised by either of the above reagents, whereas that in benzyl chloride is rapidly oxidised: this rapid oxidation is due to the fact that with an aqueous oxidising agent, the benzyl chloride is first hydrolysed to benzyl alcohol, which then undergoes the normal oxidation of a primary alcohol to the corresponding carboxylic acid.

In the following preparation, the oxidation of benzyl chloride instead of toluene is therefore given in order to reduce the time required. It should be borne in mind, however, that the procedure is otherwise independent of the nature of the side chain.

Required: Anhydrous sodium carbonate, 5 gms.; potassium permanganate, 10 gms.; benzyl chloride, 5 c.c.; sodium sulphite, *ca.* 20 gms.

To 200 c.c. of water contained in a 500 c.c. bolt-head flask add in turn 5 gms. of anhydrous sodium carbonate, 10 gms. of potassium permanganate, and finally 5 c.c. (5·5 gms.) of benzyl chloride. Fit the flask with a reflux water-condenser, and boil the mixture gently for 1–1½ hours, *i.e.*, until the reaction is complete and the liquid running down from the condenser contains no oily drops of unchanged benzyl chloride. During this boiling, the permanganate is slowly reduced, and manganese dioxide separates as a dark brown precipitate. Now cool the flask, and add concentrated hydrochloric acid (about 50 c.c.) cautiously until the mixture is strongly acid, and all the benzoic acid has been precipitated. Then add a 20% aqueous solution of crystalline sodium sulphite (about 100 c.c.) slowly with shaking until the manganese dioxide is completely dissolved* and only the white precipitate of benzoic acid remains. When the mixture is quite cold, filter off the benzoic acid at the pump, and wash well with water. Recrystallise from boiling water. The benzoic acid is obtained as colourless needles, m.p. 121°: yield, about 4·5 gms.

Benzoyl Chloride. C_6H_5COCl.

One of the general methods for the preparation of acid chlorides is the action of phosphorus pentachloride on the corresponding carboxylic acid:

$$RCOOH + PCl_5 = RCOCl + POCl_3 + HCl$$

One disadvantage of this method is that it is sometimes difficult to separate the acid chloride sharply from the phosphorus oxychloride by fractional distillation, and unless the boiling-points of these two substances are fairly wide apart, traces of the oxychloride will occasionally pass over in the vapour of the acid chloride. If, however, thionyl chloride is used instead of phosphorus

$$RCOOH + SOCl_2 = RCOCl + SO_2 + HCl$$

pentachloride, this difficulty does not arise, as the acid chloride is now the only liquid product of this reaction.

Required: Benzoic acid, 20 gms.; thionyl chloride, 15 c.c.

For this preparation, which must be performed in the fume-cupboard, assemble the apparatus shown in Fig. 51(A). **C** is a 150 c.c. distilling-flask, to the neck of which is fitted a reflux single-surface water-condenser **D**, closed at the top **E** by a calcium chloride tube. The side-arm of **C** carries a cork **F** which fits the end **E** of the condenser for subsequent distillation. The side-arm of **C** is meanwhile plugged by a small rubber cork, or by a short length of glass rod.

Place 20 gms. of dry powdered benzoic acid in **C**, add 15 c.c. (25 gms., *i.e.*, a 30% excess) of thionyl chloride and some fragments of porcelain, and then clamp the apparatus on a boiling water-bath as shown so that no liquid can collect in the side-arm

---

* Sulphur dioxide reacts with manganese dioxide giving the soluble colour-less manganese dithionate: $MnO_2 + 2SO_2 = MnS_2O_6$. Some manganese sulphate is also formed: $MnS_2O_6 + MnO_2 = 2MnSO_4$. In the presence of hydrochloric acid, some of the dioxide is also reduced to the monoxide, which then dissolves to give manganous chloride, $MnCl_2$.

of **C**. Heat for one hour (with occasional gentle shaking), by which time the evolution of gas will be complete. Cool the flask **C**,

FIG. 51.

detach the condenser and fit it to the side-arm for distillation, using a 360° thermometer for the neck of **C**. To the lower end of the condenser fit a small conical flask **G** (Fig. 51(B)) by a cork carrying also a calcium chloride tube. In place of the conical flask **G**, a small Buchner flask may be used with the calcium chloride tube fitted to the side-arm, but in either case a duplicate flask for the second fraction should be available.

Now distil the contents of **C** by heating carefully over a gauze. A small initial fraction of unchanged thionyl chloride boiling at 78–80° comes over, and the temperature then rises rapidly to 194°. Directly this happens, stop the distillation, allow the condenser to drain thoroughly, and then replace **G** by the duplicate receiver. Run the water out of the condenser so that it acts as an air-condenser, and then continue the distillation. Collect the benzoyl chloride as the fraction boiling at 194–198°. Yield, 19 gms.

In the distilling-flask remains a very small high-boiling fraction of benzoic anhydride (b.p. 366°), formed by the dehydrating action of the thionyl chloride on the benzoic acid :

$$2C_6H_5COOH + SOCl_2 = (C_6H_5CO)_2O + SO_2 + 2HCl.$$

Benzoyl chloride is a colourless highly refractive liquid, having b.p. 198° and d, 1·21. It has a very irritating odour, and its vapour causes copious watering of the eyes. Benzoyl chloride has similar properties to acetyl chloride, but is much less reactive, *e.g.*, it is only slowly hydrolysed by cold water to benzoic acid and hydrochloric acid. It is largely used as a reagent for identifying alcohols and primary and secondary amines (see below).

For reactions of benzoyl chloride, see p. 274.

3:5-Dinitrobenzoyl Chloride. $(NO_2)_2C_6H_3COCl$.

This preparation illustrates the use of phosphorus pentachloride for the preparation of acyl chlorides: in this case no difficulty is experienced in separating the 3:5-dinitrobenzoyl chloride from the phosphorus oxychloride formed simultaneously (*cf.* p. 187), because the former is readily isolated as a crystalline solid. This acyl chloride is used extensively for the preparation of crystalline derivatives of alcohols, phenols, amines and amino-acids (*cf*, pp. 251, 255, 289).

Required: 3:5-Dinitrobenzoic acid, 15 gms.; phosphorus pentachloride, 17 gms.

Assemble in a fume-cupboard the apparatus shown in Fig. 51(A). Place 15 gms. of 3:5-dinitrobenzoic acid and 17 gms. of phosphorus pentachloride in the flask **C**, and heat the mixture in an oil-bath for $1\frac{1}{4}$ hours. Then reverse the condenser as shown in Fig. 51(B), but replace the calcium chloride tube by a tube leading to a water-pump, the neck of the reaction-flask **C** being closed with a rubber stopper. Now distil off the phosphorus oxychloride under reduced pressure by heating the flask **C** in an oil-bath initially at 25–30°, increasing this temperature ultimately to 110°. Then cool the flask, when the crude 3:5-dinitrobenzoyl chloride will solidify to a brown crystalline mass. Yield, 16 gms., *i.e.*, almost theoretical. Recrystallise from carbon tetrachloride. The chloride is obtained as colourless crystals, m.p. 66–68°. Yield, 13 gms. Further recrystallisation of small quantities can be performed using petrol (b.p. 40–60°). The chloride is stable almost indefinitely if kept in a calcium chloride desiccator.

The Schotten-Baumann Reaction. I. Benzoylation.

Acetylation (*i.e.*, the introduction of the acetyl group, CH_3CO –) as a means of characterising and identifying hydroxy-compounds and primary and secondary amines has already been described (p. 79). It is, however, frequently preferable to introduce an aromatic acyl group (such as the *benzoyl* group, C_6H_5CO –) for this purpose rather than the acetyl group. Benzoylation has two important advantages over acetylation: (*a*) acetyl chloride and acetic anhydride are so readily hydrolysed that acetylation has usually to be performed in absence of water; benzoyl chloride, C_6H_5COCl, is so slowly hydrolysed by water that benzoylation can be carried out freely in an aqueous medium; (*b*) benzoyl derivatives usually have higher melting-points than the corresponding acetyl compounds, and are usually much less soluble in most solvents: they can therefore be more readily crystallised. Moreover, benzoyl compounds are all insoluble in water and can thus be readily isolated from the crude reaction product, whereas acetyl compounds (particularly of the aliphatic amines) are frequently soluble in water and therefore difficult to isolate.

In the *Schotten-Baumann* method of benzoylation, the hydroxyl- or amino-compound (or a salt of the latter) is dissolved or suspended in an excess of 10% aqueous sodium hydroxide solution, a small excess (about 10% more than the theoretical amount) of benzoyl chloride is then added and the mixture vigorously shaken. Benzoylation proceeds smoothly under these conditions, and the solid benzoyl compound, being insoluble in water, separates out. The sodium hydroxide then hydrolyses the excess of benzoyl chloride, giving sodium

$$C_6H_5COCl + 2NaOH = NaCl + C_6H_5COONa + H_2O$$

chloride and benzoate, which remain in solution.

Thus phenol when subjected to the Schotten-Baumann reaction first dissolves in the sodium hydroxide to give sodium phenoxide, which then undergoes

$$C_6H_5CO|Cl + Na|OC_6H_5 = C_6H_5COOC_6H_5 + NaCl$$

benzoylation to give phenyl benzoate. An aqueous suspension of aniline similarly gives benzoyl-aniline, or phenyl-benzamide (frequently called benz-

$$C_6H_5NH|H + Cl|COC_6H_5 = C_6H_5NHCOC_6H_5 + HCl$$

anilide); whilst monomethylaniline gives benzoyl-monomethylaniline or phenyl-

$$C_6H_5N(CH_3)|H + Cl|COC_6H_3 = C_6H_5N(CH_3)COC_6H_5 + HCl$$

methyl-benzamide. Tertiary amines clearly cannot react in this way.

When these benzoyl compounds separate in the course of the Schotten-Baumann reaction, they frequently occlude traces of unchanged benzoyl chloride, which thus escapes hydrolysis by the alkali: it is advantageous therefore to recrystallise the benzoyl compounds whenever possible from alcohol or methylated spirit, since these solvents will esterify the unchanged chloride and so remove the latter from the recrystallised material.

Occasionally benzoyl chloride gives a product which does not crystallise well: in such cases the difficulty may frequently be overcome by using *p*-nitrobenzoyl chloride, $NO_2C_6H_4COCl$, or 3:5-dinitrobenzoyl chloride, $(NO_2)_2C_6H_3COCl$ (p. 189), which usually give highly crystalline derivatives.

Phenyl Benzoate. $C_6H_5COOC_6H_5$.

Required: Phenol, 5 gms.; benzoyl chloride, 9 c.c.

Dissolve 5 gms. of phenol in 70 c.c. of 10% sodium hydroxide solution contained in a strong wide-mouthed bottle of about 200 c.c. capacity. Then add 9 c.c. (11 gms.) of benzoyl chloride, cork the bottle securely and shake the mixture vigorously for 15 minutes. At the end of this time the reaction should be complete, and a solid product obtained, although a faint smell of unchanged benzoyl chloride may possibly still persist, owing to slight occlusion by the solid product, absorption by the cork, *etc.* Filter off the solid ester at the pump, breaking up any lumps on the filter with a spatula, and then wash thoroughly with water and drain. Recrystallise the crude ester from methylated spirit: for this purpose use a quantity of the hot solvent approximately twice the minimum required for complete solution, in order to ensure that the phenyl benzoate does not separate until the temperature of the solution has fallen below the melting-point of the ester: filter the hot solution if necessary through a funnel preheated by the filtration of some boiling solvent. Phenyl benzoate is thus obtained as colourless crystals, m.p. 69°: yield, 8 gms.

Hydrolysis of Phenyl Benzoate. The hydrolysis of phenyl benzoate (and of phenol esters generally) is of particular interest, because both products of hydrolysis are acidic in type: if the hydrolysis is carried out with sodium

$$C_6H_5COOC_6H_5 + H_2O = C_6H_5COOH + C_6H_5OH$$

hydroxide, both compounds remain in solution as their sodium derivatives. They may, however, be separated by acidifying the solution (in order to liberate both acid and phenol) and then adding an excess of sodium carbonate. The benzoic acid readily displaces carbonic acid giving sodium benzoate, whereas the phenol is too weakly acidic to give a similar reaction and so remains free in solution (*cf*. p. 262).

Boil a mixture of 2 gms. of phenyl benzoate and 25 c.c. of 10% aqueous sodium hydroxide* in a 100 c.c. conical flask under reflux until the molten ester has completely disappeared (about 1 hour). During the boiling, a small quantity of unchanged ester may have volatilised in the steam and crystallised again in the condenser: therefore pour about 5 c.c. of 10% sodium hydroxide solution down the condenser to dislodge this ester, and continue the boiling for a further 10 minutes until the solution is clear. Cool the solution in ice-water, and then add dilute sulphuric acid with stirring until a faint but *permanent* precipitate of benzoic acid is produced (test with litmus-paper to ensure that solution is acidic). Now add dilute sodium carbonate solution with *vigorous* stirring until the precipitate is just redissolved and the solution is definitely alkaline to litmus-paper. Extract the solution twice with ether, dry the united ethereal extracts with potassium carbonate, and after filtering, distil off the greater part of the ether. Pour the remainder whilst hot into an evaporating-basin; the phenol will crystallise when the residual ether has evaporated. Confirm the identity of the phenol by the tests given on p. 254. Meanwhile, add hydrochloric acid to the aqueous solution from the ether extraction: the sodium carbonate is first neutralised and the benzoic acid then precipitated. Filter off the benzoic acid at the pump, wash with water, and then recrystallise from boiling water. Benzoic acid is obtained as colourless crystals, m.p. 121°.

Benzanilide (Benzoyl-aniline). $C_6H_5NHCOC_6H_5$.

Required: Aniline, 5 c.c.; benzoyl chloride, 7 c.c.

Add 5 c.c. (5·2 gms.) of aniline to 75 c.c. of 10% aqueous sodium hydroxide solution contained in a wide-necked bottle as

---

* If about 10 c.c. of alcohol are added to the mixture, the time required for complete hydrolysis is reduced to about 20 minutes, and any volatilised ester which tends to collect in the condenser is redissolved and returned to the flask. When hydrolysing an unknown ester (p. 268) for identification purposes, however, it is often best to omit the alcohol to avoid confusion.

before, and then add 7 c.c. (8·5 gms.) of benzoyl chloride, and shake vigorously for 15–20 minutes. The mixture becomes warm, and the crude benzoyl derivative separates as a white powder, or, if the shaking has not been sufficiently vigorous, as small pellets: when the reaction is complete, filter off the product at the pump, break up any pellets with a spatula on the filter, and then thoroughly wash with water and drain. Recrystallise the benzanilide from hot methylated spirit: for this purpose use rather more of the hot solvent than the minimum required for complete solution, and filter the latter through a funnel preheated by the filtration of some of the boiling solvent, as the benzanilide may crystallise rapidly as the solution cools: it is only slightly soluble in cold methylated spirit. Benzanilide is thus obtained as colourless crystals, m.p. 163°: yield, 9 gms.

For reactions of benzanilide, see p. 287.

Hydrolysis of Benzanilide. For this hydrolysis, it is necessary to use 70% sulphuric acid (see Hydrolysis of Acetanilide, p. 80). Add 4 gms. of benzanilide to 40 c.c. of 70% sulphuric acid, and boil the mixture gently in a small flask under a reflux water-condenser for 30 minutes. Hydrolysis will now be complete, but much of the benzoic acid will have vaporised in the steam and then solidified in the conden-

$$C_6H_5NHCOC_6H_5 + H_2O + H_2SO_4 = C_6H_5NH_2,H_2SO_4 + C_6H_5COOH$$

ser. Therefore remove the flask, run the water out the condenser jacket, and then pour about 50 c.c. of hot water down the inner tube, which is held vertically over a beaker. The benzoic acid is thus dislodged and largely dissolved. Then add the hot solution from the flask, and cool in ice-water. Benzoic acid rapidly crystallises, but at this dilution the aniline sulphate, although sparingly soluble, does not separate. Filter off the benzoic acid, wash with water, drain, and apply the tests given on p. 261. Note the m.p. (121°). With the filtrate, perform the tests for aniline (p. 282).

Benzyl *p*-Nitrobenzoate. $NO_2C_6H_4COOCH_2C_6H_5$.

A crystalline derivative of benzyl alcohol cannot be obtained by using benzoyl chloride, because the benzyl benzoate, $C_6H_5COOCH_2C_6H_5$, so obtained has m.p. 18°, and is thus usually liquid: the present preparation illustrates therefore the use of a substituted benzoyl chloride (*p*-nitrobenzoyl chloride, m.p. 75°) in order to obtain a crystalline derivative of suitably high m.p.

Required: Benzyl alcohol, 2 c.c.; *p*-nitrobenzoyl chloride, 3·8 gms.
Place 2 c.c. of benzyl alcohol in a boiling-tube and add 12 c.c. of 10% sodium hydroxide solution: add also 12 c.c. of water to moderate the subsequent reaction, otherwise the rise in temperature may cause hydrolysis of some of the ester produced. Now add 3·8 gms. of finely powdered *p*-nitrobenzoyl chloride, and shake the well-corked tube

vigorously. The mixture becomes warm, and the solid ester rapidly separates, the reaction being complete after about 5 minutes' shaking. Filter the ester at the pump, wash with dilute sodium hydroxide solution, then thoroughly with water, and drain. Recrystallise from methylated spirit, allowing the hot solution to cool slowly at first: finally cool in ice-water. The benzyl *p*-nitrobenzoate separates in colourless crystals, m.p. 84°. Yield, 3·5 gms.

Methyl 3 : 5-Dinitrobenzoate. $(NO_2)_2C_6H_3COOCH_3$

The reaction between 3:5-dinitrobenzoyl chloride and compounds containing the OH, NH_2, or NH groups is very rapid, and therefore is particularly suitable for identification purposes (*cf.* p. 189). It is usual to have sodium hydroxide present during the reaction with phenols, amines and amino-acids, but this is not necessary with alcohols if they are dry.

Required: 3:5-Dinitrobenzoyl chloride, 2 gms.; methyl alcohol, 5 c.c.

Place 2 gms. of powdered 3:5-dinitrobenzoyl chloride in a small conical flask, add 5 c.c. of dry methyl alcohol, and warm on a water-bath until the solid has dissolved. Cool and filter off the 3:5-dinitrobenzoate which has separated. Recrystallise from ethyl alcohol* or petrol (b.p. 60–80°). The ester separates in colourless crystals, m.p. 108°. Yield, 1·3 gms.

The Schotten-Baumann Reaction. II. Sulphonylation.

The Schotten-Baumann reaction may also be carried out, using, for example, benzene sulphonyl chloride, $C_6H_5SO_2Cl$ (*i.e.*, the acid chloride of benzene sulphonic acid, $C_6H_5SO_2OH$) in place of benzoyl chloride, and similar derivatives are obtained. Thus when phenol is dissolved in an excess of 10% sodium hydroxide solution, and then shaken with a small excess of benzene sulphonyl

$$C_6H_5SO_2|Cl + Na|OC_6H_5 = C_6H_5SO_2OC_6H_5 + NaCl$$

chloride, phenyl benzene sulphonate, a crystalline ester, is readily formed, and the excess of the sulphonyl chloride then undergoes hydrolysis by the alkali, giving the soluble sodium benzene sulphonate. A suspension of aniline in sodium hydroxide when similarly treated with benzene sulphonyl chloride gives benzene sulphonyl-aniline, whilst monomethylaniline gives benzene sulphonyl-methylaniline: alternatively, these two compounds may be regarded as being

$$C_6H_5NH|H + Cl|SO_2C_6H_5 = C_6H_5NHSO_2C_6H_5 + HCl$$

$$C_6H_5N(CH_3)|H + Cl|SO_2C_6H_5 = C_6H_5N(CH_3)SO_2C_6H_5 + HCl$$

mono-and di-substituted derivatives of benzene sulphonamide, $C_6H_5SO_2NH_2$ and thus termed benzene sulphon-phenyl-amide, and benzene sulphon-methyl-phenyl-amide respectively. Sulphonylation, like benzoylation, can there-

---

* Esters of one alcohol should not normally be recrystallised from another alcohol. In the above case, however, no interchange of alkyl groups occurs on rapid recrystallisation.

H

fore be used to obtain crystalline derivatives of hydroxyl compounds, and also of primary and secondary amines: tertiary amines cannot undergo sulphonylation. There is, however, one important difference between the benzoyl and the sulphonyl derivatives of amines. It has been shown that primary and secondary amines, when treated with benzoyl chloride, give mono- and di-substituted derivatives of benzamide, and when treated with benzene sulphonyl chloride, give similar derivatives of benzene sulphonamide. A carboxylic acid amide, such as benzamide, possesses only very weak amphoteric properties (p. 92), and is therefore practically neutral, and its derivatives are consequently insoluble in dilute aqueous solutions of alkalis or acids. A sulphonic acid amide, such as benzene sulphonamide, is devoid of basic properties, but has its acidic properties correspondingly increased, and therefore each of the hydrogen atoms in the $-NH_2$ group can in turn show marked acidic properties. It follows that sulphonamides and their mono-substitution derivatives are definitely acidic and will therefore dissolve freely in sodium hydroxide solution, although they are insoluble in acids: their di-substitution derivatives, having no acidic hydrogen atoms, are neutral and therefore insoluble in both alkalis and acids.

The acidic properties of sulphonamides and their mono-substitution derivatives are particularly well illustrated in the alkyl-substitution compounds, which by reason of these properties can be prepared by two distinct methods. Thus mono- and di-ethylamine, when subjected to the Schotten-Baumann reaction using benzene sulphonyl chloride, give benzene sulphon-ethylamide, and benzene sulphon-diethylamide respectively. These compounds can also

$$C_6H_5SO_2Cl + HNHC_2H_5 = C_6H_5SO_2NHC_2H_5 + HCl$$
$$C_6H_5SO_2Cl + HN(C_2H_5)_2 = C_6H_5SO_2N(C_2H_5)_2 + HCl$$

be prepared from benzene sulphonamide by direct substitution. If an alcoholic solution of the sulphonamide is treated with sodium ethoxide, the sulphon-sodio-amide is formed and may crystallise out: if this compound is then heated with ethyl bromide or iodide, the sulphon-ethylamide (A) is formed. The latter still retains an acidic hydrogen atom and therefore, when

$$C_6H_5SO_2NH_2 \xrightarrow{\text{NaOC}_2\text{H}_5} C_6H_5SO_2NHNa \xrightarrow{\text{C}_2\text{H}_5\text{I}} C_6H_5SO_2NHC_2H_5 \quad (A)$$

treated in alcoholic solution with sodium ethoxide, gives the sulphon-sodio-

$$C_6H_5SO_2NHC_2H_5 \xrightarrow{\text{NaOC}_2\text{H}_5} C_6H_5SO_2NNaC_2H_5 \xrightarrow{\text{C}_2\text{H}_5\text{I}} C_6H_5SO_2N(C_2H_5)_2 \quad (B)$$

ethylamide, which when heated in turn with ethyl iodide, gives the neutral sulphon-diethylamide (B).

Hinsberg has based a method of separating primary, secondary and tertiary amines upon the solubility of mono-substituted sulphonamides in sodium hydroxide solution. If, for example, a mixture of aniline, monomethylaniline and di-methylaniline is shaken with benzene sulphonyl chloride in the presence of an excess of sodium hydroxide solution, the aniline gives benzene sulphonyl-aniline, $C_6H_5NHSO_2C_6H_5$, which, being acidic, remains dissolved in the alkaline solution. The monomethylaniline gives benzene sulphonyl-methylaniline, $C_6H_5N(CH_3)SO_2C_6H_5$, which, being neutral, is insoluble and therefore separates out. The dimethylaniline is unaffected. When the sulphonylation is complete, the unchanged dimethylaniline can therefore be recovered by steam-distillation. The reaction product is then cooled and the insoluble sulphonyl-methylaniline filtered off. The filtrate is then acidified, and the sulphonyl-aniline thus precipitated. Hydrolysis of these two sulphonyl compounds then regenerates the secondary and primary amines respectively.

Although benzene sulphonyl chloride has for simplicity been used in the above discussion, toluene p-sulphonyl chloride, $CH_3C_6H_4SO_2Cl$, is more frequently used in the laboratory, owing to its much lower cost, the latter being due in turn to the fact that toluene p-sulphonyl chloride is a by-product in the commercial preparation of saccharin. Toluene p-sulphonyl chloride is a crystalline substance, of m.p. 68°: the finely powdered chloride will, however, usually react readily with amines in the Schotten-Baumann reaction; it does not react so readily with alcohols, but the reaction may be promoted considerably by first dissolving the chloride in some inert water-soluble solvent such as acetone.

Phenyl Toluene p-Sulphonate. $CH_3C_6H_4SO_2OC_6H_5$.

Required: Phenol, 4 gms.; 10% sodium hydroxide, 25 c.c.; toluene p-sulphonyl chloride, 9 gms.; acetone, 40 c.c.

Dissolve 4 gms. of phenol in 25 c.c. of 10% aqueous sodium hydroxide solution contained in a 150 c.c. conical flask, and then add a solution of 9 gms. of toluene p-sulphonyl chloride in 40 c.c. of cold acetone: cork the flask *securely* and shake it vigorously for 15–20 minutes. When the mixed solutions are first shaken, a fine emulsion forms and the mixture becomes warm: on continued shaking (which prevents the emulsion from separating into two well-defined layers) the fine oily drops crystallise as the temperature falls, and when the shaking is complete, a crop of small heavy crystals will have separated from the clear supernatant liquid. Now cool the flask in water, and then pour the contents into about 150 c.c. of water, finally washing out the flask to remove any crystals adhering to the sides. Filter the well-stirred aqueous mixture at the pump, wash the crystals thoroughly with water, and drain. Recrystallise the product from methylated spirit, of which about 120 c.c. will be required. Phenyl toluene p-sulphonate is thus obtained as colourless crystals, m.p. 95°: yield, 9–10 gms.

Separation of a Mixture of Aniline, Monomethylaniline, and Dimethylaniline. Hinsberg's Method.

The principle of this method has been explained above. The reaction is best carried out in a wide-necked 250 c.c. conical flask for which a cork having the usual two delivery-tubes for steam-distillation is available: when the sulphonylation is complete, the reaction product can then be steam-distilled without transference to another vessel.

Required: Aniline, 4 c.c.; monomethylaniline, 4 c.c.; dimethyl-aniline, 4 c.c.; toluene *p*-sulphonyl chloride, 16 gms.

Prepare a mixture containing 4 c.c. of each of the above three amines. Place the mixture in the conical flask, add 60 c.c. of 10% sodium hydroxide solution, and also 60 c.c. of water to moderate the subsequent reaction. Add 16 gms. of finely powdered toluene *p*-sulphonyl chloride, cork the flask securely and shake the contents vigorously for 20–30 minutes: the mixture becomes warm, and a fine emulsion of the unchanged dimethylaniline and the molten sulphonyl-methylaniline forms in the alkaline solution. Finally the temperature falls towards the end of the above period of shaking. Now replace the cork by the steam-distillation fitting, and steam-distil the reaction mixture until fine drops of dimethylaniline can no longer be detected in the distillate leaving the condenser. Then stop the distillation, and cool the reaction mixture by shaking the flask in a stream of cold water under the tap, in order to ensure that the sulphonyl-methylaniline solidifies in small particles and not in one large hard lump.

Extract the dimethylaniline by shaking the distillate in a separating-funnel with a few c.c. of ether, and then dry the ethereal solution over potassium carbonate: heat the filtered ethereal solution in an evaporating-basin on the water-bath until the ether has evaporated and pure dimethylaniline remains. Yield, almost theoretical.

Meanwhile, filter the original cold reaction product at the pump, and wash the sulphonyl-methylaniline on the filter first with 10% sodium hydroxide solution (to ensure complete removal of the sulphonyl-aniline) and then with water: drain thoroughly. Recrystallise from alcohol: toluene *p*-sulphonyl-methylaniline, $C_6H_5N(CH_3)SO_2C_6H_4CH_3$, is thus obtained as colourless crystals m.p. 95°: yield, 7·5 gms.

Finally, add an excess of concentrated hydrochloric acid slowly with stirring to the alkaline filtrate remaining from the original reaction product. As the solution becomes acid, the sulphonyl-aniline separates as a thick sticky syrup which, when stirred, rapidly crystallises. Cool the mixture in ice-water if necessary, and then filter off the solid product at the pump, wash well with water, and drain. Recrystallise from a mixture of 2 volumes of alcohol and 1 volume of water: to prevent the sulphonyl-aniline from separating as an emulsion, allow the hot solution to cool spontaneously (with occasional stirring) until crystallisation starts, and then cool in ice-water to complete the process. The toluene p-sulphonyl-aniline, $C_6H_5NHSO_2C_6H_4CH_3$, when filtered and drained is obtained as colourless crystals, m.p. $102°$: yield, 6 gms.

The aniline and the monomethylaniline can be obtained from their respective sulphonyl derivatives by hydrolysis with 70% sulphuric acid (preparation, p. 80), the mixture of the sulphonyl compound and the acid being gently boiled under reflux: to illustrate the *separation* of the three amines, however, this is not necessary.

The chief disadvantage of Hinsberg's method is that partial hydrolysis of the two sulphonyl amines by the sodium hydroxide may occur during the steam-distillation: if, however, only a small excess of the hydroxide is used in the sulphonylation, this hydrolysis becomes negligible, particularly as the sulphonyl amides are far less readily hydrolysed by alkalis than by acids. This point does not arise in the separation of a similar mixture of *aliphatic* amines, since all the lower members are soluble in water. Therefore if a mixture of mono-, di- and tri-ethylamine were treated as above with toluene p-sulphonyl chloride, the sulphonyl mono-ethylamine, $C_2H_5NHSO_2C_6H_4CH_3$, and the unchanged tri-ethylamine would remain dissolved in the sodium hydroxide solution, whilst the neutral sulphonyl diethylamine $(C_2H_5)_2NSO_2C_6H_4CH_3$, would separate, and could then be filtered off. Acidification of the filtrate would then precipitate the sulphonyl mono-ethylamine, whilst the tri-ethylamine remained in solution as a salt of the acid. After filtering off the sulphonyl mono-ethylamine, the filtrate could be made alkaline again, and the liberated tri-ethylamine steam-distilled off from the crude residual solution.

Toluene p-Sulphonamide. $CH_3C_6H_4SO_2NH_2$.

Toluene p-sulphonyl chloride reacts with aqueous ammonia to give the

$$CH_3C_6H_4SO_2|Cl + H|NH_2 = CH_3C_6H_4SO_2NH_2 + HCl$$

sulphonamide, but the reaction is slow. A more rapid reaction may be obtained by heating the sulphonyl chloride with ammonium carbonate, which dissociates readily into carbon dioxide and ammonia, and converts the chloride almost quantitatively into the amide.

Required : Toluene p-sulphonyl chloride, 5 gms.; ammonium carbonate, 10 gms.

Thoroughly mix 5 gms. of toluene p-sulphonyl chloride and 10 gms. of ammonium carbonate by grinding together in a mortar until a fine uniform powder is obtained. Then heat the mixture in an evaporating-basin on a boiling water-bath for 15–20 minutes, stirring the mixture *continuously* with a glass rod meanwhile. Conversion of the chloride to the amide is now complete and only a small quantity of unchanged ammonium carbonate remains. Recrystallise the powder from about 120 c.c. of boiling water. Toluene p-sulphonamide is thus obtained in colourless crystals, m.p. 137°. Yield 4·2–4·4 gms.

Toluene p-sulphonamide is almost insoluble in cold water, but dissolves readily in sodium hydroxide solution (as the sodium derivative) and is immediately reprecipitated on the addition of strong acids. To show the formation of the sodium derivative, dissolve about 0·2 gm. of metallic sodium in about 10 c.c. of alcohol, cool the solution, and then add it to a solution of 1 gm. of the sulphonamide in 20 c.c. of cold alcohol. On shaking the mixture, fine white crystals of the sodium derivative, $CH_3C_6H_5SO_2NHNa$, rapidly separate, and may be obtained pure by filtering at the pump, and washing first with a few c.c. of alcohol, and then with ether.

Toluene p-Sulphon-sodio-chloro-amide ("Chloramine-T"), $CH_3C_6H_4SO_2NNaCl,3H_2O$, and Toluene p-Sulphon-dichloro-amide ("Dichloramine-T"), $CH_3C_6H_4SO_2NCl_2$.

When toluene p-sulphonamide is dissolved in an excess of sodium hypochlorite solution, toluene p-sulphon-sodio-chloro-amide is formed, and, being soluble in water, does not crystallise unless concentrated solutions are used:

$$CH_3C_6H_4SO_2NH_2 + NaClO = CH_3C_6H_4SO_2NNaCl + H_2O$$

This compound is similar in type to the sodium acet-bromoamide, $CH_3CONNaBr$, which is an intermediate compound in Hofmann's amine synthesis (p. 98). If a weak acid (such as acetic acid) is now added to the solution of the sodio-chloro-amide, the latter compound reacts with the hypochlorous acid giving the sulphon-dichloro-amide, which being insoluble in water, rapidly separates:

$$CH_3C_6H_4SO_2NNaCl + HOCl + CH_3COOH$$
$$= CH_3C_6H_4SO_2NCl_2 + CH_3COONa + H_2O$$

When the sulphon-dichloro-amide is gently boiled with sodium hydroxide solution, the reverse change occurs, and the sodio-chloro-amide crystallises out at suitable concentration:

$$CH_3C_6H_4SO_2NCl_2 + 2NaOH = CH_3C_6H_4SO_2NNaCl + NaOCl + H_2O$$

The sodio-chloro-amide can thus be made either directly from toluene p-sulphonamide or from the intermediate dichloro-amide. The sodio-chloro-amide and the dichloro-amide are known commercially as Chloromine-T and Dichloramine-T respectively.

DICHLORAMINE-T. Dilute 80 c.c. of *freshly prepared* 2N sodium hypochlorite solution (preparation, p. 426) with 80 c.c. of water, and then add with stirring 5 gms. of finely powdered toluene p-sulphonamide, a clear solution being rapidly obtained. Cool in ice-water, and then add about 50 c.c. of a mixture of equal volumes of glacial acetic acid and water *slowly* with stirring until precipitation is complete: the dichloro-amide separates at first as a fine emulsion, which rapidly forms brittle colourless crystals. Filter off the latter at the pump, wash well with water, drain thoroughly, and dry without delay either with drying-paper or (better) in a desiccator. Yield, 6·8–7·0 gms. (theoretical). The dichloramine-T is thus obtained in a high state of purity: it may, however, be crystallised with very little loss from 60–80° petrol, and obtained as needles, m.p. 83°.

CHLORAMINE-T. (*a*) *From Dichloramine-T.* For this purpose use dichloramine-T which has been prepared as above, and thoroughly drained but not necessarily dried. Heat 40 c.c. of 10% sodium hy-droxide solution in a beaker over a gauze until the solution is almost boiling, and then add the dichloramine-T in small quantities, stirring the mixture gently after each addition until a clear solution is obtained. When the addition is complete, cool the solution in ice-water, whereupon the chloramine-T will rapidly separate in colourless crystals. Filter at the pump, and drain thoroughly. Yield, 8 gms. (almost theoretical). The chloramine-T, which is now practically pure, may if desired be recrys-tallised from a small quantity of hot water: dry the final product with drying-paper or in a calcium chloride desiccator, as water of crystal-lisation is readily lost over sulphuric acid or in a vacuum. Chlor-amine-T has no definite m.p., for on heating it first loses water of crystallisation and then decomposes vigorously at 175–180°.

(*b*) *Direct from toluene p-sulphonamide.* Mix 45 c.c. of the freshly prepared 2N sodium hypochlorite solution and 40 c.c. of 10% sodium hydroxide solution in a 200 c.c. conical flask, and then add 5 gms. of finely powdered toluene *p*-sulphonamide. Shake the corked flask vigorously for 3–5 minutes, whereupon the sulphonamide will dissolve and be largely replaced by white crystalline chloramine-T. Now warm the mixture in the open flask until a clear solution is obtained (in order to ensure removal of any dichloramine-T) and then cool. The chlor-amine-T separates on slow cooling in needles, and on quick cooling in characteristic leaflets. Filter, drain, and dry. Yield 7·5 gms.

Both chloramine-T and dichloramine-T have marked antiseptic properties, chloramine-T being most frequently used because of its solubility in water. Aqueous solutions of chloramine-T can be used either for external application, or for internal application to the mouth, throat, *etc.*, as chloramine-T in moderate quantities is non-toxic: its aqueous solution can also be effectively used when the skin has come in contact with many of the vesicant liquid "poison-gases," as the latter are frequently organic sulphur or arsenic derivatives which combine with or are oxidised by chloramine-T and are thus rendered harmless.

Both chloramine-T and dichloramine-T can be readily estimated, because they liberate iodine from potassium iodide quantitatively in the presence of acetic acid. For this purpose, a solution of a known quantity of chloramine-T in water containing acetic acid, or dichloramine-T in acetic acid itself, is diluted with an excess of potassium iodide solution, and the iodine is then

$$CH_3C_6H_4SO_2NNaCl + 2KI + 2CH_3COOH$$
$$= CH_3C_6H_4SO_2NH_2 + NaCl + I_2 + 2CH_3COOK$$
$$CH_3C_6H_4SO_2NCl_2 + 4KI + 4CH_3COOH$$
$$= CH_3C_6H_4SO_2NH_2 + 2HCl + 2I_2 + 4CH_3COOK$$

estimated by direct titration with standard sodium thiosulphate solution.

Aromatic Ketones.

Aromatic ketones may be divided into two classes:

(1) The true ketones, in which the $>CO$ group is in the side chain, the most common examples being acetophenone or methyl phenyl ketone, $C_6H_5COCH_3$, and benzophenone or diphenyl ketone, $C_6H_5COC_6H_5$. These ketones are usually prepared by a modification of Friedel and Crafts' reaction, an aromatic hydrocarbon being treated with an acyl chloride (either aliphatic or aromatic) in the presence of aluminium chloride. Thus benzene reacts with acetyl chloride

$$C_6H_5\underline{H + Cl}COCH_3 = C_6H_5COCH_3 + HCl$$

readily in these circumstances to give acetophenone.

(2) The quinones, in which the carbon of the $>CO$ group is part of the ring; for this reason, the properties of the $>CO$ group are sufficiently modified to make the quinones quite distinct from the true ketones of class (1). Quinones may often be prepared by direct oxidation of the corresponding hydrocarbon: thus anthracene (A) on oxidation gives anthraquinone (B) whilst phenanthrene (C) gives phenanthraquinone (D), these quinones being

(A)   (B)   (C)   (D)

examples of *para* and *ortho* quinones respectively. The specific term quinone is usually applied to *p*-benzoquinone (F) which cannot easily be prepared by the direct oxidation of benzene on a laboratory scale. It can, however, be readily

(E)   (F)

prepared by the addition of a mild oxidising agent, such as ferric chloride, to an aqueous solution of hydroquinone (E), a reaction which is readily reversible by reducing agents such as sulphur dioxide: it is also technically prepared by the more complicated oxidation of compounds such as aniline.

The preparation of a member of each of the above classes of ketones is given below.

Acetophenone. $C_6H_5COCH_3$.

Required: Aluminium chloride, 30 gms.; benzene, 75 c.c.; acetyl chloride, 20 c.c.

30 Gms. of anhydrous *finely powdered* aluminium chloride* are placed in a 300 c.c. *dry* round-bottomed bolt-head flask, and 75 c.c. of dry benzene (free from toluene) are added. A reflux water-condenser is fitted to the flask, and a small dropping-funnel in turn is then fitted securely in the top of the condenser by means of a cork having a shallow V-shaped groove cut vertically in the side to give open access to the air. The contents of the flask are cooled in a basin of cold water (ice-water must not be used, in case the benzene crystallises): 20 c.c. (22 gms.) of acetyl chloride are then placed in the dropping-funnel, and allowed to run *slowly* down the condenser into the flask, the latter being shaken from time to time to ensure thorough mixing of the contents. When all the acetyl chloride has been added, the flask must be heated *in* a water-bath at 50° for 1 hour in order to complete the reaction, a vigorous evolution of hydrogen chloride occurring meanwhile. The heating should therefore be carried out in the fume-cupboard, the dropping-funnel being replaced by a calcium chloride tube, bent downwards as in Fig. 45, p. 76. Alternatively, the heating may be carried out in the open laboratory, in which case a delivery-tube should be securely fitted at one end to the top of the condenser, and at the other end to the stem of an inverted glass filter-funnel, the latter being placed in a beaker of water so that the rim dips *just* below the surface: the hydrogen chloride is thus absorbed without risk of the water "sucking back" through the tube into the reaction mixture.

When the heating is complete, the reaction mixture is cooled and then poured into 200 c.c. of water contained in a flask of about 750 c.c. capacity. The flask is then corked and vigorously shaken, cooling in water if necessary: aluminium chloride and hydrogen chloride are thus extracted by the water, whilst the acetophenone remains dissolved in the benzene. The mixture is then poured into a separating-funnel, and the lower aqueous layer run off: the benzene solution is shaken with a dilute aqueous

---

* Aluminium chloride is usually supplied by dealers either in stoppered bottles or in sealed glass flasks. Great care should be taken in opening the sealed flasks, as they frequently contain hydrogen chloride under considerable pressure. The flask or tube should first be chilled in ice-water or ice-salt, and then enveloped in a thick duster so that only the tip of the neck protrudes. A scratch is made across the neck with a sharp file and the scratch then touched with the hot end of a fine glass rod: the end of the neck may fly off with great violence and should therefore be pointing in a safe direction.

H*

sodium hydroxide solution to ensure complete removal of hydrogen chloride, and the benzene is again separated, and then dried over calcium chloride for about 15 minutes. The dry solution is filtered and the benzene removed by distillation. For this purpose, a 100 c.c. distilling-flask containing some fragments of unglazed porcelain is fitted with a dropping-funnel and a water-condenser: a portion of the benzene solution is run into the flask, which is then heated on a sand-bath, the remainder of the solution being added as the benzene distils over. (Alternatively, the flask may be heated *in* a boiling water-bath, since benzene will not readily distil from a flask heated on a water-bath.) When almost all the benzene has been removed, the dropping-funnel is replaced by a 360° thermometer, and the water-condenser by a short air-condenser similar to that used in the preparation of acetamide (p. 89). The distillation is then continued by careful heating over a gauze, and the acetophenone finally collected as the fraction of b.p. 195–202°. Yield, 20 gms. This fraction should be collected directly into a weighed specimen-tube, and should crystallise readily when the tube is cooled in ice-water. If it does not crystallise, it should be redistilled.

Acetophenone is a colourless compound, having m.p. 20° and b.p. 201°; except in cold weather it is therefore usually a liquid, of d, 1·03. It has only a faint odour. Acetophenone was at one time used medicinally under the name of *hypnone* as a soporific, but for this purpose it has now been largely superseded by other and more suitable drugs.

For reactions of acetophenone, see p. 260.

The student should note that ketones in class (1), *i.e.*, those having the $>CO$ group in the side chain, will form additive compounds with sodium bisulphite *only* if this $>CO$ group is not directly joined to the benzene ring: acetophenone therefore will not form such compounds, whereas benzyl methyl ketone, $C_6H_5CH_2COCH_3$, will do so. Many quinones, particularly *ortho* quinones such as phenanthraquinone, form additive compounds with sodium bisulphite.

Acetophenone Phenylhydrazone. $CH_3(C_6H_5)C:N·NHC_6H_5$.

Required: Acetophenone, 2 c.c.; phenylhydrazine, 2·5 c.c.; acetic acid, 5 c.c.

Dissolve 2 c.c. (2 gms.) of acetophenone in 10 c.c. of glacial acetic acid contained in a boiling-tube for which a well-fitting cork is available. Dissolve 2·5 c.c. of phenylhydrazine in a mixture of 5 c.c. of glacial acetic acid and 5 c.c. of water, and add this solution to that of the acetophenone, at once corking and vigorously shaking the boiling-tube. The mixture becomes warm, and the phenylhydrazone rapidly separates as fine colourless crystals. After 5 minutes' shaking, cool the tube in cold water, and then filter the contents at the pump: wash the crystals on the filter with *dilute* acetic acid and then with water. Recrystallise the phenylhydrazone from alcohol (*not* from methylated spirit, which causes decomposition) and dry thoroughly: m.p. 105°. Yield, 3·0–3·5 gms. The phenylhydrazone, after standing for a few days, develops a brown colour and ultimately decomposes.

Acetophenone similarly gives an oxime, $CH_3(C_6H_5)C:NOH$, of m.p. 59°: owing to its lower m.p. and its greater solubility in most liquids, it is not as suitable as the phenylhydrazone for characterising the ketone. Its chief use is for the preparation of α-phenyl-ethylamine, $CH_3(C_6H_5)CHNH_2$, which can be readily obtained by the reduction of the oxime, and which can then be resolved by *l*-malic acid into optically active forms. The optically active amine is frequently used in turn for the resolution of racemic acids.

Acetophenone-semicarbazone. $CH_3(C_6H_5)C:N \cdot NHCONH_2$.

Aldehydes and ketones may frequently be identified by their *semicarbazones*, obtained by direct condensation with semicarbazide (or amino-urea), $NH_2NHCONH_2$, a compound which is a monacidic base and usually available as its monohydrochloride, $NH_2CONHNH_2,HCl$. Semicarbazones are particularly useful for identification of compounds (such as acetophenone) of which the oxime is too soluble to be readily isolated and the phenylhydrazone is unstable: moreover, the high nitrogen content of semicarbazones enables very small quantities to be accurately analysed and so identified. The general conditions for the formation of semicarbazones are very similar to those for oximes and phenylhydrazones (pp. 66, 177): the free base must of course be liberated from its salts by the addition of sodium acetate.

Required: Semicarbazide hydrochloride, 2 gms.; anhydrous sodium acetate, 1·8 gms.; acetophenone, 2 c.c.

Add first 2·0 gms. of powdered semicarbazide hydrochloride and then 1·8 gms. of anhydrous sodium acetate (or 2·5 gms. of the crystalline acetate) to 10 c.c. of water, and warm gently until a clear solution is obtained. Then add a solution of 2 c.c. (2 gms.) of acetophenone in 10 c.c. of rectified spirit, and warm the mixed solutions gently on a water-bath for 15 minutes. The semicarbazone rapidly crystallises

$$CH_3(C_6H_5)C[O + H_2]N \cdot NHCONH_2 =$$
$$CH_3(C_6H_5)C:NNHCONH_2 + H_2O$$

whilst the solution is still being heated. Finally cool, filter off the acetophenone-semicarbazone, wash thoroughly with water, and drain. Yield, 2·9–3·0 gms. (theoretical). The semicarbazone when dry has m.p. 197–198° and is practically pure. It may be recrystallised from methylated spirit or alcohol, and obtained as colourless crystals, m.p. 201°.

Anthraquinone. $C_6H_4 \diagdown \begin{matrix} CO \\ CO \end{matrix} \diagup C_6H_4.$

Anthracene is oxidised by chromium trioxide, CrO_3, to anthraquinone. As the reaction is carried out in solution, a solvent is required which will dissolve both the anthracene and the chromium trioxide, and at the same time be unaffected by the vigorous oxidising action of the latter compound: acetic acid fulfils these conditions admirably.

Required: Anthracene, 10 gms.; acetic acid, 150 c.c.; chromium trioxide, 20 gms.

Assemble an apparatus precisely similar to that used for the previous preparation of acetophenone, *viz.*, a 500 c.c. bolt-head flask having a reflux water-condenser, into the top of which is fitted a 100 c.c. dropping-funnel by means of a cork having a V-shaped groove cut vertically in the side to allow escape of air. Place 10 gms. of finely powdered anthracene and 100 c.c. of glacial acetic acid in the flask, mix thoroughly by shaking and then heat the flask over a gauze so that the acetic acid boils gently under reflux, and the greater part of the anthracene goes into solution. Then dissolve 20 gms. of chromium trioxide in 15 c.c. of water, add 50 c.c. of glacial acetic acid, and pour the well-stirred mixture into the dropping-funnel. Now allow the chromium oxide solution to run drop by drop down the condenser at such a rate that the total addition takes about 40 minutes. As the oxidation proceeds, the anthracene dissolves up completely in the boiling acetic acid. When the addition of the chromium oxide solution is complete, continue the boiling for a further 20 minutes, and then allow the solution to cool somewhat before pouring it into a large excess (about 500 c.c.) of cold water. The crude anthraquinone separates as a greenish-grey powder. Stir the mixture vigorously in order to wash out as much acetic acid and chromium derivatives as possible from the anthraquinone, and then filter off the latter under *gentle* suction of the pump, wash it thoroughly on the filter with hot water, then with a hot *dilute* solution of sodium hydroxide, and finally with much cold water, before draining it well. Dry the anthraquinone as completely as possible by pressing it between several thick sheets of drying-paper. Yield, 10–11 gms. (almost theoretical).

Anthraquinone sublimes readily on being heated, and may easily be obtained in a high state of purity by this method. Assemble the apparatus shown in Fig. 10, p. 23. Place about half of the crude product in the small evaporating-basin, and first warm the latter gently over a gauze (using a *very* small flame) in order to dry the product completely: when the evolution of steam is no longer perceptible, place over the basin a filter-paper through which a number of small holes (about 2 mms. in diameter) have been pierced upwards. Then place in turn a cold dry filter-funnel (of slightly smaller diameter than the basin) over the filter-paper, and heat the basin rather more strongly than before, at the same time protecting the apparatus from draughts. After a few minutes, the vapour of the anthraquinone passes through the holes, and condenses on the upper surface of the filter-paper and on the walls of the funnel in beautiful long yellow needles: these are pure and have m.p. 273°. During the process of sublimation, adjust the rate of heating so that the anthraquinone is slowly yet steadily volatilised, but the funnel does not become more than slightly warm.

Recrystallise the remaining half of the crude anthraquinone from boiling acetic acid, using animal charcoal: filter the hot solution through a Buchner funnel which has been preheated by the filtration of some of the boiling solvent, as the anthraquinone crystallises rapidly as the solution cools. Cool the filtrate in cold water and then filter at the pump, drain, wash with methylated spirit and dry. Yield, 4–5 gms.

For reactions of anthraquinone, see pp. 280, 281.

Anthraquinone is of great technical importance, as many of its derivatives form valuable dyes: notable among these are the hydroxy-derivatives (alizarin, *etc.*), the amino-derivatives (indanthrene, *etc.*) and the sulphonic acids.

ω-Dimethylamino-propiophenone Hydrochloride.
$C_6H_5COCH_2CH_2N(CH_3)_2$. (The Mannich Reaction.)

The *Mannich Reaction* involves the condensation of formaldehyde with ammonia or a primary or secondary amine and with a third compound containing a reactive methylene group: these compounds are most frequently those in which the methylene group is activated by a neighbouring keto group. Thus when acetophenone is boiled in alcoholic solution with paraformaldehyde and dimethylamine hydrochloride, condensation occurs readily with the formation of

$$C_6H_5COCH_3 + H_2CO + (CH_3)_2NH,HCl = C_6H_5COCH_2CH_2N(CH_3)_2,HCl$$

ω-dimethylamino-propiophenone hydrochloride. The reaction therefore affords a ready synthesis of certain keto-amines.

It will be clear that the above reaction, if carried out with ammonia would give a primary amine, and if performed with a primary amine would give a secondary amine. Furthermore, if the above reaction were carried out with monomethyl-

(A) $C_6H_5COCH_2CH_2NH(CH_3)$. $(C_6H_5COCH_2CH_2)_2NCH_3$ (B)

amine hydrochloride, the initial product would be the hydrochloride of ω-methylamino-propiophenone (A), but this compound could react again to give the compound (B). In the reaction described below, such secondary reactions do not occur.

Required: Acetophenone, 5 gms.; paraformaldehyde, 1·25 gms.; dimethylamine hydrochloride, 3·5 gms.

NOTE. Dimethylamine hydrochloride is a deliquescent substance: the sample if damp should be dried in a vacuum desiccator and then rapidly weighed before use.

Add 5 c.c. (5 gms.) of acetophenone, 1·25 gms. of finely powdered paraformaldehyde, and 3·5 gms. of dry dimethylamine hydrochloride to 8 c.c. of absolute alcohol, and then boil the mixture under reflux for 1·5 hours. Filter the solution (which is now almost entirely clear) through a preheated filter-funnel, and cool the filtrate in ice-water with stirring. The ω-di-methylamino-propiophenone hydrochloride rapidly separates as white crystals; filter off the crystals at the pump and recrystallise from a small quantity of alcohol: m.p. 155–156°. Yield, 2·5 gms.

Ethyl Acetoacetate. $CH_3COCH_2COOC_2H_5$. (Claisen Condensation.)

Ethyl acetoacetate is a tautomeric substance which at room temperature exists as an equilibrium mixture of the *keto* and *enol* forms, the latter form being present to the extent of about 7%.

$$CH_3COCH_2COOC_2H_5 \rightleftharpoons CH_2C(OH):CHCOOC_2H_5$$
keto   *enol*

It is readily prepared by the action of metallic sodium on dry ethyl acetate. The reaction, which occurs only in the presence of a trace of alcohol, is complex, but may be considered (in effect) as a condensation of two molecules of ethyl acetate under the influence of sodium ethoxide, the sodium derivative of the *enol* form being thus obtained. Clearly, only a trace of alcohol is thus initially

$$CH_3CO|OEt + H|CH_2COOC_2H_5 + C_2H_5ONa =$$
$$CH_3C(ONa):CHCOOC_2H_5 + 2C_2H_5OH$$

required. Treatment of the crude sodium derivative with a weak acid, *e.g.*, dilute acetic acid, then gives the normal equilibrium mixture of the *keto* and *enol* forms.

This preparation was discovered independently by Geuther (1863) and by Frankland and Duppa (1865). The reaction was subsequently investigated in detail and so widely extended by Claisen that it has become solely a specific example of the more general process known as the Claisen Condensation.*

* This Condensation should not be confused with the *Claisen Reaction*, which is the condensation of an aldehyde with (i) another aldehyde, or (ii) a ketone, under the influence of *sodium hydroxide*, and with the elimination of *water*. For details, see Dibenzal-acetone, p. 179.

Claisen showed that an ester under the influence of sodium ethoxide would not only condense with itself (as in the preparation of ethyl acetoacetate), but also with (i) another ester, (ii) a ketone, if of formula RCH_2COR, (iii) a nitrile, if of formula RCH_2CN, in each case with the elimination of alcohol. Examples of these modifications are:

(i) $C_6H_5CO|OC_2H_5 + H|CH_2COOC_2H_5 = C_6H_5COCH_2COOC_2H_5 + C_2H_5OH$

   Ethyl benzoate   Ethyl acetate   Benzoyl-acetic ester.

(ii) $CH_3CO|OC_2H_5 + H|CH_2COCH_3 = CH_3COCH_2COCH_3 + C_2H_5OH$

   Ethyl acetate   Acetone   Acetyl-acetone.

(iii) $C_2H_5OOC\cdot CO|OC_2H_5 + H|CH_2CN = C_2H_5OOC\cdot COCH_2CN + C_2H_5OH$

   Ethyl oxalate   Acetonitrile β-Cyano-pyruvic ester.

Many other examples of the Claisen Condensation will be found in textbooks of theoretical organic chemistry.

Required: Ethyl acetate, 200 c.c.; sodium, 15 gms.; saturated brine, 200 c.c.

The ethyl acetate used in the preparation must first be dried. For this purpose place about 200 c.c. of ethyl acetate over granular calcium chloride, shake thoroughly and allow to stand, preferably overnight: then filter through a fluted filter-paper directly into a distilling-flask fitted with a water-condenser and distil carefully over a gauze. Use rubber stoppers for the distillation apparatus, as bark corks contain appreciable quantities of water.

Fit a 750 c.c. bolt-head flask (also by a rubber stopper) to a reflux water-condenser closed at the top by a calcium chloride tube: ensure that flask and condenser are quite dry. Place 150 c.c. of the dried ethyl acetate in the flask and add 15 gms. of sodium. The sodium for this purpose should preferably be added in the form of wire directly from a sodium press (Fig. 39, p. 56): alternatively the sodium may be added as thin slices, but in this case each slice should be quickly pressed between drying-paper before being added to the acetate to remove the wet film which may have formed during the weighing and cutting of the metal. Now heat the mixture on the water-bath. Very little reaction occurs whilst the acetate is still cold, but on warming a vigorous reaction ensues and hydrogen is evolved. Continue heating until a clear pale brown liquid entirely free from metallic sodium is obtained—this usually requires 2–2½ hours' heating, depending largely on the initial condition of the sodium. Then cool thoroughly and add dilute acetic acid (1:1 by volume) cautiously with shaking until the liquid is just definitely acid to litmus-paper; the addition of the acid first causes the formation of a semi-solid white mass which redissolves to a clear solution as the mixture becomes acid. Pour the solution into about 200 c.c. of cold almost saturated brine contained in a separating-funnel and shake the mixture vigorously. The ethyl acetoacetate separates sharply above the brine solution. Run off the lower layer of brine and then transfer the ester to a conical flask; add some powdered anhydrous sodium sulphate, and allow to stand for about 30 minutes with occasional shaking.

Meanwhile fit up a Claisen flask (of about 175 c.c. capacity) with a fine capillary and thermometer (see Fig. 13(A), p. 30), taking care that the range of temperature of 70°–100° is not obscured by the cork. Then filter the crude ester at the pump using a Buchner funnel and flask, quickly drain the residue of sodium sulphate in the funnel, and then rinse out the conical flask with a few c.c. of the original dried ethyl acetate, filtering the latter through the sodium sulphate residue into the ester below. Pour the latter into the Claisen flask, add some unglazed porcelain and, temporarily discarding the capillary and thermometer, cork the necks of the flask, connect it to a water-condenser and then place it *in* a boiling water-bath. The greater part of the unchanged ethyl acetate now distils over. When distillation ceases, remove the flask, replace the capillary and thermometer, and fit an apparatus for vacuum-distillation to the Claisen flask: for this purpose the Perkin triangle apparatus (Fig. 15, p. 33) is preferable, but the more simple apparatus shown in Fig. 13(A), p. 30, gives very good results. When a steady low pressure is attained in the apparatus, heat the Claisen flask in an oil-bath, increasing the temperature of the bath cautiously so that the distillation proceeds slowly. The boiling-point of the distillate rises slowly as the low-boiling impurities come over first, and finally becomes almost constant as the ethyl acetoacetate distils. Therefore ensure by slow distillation that the low-boiling impurities pass over as completely as possible before the ethyl acetoacetate starts to distil: if the apparatus shown in Fig. 13(A) is used, the receiver must of course be changed at this stage. The distillation of the acetoacetate can readily be recognised from the following boiling-points, 73°/15 mm., 82°/20 mm., 87°/30 mm., 92°/40 mm., and a fraction boiling over a range of 3–5° should be collected. Yield, 40–45 gms. A brown residue remains in the flask.

Refractionation of the low-boiling impurities gives a further quantity of the acetoacetate, but if the initial distillation has been carefully conducted, the amount recovered is less than 1 gm., and the refractionation is not worth while. If possible, complete the preparation in one day. If this is not possible, it is best to allow the cold crude sodium derivative (before acidification) to stand overnight, the flask being closed by a cork carrying a calcium chloride tube; the yield will now fall to about 38 gms. Alternatively, the crude ester may be allowed to remain overnight in contact with the sodium sulphate, but in this case the yield will fall to about 30 gms.

The ethyl acetoacetate obtained as above is sufficiently pure for most purposes: it should, however, be refractionated under reduced pressure if a sample of specially high purity is required.

If a vacuum-distillation apparatus is not available for the above preparation, the crude product may be distilled at atmospheric pressure and the acetoacetate collected as the fraction boiling at 175–185°. A pure preparation cannot be obtained in this way, however, because the ester decomposes slightly when distilled at atmospheric pressure.

Ethyl acetoacetate is a colourless liquid, d, 1·03, slightly soluble in water, but almost insoluble in brine. It has a faint but pleasant odour. It is widely used in chemical syntheses.

Demonstrate both the presence and the interconversion of the *keto* and *enol* forms in the ester thus:

(1) Dissolve about 1 c.c. of the ester in about 3 c.c. of alcohol and then add 2–3 drops of aqueous ferric chloride solution. A deep violet-red coloration at once appears. This is strong evidence for the presence of the *enol* form, since similar colorations with ferric chloride are given by most phenols (p. 254) and many higher aliphatic hydroxy-compounds. Now pour the solution into about 100 c.c. of distilled water in a beaker and add bromine water *drop* by *drop* with vigorous stirring until the solution *just* becomes colourless. On standing, the violet-red ferric chloride coloration soon reappears with increasing intensity. The bromine has thus added on at the double bond of the *enol* form, giving the unstable dibromo derivative (A), which readily loses hydrogen

$$CH_3C(OH){:}CHCOOC_2H_5 \xrightarrow{Br_2} CH_3C(OH)Br{\cdot}CHBrCOOC_2H_5 \xrightarrow{-HBr}$$
$$(A)$$
$$CH_3CO{\cdot}CHBrCOOC_2H_5$$
$$(B)$$

bromide to give the monobrom-*keto* ester (B). Since the violet-red ferric chloride coloration is given only by the *enol* form, the temporary removal of the latter by the bromine causes the solution to become momentarily colourless. Some of the unchanged *keto* form then changes over to the *enol* in order to re-establish the original equilibrium, and the ferric chloride coloration therefore reappears. The process can be repeated several times by the subsequent addition of bromine. If a *slight* excess of bromine water is originally added after the solution becomes colourless, the slow fading of the yellow bromine solution can be observed as it reacts with the *enol* form, then the solution becomes momentarily colourless, and finally the violet-red coloration reappears as before.

(2) To 2 c.c. of the ester in a test-tube add slightly more than the same volume of a cold *saturated* aqueous copper acetate solution. The blue colour of the latter turns immediately to a pale green. Now shake the tube vigorously in order to produce an emulsion of the ester in the aqueous layer. Scratch the sides of the tube with a rod, and shake vigorously as before. Crystallisation may be delayed for about 5 minutes, but, when once started, rapidly gives a copious precipitate of the pale green cupric derivative (C) of the *enol* form. If the contents of the tube are now shaken with chloroform, the crystals of the cupric compound readily dissolve in the lower chloroform layer, showing clearly that it is not a normal ionised salt.

$$CH_3C:CH \cdot C \cdot OC_2H_5$$

$$CH_3COCH_2COOC_2H_5 + NaHSO_3$$

$$\downarrow$$

$$CH_3C(OH).CH_2COOC_2H_5$$

$$SO_3Na \ (D)$$

$$CH_3\overset{|}{C}:CH \cdot C \cdot OC_2H_5 \ (C)$$

(3) To 2 c.c. of the ester, add 2–3 drops of a saturated *freshly prepared* solution of sodium bisulphite. On shaking, a gelatinous precipitate of the bisulphite addition product (D) of the *keto* form separates, and on standing for 5–10 minutes usually crystallises out. This is a normal reaction of a ketone (see p. 260): hydrogen cyanide adds on similarly to give a cyanhydrin.

Note. To obtain satisfactory results with tests (2) and (3), pure redistilled ethyl acetoacetate should be used.

For further experimental evidence for the presence of the *enol* form, see Tests 1, 2 (*a*) and 2 (*b*), pp. 215, 216.

SYNTHETIC USE OF ETHYL ACETOACETATE. In view of the great importance of the ester in synthetic work, the following practical points concerning its use should be borne in mind.

Mono- and Di-substitution Derivatives. The enolic sodium derivative of ethyl acetoacetate (E) is prepared by mixing alcoholic solutions of the ester and of sodium ethoxide. It should not be prepared by the direct action of metallic sodium on the ester, as the reaction is slow and the nascent hydrogen evolved reduces some of the ester to ethyl β-hydroxy-butyrate, $CH_3CH(OH)CH_2COOEt$.

When the sodium derivative, which is used in alcoholic solution without intermediate isolation, is boiled with an alkyl halide, *e.g.*, methyl iodide,

$$\text{CH}_3\text{COCH}_2\text{COOEt} \xrightarrow{\text{NaOEt}} \text{CH}_3\text{C(ONa):CHCOOEt} \xrightarrow{\text{MeI}} \text{CH}_3\text{COCH(Me)COOEt}$$
$$\text{(E)} \qquad\qquad\qquad \text{(F)}$$

$$\text{CH}_3\text{COCH(Me)COOEt} \xrightarrow{\text{NaOEt}} \text{CH}_3\text{C(ONa):C(Me)COOEt} \xrightarrow{\text{EtI}}$$
$$\text{(F)} \qquad\qquad\qquad \text{(G)} \quad \text{CH}_3\text{COC(Me)(Et)COOEt}$$
$$\text{(H)}$$

the methyl derivative (F) of the ketonic form is produced. The latter can then be treated again with sodium ethoxide (both in alcoholic solution as before), and the enolic sodium derivative (G) of the methyl compound thus formed. The latter can then be boiled in solution as before with an alkyl halide such as ethyl iodide, and the methyl-ethyl compound (H) obtained. It follows therefore that (1) even with a large excess of sodium ethoxide, a di-sodium derivative cannot be obtained and therefore a di-substituted derivative (H) must be prepared through the intermediate formation of the mono-substituted derivative (F); (2) the substituent groups* must be alkyl groups or substituted alkyl groups such as benzyl, $\text{C}_6\text{H}_5\text{CH}_2 -$, and that aryl groups cannot be introduced, because, e.g., iodo-benzene would not react with sodium derivatives such as (E) or (G). Therefore the synthesis of aryl compounds has usually to be accomplished by entirely different means, such as by the Grignard reagent.

Hydrolysis. Ethyl acetoacetate when treated with cold dilute sodium hydroxide solution gives the sodium salt of acetoacetic acid. This acid is unstable, and readily breaks down into acetone and carbon dioxide: it is of considerable

$$\text{CH}_3\text{COCH}_2\text{COOH} = \text{CH}_3\text{COCH}_3 + \text{CO}_2$$

physiological importance, as it occurs with acetone in diabetic urine, both compounds being initially formed from β-hydroxy-butyric acid.

The important methods of hydrolysis of acetoacetic ester derivatives are however:

(1) *Ketonic Hydrolysis.* Hot dilute caustic alkalis first hydrolyse off the ethyl group, and then remove carbon dioxide, a mono- or di-substituted acetone being thus obtained:

$$\text{CH}_3\text{COCH(Me)}\;|\text{COO}|\text{Et} \qquad\qquad \text{CH}_3\text{COC(Me)(Et)}\;|\text{COO}|\;\text{Et}$$
$$\downarrow \quad \text{H} \quad |\text{OH} \qquad\qquad\qquad\qquad \downarrow \quad \text{H} \quad |\text{OH}$$
$$\text{CH}_3\text{COCH}_2\text{Me} + \text{CO}_2 + \text{EtOH} \qquad \text{CH}_3\text{COCHMeEt} + \text{CO}_2 + \text{EtOH}$$

---

* Acyl halides, both aliphatic and aromatic, react with the sodium derivative, but the product depends largely on the solvent used. Thus acetyl chloride reacts with the sodium derivative (E) in alcoholic solution to give mainly the C-derivative (1) and in pyridine solution to give chiefly the O-derivative (2). These isomeric compounds can be readily distinguished, because the C-derivative (1) can still by enolisation act as a weak acid and is therefore

$$\text{(1) CH}_3\text{COCHCOOEt} \qquad\qquad \text{(2) CH}_3\text{C:CHCOOEt}$$
$$| \qquad\qquad\qquad\qquad\qquad\qquad |$$
$$\text{COCH}_3 \qquad\qquad\qquad\qquad\qquad \text{OCOCH}_3$$

soluble in alkalis, while the O-derivative (2) is neutral and insoluble in alkalis.

(2) *Acidic Hydrolysis.* Hot concentrated caustic alkalis first hydrolyse off the ethyl group, and then split the molecule to give one equivalent of acetic acid and one equivalent of the mono-or di-substituted acetic acid (as their alkali salts).

$$CH_3CO\vert CH(Me)COO\vert Et \qquad\qquad CH_3CO\vert C(Me)(Et)COO\vert Et$$
$$OH\vert H \quad\downarrow\quad H\vert OH \qquad\qquad OH\vert H \quad\downarrow\quad H\vert OH$$
$$CH_3COOH+MeCH_2COOH+EtOH \qquad CH_3COOH+MeEtCHCOOH+EtOH$$

In brief, suitable hydrolysis of ethyl acetoacetate derivatives will give mono- or di-*alkyl* substituted acetones or acetic acids. Tri-substituted acetones or acetic acids cannot be obtained: moreover, the di-substituted acetones must have the two substituents joined to the same carbon atom, symmetrically substituted ketones not being obtainable from the ester by the above methods.

Methyl-phenyl-pyrazolone.

The preparation of methyl-phenyl-pyrazolone illustrates one of the synthetic uses of ethyl acetoacetate, as distinct from those involving the hydrolysis of substitution derivatives.

If ethyl acetoacetate is warmed with an equivalent quantity of phenyl-hydrazine, the corresponding phenylhydrazone (A) is readily formed. On

$$CH_3C\vert O + H_2\vert NNHC_6H_5 \qquad\qquad CH_3C:NNHC_6H_5$$
$$\vert \qquad\qquad = H_2O + \qquad \vert$$
$$CH_2COOC_2H_5 \qquad\qquad\qquad CH_2COOC_2H_5 \ (A)$$

further heating, ring formation occurs with the loss of alcohol and the pro-

$$CH_3C:N\cdot N\cdot \vert H\vert C_6H_5 \qquad\qquad CH_3C:N\cdot NC_6H_5$$
$$\vert \qquad\qquad\qquad = C_2H_5OH + \qquad \vert \quad \vert$$
$$CH_2CO\vert OC_2H_5\vert \qquad\qquad\qquad CH_2-CO \quad (B)$$

duction of methyl-phenyl-pyrazolone (B). To indicate the position of the substituents in the pyrazolone ring, the atoms in this ring are numbered as shown, and the compound is thus 3-methyl-1-phenyl-5-pyrazolone.

$$CH_3C:N\cdot NC_6H_5$$
$$\vert\ \ ^{3}\ ^{2}\ ^{1}\ \vert$$
$$\vert\ _{4}\quad_{5}\ \vert$$
$$CH_2-CO$$

Required: Ethyl acetoacetate, 6·2 c.c.: phenylhydrazine, 5 c.c.

Mix 6·2 c.c. (6·4 gms.) of pure ethyl acetoacetate and 5·0 c.c. of pure phenylhydrazine* in an evaporating-basin of about 75 c.c. capacity, add 0·5 c.c. of acetic acid and then heat the mixture on a boiling water-bath (preferably in a fume-cupboard) for 1 hour, occasionally stirring the mixture with a short glass rod. Then allow the heavy yellow syrup to cool somewhat, add 30–40 c.c. of ether, and stir the mixture vigorously, when the syrup, which is insoluble in ether, will solidify. (*Note.* If the laboratory has been "inoculated" by previous preparations, the syrup may solidify

* The use of impure reactants may give a deep red syrup and delay considerably the final solidification: they should, therefore, be redistilled in a vacuum before use.

whilst still on the water-bath: in this case the solid product when cold must be chipped out of the basin, and ground in a mortar with the ether.) Now filter the product at the pump, and wash the solid material thoroughly with ether. Recrystallise the product from a small quantity of a mixture of equal volumes of water and alcohol. The methyl-phenyl-pyrazolone is obtained as colourless crystals, m.p. 127°. Yield of recrystallised material, 6·0–6·5 gms.

The tautomerism shown by the pyrazolones is of considerable interest. Thus the above methyl-phenyl-pyrazolone when fused or in solution can exist in the tautomeric forms (C), (D), and (E).

$$CH_3C : N \cdot NC_6H_5 \qquad CH_3C \cdot NH \cdot NC_6H_5 \qquad CH_3C : N \cdot NC_6H_5$$
$$\mid \quad \mid \quad \rightleftharpoons \quad \| \quad \mid \quad \rightleftharpoons \quad \mid \quad \mid$$
$$CH_2 \!-\! CO \ (C) \qquad CH \!-\!\!-\! CO \ (D) \qquad CH = C(OH) \ (E)$$

When the methyl-phenyl-pyrazolone is heated with methyl iodide in methyl alcoholic solution, it acts in the form (D), the – NH – group undergoing methylation, with the formation of the hydriodide of 2:3-dimethyl-1-phenyl-5-pyrazolone, or *antipyrine* (F), a drug used (either as the free base or as the

$$CH_3C \cdot N(CH_3) \cdot NC_6H_5 \qquad CH_3C \cdot N(CH_3) \cdot NC_6H_5$$
$$\| \quad \mid \qquad \qquad \| \quad \mid$$
$$CH \!-\!\!-\!\!-\! CO \ (F) \qquad (CH_3)_2N \cdot C \!-\!\!-\!\!- CO \ (G)$$

salicylate) to remove pain and also to reduce the body temperature. Antipyrine in turn can be converted to 2:3-dimethyl-4-(dimethylamino)-1-phenyl-5-pyrazolone, or *pyramidon* (G), a drug which has physiological properties similar to those of antipyrine, but which is effective in smaller doses and is more free from harmful after-effects.

Ethyl Malonate. $CH_2(COOC_2H_5)_2$.

A concentrated solution of monochloro-acetic acid is neutralised with sodium bicarbonate, and then heated with potassium cyanide, whereby sodium cyano-acetate is obtained:

$$CH_2ClCOONa + KCN = CH_2(CN)COONa + KCl$$

The crude product is evaporated to dryness and then heated with a mixture of alcohol and sulphuric acid: the cyano group is thus hydrolysed giving malonic acid, which then undergoes esterification to give diethyl malonate.

$$CH_2 \overset{\diagup COONa}{\underset{\diagdown CN}{}} \quad \xrightarrow{\text{Hydrolysis}} \quad CH_2 \overset{\diagup COOH}{\underset{\diagdown COOH}{}} \quad \xrightarrow{\text{Esterification}} \quad CH_2 \overset{\diagup COOC_2H_5}{\underset{\diagdown COOC_2H_5}{}}$$

Required: Monochloro-acetic acid, 30 gms.; sodium bicarbonate, 30 gms.; potassium cyanide, 24 gms.; sulphuric acid, 50 c.c.; rectified spirit, 70 c.c.

The first part of this preparation (as far as the solidification of the sodium cyano-acetate) *must be carried out in the fume-cupboard.* Add 30 gms. of monochloro-acetic acid to 60 c.c. of water contained in a wide evaporating-basin (about 12–15 cm. in diameter) and warm the mixture gently on a sand-bath until the temperature reaches about 55°, using a 260° thermometer as a stirrer for this purpose. Now add powdered sodium bicarbonate (about 30 gms.) in small quantities at a time with stirring until the evolution of carbon dioxide is complete, and the solution is just alkaline to litmus-paper: during this operation keep the temperature of the mixture between 55° and 60°. Now remove the basin from the sand-bath and cautiously add 24 gms. of powdered potassium cyanide,* continuing the stirring both during and after the addition. The temperature of the mixture rises spontaneously after the addition is complete and the cyanide rapidly dissolves. When the temperature of the well-stirred mixture reaches 90–95°, a vigorous effervescence usually occurs for a few seconds and then rapidly subsides. When this reaction is over, replace the basin on the sand-bath and heat gently, meanwhile stirring the brown solution with the thermometer until the temperature reaches 135° (about 30 minutes' heating is usually required). Maintain the temperature at 135° for a further 5 minutes, and then remove the basin from the sand-bath and continue stirring until the product solidifies.

Without undue delay, chip out the brown solid mass (which is deliquescent when cold) and place the coarsely broken mass in a 400 c.c. round-bottomed flask fitted with a reflux water-condenser: add 20 c.c. of rectified spirit and shake well around until the product is uniformly wet. Now add 50 c.c. (92 gms.) of concentrated sulphuric acid *carefully* with shaking to 50 c.c. (40 gms.) of rectified spirit in a 200 c.c. conical flask, keeping the mixture well cooled in ice-water during the addition. Pour this solution in small portions down the reflux condenser, shaking well after each addition. When the addition is complete, heat the flask on a boiling water-bath for 1 hour, with occasional shaking. Then allow it to cool somewhat (the contents will become almost solid if allowed to become quite cold), add 70 c.c. of water down the condenser, and shake vigorously. Filter any insoluble material at the pump, and wash the residue on the filter several times with a few c.c. of ether. Transfer the filtrate (with the ether washings) to a separating-funnel and extract several times with ether. Discard the aqueous layer, return the united ethereal

* See footnote, p. 150.

extracts to the funnel, and shake them *cautiously* with sodium carbonate solution several times until no further evolution of carbon dioxide occurs: traces of sulphuric acid and of alcohol are thus removed. Finally separate the ethereal layer and dry it over granular calcium chloride in a small conical flask for at least 30 minutes.

Meanwhile fit up an apparatus for ether distillation precisely similar to that shown in Fig. 48 (p. 123), except that a 100 c.c. Claisen flask is used instead of the simple distillation-flask shown in the figure. The dropping-funnel is fitted to the main neck of the Claisen flask, the side-neck being corked. Filter the dry ethereal solution through a fluted filter-paper directly into the dropping-funnel, finally washing the conical flask and the calcium chloride with a few c.c. of fresh ether. Then distil off the ether in the usual way, allowing the solution to fall from the dropping-funnel into the flask as fast as the ether itself distils over—*observe all the usual precautions for ether distillations*. When the distillation of the ether is complete and only the crude ester remains in the Claisen flask, fit up the latter for vacuum-distillation, using either the simple apparatus shown in Fig. 13(A) (p. 30) or a Perkin triangle with condenser (Fig. 15, p. 33), and heating the flask in an oil-bath. The ethyl malonate usually distils as a sharp fraction boiling over a range of about 2–3°: it may be recognised from the following b.p.s: 93°/16 mm., 105°/26 mm. Yield, about 35 gms. If necessary the ethyl malonate may be distilled at atmospheric pressure, at which it has b.p. 198°: slight decomposition occurs in these circumstances, however, and the distillate, although colourless, has a slightly acrid odour.

Diethyl malonate is a colourless liquid, d, 1·07; it has a faint pleasant odour, and is only slightly soluble in water.

Ethyl malonate, like ethyl acetoacetate, exists as a tautomeric mixture of *keto* and *enol* forms, although in the case of ethyl malonate

$$C_2H_5OOC \cdot CH_2COOC_2H_5 \rightleftharpoons C_2H_5OOC \cdot CH:C(OH)OC_2H_5$$
keto   *enol*

the proportion of *enol* form present at room temperature is exceedingly small. Experimental evidence for the presence of the *enol* form is, however, given by the following tests:

(1) To 2 c.c. of a freshly prepared dilute aqueous solution of sodium nitroprusside, add 2 drops of ethyl malonate and shake: then add 2–3 drops of 10% aqueous sodium hydroxide solution and shake again. A red coloration at once appears, but fades in a few minutes to a pale brown.

(2) (*a*) Dissolve about 0·1 gm. of *pure m*-dinitrobenzene in 2–3 c.c.

of alcohol, and then add an equal volume of 10% aqueous sodium hydroxide solution. (Ignore traces of the dinitrobenzene that may be reprecipitated by the soda.) Now add 2 drops of ethyl malonate and shake. A deep reddish-violet coloration is produced, but rapidly changes to a deep red.

(b) Dissolve 0·2 gm. of 3:5-dinitrobenzoic acid in 2–3 c.c. of 10% aqueous sodium hydroxide solution, and then add 2 drops of ethyl malonate and shake. A violet coloration is produced, rapidly fading to red and eventually to pale yellow. Excess of the malonate discharges the red colour rapidly, giving the yellow solution.

Precisely similar results are obtained with ethyl acetoacetate, except that in tests 2 (a) and 2 (b) the deep red coloration is produced without a preliminary violet coloration.

These coloration changes are given by most compounds which possess the enolic group $-CH:C(OH)-$, or which by tautomeric change can produce this group: for further examples, see Tests 6 (a) and 6 (b) for Ketones, p. 261.

SUBSTITUTION DERIVATIVES OF ETHYL MALONATE. Ethyl malonate resembles ethyl acetoacetate in that it gives rise to mono- and di-substituted derivatives in precisely similar circumstances. Thus when alcoholic solutions of ethyl malonate and of sodium ethoxide are mixed, the sodium derivative (A) of the enol form is produced in solution. On boiling this solution with an *alkyl* halide, e.g., methyl iodide, the methyl derivative (B) of the keto form is obtained. When this is treated again in alcoholic solution with sodium ethoxide, the

$$EtOOC \cdot CH:C(ONa)OEt \xrightarrow{MeI} EtOOC \cdot CH(Me)COOEt \xrightarrow{NaOEt}$$
$$\text{(A)} \qquad\qquad\qquad \text{(B)}$$

$$EtOOC \cdot C(Me):C(ONa)OEt \xrightarrow{EtI} EtOOC \cdot C(Me)(Et)COOEt$$
$$\text{(C)} \qquad\qquad\qquad \text{(D)}$$

corresponding sodium derivative (C) is formed: this in turn when boiled in alcoholic solution with any alkyl halide, e.g., ethyl iodide, gives the methyl-ethyl derivative (D), i.e., the diethyl ester of methyl-ethyl malonic acid. In this way, any mono-substituted (B) or di-substituted (D) alkyl derivative may be obtained.

Hydrolysis. Ethyl malonate and its derivatives are usually readily hydrolysed on boiling with aqueous alkalis, the salts of the corresponding dicarboxylic acids being thus obtained: the course of this hydrolysis is unaffected by the concentration of the alkali used. The free acids, having two –COOH groups joined to one carbon atom, are unstable when heated, and immediately above their melting-points (or sometimes in boiling aqueous solution) lose carbon dioxide, a monobasic acid being obtained. Thus the mono-substituted ester (B) on hydrolysis gives mono-methyl-malonic acid (E) which on being heated to its m.p. gives methyl-acetic or propionic acid (F). The di-substituted ester (D) similarly gives first methyl-ethyl-malonic acid (G) and then methyl-ethyl-acetic acid (H).

EtOOC·CH(Me)COOEt $\longrightarrow$ H$\lfloor$OOC$\rfloor$CH(Me)COOH $\longrightarrow$

   (B)   (E)   CH$_2$(Me)COOH + CO$_2$

                  (F)

EtOOC·C(Me)(Et)COOEt $\longrightarrow$ H$\lfloor$OOC$\rfloor$C(Me)(Et)COOH $\longrightarrow$

   (D)   (G)   CH(Me)(Et)COOH + CO$_2$

                  (H)

It follows therefore that ethyl malonate can be used (just as ethyl aceto-acetate) to prepare any mono- or di-substituted acetic acid: the limitations are identical, namely the substituents must necessarily be alkyl groups (or aryl-alkyl groups such as $C_6H_5CH_2$), and tri-substituted acetic acids cannot be prepared. Ethyl malonate undergoes no reaction equivalent to the ketonic hydrolysis of ethyl acetoacetate, and the concentration of the alkali used for the hydrolysis is therefore not important.

Ethane Tetracarboxylic Ethyl Ester.
$(C_2H_5OOC)_2CH\cdot CH(COOC_2H_5)_2$.

When an alcoholic solution of the sodium derivative of ethyl malonate is shaken with a solution of iodine, the latter withdraws the sodium, and the ethyl malonate residues link together in pairs to give the tetra-ethyl ester of

$$I_2 + \begin{array}{l} Na\lceil CH(COOC_2H_5)_2 \\ \\ Na\lfloor CH(COOC_2H_5)_2 \end{array} = \begin{array}{l} CH(COOC_2H_5)_2 \\ | \\ CH(COOC_2H_5)_2 \end{array} + 2NaI$$

sym-ethane tetracarboxylic acid.

Required: Alcohol, 30 c.c.; sodium, 1·4 gms.; iodine, 7·7 gms.; ethyl malonate, 9 c.c.; sodium thiosulphate solution.

Place 30 c.c. of alcohol in a 100 c.c. conical flask fitted to a reflux water-condenser, and then add 1·4 gms. of sodium cut into small pieces. The sodium rapidly dissolves to give a solution of sodium ethoxide, the alcohol boiling under the heat of the reaction. When the sodium has completely dissolved, detach the flask and cool it in ice-water.

While the sodium ethoxide solution is cooling, prepare a solution of 7·7 gms. of finely powdered iodine in 60 c.c. of ether. *When this solution is ready*, add 9 c.c. (9·6 gms.) of ethyl malonate to the alcoholic sodium ethoxide solution, mix well and then allow to stand for 30–60 seconds (*not longer*): then cautiously add the ethereal solution of the iodine, mixing *thoroughly* during the addition in order to avoid local overheating by the heat of the re-action. (If, after the ethyl malonate has been added to the sodium ethoxide, a considerable delay occurs before the iodine is added, the yield of the final product is markedly decreased.)

Now cork the flask securely, and shake it vigorously for about

5 minutes: the solution should now have only a faint brown colour due to unchanged iodine. Cool the mixture in ice-water, pour it into a separating-funnel, and extract it twice with water to remove sodium iodide and most of the alcohol. Then shake the residual ethereal solution with a dilute aqueous solution of sodium thiosulphate: the excess of iodine is thus removed and the ethereal solution becomes colourless. Separate the ether, dry it over calcium chloride for about 20 minutes, and then filter it through a fluted filter-paper directly into a 100 c.c. conical flask. Fit the latter with a delivery knee-tube and water-condenser, and then, observing all the usual precautions, distil off the ether on a water-bath until about 10–15 c.c. remain. Pour this solution whilst still hot into a small evaporating-basin and swirl it gently around: the hot ether rapidly evaporates and the ethane tetracarboxylic ester crystallises out. Allow it to stand exposed to the air for about 10–15 minutes, and then well press the crystals between several layers of thick drying-paper to remove any liquid residue. Recrystallise from a small quantity of rectified spirit or of light petroleum (b.p. 40–60°). The ester is obtained as colourless crystals, m.p. 76°: yield, 6·0–6·5 gms.

This tetra-ethyl ester is difficult to hydrolyse: the corresponding tetra-methyl ester can, however, be hydrolysed to give ethane tetracarboxylic acid, $(HOOC)_2CH \cdot CH(COOH)_2$. The latter readily loses 2 molecules of carbon dioxide (on being heated or even on boiling with water) to give succinic acid, $HOOC \cdot CH_2 \cdot CH_2COOH$.

Ethane tetracarboxylic ethyl ester can be regarded as composed of two malonic ester residues, each acting as a mono-alkyl substituent to the other. The two remaining hydrogen atoms therefore still retain acidic properties, and consequently the ester gives with sodium ethoxide a di-sodium derivative,

$$
\begin{array}{ccc}
NaC(COOEt)_2 & & C(COOEt)_2 \\
| & +\ I_2\ = & \| & +\ 2NaI \\
NaC(COOEt)_2 & & C(COOEt)_2
\end{array}
$$

which when treated with iodine gives in turn ethylene tetracarboxylic ethyl ester, m.p. 57°.

The Grignard Reagent.

Grignard reagents are prepared by the interaction of alkyl or aryl halides (of general formula RX) with magnesium in the presence of ether, or (much more rarely) certain other solvents. Although the ether certainly takes part both in the formation and the composition of the Grignard reagent, the formation of the latter can, for the purpose of interpreting its reactions, be represented as a simple addition:

$$RX + Mg = RMgX.$$

For the preparation of the Grignard reagent, the following factors should be noted:

(1) Alkyl and aryl iodides *usually* react with magnesium more rapidly than the corresponding bromides, and the bromides very much more rapidly than the chlorides. Aryl (as distinct from alkyl) chlorides have usually only a slow reaction with magnesium and are therefore very rarely used. With alkyl and aryl iodides in particular, however, a side reaction often occurs with the formation of a hydrocarbon and magnesium iodide:

$$2RI + Mg = R-R + MgI_2$$

Hence as a general rule the bromides are used.

(2) The formation of the Grignard reagent is inhibited by traces of water, which also decompose the reagent when it is formed. Therefore the apparatus used must be thoroughly dry, and the ether anhydrous (p. 55). Specially prepared magnesium turnings* should preferably be used: if magnesium ribbon is employed, it should first be drawn through two layers of fine emery paper to remove the superficial film of oxide, *etc.*

(3) In spite of these precautions, it is sometimes found difficult to start the formation of the reagent, although when once the formation has started, it proceeds with increasing speed. In such cases it is advisable to add a small crystal of iodine, which is allowed to fall through the ethereal solution of the organic halide on to the surface of the magnesium below. If the mixture is undisturbed, a local concentration of iodine in solution is thus obtained in immediate contact with the magnesium: the latter then usually becomes reactive, and the formation of the Grignard reagent, starting in the immediate neighbourhood of the iodine, rapidly spreads throughout the magnesium turnings. Alternatively, a trace of methyl iodide can be added to the ether to stimulate the reaction with the magnesium, although the resulting Grignard solution will then contain minute quantities of methyl magnesium iodide.

No attempt is made to isolate the Grignard reagent from its ethereal solution before use. The reagent (usually also in ethereal solution) is added to the solution of the Grignard reagent, and when the reaction is complete the product is hydrolysed.

The method of hydrolysis depends on the nature of the product. It is usually sufficient to add dilute sulphuric acid to the ethereal solution and to shake thoroughly, when the magnesium enters the aqueous solution, whilst the organic compound remains in the ether. Alternatively, however, the ethereal solution may be poured on to ice and water, and then treated with dilute sulphuric acid. Should the product be very unstable, the hydrolysis can be carried out with an aqueous solution of ammonium chloride. In the following examples the hydrolysis is usually shown as a simple double decomposition with

* Supplied for this purpose by chemical dealers.

water, giving magnesium hydroxy-iodide: it will be understood that the latter dissolves in the dilute acid to give a mixture of magnesium iodide and sulphate.

SYNTHETIC USE OF GRIGNARD REAGENTS. Grignard reagents can be used to synthesise a wide variety of organic compounds, and are consequently of very great value in organic chemistry: the *chief* reactions are summarised in the following table, in which magnesium methyl iodide (denoted as MeMgI, in order to differentiate the methyl group introduced by the reagent from any methyl groups already present in the organic compound) is used as a typical Grignard reagent.

(1) Water, alcohols and hydroxy compounds generally, and also primary and secondary amines, give the *hydrocarbon* corresponding to the Grignard reagent,

$$Me\!:\!MgI + HO\!:\!H = MeH + Mg(OH)I$$

$$Me\!:\!MgI + EtO\!:\!H = MeH + Mg(OEt)I$$

$$Me\!:\!MgI + EtNH\!:\!H = MeH + Mg(NHEt)I$$

(2) Oxygen is directly absorbed, and the product on hydrolysis gives the corresponding *alcohol*.

$$MeMgI \xrightarrow{O} MeOMgI \qquad MeO\!:\!MgI + HO\!:\!H = MeOH + Mg(OH)I$$

(3) Carbon dioxide is similarly absorbed, and gives the corresponding *carboxylic acid*.

$$MeMgI \xrightarrow{CO_2} MeCOOMgI$$

$$MeCOO\!:\!MgI + HO\!:\!H = MeCOOH + Mg(OH)I$$

(4) Aldehydes form addition products at the double bond of the carbonyl (>C:O) group, and hydrolysis gives *secondary alcohols*. Thus acetaldehyde gives *iso*-propyl alcohol:

$$CH_3C\!\!\stackrel{\displaystyle /H}{\diagdown O} + MeMgI = CH_3\!\!\stackrel{\displaystyle /H}{\underset{\diagdown Me}{C}}\!\!-OMgI$$

$$CH_3\!\!\stackrel{\displaystyle /H}{\underset{\diagdown Me}{C}}\!\!-O\!:\!MgI + HO\!:\!H = CH_3\!\!\stackrel{\displaystyle /H}{\underset{\diagdown Me}{C}}\!\!-OH + Mg(OH)I$$

Note. Formaldehyde is a special case. It reacts similarly, but a *primary alcohol* is necessarily produced. This alcohol, however, will always contain one carbon atom more than that obtained in Reaction (2).

$$HC\!\!\stackrel{\displaystyle /H}{\diagdown O} + MeMgI = HC\!\!\stackrel{\displaystyle /H}{\underset{\diagdown Me}{}}\!\!-OMgI$$

$$\overset{\displaystyle H}{\underset{\displaystyle Me}{HC}}\!\!-\!\!O\,\lvert MgI + HO\rvert H = MeCH_2OH + Mg(OH)I$$
Ethyl alcohol

This reaction is of great value for ascending the homologous series of alcohols:

$$ROH \rightarrow RBr \rightarrow RMgBr \rightarrow RCH_2OH$$

(5) Ketones similarly give *tertiary alcohols*.

$$\underset{CH_3}{\overset{CH_3}{>}}C:O + MeMgI = \underset{CH_3}{\overset{CH_3}{>}}C\underset{Me}{\overset{OMgI}{<}}$$
Acetone

$$\underset{CH_3}{\overset{CH_3}{>}}C\underset{Me}{\overset{O\lvert MgI + HO\rvert H}{<}} = \underset{CH_3}{\overset{CH_3}{>}}C\underset{Me}{\overset{OH}{<}} + Mg(OH)I.$$
Tertiary butyl alcohol

Note.—Grignard reagents readily act as dehydrating agents by virtue of Reaction (1). Since aliphatic tertiary alcohols usually readily lose water, an excess of the Grignard reagent may take the above reaction one stage further to give an unsaturated hydrocarbon.

$$\underset{CH_3}{\overset{CH_3}{>}}C\underset{Me}{\overset{OH}{<}} \quad -H_2O = \underset{CH_3}{\overset{CH_2}{>}}C-Me$$

(6) Esters (a) and acid chlorides (b) readily react with Grignard reagents to give ketones, which immediately react with a second equivalent of the reagent as in (5) to give *tertiary* alcohols as before.

(a) $CH_3C:O\!\!\diagup^{\lvert OEt + IMg\rvert Me} = CH_3C:O\!\!\diagup^{Me} + Mg(OEt)I$
Ethyl acetate

(b) $CH_3C:O\!\!\diagup^{\lvert Cl + IMg\rvert Me} = CH_3C:O\!\!\diagup^{Me} + MgClI*$
Acetyl chloride

(7) Non-metallic halides and covalent metallic halides give their *organic* derivatives.

$$As\lvert Cl_3 + 3IMg\rvert Me = AsMe_3 + 3MgClI$$

$$Sn\lvert Cl_4 + 4IMg\rvert Me = SnMe_4 + 4MgClI$$

$$Hg\lvert Cl_2 + 2IMg\rvert Me = HgMe_2 + 2MgClI$$

Since Grignard reagents can easily be obtained from aryl halides, they are of special value in the synthesis of many aromatic compounds, particularly as, for reasons already stated (pp. 211, 216), aromatic compounds cannot generally be prepared by means of ethyl acetoacetate and ethyl malonate.

* *i.e.*, equimolecular quantities of magnesium chloride and iodide.

Triphenyl-carbinol, $(C_6H_5)_3COH$, from Ethyl Benzoate and Phenyl Magnesium Bromide. (Grignard Reaction 6 (a).)

Required: Bromobenzene, 10·5 c.c.; dry ether, 50 c.c.; granulated magnesium, 2·5 gms.

Fit a 250 c.c. round-bottomed flask to a reflux water-condenser (each being *thoroughly* dry) and close the top of the condenser with a calcium chloride tube. Dissolve 10·5 c.c. (15·7 gms.) of dry bromobenzene in 50 c.c. of *anhydrous* ether (preparation, p. 55), and add about half this solution of 2·5 gms. of granulated magnesium contained in the round-bottomed flask, meanwhile keeping the rest of the ethereal solution in a small, well-corked conical flask. Now, since the formation of phenyl magnesium bromide seldom begins spontaneously, add a crystal of iodine carefully to the magnesium mixture so that it rests on top of the metal and there slowly dissolves. If the mixture is allowed to stand quietly, the formation of the Grignard reagent will probably start in the neighbourhood of the iodine within a few minutes (being accompanied by a cloudiness and complete disappearance of the iodine), and will then continue with increasing vigour until the ether is boiling. (If this does not happen, warm the mixture carefully (without shaking) on the water-bath and then, when the action begins, turn out the gas.) When the boiling of the ether begins to cease, pour about 10 c.c. of the remainder of the ethereal solution of the bromobenzene down the reflux condenser, at once replacing the calcium chloride tube. Continue in this way until all the bromobenzene has been added, the solution in the flask boiling steadily meanwhile. If the bromobenzene solution is added too rapidly, check excessive boiling of the ether by immersing the flask in cold water for a few minutes, taking care, however, not to stop the reaction entirely.

When the addition of the bromobenzene is complete and the ether is boiling gently, reheat the flask on the water-bath for a further 15 minutes to ensure completion of the reaction: the solution will now be slightly dark in colour, and only a trace of metallic magnesium should remain.

Now remove the flask from the water-bath, and *slowly* add a solution of 5 c.c. (5·2 gms.) of dry ethyl benzoate in 15 c.c. of anhydrous ether down the condenser in small quantities at a time, mixing the contents of the flask thoroughly between each addition. When the boiling of the ether again subsides, return the flask to the water-bath and reheat for a further 15 minutes. Then cool the mixture in ice-water, and carefully pour off the ethereal solution into a mixture of about 60 c.c. of dilute sulphuric acid and 100 gms. of crushed ice contained in a flask of about 300 c.c. capacity fitted for steam-distillation, taking care to leave behind any unchanged magnesium. Add about 100 c.c. water, and then fit securely to the lower end of the condenser (as a receiver) a Buchner flask, the side-tube carrying a piece of rubber tubing which falls well below the level of the bench. Steam-distil the ethereal mixture for about 30 minutes: discard the distillate, which contains the ether, possibly a trace of unchanged ethyl benzoate, and also any diphenyl, $C_6H_5C_6H_5$, which has been formed. The residue in the flask contains the triphenyl-carbinol, which solidifies when the liquid is cooled. Filter this residual product at the pump, wash the triphenyl-carbinol *thoroughly* with water, drain, and then dry by pressing between several layers of thick drying-paper. Yield of crude dry product, 8 gms. The triphenyl-carbinol can be recrystallised from methylated spirit (yield, 6 gms.), or, if quite dry, from benzene, and so obtained as colourless crystals, m.p. 162°.

Ethyl β-Phenyl-β-hydroxy-propionate.
$C_6H_5CH(OH)CH_2COOEt.$ (Reformatsky Reaction.)

The *Reformatsky Reaction* consists of the interaction of an ester of an α-halogeno-acid with an aldehyde, a ketone or another ester in the presence of zinc. For example, if a mixture of ethyl bromoacetate and benzaldehyde is heated with zinc, the latter undoubtedly first combines with the ethyl bromo-acetate to form a Grignard-like reagent (reaction A), which then adds on to the benzaldehyde just as a Grignard reagent would do (reaction B). The complex so formed, on acidification gives ethyl β-phenyl-β-hydroxy-propionate (reaction C). Note that reaction A could not satisfactorily be carried out using

$$BrCH_2COOC_2H_5 + Zn \longrightarrow BrZnCH_2COOC_2H_5 \ (A)$$

$$C_6H_5CHO + BrZnCH_2COOC_2H_5 \longrightarrow C_6H_5\overset{H}{\underset{CH_2COOC_2H_5}{C}}-OZnBr \qquad (B)$$

$$C_6H_5\overset{H}{\underset{CH_2COOC_2H_5}{C}}-OZnBr \xrightarrow{\text{dilute acid}} C_6H_5CH(OH)CH_2COOC_2H_5 \ (C)$$

magnesium instead of zinc, because the magnesium Grignard reagent as fast as it was formed would react with the ester grouping (p. 221). The Reformatsky reaction is therefore of great value for the preparation of β-hydroxy acids, and also for the preparation of αβ-unsaturated acids, to which the β-hydroxy acids can often be readily converted by dehydration.

Note also that if another ester, of general formula $R \cdot COOC_2H_5$, were used in place of benzaldehyde in the above reaction, a similar complex would be formed,

$$R \cdot \overset{O}{\overset{\|}{C}} - OC_2H_5 \longrightarrow R \cdot \overset{OZnBr}{\underset{OC_2H_5}{\overset{|}{C}}} - CH_2COOC_2H_5 \longrightarrow R \cdot \overset{OH}{\underset{OC_2H_5}{\overset{|}{C}}} - CH_2COOC_2H_5$$

$$\longrightarrow R \cdot CO \cdot CH_2COOC_2H_5$$

and on acidification would give an unstable β-hydroxy-β-ethoxy ester, which would very readily lose alcohol with the formation of a β-keto-ester.

Required: Zinc powder, 20 gms.; ethyl bromoacetate, 28 c.c.; benzaldehyde, 32 c.c.

PREPARATION OF REAGENTS. It is essential for this preparation that the zinc powder should be in an active condition. For this purpose, it is usually sufficient if a sample of ordinary technical zinc powder is vigorously shaken in a flask with pure ether, and then filtered off at the pump, washed once with ether, quickly drained and without delay transferred to a vacuum desiccator. If, however, an impure sample of zinc dust fails to respond to this treatment, it should be vigorously stirred in a beaker with 5% aqueous sodium hydroxide solution until an effervescence of hydrogen occurs, and then filtered at the pump, washed *thoroughly* with distilled water, and then with alcohol and ether, and dried as before in a vacuum desiccator. The ethyl bromoacetate (b.p. 159°) and the benzaldehyde (b.p. 179°) should be dried and distilled before use.

A 250 c.c. flask is fitted (preferably by means of a three-necked adaptor) with a mercury-sealed stirrer (Fig. 19, p. 19), a reflux water-condenser, and a dropping-funnel. The dried zinc powder (20 gms.) is placed in the flask, and a solution of 28 c.c. of ethyl bromoacetate and 32 c.c. of benzaldehyde in 40 c.c. of dry benzene containing 10 c.c. of dry ether is placed in the dropping-funnel. Approximately 10 c.c. of this solution is run on to the zinc powder, and the mixture allowed to remain unstirred until (usually within a few minutes) a vigorous reaction occurs. The stirrer is now started, and the rest of the solution allowed to run in drop-wise over a period of about 30 minutes so that the initial reaction is steadily maintained. The flask is then heated on a water-bath for 30 minutes with continuous stirring, and is then cooled in an ice-water bath. The well-stirred product is then hydrolysed by the addition of 120 c.c. of 10% sulphuric acid. The mixture is transferred to a separating-funnel, the lower aqueous layer discarded, and the upper benzene layer then extracted twice with 20 c.c. of 10% sulphuric acid, then with 20 c.c. of 10 % sodium carbonate solution, twice again with the dilute sulphuric acid, and finally twice with 20 c.c. of distilled water. The benzene solution is then separated and dried over anhydrous magnesium sulphate or (more slowly) over sodium sulphate.

A 75 c.c. Claisen flask is fitted with a small dropping-funnel in the main neck, and the filtered benzene solution then run into the flask from the funnel at approximately the rate at which the benzene is being distilled off by heating the flask in an oil-bath. When the solvent has thus been removed, the residue is allowed to cool whilst the funnel is replaced by the usual capillary tube, and the distillation is then continued at low pressure obtained by an efficient water-pump. The ester is obtained as a colourless liquid, b.p. 145–155°/15 mm.: yield, 27–30 gms. A second distillation gives a product of sharper boiling-point. If during the distillation the ester tends to decompose with foaming, it indicates that the above washing has not been sufficiently thorough: the application of a lower pressure (e.g., ca. 5 mm. by means of an oil-pump) will usually give smooth distillation without decomposition. The ester has b.p. 128–130°/5 mm.

Ethyl-benzene. $C_6H_5C_2H_5$. (The Fittig Reaction.)

Two methods may conveniently be used to ascend the homologous series of aromatic hydrocarbons:

(1) *The Friedel and Crafts Reaction*, in which an aromatic hydrocarbon reacts with an alkyl halide under the influence of aluminium chloride:

$$C_6H_5 \vert H + Br \vert C_2H_5 = C_6H_5C_2H_5 + HBr$$

The preparation of acetophenone (p. 201) is a modification of this method, the alkyl halide being replaced by an acid chloride, with the consequent formation of a ketone.

(2) *The Fittig Reaction*, in which sodium reacts with a mixture of an aryl and an alkyl halide, forming the sodium halide and the corresponding hydrocarbon:

$$C_6H_5 \vert Br + 2Na + Br \vert C_2H_5 = C_6H_5C_2H_5 + 2NaBr$$

This reaction is precisely parallel to the Wurtz Reaction in the aliphatic series, by which, for instance, n-butane can be obtained by the action of sodium on ethyl bromide.

$$2C_2H_5Br + 2Na = C_2H_5C_2H_5 + 2NaBr$$

The Fittig Reaction is employed in the following preparation of ethyl-benzene.

[NOTE. Hydrocarbons such as ethyl-benzene can also be prepared by the *Clemmensen* reduction of the corresponding ketone. This is exemplified by the reduction of p-methylacetophenone (p. 228)].

I

Required: Sodium, 22·5 gms.; dry ether, 100 c.c.; bromobenzene, 34 c.c.; ethyl bromide, 31 c.c.

Using the sodium press described on p. 56, press 22·5 gms. of
sodium into wire, and allow the latter to fall directly into 100
c.c. of *anhydrous* ether (preparation, p. 55) contained in a 750
c.c. round-bottomed flask. Fit the latter with an efficient
(preferably double-surface) reflux water-condenser, and stand the
flask on a cork ring. Now pour down the condenser a mixture of
34 c.c. (50 gms.) of dry bromobenzene and 31 c.c. (45·5 gms.,
i.e., a 30% excess) of ethyl bromide. Close the top of the
condenser with a calcium chloride tube and shake the mixture
thoroughly. After 10–15 minutes, the reaction will cause the
ether to boil steadily. Shake the mixture occasionally during the
next two hours in order to prevent the wire from becoming coated
with sodium bromide, but do not cool the flask unless the boiling
of the ether becomes very vigorous: ultimately a bluish-grey
sludge forms in the mixture, in addition to unchanged wire.
Allow the mixture to stand in this way for a total period of at least
3 hours, and preferably overnight—in the latter case ensure that
the condenser-water is turned off during the night.

Now assemble the apparatus for ether distillation shown in
Fig. 48, p. 123, except that, in place of the small distilling-flask
A, use a wide-necked 100 c.c. bolt-head flask, closed by a cork
carrying the dropping-funnel **B** and also a bent delivery-tube (or
"knee-tube") for connection to the condenser **C**. Carefully
decant the ethereal solution of the ethyl-benzene into the dropping-
funnel **B**, leaving as much solid material behind in the 750 c.c.
flask as possible: wash this solid residue with a further quantity
of ether, decanting the latter in turn into the dropping-funnel.
(The residue in the flask may still contain some unchanged
sodium: therefore place some methylated spirit in the flask, and
then, *when all effervescence has subsided*, dilute carefully with
water, and finally pour into the sink.) Now distil the ether,
running the ethereal solution into the bolt-head flask as fast as the
ether itself distils over, and observing all the usual precautions
for ether-distillations (p. 123). When no more ether distils over,
detach the bolt-head flask, and fit to it a short fractionating
column, similar to that shown in Fig. 12(B), p. 28, a water-condenser being then connected in turn to the column. Carefully
fractionate the crude ethyl-benzene, collecting the fraction of b.p.
130–135°. Yield, 16 gms.

Ethyl-benzene is a colourless liquid of b.p. 134°, and *d*, 0·876:
it has only a faint odour.

p-Ethyl-toluene. $C_2H_5\cdot C_6H_4\cdot CH_3$. (Clemmensen Reduction.)

Many aldehydes and ketones can be reduced directly by *Clemmensen's* method, in which the aldehyde or ketone is boiled with dilute hydrochloric acid and amalgamated zinc. *p*-Methylacetophenone (or *p*-tolyl-methyl-ketone) is reduced under these conditions to *p*-ethyl-toluene. An excess of the reducing agent is employed in order to prevent the formation of unsaturated hydrocarbons.

The *p*-methylacetophenone is readily prepared by the Friedel-Crafts' reaction (*cf.* p. 200), toluene being treated with acetyl chloride in the presence of aluminium chloride. The toluene is employed in considerable excess so that it

$$CH_3 \bigodot + ClCOCH_3 \longrightarrow CH_3 \bigodot COCH_3 + HCl$$

may act both as a reagent and a solvent. Note that in this reaction *ortho*-substitution is negligible, and the pure *p*-methylacetophenone is obtained.

p-METHYLACETOPHENONE. *Required :* Toluene, 250 c.c.; acetyl chloride, 35 c.c.; aluminium chloride, 40 gms.

Fit a 500 c.c. flask (preferably by means of a three-necked adaptor) with a stirrer having a mercury (or other type of) seal, a dropping-funnel and, by means of the third outlet, with a calcium chloride tube. Place 250 c.c. of *dry* toluene and 40 gms. of aluminium chloride in the flask, and cool the latter in an ice-water bath inside a fume-cupboard. (Ensure that the aluminium chloride is a fresh sample, *i.e.*, that it has not been long stored in a previously opened bottle, and pulverise it if necessary immediately before use.) When the mixture has been thoroughly cooled, place 35 c.c. of acetyl chloride in the dropping-funnel, and allow it to run drop-wise into the flask over a period of 30 minutes, maintaining the stirring and cooling throughout. Hydrogen chloride is steadily evolved. When the addition of the acetyl chloride is complete, replace the ice-bath by a water-bath, and maintain the temperature of the latter at 20–25° for 2 hours with constant stirring. During this period hydrogen chloride continues to be liberally evolved, and the product darkens considerably in colour. Now pour the product into 500 c.c. of dilute hydrochloric acid in a separating-funnel, and shake the mixture thoroughly: this operation removes the dark colour, and the toluene solution becomes yellow. Run off the lower acid layer, and extract the toluene three times with water. Finally dry the toluene over calcium chloride.

Fit a 75–100 c.c. Claisen flask with a small dropping-funnel in the main neck, and a water-condenser to the side-arm, and then run the filtered toluene solution slowly into the flask at such a rate that the volume of solution entering is approximately the same as that of the toluene (b.p. 111°) distilling over. When the unchanged toluene has thus been removed, replace the funnel by a capillary tube, and continue the distillation under reduced pressure by means of a water-pump. The *p*-methylacetophenone is obtained as a colourless liquid, b.p. 110–112°/15 mm., leaving a dark residue in the flask. Yield 20–25 gms. The ketone may require redistillation to obtain a sharply-boiling fraction. It can be distilled at atmospheric pressure, and has b.p. 220–224°/760 mm.

p-ETHYL-TOLUENE.   *Required:* *p*-Methylacetophenone, 15 gms.; granulated zinc, 40 gms.; mercuric chloride, 5 gms.

To prepare the amalgamated zinc, place 40 gms. of granulated zinc in a 750 c.c. flask, and clean the surface by first shaking the zinc with a small quantity of acetone, then decanting off the acetone and repeating the process with distilled water. Dissolve 5 gms. of mercuric chloride in 100 c.c. of distilled water containing 5 c.c. of concentrated hydrochloric acid, add the solution to the zinc, and shake the mixture gently for about 5 minutes. Decant the solution from the amalgamated zinc, and then pour on to the latter 200 c.c. of water and 200 c.c. of concentrated hydrochloric acid. Add 15 gms. of *p*-methylacetophenone, fit the flask to a reflux water-condenser, and boil the mixture for 6 hours: during the latter half of this period add 30 c.c. of concentrated hydrochloric acid, *ca.* 5 c.c. at a time, down the condenser.

Cool the mixture and pour the liquid reaction product into a separating-funnel. Rinse out the flask (which may contain some unchanged zinc) with ether, pour the latter into the funnel, and extract the aqueous solution with the ether. Repeat the extraction with a second quantity of ether, unite the ether extracts, wash them by extracting once with water, and then dry the ethereal extract over sodium sulphate.

Filter the dried extract, and then distil off the ether from a small flask, using the customary precautions: if the volume of ether is large, fit a dropping-funnel to the flask so that the ethereal extract can be run into the flask as the ether distils off. When the ether has been removed, replace the water-condenser by an air-condenser, and continue the distillation. The *p*-ethyl-toluene distils at 161–162° as a colourless liquid. Yield, 10 gms.

Quinoline. C_9H_7N. (Skraup's Synthesis.)

When a mixture of aniline, nitrobenzene, glycerol and concentrated sulphuric acid is heated, a vigorous reaction occurs with the formation of quinoline. It is probable that the sulphuric acid first dehydrates the glycerol giving acrolein or acraldehyde (A), which then condenses at its double bond with the amino group of the aniline to give acrolein-aniline (B). The latter in its *enol*

$$CH_2(OH) \cdot CH(OH) \cdot CH_2(OH) \ - \ 2H_2O \ = \ CH_2:CH \cdot CHO \ (A)$$
$$C_6H_5NH_2 + CH_2:CH \cdot CHO \ = \ C_6H_5NHCH_2CH_2CHO \ (B)$$

form (C) then undergoes ring-closure to give the unstable intermediate compound (D), which is at once oxidised by the nitrobenzene to quinoline (E).

The nitrobenzene is thus itself reduced to aniline, which can then react as before.

When the crude reaction product is made alkaline and steam-distilled, a mixture of quinoline and some unchanged aniline passes over. Pure quinoline can be isolated from this mixture by one of the following methods:

(1) The mixed bases are dissolved in dilute hydrochloric acid and sodium nitrite solution added. The aniline is thus diazotised and, if the mixture is subsequently boiled, converted into phenol. The solution is then made alkaline and steam-distilled, the quinoline passing over, while the phenol remains behind in the alkaline solution.

(2) The mixed bases are boiled with an acetic acid-acetic anhydride mixture to convert the aniline into acetanilide. The product is poured into water, when the acetanilide crystallises out while the quinoline remains in solution as quinoline acetate. The acetanilide is filtered off, and the filtrate made alkaline and steam-distilled.

(3) The mixed amines are dissolved in hydrochloric acid and zinc chloride solution added. The quinoline chlorozincate,* $(C_9H_7N)_2,H_2ZnCl_4$, crystallises out, being almost insoluble in water, while the aniline chlorozincate remains in solution. The quinoline chlorozincate is then filtered off and decomposed by alkalis, and the liberated quinoline extracted with ether or steam-distilled.

Of the above methods for separating the amines, number (3) is the best.

Required: Aniline, 24 c.c.; nitrobenzene, 13 c.c.; anhydrous glycerol, 62 c.c.; sulphuric acid, 36 c.c.; zinc chloride, 23 gms.

The reaction is carried out in a 2-litre *long-necked* round-bottomed flask, to which is fitted an efficient reflux water-condenser, capable of condensing a sudden rush of vapour without choking. For this purpose, a long bulb-condenser, similar to that shown in Fig. 3(A) (p. 90) is best, but the inner tube must be of wide bore (at least 12 mm.). Alternatively, an air-condenser of wide bore may be used, and a short double-surface water-condenser fitted to its top. A steam-distillation fitting for the flask should also be prepared in advance, so that the crude product can subsequently be steam-distilled directly from the flask. The glycerol used in the preparation must be anhydrous, and should therefore be dehydrated by the method described on p. 85.

Place 24 c.c. (24·5 gms.) of aniline, 13 c.c. (15·5 gms.) of

---

* These chlorozincates must not be confused with the non-ionic compounds which quinoline and aniline bases give with neutral zinc chloride: the latter have the formulae $[(C_9H_7N)_2ZnCl_2]$ and $[(C_6H_7N)_2ZnCl_2]$ respectively, and both are only slightly soluble in water.

nitrobenzene,* and 62 c.c. (75 gms.) of the anhydrous glycerol in the flask and mix thoroughly. (If the glycerol is still warm from the dehydration, cool the mixture in water.) Now add slowly 36 c.c. (66 gms.) of concentrated sulphuric acid, shaking the mixture thoroughly during the addition. The mixture at first becomes semi-solid owing to the separation of aniline sulphate, but later becomes mobile as the temperature rises during the further addition of the acid. Now add some fragments of un-glazed porcelain, fit the reflux condenser to the flask, and support the latter on a gauze-covered tripod, preferably in a fume-cupboard; clamp the condenser so that it is inclined at about 60° to the horizontal, as "choking" is less likely in this position than in a vertical position. Now heat the flask cautiously with a Bunsen flame: *immediately* the reaction starts and bubbles of vapour form in the liquid, turn out the gas. (It is advisable to have a duster soaked in cold water at hand: if, when the reaction starts, the duster is wrapped around the upper part of the body of the flask, the risk of the condenser choking becomes negligible.)

When the vigorous reaction subsides, replace the gauze by a sand-bath and boil the mixture gently for 3 hours. By this time the reaction is complete, and no unchanged nitrobenzene should remain. Then add about an equal volume of water, cool, and add concentrated sodium hydroxide solution until the mixture is definitely alkaline to litmus-paper. Steam-distil the product until the crude quinoline has been driven completely over and the distillate leaving the condenser is no longer turbid (usually about 700 c.c.). Extract the quinoline with ether and then either distil off the ether taking the customary precautions, or, if the amount of ether used is small, evaporate the ether in an open basin on a water-bath, the gas being turned out immediately before the basin is placed in position. (Chloroform may be used instead of ether, but its complete removal from the quinoline requires distil-lation.) Dissolve the crude residual quinoline in 200 c.c. of dilute hydrochloric acid (1 vol. concentrated acid to 4 vols. water), warm the solution to about 60°, and add a solution of 23 gms. of zinc chloride in 40 c.c. of dilute hydrochloric acid. The quinoline chlorozincate soon starts to crystallise. Cool the well-stirred mixture thoroughly in ice-water and when crystallisation is complete, filter at the pump, wash well with dilute hydrochloric acid, and drain.

* The initial reaction proceeds more smoothly if 37 gms. of *dry* arsenic acid are used in place of the nitrobenzene for oxidation purposes. The yields when arsenic acid is used are, however, uncertain and often low.

Transfer the quinoline chlorozincate to a beaker, add a small quantity of water, and then add 10% sodium hydroxide solution until the initial precipitate of zinc hydroxide completely redissolves, and the free quinoline separates. Transfer the mixture to a separating-funnel, wash out the beaker with ether, adding the washings also to the solution in the funnel, and then extract the quinoline twice with ether. Dry the united ethereal extracts by adding an ample quantity of powdered potassium hydroxide and allowing the mixture to stand overnight. Then filter the ethereal solution, wash the residual potash with more ether and then distil off the ether from a small (75 c.c.) flask with the usual precautions (Fig. 48, p. 123). Then replace the water-condenser by an air-condenser and distil the quinoline. Collect the fraction of b.p. 234–237°. Yield, 18 gms.

Quinoline is a colourless liquid, having b.p. 236° and d, 1·095. It has an odour similar to, but fainter than, that of pyridine: unlike pyridine, it is almost insoluble in water.

1:2:3:4-Tetrahydro-carbazole. (The Fischer Indolisation Reaction.)

The *Fischer Indolisation Reaction* occurs when the phenylhydrazone of a suitable aldehyde or ketone undergoes cyclisation with loss of ammonia, under the influence of various reagents, such as zinc chloride, alcoholic hydrogen chloride, or acetic acid. For example, the phenylhydrazone of acetophenone (p. 202) when heated with zinc chloride gives 2-phenylindole:

$$CH_3$$
$$C_6H_5NHNH_2 + CH_3COC_6H_5 \longrightarrow C_6H_5NHN{:}\dot{C}{\cdot}C_6H_5$$

(For the mechanism of this reaction, see Robinson and Robinson, *J.C.S.*, 1918, **113**, 639; *1924*, **145**, 827.) The reaction is of wide application: for example, the use of phenyl-methyl-hydrazine, $C_6H_5(CH_3)N{\cdot}NH_2$, in the above reaction gives 1-methyl-2-phenylindole, whereas pyruvic acid, $CH_3{\cdot}CO{\cdot}COOH$, when converted to its phenylhydrazone and then indolised, gives indole-2-carboxylic acid. The ease of cyclisation of various hydrazones varies greatly. Indole itself cannot be prepared from acetaldehyde-phenylhydrazone: on the other hand, the phenylhydrazones of some saturated cyclic ketones undergo cyclisation very readily even when boiled with acetic acid. This is illustrated in the following preparation, in which *cyclo*hexanone is converted to its phenylhydrazone, and the latter, without isolation, is converted to 1:2:3:4-tetrahydrocarbazole by boiling with acetic acid:

$$C_6H_5NH\cdot NH_2 + \quad \begin{array}{c} CH_2 \\ H_2C \quad CH_2 \\ | \qquad | \\ OC \quad CH_2 \\ CH_2 \end{array} \longrightarrow \quad C_6H_5NH\cdot N:C \begin{array}{c} CH_2 \\ H_2C \quad CH_2 \\ | \qquad | \\ CH_2 \\ CH_2 \end{array} \longrightarrow$$

Required: *Cyclo*hexanone, 9 c.c.;   phenylhydrazine, 8 c.c. Dissolve 8·8 gms. (9·0 c.c.) of *cyclo*hexanone in 80 c.c. of glacial acetic acid, add 8 c.c. of phenylhydrazine, and boil the solution under reflux for 5 minutes. Cool the solution, when the tetrahydrocarbazole will crystallise out. Filter at the pump, drain well, and recrystallise either from aqueous alcohol or aqueous acetic acid. The tetrahydrocarbazole is obtained as colourless crystals, m.p. 118°: yield of recrystallised material, 6 gms.

If cold saturated alcoholic solutions of the recrystallised tetrahydrocarbazole and of picric acid are mixed and stirred, the chocolate-brown picrate of the carbazole slowly crystallises. After it has been filtered off at the pump, washed with a small quantity of alcohol, and dried, it has m.p. 145–146°.

9:10-Dihydroanthracene-9:10-*endo*-αβ-succinic Anhydride. (The Diels-Alder Reaction.)

The *Diels-Alder Reaction* consists in the direct combination of a compound containing a conjugated diene system with a reagent which possesses a double or triple bond activated by suitable adjacent groups. Examples of such reagents are maleic anhydride, *p*-benzoquinone, acraldehyde and acetylene dicarboxylic esters. Combination always occurs at the 1,4 positions of the diene system:

thus butadiene combines with *p*-benzoquinone as shown above; in this case a second molecule of butadiene can similarly add on to the opposite side of the *p*-benzoquinone ring.

The Diels-Alder Reaction usually occurs readily: it is of great value (*a*) for diagnosing the presence of a conjugated diene grouping, (*b*) for synthetic purposes in the preparation of cyclic systems.

In the following preparation, this reaction is exemplified by the union of anthracene with maleic anhydride, to form 9:10-dihydroanthracene-9:10-*endo*-αβ-succinic anhydride: note that as a result of this reaction both the outer rings of the anthracene system become truly aromatic in character.

Required: Anthracene, 2 gms.; maleic anhydride, 1 gm.

Add 2 gms. of anthracene and 1 gm. maleic anhydride to 25 c.c. of dry xylene, and boil the mixture under reflux: during the early stages of the heating, keep the mixture gently shaken until a clear solution is obtained, otherwise a portion of the reagents may adhere to the base of the flask and darken because of local over-heating. After boiling for 20 minutes, cool the solution, when the addition product will rapidly crystallise. Filter at the pump, and drain well. (Yield of crude material, which is almost pure, *ca.* 2·7 gms.) Recrystallise from about 25 c.c. of xylene with the addition if necessary of a small quantity of animal charcoal: filter the solution through a small preheated funnel, as the solute rapidly crystallises as the solution begins to cool. Place the recrystallised material in a vacuum desiccator, preferably over fresh paraffin-wax shavings to absorb traces of xylene. The additional product is obtained as colourless crystals, m.p. 256–258°. Yield *ca.* 2 gms.

1*

PART III

REACTIONS AND IDENTIFICATION OF ORGANIC COMPOUNDS

THE following pages contain an account of the chief reactions of the commoner organic compounds, arranged in a series of short sections with a view to the identification of an unknown organic compound. The first eight sections contain various preliminary tests which should be applied to an unknown compound in order to obtain *general* information with regard to its identity. Each of the remaining seventeen sections is devoted to one class of organic compound, and a description is given of the general reactions of members of this class and then of any important special reactions which individual members may show. Only the commoner members of each class are described, because it is considered desirable that students should get a thorough grasp of the reactions of these members before they proceed to wider and more ambitious schemes for the identification of organic compounds.

The following is a list of the sections, together with a complete catalogue of the compounds included:

SECTION:
1. Heating on a crucible lid.
2. Identification of elements present.
3. Heating with soda-lime.
4. Treatment with sodium hydroxide solution.
5. Treatment with sodium carbonate solution.
6. Treatment with concentrated sulphuric acid.
7. Reactions and colorations with ferric chloride solution.
8. Reaction with 2:4-dinitrophenylhydrazine.
9. Alcohols. *Methyl alcohol, ethyl alcohol,* iso*propyl alcohol,* n-*butyl alcohol, glycol, glycerol, benzyl alcohol,* cyclohexanol.
10. Phenols. *Phenol,* o-, m- *and* p-*cresol, catechol, resorcinol, hydroquinone,* α- *and* β-*naphthol.*
11. Aldehydes. *Formaldehyde, metaformaldehyde, acetaldehyde, paraldehyde, chloral hydrate, benzaldehyde, salicylaldehyde.*
12. Ketones. *Acetone, acetophenone, benzophenone.*
13. Acids. *Formic, acetic, oxalic, succinic, lactic, tartaric, citric, benzoic, salicylic, phthalic, and cinnamic acids.*

234

14. **Esters.** *Methyl and ethyl esters of all the acids in Section* 13 *(except lactic and citric acids); benzyl acetate; phenyl esters of acetic, benzoic and salicylic acids.*

15. Ammonium salts, amides, imides, nitriles.

(A) *Ammonium salts of acids given in Section* 13 *(except lactic acid).*

(B) *Formamide, acetamide, oxamide, urea, benzamide, salicylamide.*

(C) *Succinimide, phthalimide.*

(D) *Acetonitrile, benzonitrile.*

16. Acid chlorides and Anhydrides.

(A) *Acetyl chloride, benzoyl chloride.*

(B) *Acetic, succinic and phthalic anhydrides.*

17. **Carbohydrates.** *Glucose, fructose, sucrose, maltose, lactose, starch.*

18. **Quinones.** *Benzoquinone, anthraquinone.*

19. **Amines.** (A) Primary aromatic amines. *Aniline, o-, m- and p-toluidine, α- and β-naphthylamine.*

(B) Secondary aromatic amines. *Monomethylaniline, diphenylamine.*

(C) Tertiary aromatic amines. *Dimethylaniline, triphenylamine.*

(D) Heterocyclic amines. *Hexamethylene-tetramine, pyridine, quinoline.*

20. **Anilides.** *Acetanilide, benzanilide.*

21. Amino-acids.

(A) Amino-aliphatic carboxylic acids. *Glycine, tyrosine,* cystine.**

(B) Amino-aromatic carboxylic acids. *Anthranilic acid.*

(C) Amino-aromatic sulphonic acids. *Sulphanilic acid.*

22. Nitro-compounds.

(A) Nitro-hydrocarbons. *Nitrobenzene, p-nitrotoluene, m-dinitrobenzene.*

(B) Nitro-phenols. *o- and p-Nitrophenols.*

(C) Nitro-anilines. *o-, m-, and p-Nitro-anilines.*

23. **Purines.** *Uric acid.*

24. **Halogeno-hydrocarbons.** *Methyl iodide, ethyl bromide and iodide, chloroform, iodoform, carbon tetrachloride, chlorobenzene, bromobenzene, iodobenzene, benzyl chloride.*

25. **Hydrocarbons.** *Benzene, toluene, naphthalene, anthracene, petrol.*

Ethers as a class (diethyl ether, anisole, phenetole) have been omitted, primarily because there is no readily applied reaction or test which is characteristic solely of the ether grouping. Diethyl ether can at once

---

* Tyrosine and cystine have been included primarily for students of biochemistry, physiology and medicine; these two amino-acids might, however, be omitted by other students.

be recognised by its odour, but in addition its inflammable nature makes it unsuitable for attempted identification by students.

In each of the Sections 9–25, the chief physical properties of the compounds concerned are first briefly indicated: a list of the general reactions* is then given, followed by practical directions for the application or illustration of these general reactions. Finally, any important special reactions of individual members are described.

It is suggested that students should work systematically through these sections, undertaking one or more sections at each practical class, according to the time available. It is strongly recommended, however, that after the first or second practical class, students should always be given two or three unknown compounds at each class, and should then obtain as much information with regard to the chemical character of the compounds as their previous work allows, a complete identification not in general being expected until the end of the sections is reached. In this way the student's knowledge of the organic reactions is consolidated as he proceeds through the sections, his experience of the general method of identification steadily increases, and the investigation of the unknown compounds forms a welcome break from the systematic pursuit of the sectional work.

NOTE. It is not expected that a student will attempt to memorise all the colour tests given in Part III. He might for example be expected to know the Liebermann Nitroso Reaction for phenol itself (p. 255). Details of the divergence from the "standard" result are recorded primarily for reference, so that a student will not be diverted from his line of investigation if he observes that a "suspected" phenol does not respond exactly to the standard colour changes.

Section 1. Heating on a Crucible Lid.

Heat a small portion of the following substances on an inverted porcelain or nickel crucible lid. At first, heat one side of the lid *gently*, so that the heat travels along the lid to the organic substance: later heat the lid more strongly. Note carefully in particular (*a*) the change in appearance, (*b*) whether readily inflammable, (*c*) any odour produced, (*d*) whether a non-volatile residue is left.

It must be emphasised that the following substances are merely representative of widely different classes of compounds, and that the test when applied to an unknown compound often provides only a *general* indication of the pro-

---

* The success of the test-tube reactions described in Sections 9–25 depends largely on the use of the reagents in the correct proportions. The quantities specified are given as a guide for this purpose, but need not in general be rigidly adhered to.

bable class to which the compound belongs. Moreover, the behaviour of a compound when heated is often determined more by the nature of its substituent groups than by its general character.

Alcohol.—Burns rapidly with a clear flame. Typical of many aliphatic substances.

Aniline.—Burns with a very smoky flame, clouds of soot being produced. Typical of many aromatic substances.

Ethylene dibromide.—Does not burn until vapour becomes hot and then burns with a slightly smoky flame. Typical of substances rich in halogens such as chloroform, chloral hydrate, and carbon tetrachloride. (Note, however, that iodoform evolves copious fumes of iodine when heated in this way.)

Sodium benzoate.—Burns with great difficulty, and after prolonged heating leaves a white infusible residue of Na_2CO_3. Scrape this residue into a test-tube, and test for carbonate in the usual way. Typical of alkali salts of carboxylic acids.

In similar circumstances, silver salts leave a residue of metallic silver; lead and copper salts usually leave a residue of the corresponding oxide; calcium and barium salts leave a residue of the carbonate or oxide. Identify the metal in all such cases by the usual tests of qualitative inorganic analysis. Metals other than the above are seldom encountered in elementary qualitative analysis.

Sodium sulphanilate.—Burns with difficulty, leaving a residue of (chiefly) sodium sulphide. Add dil. HCl, and confirm without delay the evolution of H_2S by means of a filter-paper moistened with lead acetate solution. Typical of salts of the sulphonic acids.

Acetone sodium bisulphite.—Almost non-inflammable, leaving a colourless residue of sodium sulphite and sulphate. Transfer residue to a test-tube, add dil. HCl, warm, and confirm the SO_2 evolved.

Cane sugar.—Melts, darkens, then chars, and finally burns, with a marked odour of burnt sugar. Typical of the changes given by mono- and di-saccharides.

Tartaric acid and tartrates also swell up, blacken and give an odour resembling burnt sugar. Citrates and lactates also char, and give off odours resembling burnt sugar.

A large variety of organic compounds char without melting, *e.g.*, starch, oxamide, sulphonic acids, uric acid, *etc.*

NOTE. (1) Care should be taken to distinguish between a residue of carbon which may be very difficult to burn off completely, and a really non-volatile residue due to the presence of a metallic derivative. Thus for instance starch leaves a hard black residue of carbon which can best be burned away by moistening with a saturated solution of ammonium nitrate and then reheating.

(2) Aqueous solutions do not usually ignite even though the solute is highly inflammable, *e.g.*, an aqueous solution of alcohol containing less than 50% of the latter. When aqueous solutions of solid substances are heated on a crucible lid, they usually "spit" vigorously immediately before solidification.

Section 2.   Identification of Elements present in an Organic Compound.

1. Carbon and Hydrogen. The presence of these elements is usually assumed. If a direct test is required, a mixture of about 0·5 gm. of the powdered substance and 3–4 gms. of finely powdered copper oxide is heated in the tube **A** (Fig. 52) and the

FIG. 52.

gases issuing from the delivery-tube are then collected above the lime-water in the tube **B**. When the delivery-tube is withdrawn and the tube **B** closed and shaken, a white precipitate indicates carbon dioxide, and hence the presence of carbon. (Alternatively, the delivery-tube may dip into the lime-water during the heating, but in this case the lime-water is apt to "suck back" into **A** if the heating is irregular.) If the compound contains sulphur, the issuing gases must first be passed through a solution of potassium dichromate in dilute sulphuric acid to remove the sulphur dioxide (which is oxidised to sulphuric acid) before passing into lime-water.

A mist of condensed water on the upper portion of the tube **A** indicates the presence of hydrogen. To detect the presence of hydrogen in this way, however, the copper oxide must first be strongly heated in a crucible and then allowed to cool in a good desiccator: otherwise the water normally absorbed by the very hygroscopic copper oxide will always give a mist on the tube **A**.

2. Nitrogen.   The Lassaigne Sodium Test.*

This test is general for organic nitrogen compounds. The organic compound is heated with molten sodium, the nitrogen present thus forming sodium cyanide. The latter is extracted with water and then identified by first adding ferrous sulphate solution and then boiling the alkaline mixture in order to convert the cyanide to ferrocyanide:

$$6NaCN + Fe(OH)_2 = Na_4[Fe(CN)_6] + 2NaOH$$

Ferric chloride solution is then added to convert the sodium ferrocyanide to the deep blue ferric ferrocyanide (or Prussian Blue), dilute sulphuric acid being also added to dissolve any ferrous and ferric hydroxides present in the other-

$$3Na_4[Fe(CN)_6] + 4FeCl_3 = Fe_4[Fe(CN)_6]_3 + 12NaCl$$

* For Middleton's sodium carbonate-zinc method for the detection of elements, see p. 243.

wise alkaline solution. The blue coloration is thus a definite test for nitrogen in the original organic compound.

Place about 0·1 gm. of the organic compound* in a short hard-glass test-tube, and add two small pellets of metallic sodium (roughly 3 mm. in diameter). Grasping the tube firmly with a test-tube holder, heat the mixture in a Bunsen flame, at first *gently* and then, after any initial reaction† has subsided, more vigorously until fumes have ceased to be evolved and a well-roasted product has been obtained. While holding the tube in *a vertical position*, plunge it firmly and without delay into about 20 c.c. of *distilled* water contained in a small clean mortar. A vigorous action occurs as the tube fractures and the excess of sodium oxide reacts with the water: hence the need to hold the tube vertically in the water until all reaction has ceased, in case a portion of the contents should be blown out. Plunging the end of the tube into water should *always* be performed immediately after heating: if the tube is allowed to cool somewhat beforehand, the reaction may then be far more violent.

The sodium fusion and extraction, if performed strictly in accordance with the above directions, should be safe operations. In crowded laboratories, however, additional safety may be obtained by employing the following modification. Suspend the hard-glass test-tube by the rim through a hole in a piece of stout copper sheet (Fig. 53). Place 1–2 pellets of sodium in the tube, and heat gently until the sodium melts. Then drop the organic compound, in *small quantities* at a time, down the tube, allowing the reaction to subside after each addition before the next is made. (If the compound is liquid, allow two or three small drops to fall at intervals from a fine dropping-tube directly on to the molten sodium.) Then heat the complete mixture as before until no further reaction occurs. Next push the tube upwards partly out of the copper sheet by a piece of clean wire gauze, grasp the neck firmly with a test-tube holder, and transfer the tube to a fume-cupboard. There reheat the tube, and then without delay plunge it as before into about 20 c.c. of distilled water contained in a mortar placed immediately behind a small sheet of plate-glass clamped vertically to act as a screen.

FIG. 53.

The first method should be used, however, by experienced students, as it has the advantage that the initial reaction of the compound with the

---

* Note that, in addition to the recognised unstable compounds (such as polynitro derivatives), *chloroform* and *carbon tetrachloride* should never be submitted to Lassaigne's sodium test, as violent explosions may result.

† If a vigorous initial reaction occurs, remove the tube from the flame until the reaction subsides, and then continue heating.

sodium as the cold mixture is warmed can be observed, and frequently gives an indication of the general nature of the compound: thus a vigorous reaction in the cold, or immediately on gentle warming, may indicate an acidic substance, whereas a vigorous reaction after the mixture has been gently heated may indicate a compound rich in oxygen; evolution of violet vapour of iodine indicates a substance rich in iodine, *etc.*

Now grind up the mixture of solution and glass in the mortar to ensure extraction of the sodium salts, and then filter. Divide the filtrate into three portions, reserving two portions for testing for halogens and sulphur.

Dissolve about 0·5 gm. of ferrous sulphate crystals in a *small* quantity of warm water, and add the solution to the first portion of the filtrate contained in a boiling-tube. An immediate dark greenish-grey* precipitate of ferrous hydroxide should occur: if the mixture remains clear, add a few c.c. of sodium hydroxide solution. Now boil the mixture gently for a few minutes to ensure formation of the ferrocyanide, cool under the tap, add *one drop* of ferric chloride solution, and then acidify with dilute sulphuric acid. A greenish-blue coloration, sometimes followed slowly by an actual precipitation of Prussian blue, indicates nitrogen. If only a green coloration is obtained, it often indicates insufficient reaction with the sodium: if, however, such a solution is filtered, "specks" of deep blue material can frequently be seen collected on the filter-paper and are a clear indication of the presence of nitrogen.

(1) Some nitrogenous organic compounds react very slowly with sodium even under the above conditions of fusion, and give in consequence only a feeble indication for nitrogen. If, in spite of this feeble indication, the general properties of the substance point to the presence of nitrogen, repeat the fusion using the apparatus shown in Fig. 53, but heat the sodium until it boils gently in the vertical tube. Then drop the substance, in *very small portions* at a time, down the tube, so that it falls through the column of sodium vapour into the boiling metal. Nitrogen is often yielded up under these conditions when the former less drastic method fails.

(2) Lassaigne's test is obviously a test also for carbon in the presence of nitrogen. It can be used therefore to detect nitrogen in carbon-free inorganic compounds, *e.g.*, complex nitrites, amino-sulphonic acid derivatives, *etc.*, but such compounds must before fusion with sodium be mixed with some non-volatile nitrogen-free organic compound such as starch.

---

* If the original compound contains sulphur, a black precipitate **may** be produced at this stage.

The Soda-lime Test. Certain classes of nitrogenous organic compounds (*e.g.*, amides, *etc.*) evolve ammonia when heated with soda-lime. In view of the limited application of this test, however, it may well be reserved for Section 3, where it is included with other compounds reacting with soda-lime.

Halogen. (1) THE BEILSTEIN TEST. For this very rapid test, which should precede Lassaigne's sodium test for halogen, secure a fragment of copper oxide **C** (Fig. 54(A)) by a platinum wire **D** held in turn by a glass rod: the latter may conveniently be thrust through a cork which fits a short test-tube so that the wire may be safely carried in the pocket. An alternative and cheaper apparatus for large classes consists of a piece of fine copper gauze **E** about 2 cm. square (Fig. 54(B)) securely rolled around one end of a stout copper wire carrying a cork for use as a holder. Heat the copper oxide **C** (or the copper gauze **E**) in a Bunsen flame until any initial green coloration caused by impurities on the copper has disappeared. Withdraw the wire, and dip the hot oxide (or the oxidised

(A)   (B)

FIG. 54.

gauze) into a small quantity of the *powdered* organic compound, *e.g.*, chloral hydrate. Now return the oxide to the flame, inserting the wire into the vertical edge of the flame about one inch from the top of the burner. A bright green coloration, often lasting only a few seconds, indicates halogen in the organic compound.

This test depends on the hot copper oxide decomposing a small quantity of the organic compound with the formation of the corresponding copper halide, which, being volatile at high temperatures, gives the usual green copper coloration. A few halogen-free amides, such as urea, thio-urea, and some pyridine compounds, give volatile cuprous cyanide under these conditions, however, and therefore also give the green coloration. It can be said therefore that a *negative* result for halogen is decisive, whereas a *positive* result means that halogen is *probably* present. The great value of this test for halogen is that, unlike the Lassaigne test, it is usually unaffected by the presence of nitrogen, and thus gives a *rapid* indication of the definite absence or probable presence of halogen.

(2) THE LASSAIGNE SODIUM TEST. (*a*) *Nitrogen being absent.* In this case the halogen has been converted during the sodium fusion into the corresponding sodium halide. Therefore acidify the second portion of the filtrate with dilute nitric acid

and add silver nitrate solution. A white or yellow precipitate indicates halogen.

(b) *Nitrogen being present.* In' this case, if silver nitrate is added to the acidified solution, a white precipitate of silver cyanide will be obtained and will be mixed with silver halide if halogen is present: it is necessary therefore either (i) to remove cyanide before testing for halogen, or (ii) to test for silver halide in a possible mixture of silver cyanide and halide.

(i) Take a portion of the clear filtrate from the sodium fusion, make it *just* acid with dilute nitric acid, and then evaporate it to about half-bulk by gentle boiling in an evaporating-basin. The very volatile hydrogen cyanide is thus driven off. Now cool and test for halogen by addition of silver nitrate. Note furthermore that if the organic compound contains sulphur, the hydrogen sulphide liberated by the dilute nitric acid will be driven off with the hydrogen cyanide during the evaporation, and the final precipitate of silver halide will therefore be entirely free also from silver sulphide.

(ii) Treat the clear filtrate with dilute nitric acid and silver nitrate (as in (a) above), and add mercurous nitrate drop by drop. Note that the white precipitate of silver salts turns black (showing the presence of silver cyanide). Now add an *excess* of mercurous nitrate: the black precipitate redissolves, but the silver halide remains undissolved.

To determine which halogen is present, take 1–2 c.c. of the filtrate from the sodium fusion, and add dilute sulphuric acid until *just* acid to litmus. Add about 1 c.c. of benzene and then about 1 c.c. of chlorine water and shake. A yellowish-brown colour in the benzene indicates bromine, and a violet colour iodine. If neither colour appears, the halogen is chlorine. The result may be confirmed by testing the solubility of the silver halide (free from cyanide) in *dilute* ammonia solution: silver chloride is readily soluble, whereas the bromide dissolves with difficulty, and the iodide not at all.

Sulphur. THE LASSAIGNE SODIUM TEST. The sodium fusion will have converted any sulphur present in the original compounds to sodium sulphide. Dissolve a few crystals of sodium nitroprusside, $Na_2[Fe(CN)_5NO],2H_2O$, in water, and add the solution to the third portion of the filtrate obtained from the sodium fusion. A brilliant purple coloration (resembling permanganate) indicates sulphur; the coloration slowly fades on standing. *Note.* (i) Sodium nitroprusside is unstable in aqueous solution and therefore the solution should be freshly prepared on each occasion. (ii) This is a *very* delicate test for sulphides, and it is essential therefore that all apparatus, particularly test-tubes, should be quite clean.

The following compounds are suggested for practising the identification of these elements:

(a) *Nitrogen.* Benzamide, ammonium benzoate, *p*-toluidine, glucosazone, acetanilide and benzanilide (require care to obtain definite blue coloration).

(b) *Halogen.* Chloral hydrate, sodium chloro-acetate, chlorobenzene, *p*-chlorophenol, dichlorhydrin, bromobenzene, iodobenzene.

(c) *Nitrogen and Halogen.* Aniline hydrochloride, ammonium chloro-acetate, *p*-chloro-acetanilide, suitable mixtures of (a) and (b).

(d) *Sulphur.* Potassium ethyl sulphate, acetone sodium bisulphite, benzaldehyde sodium bisulphite, toluene *p*-sulphonic acid and salts.

(e) *Nitrogen and Sulphur.* Sulphanilic acid, toluene *p*-sulphonamide, thiocarbanilide, aniline sulphate.

(f) *Nitrogen, Halogen and Sulphur.* Chloramine-T, suitable mixtures of (c) and (d), and (c) and (e).

It is essential that students practise these tests until they can be reasonably certain of accurate results with unidentified compounds. The following scheme for the identification of organic compounds is based largely on an initial classification of the compounds according to the elements they contain: hence an error in the identification of these elements may lead a student completely astray throughout the subsequent investigation.

Sodium Fusion on Semi-micro scale. The Lassaigne test can be readily carried out with as little as 0·01 gm. of material, using sodium pellets about 2 mm. in diameter in a tube about $3'' \times \frac{3}{8}''$. After fusion, the red-hot tube is plunged into distilled water in a porcelain crucible. The mixture is then heated, filtered and tested as already described.

The Sodium Carbonate-Zinc Method for Detecting Nitrogen, Halogens and Sulphur in Organic Compounds.

This method, due to Middleton (*Analyst*, 1935, **60**, 154), has the advantage over Lassaigne's method (pp. 238–242) that the use of metallic sodium is avoided: it has the disadvantage, however, that the reagents are not so readily obtained pure, and the method requires rather more time.

The organic compound is heated with a mixture of sodium carbonate and zinc dust, when nitrogen and halogens are split off as sodium cyanide and halides respectively, and sulphur as zinc sulphide. The sodium cyanide and halides are extracted with water and detected as in Lassaigne's method: the zinc sulphide in the residue is decomposed with acid and the hydrogen sulphide then detected with lead acetate paper. In these circumstances compounds which contain both nitrogen and sulphur do not give thiocyanates, a further minor advantage which the method has over Lassaigne's method.

Preparation of the Reagent. Grind thoroughly together in a dry mortar 25 gms. of pure anhydrous ("Analar") sodium carbonate and 50 gms. of the purest obtainable zinc dust. Preserve the reagent in a wide-necked stoppered bottle until required.

Zinc dust of good quality usually contains only negligible quantities of halogen and sulphur, and is nitrogen-free. A blank for these elements should, however, be made with every fresh batch of reagent prepared: if perceptible traces of halogen or sulphur are present, a blank or control test must be performed side by side with that on the organic compound, and the results compared.

The Fusion. (i) *Solid Compounds.* Place about 0·2 gm. of the powdered compound in a small dry hard-glass test-tube, add sufficient of the reagent to give a column about 1 cm. high and then shake the closed tube until the contents are thoroughly mixed. Now add more reagent (without mixing with the material already in the tube) until a total height of about 3–4 cms. is obtained.

(ii) *Liquid Compounds.* Fill the hard-glass tube to a height of about 1 cm. with the reagent. Add 2–3 drops of the liquid to be tested, and allow it to soak well into the reagent. Now add more reagent (without mixing) until a total height of about 4 cm. is obtained.

Now proceed as follows for both solid and liquid compounds. By means of a test-tube holder, hold the tube in a horizontal position, and by means of a small flame *gently* heat the mixture at the open end. Increase the size of the flame gradually until the mixture is red-hot at this end. Now slowly and cautiously extend the heating towards the closed end until the whole of the mixture is red-hot. (If during the extension of the heating, the mixture tends to be pushed out of the tube by the evolution of gas, stop the heating momentarily, and rotate the tube whilst still in a horizontal position in order to redistribute the contents: then continue the heating cautiously.) Finally heat the tube strongly in a vertical position for a short time. While the end of the tube is still red-hot, plunge the tube vertically into about 20 c.c. of cold distilled water in an evaporating-basin. Boil the contents of the dish gently, allow to cool slightly and then decant the supernatant liquid through a filter. Retain the residue in the basin for the sulphur test. Divide the clear filtrate into two portions.

NITROGEN. To one portion of the filtrate, add 2–3 c.c. of sodium hydroxide solution, then add ferrous sulphate solution and proceed as in the Lassaigne nitrogen test (p. 240). Note, however, that the final acidification with dilute sulphuric acid must be made with care, owing to the vigorous evolution of carbon dioxide from the carbonate present.

HALOGENS. Test the second portion of the filtrate for halogens in the usual way, as described under the Lassaigne halogen test (p. 241). Note that cyanides if present must first be eliminated as usual.

SULPHUR. Moisten the centre of a filter-paper with lead acetate solution. Then add about 10 c.c. of dilute hydrochloric acid to the residue in the evaporating-basin, and at once cover the latter with the paper. If zinc sulphide is present in the residue, the hydrogen sulphide evolved will give a *definite* dark brown coloration with the lead acetate paper. The presence of hydrogen sulphide can often be confirmed by its odour.

Section 3. Heating with Soda-lime.

Mix about 0·2 gm. of each of the following powdered substances with about 1 gm. of powdered soda-lime, preferably by grinding in a small clean mortar. The odour of ammonia in the cold usually indicates an ammonium salt, that of chloroform indicates chloral hydrate. Place the intimate mixture in a hard-glass test-tube (which thus should be not more than half-full), close the tube by a cork and delivery-tube, and then incline the tube as shown in Fig. 55, so that any liquid which subsequently condenses cannot run back into the hot part of the tube. Now heat the tube very gently at first and then more strongly. A non-condensible product such as hydrogen or methane is best detected by collecting a sample of the gas in a test-tube as shown in Fig. 55(A). A condensible product such as benzene or phenol should be collected by twisting the delivery-tube downwards and collecting the liquid in a few c.c. of water in a test-tube as shown in Fig. 55(B).

FIG. 55.

Substance	Class	Result
Ammonium acetate CH_3COONH_4	Ammonium salts	Ammonia evolved in the cold (turns moist red litmus-paper blue). Methane may be evolved by stronger and more prolonged heating.
Acetamide CH_3CONH_2 Urea H_2NCONH_2	Acid amides	Ammonia evolved.
Glycine H_2NCH_2COOH	Amino-carboxylic acids	Methylamine evolved (fishy odour, alkaline reaction).
Sodium acetate CH_3COONa	Carboxylic acids and salts	Methane evolved.
Sodium succinate $(CH_2COONa)_2$	,,	Ethane evolved.
Sodium benzoate C_6H_5COONa	,,	Yields benzene (odour).
Sodium formate HCOONa Sodium oxalate $(COONa)_2$	,,	Hydrogen evolved.

Substance	Class	Result
Sodium salicylate HOC_6H_4COONa	Carboxylic acids and salts	Yields phenol (odour, and also violet coloration when $FeCl_3$ is added to aqueous solution).
Cane sugar $C_{12}H_{22}O_{11}$	Carbohydrates	Odour of burnt sugar.
Tartaric acid $[CH(OH)COOH]_2$ Citric acid $C_3H_4(OH)(COOH)_3$	Some aliphatic hydroxy-acids and their salts	Odour resembling burnt sugar.
Chloral hydrate $CCl_3CH(OH)_2$		Chloroform (characteristic odour, heavier than water).
Sulphanilic acid $H_2NC_6H_4SO_3H$	Amino-aromatic sulphonic acids	Yields aniline (violet and then brown coloration with bleaching powder solution).
Anthranilic acid $H_2NC_6H_4COOH$	Amino-aromatic carboxylic acids	Yields aniline.
Cinnamic acid $C_6H_5CH:CHCOOH$	Unsaturated aromatic acid	Yields benzene and usually some styrene ($C_6H_5CH:CH_2$, colourless oily liquid, insoluble in water, pleasant characteristic odour).
Uric acid $C_5H_4N_4O_3$	Purine	Ammonia evolved.

NOTE (1) There is no satisfactory way of distinguishing between ethane and methane, both of which burn with an almost non-luminous flame: this fact however is quite unimportant at this stage of the investigation. Hydrogen also burns with a non-luminous flame and when the open end of a test-tube full of the gas is placed in a Bunsen flame, a mild explosion with a very characteristic report takes place.

(2) It frequently happens that more than one volatile product is evolved, a fact which may be of considerable value. For example, benzamide, $C_6H_5CONH_2$, will give off first ammonia, and then benzonitrile and benzene on stronger heating: salicylamide, $HOC_6H_4CONH_2$, will give off ammonia and then phenol.

It must be emphasised that the above reactions are solely of an exploratory nature, and serve merely to indicate the *probable* class to which the compound belongs.

Section 4. Treatment with concentrated NaOH solution.

Place about 0·2 gm. of the following substances in a boiling-tube and add about 5 c.c. of 30% aqueous NaOH solution. Note any reaction in the cold. Then add a small piece of un-glazed porcelain (to prevent "bumping"), and boil gently for a few minutes. Note any further reaction.

Substance	Class	Result
Ammonium acetate CH_3COONH_4	Ammonium salt of any acid	Ammonia evolved in the cold.
Acetamide CH_3CONH_2	Acid amides	
Acetonitrile CH_3CN	Acid nitriles	Ammonia evolved on heating.
Phthalimide $C_6H_4(CO)_2NH$	Imides of dibasic acids	
Acetanilide $C_6H_5NHCOCH_3$	Acid anilides	Hydrolysis takes place *very slowly*, and after heating for some time aniline is liberated.
Aniline hydrochloride $C_6H_5NH_2,HCl$	Salts of aromatic amines	Aniline is liberated in the cold and floats on the surface.
Ethyl benzoate $C_6H_5COOC_2H_5$	Esters of aromatic acids	Hydrolyses to alcohol and acid on being heated for a few minutes. Cool, add a few c.c. of water and then conc. HCl, and cool again. Crystals of benzoic acid separate out. Complete hydrolysis cannot be carried out effectively on a test-tube scale. (see p. 268).
Acetaldehyde CH_3CHO (aqueous solution)	Aliphatic aldehydes (not given by formaldehyde)	On heating gives a yellow resin having a characteristic colour.
Benzaldehyde C_6H_5CHO	Aromatic aldehydes	Undergoes Cannizzaro's reaction, giving benzyl alcohol and benzoic acid (p. 179). Warm gently for several minutes, cool, add a few c.c. of water and then conc. HCl, and cool again. Crystals of benzoic acid separate out on scratching the sides of the tube with glass rod. The Cannizzaro reaction cannot be carried out very satisfactory on a test-tube scale.
Chloral hydrate $CCl_3CH(OH)_2$		On gentle warming gives chloroform, which separates out as oily liquid, characteristic odour.
Glucose $C_6H_{12}O_6$	Certain carbohydrates	Turns brown on heating.

Section 5. Treatment with dilute Sodium Carbonate solution.

Place about 5 c.c. of Na_2CO_3 solution in a test-tube, add a few fragments of unglazed porcelain, and boil gently to ensure complete absence of bicarbonate and of free carbon dioxide. Cool the solution, add about 0·3 gm. of the substance to be tested, and at once fit a bent delivery-tube as shown in Fig. 52, p. 238. Now insert the delivery-tube into another test-tube containing lime-water, so that the end of the delivery-tube just does not touch the surface of the lime-water (if it dips below the surface of the lime-water, intermittent "sucking-back" is liable to occur later). Boil the sodium carbonate *gently* for 2–3 minutes, and then remove the delivery-tube, close the lime-water tube with the thumb and shake vigorously. A white precipitate indicates that carbon dioxide has been evolved.

The following classes of compound yield carbon dioxide when treated in this way.

(*a*) Carboxylic acids, *e.g.*, tartaric acid, benzoic acid (but not most phenols, hence this reaction can be used to distinguish between carboxylic acids and phenols, see p. 262).

(*b*) Sulphonic acids, *e.g.*, sulphanilic acid.

(*c*) Salts of weak bases, *e.g.*, aniline hydrochloride, which hydrolyses in aqueous solution to aniline and free hydrochloric acid.

(*d*) Nitrophenols, *e.g.*, *o*-nitrophenol. In these compounds the nitro group enhances the acidic properties of the phenolic grouping, which is thus able to liberate CO_2 from Na_2CO_3 solution.

NOTE. Methyl oxalate, unlike most other esters, hydrolyses very rapidly in aqueous solution: hence it will evolve CO_2 in the above test, owing to the formation of methyl alcohol and free oxalic acid.

Section 6. Action of concentrated Sulphuric Acid.

Place a *small* quantity (*i.e.*, about 0·2 gm.) of the following substances (finely powdered) in a clean dry test-tube and add about 1 c.c. of conc. H_2SO_4. Note any reaction in the cold, and then warm gently. Note any effervescence and any pronounced blackening (as distinct from mere darkening in colour).

Substance	Class	Result
Cane sugar $C_{12}H_{22}O_{11}$ Starch $(C_6H_{10}O_5)_n$ } Carbohydrates		Blackening with effervescence. CO and (or) CO_2 and SO_2 being evolved.
Tartaric acid $(CH(OH)COOH)_2$ Lactic acid $CH_3CH(OH)COOH$ } Certain hydroxy-aliphatic acids and their salts		,,

Substance	Class	Result
Citric acid $C_3H_4(OH)(COOH)_3$	Certain hydroxy-aliphatic acids and their salts	CO and CO_2 evolved, mixture turns yellow, no charring.
Resorcinol $C_6H_4(OH)_2$	Polyhydric phenols	Blackening without effervescence.
Sodium formate HCOONa	Formates	CO evolved, no blackening.
Oxalic acid $(COOH)_2,2H_2O$	Oxalates	CO and CO_2 evolved, no blackening.
Uric acid $C_5H_4N_4O_3$	Purines	Dissolves on gentle warming and is reprecipitated unchanged on dilution. The solution in conc. H_2SO_4 darkens on heating.

Section 7. Reactions and colorations with aqueous Ferric Chloride solution.

This test is frequently of great value for identification purposes, but it is essential that the conditions given below are rigidly observed, because the careless application of the reagent may give completely erroneous results.

Ferric chloride solution sometimes contains a large excess of HCl which would interfere with the following reactions. If it is very markedly acidic add *dil.* NaOH solution, drop by drop, to the ferric chloride solution until a small but permanent precipitate of ferric hydroxide is obtained. Filter this off through a small fluted filter-paper, and use the clear filtrate. The latter is still not quite neutral owing to hydrolysis, but this feeble acidity does not interfere with the tests given below.

Colorations or coloured precipitates are frequently given by the reaction of ferric chloride solution with (i) solutions of neutral salts of acids, (ii) phenols and many of their derivatives, (iii) a few amines. If a free acid is under investigation it must first be neutralised as follows: Place about 0·2 gm. of the acid in a boiling-tube and add a slight excess of ammonia solution, *i.e.*, until the solution is just alkaline to litmus-paper. Add a piece of unglazed porcelain and boil until the odour of ammonia is *completely* removed, and then cool. To the solution so obtained add a few drops of the "neutralised" ferric chloride solution. Perform this test with the following acids and note the result:

NOTE. For a very weak acid, the ammonium salt of which may dissociate rapidly on heating, conversion into the sodium salt is recommended. Place 0·2 gm. of the acid in a boiling-tube and add NaOH solution until the mixture is just alkaline to litmus-paper. Add *dil*. HNO₃ until just acid and then a slight exccess of ammonia until again just alkaline. Add a piece of unglazed porcelain, and boil until the odour of ammonia is removed, and then cool.

Substance	Class	Result*
(a) Formic acid ⎱ Acetic acid ⎰	Lower aliphatic acids	Deep red coloration. Boil for one minute and note the formation of a brown ppt. of basic ferric salt. Add dil. HCl: the ppt. dissolves, giving a clear solution.
(b) Oxalic acid		Nothing observable.
(c) Succinic acid		Buff-coloured ppt. in the cold. Add dil. H₂SO₄: the ppt. dissolves giving clear solution.
(d) Benzoic acid	Aromatic acids (except phenolic carboxylic acids)	Buff-coloured ppt. in the cold. Add dil. H₂SO₄: the ppt. dissolves, but simultaneously a white ppt. of benzoic acid is produced.
(e) Salicylic acid	Phenolic acid	Violet coloration. (Note however that a dilute solution of salicylic acid will give this coloration without any preliminary neutralisation.)

(f) Take two test-tubes **A** and **B**: in **A** place about 5 c.c. of neutralised tartaric acid solution and in **B** place 5 c.c. of distilled water. To each solution add 3–4 drops of ferric chloride solution. Place a piece of white paper under the tubes, look down their length and note that **A** is definitely yellow compared with the control tube **B**. This yellow colour is given by α-hydroxy-carboxylic-acids, *e.g.*, lactic acid, tartaric acid, citric acid.

(g) Dissolve a few crystals of phenol in water and add ferric chloride solution: a violet coloration is produced. Repeat, using 1–2 drops of *m*-cresol shaken up with about 1 c.c. of water: a violet coloration is again produced. Catechol (in dilute solution) gives a green coloration.

---

* Unless *all* the excess ammonia has been driven off in the preparation of the neutral salt, the result obtained on adding ferric chloride will be misleading owing to the precipitation of ferric hydroxide. If this is suspected, the tests should be repeated using an aqueous solution of the *pure* sodium salts of these acids for comparison.

(*h*) Dissolve 2–3 drops of *o*-toluidine in a few drops of dil. HCl and add 2–3 drops of ferric chloride solution: a green coloration is produced and is slowly replaced by a bluish-green or blue precipitate.

Section 8. Reaction with 2:4-Dinitrophenylhydrazine.

This is a test for the >C=O group. Most aldehydes and ketones readily condense with this reagent* giving yellow- or orange-coloured precipitates.

To a few drops of formalin solution add a few drops of dinitro-phenylhydrazine reagent: a yellow precipitate is produced in the cold. Acetaldehyde and acetone give orange-coloured precipitates. Dissolve water-insoluble compounds (*e.g.*, benzaldehyde, salicylaldehyde, acetophenone and benzophenone) in a small volume of methyl alcohol before adding the reagent. With benzophenone the precipitate forms slowly.

Section 9. Alcohols. –OH.

Methyl alcohol, ethyl alcohol, isopropyl alcohol, n-butyl alcohol, glycol, glycerol, benzyl alcohol, cyclohexanol.

Physical Properties. All colourless liquids. All completely miscible with water, except benzyl alcohol and *cyclo*hexanol, which are only slightly soluble. Pure glycol and glycerol are characterised by high viscosity, which falls, however, as the hygroscopic liquids absorb water from the air.

Glycol and glycerol are odourless: the other alcohols have faint odours, that of benzyl alcohol being characteristic.

GENERAL REACTIONS.

1. Give crystalline derivatives with 3:5-dinitrobenzoyl chloride.
2. Primary alcohols (·CH$_2$OH) are oxidised to aldehydes and then to acids depending upon conditions. Secondary alcohols (>CHOH) are oxidised to ketones.
3. Alcohols containing the CH$_3$CH(OH)· group give the iodoform reaction.

1. *3:5-Dinitrobenzoylation.* To 0·5 gm. of powdered 3:5-dinitro-benzoyl chloride† in a dry test-tube, add 2 c.c. of dry methyl alcohol and warm the mixture until a clear solution is obtained. Cool and filter off the solid which separates. Recrystallise from light petroleum (b.p. 60–80°). Take the m.p. of the 3:5-dinitrobenzoate formed: methyl, m.p. 108°; ethyl, m.p. 96°; *iso*propyl, m.p. 122°; *n*-butyl, m.p. 64°; glycol, m.p. 134°; glyceryl, m.p. 113°; benzyl, m.p. 114°; *cyclo*hexanyl, m.p. 112°.

2. *Oxidation.* (i) Dissolve 5 gms. of potassium dichromate in 20

---

* Details of the preparation of the reagent are given on p. 427.
† For preparation, see p. 189.

c.c. of dil. H_2SO_4 in a 100 c.c. bolt-head flask. Cool and add 1 c.c. of methyl alcohol. Fit the flask with a reflux water-condenser and warm gently: a vigorous reaction soon occurs and the solution turns green. The characteristic pungent odour of formaldehyde is usually detected at this stage. Continue to heat for 3 minutes and then fit the flask with a knee-tube (Fig. 43, p. 72) and distil off a few c.c. Test the distillate with blue litmus-paper to show that it is definitely acid. Then apply Test 3 (p. 264) for formic acid.

By a similar reaction ethyl alcohol gives acetaldehyde (tests p. 258), and *iso*propyl alcohol gives acetone (tests p. 260). *n*-Butyl alcohol gives butyraldehyde (pleasant characteristic odour and ppt. with 2:4-dinitrophenylhydrazine, m.p. 122°).

Glycol gives the non-volatile oxalic acid. After heating the mixture under reflux for 10 minutes, transfer 2 c.c. of the cold product to a test-tube and add 4 c.c. of conc. H_2SO_4. Note the production of carbon monoxide and carbon dioxide on heating (p. 265).

*Cyclo*hexanol gives the non-volatile adipic acid, $HOOC \cdot (CH_2)_4COOH$. After heating the mixture under reflux for 10 minutes, cool the flask, transfer a few c.c. of the product to a test-tube, and note the separation of white crystals of adipic acid on scratching.

(ii) *Oxidation of benzyl alcohol to benzoic acid.* Boil a mixture of 0·5 c.c. of benzyl alcohol, 25 c.c. of saturated potassium permanganate solution and 0·5 gm. of Na_2CO_3 under reflux for 15 minutes. Cool somewhat, acidify carefully with conc. HCl, and then add 25% sodium sulphite solution until the brown precipitate of manganese dioxide has dissolved. On cooling, benzoic acid crystallises out. Filter through a small Buchner funnel, wash with water and identify (see p. 262). The benzoic acid may be recrystallised from water and then has m.p. 121°.

3. *Iodoform Reaction.* To 0.5 c.c. of ethyl alcohol add 3 c.c. of 10% KI solution and 10 c.c. of NaOCl solution. Warm *gently*: fine yellow crystals of CHI_3 separate. *Iso*propyl alcohol gives CHI_3 in the cold. *Pure* methyl alcohol and the other alcohols in this section do not give the reaction.

SPECIAL REACTIONS.

Methyl alcohol (methanol). CH_3OH.

1. *Methyl salicylate test.* Heat 1 c.c. of methyl alcohol with 0·5 gm. of sodium salicylate (or free salicylic acid) and a few drops of conc. H_2SO_4 *gently* for 1 minute. Cool, pour into a few c.c. of cold water in a boiling-tube, and shake. Note the odour of methyl salicylate (oil of wintergreen).

Ethyl salicylate (prepared by the same method) has an odour similar to that of methyl salicylate but less intense: it is therefore usually impracticable to attempt to distinguish methyl and ethyl alcohols by this test alone.

Ethyl alcohol (ethanol). C_2H_5OH.

1. *Ethyl acetate test.* Heat 1 c.c. of ethyl alcohol with 0·5 gm. of sodium acetate and a few drops of conc. H_2SO_4 *gently* for about 1 minute. Cool and pour into a few c.c. of water in a boiling-tube. Note fruity odour of the ethyl acetate.

Here again the odour of methyl acetate is similar, and the student must decide for himself what reliance he can place on the difference.

Glycerol. $CH_2OH \cdot CHOH \cdot CH_2OH$.

1. *Acrolein test.* Heat 0·5 c.c. with about 1 gm. of finely powdered potassium hydrogen sulphate. Acrolein, $CH_2:CH \cdot CHO$, produced by dehydration of the glycerol, is readily detected by its characteristic and irritating odour *(smell cautiously)*.

Benzyl alcohol. $C_6H_5CH_2OH$.

1. *Action of sulphuric acid.* To 0·5 c.c. of the alcohol, add 0·5 c.c. of conc. H_2SO_4 and shake the mixture. Heat is evolved and a white gelatinous polymer gradually separates. The reaction is hastened by warming and the product darkens.

Section 10. Phenols. −OH.

Phenol, o-, m- and p-cresol, catechol, resorcinol, hydroquinone, α- and β-naphthol.

Physical properties. All solid except *m*-cresol, $CH_3C_6H_4OH$, which is a liquid. All colourless when pure, but frequently slightly coloured due to atmospheric oxidation. All have in varying degrees a characteristic odour of " carbolic acid." Phenol, the cresols and resorcinol have a *caustic action on the skin.*

Phenol, C_6H_5OH, catechol, $o\text{-}C_6H_4(OH)_2$, resorcinol, $m\text{-}C_6H_4(OH)_2$, and hydroquinone, $p\text{-}C_6H_4(OH)_2$, are soluble in water; the remainder are sparingly soluble or insoluble in water. All phenols are soluble in sodium hydroxide solution, in some cases (*e.g.*, catechol, resorcinol, hydroquinone) with rapid darkening in colour.

GENERAL REACTIONS.*

1. Give characteristic colorations with ferric chloride.
2. Certain phenols give white precipitates with bromine water.
3. Form phthaleins.
4. Give benzoyl and 3:5-dinitrobenzoyl derivatives.
5. Certain phenols respond to the Liebermann Nitroso Reaction.

* Many of the reactions of phenols are frequently given also by their derivatives, *e.g.*, salicylic acid (p. 266) behaves like phenol towards a number of reagents.

6. Couple in alkaline solution with diazotised amines to give orange or red azo-dyes.

7. Do not liberate CO_2 from Na_2CO_3 solution (distinction from carboxylic acids).

8. Certain phenols give colorations with chloroform and alkali.

1. *Ferric chloride coloration.* To a very dilute aqueous solution of the phenol or to a minute crystal of the solid add 1 drop of ferric chloride solution. Phenol, resorcinol, *o*-, *m*-, and *p*-cresol give violet or blue colorations. Catechol gives a green coloration which rapidly darkens. Hydroquinone undergoes oxidation: it gives a deep green solution (crystals may separate) and on further addition of ferric chloride, a yellow solution of *p*-benzoquinone is obtained. α- and β-Naphthol do not give characteristic colorations.

2. *Action of bromine water.* To a concentrated aqueous solution of the phenol or to the phenol itself, add bromine water gradually. At first the bromine is decolorised and then on adding *excess* a white or yellowish-white precipitate of a polybromo-derivative is produced with all except catechol, hydroquinone, α- and β-naphthol. On adding 1 drop of bromine water to catechol, a deep red coloration is produced immediately.

On gradually adding bromine water to a solution of hydroquinone, a deep red coloration is produced, followed by the separation of deep green crystals which then dissolve giving a yellow solution.

α- and β-Naphthol will decolorise bromine water, but usually no precipitate of the bromo compound can be obtained.

The test is not very satisfactory with those phenols which are insoluble in water, owing to the difficulty of distinguishing the bromo-compound from the original phenol.

3. *Phthalein reaction.* Place in a dry test-tube about 0·2 gm. of the phenol and an equal quantity of phthalic anhydride (or acid), moisten with 2 drops (not more) of conc. H_2SO_4 and gently fuse together for about 1 minute. Allow to cool somewhat, and then add 10% NaOH solution in excess. Characteristic colorations are produced as follows: phenol, red (phenolphthalein); *o*-cresol, red; *m*-cresol, bluish-purple; *p*-cresol, nil; catechol, usually blue (alizarin) although this requires longer, but not stronger, heating; resorcinol, green fluorescent solution (fluorescein); hydroquinone, deep purple; α-naphthol, green; β-naphthol, very faint green with slight fluorescence.

4. *Benzoylation* (*cf.* p. 190). Dissolve 1 gm. of the phenol in about 15 c.c. of 10% NaOH solution contained in a strong boiling-tube. Add 2 c.c. of benzoyl chloride, cork the tube securely and shake vigorously for 10 minutes. Filter, wash well, and recrystallise from methylated spirit. Take the m.p. of the benzoate formed: phenyl, m.p. 69°; *o*-cresol, liquid; *m*-cresyl, m.p. 54°; *p*-cresyl, m.p. 71°; catechyl, m.p. 84°; resorcinyl, m.p. 117°; hydroquinyl, 204°; α-naphthyl, m.p. 56°; β-naphthyl, m.p. 107°.

3:5-*Dinitrobenzoylation.* Dissolve o·5 gm. of phenol in 10 c.c. of
N.NaOH solution in a small mortar. Grind into the mortar 1·2 gms.
of powdered 3:5-dinitrobenzoyl chloride. · After one minute filter off
the solid residue, wash with dil. NaOH solution and recrystallise from
alcohol. Phenyl 3:5-dinitrobenzoate has m.p. 146°. M.p.'s of other
phenolic esters are given in the table on p. 435.

5. *Liebermann Reaction.** To 1 *minute* crystal of sodium nitrite in
a clean dry test-tube add o·5 gm. of phenol and heat very gently for
about 20 seconds; allow to cool and add twice the volume of conc.
H_2SO_4. On rotating the tube slowly in order to mix the contents, a
deep green or deep blue coloration develops (sometimes only after 1–2
minutes). Dilute cautiously with water; the solution turns red. Now
add excess of NaOH solution, the green or blue coloration reappears. The
following table indicates how phenols behave when treated in this way:
the precise tint obtained, however, may vary according to the purity of
the phenol, amount of reagents used, and temperature and time of
heating.

Substance	H_2SO_4	Dilute with water	Add NaOH solution
Phenol	deep green or blue	red	deep green or blue
o-cresol	,,	,,	,,
m-cresol	,,	brown	brownish-green
p-cresol	dirty-brown	ill defined	ill defined
resorcinol	deep blue	red	brownish-red
catechol	deep green	dirty brown	red
α-naphthol	,,	ill defined	ill defined
β-naphthol	brownish-black	,,	,,

6. *Azo-dye formation.* Dissolve 2–3 drops of aniline in 1 c.c. of
conc. HCl and add 3 c.c. of water. Shake to dissolve any hydrochloride which may have separated and cool in ice. Add a few drops
of 20% sodium nitrite solution. Add this cold diazonium solution to
a cold solution of the phenol in *excess* aqueous NaOH solution. Solutions or precipitates of azo-dyes ranging in colour from orange through
scarlet to dark red, according to the phenol used, are obtained. Note in
particular that α-naphthol gives a brownish-red, β-naphthol a scarlet
precipitate. Catechol decomposes.

7. *Sodium carbonate solution. Cf.* Section 5, p. 248. Note that

---

* The colorations produced in Liebermann's Nitroso Reaction probably
represent derivatives of *p*-nitroso-phenol, HOC_6H_4NO, obtained by the action
of nitrous acid on the phenol itself. Hence the Reaction has the following
limitations: (1) The nitroso compound used must be capable of liberating
nitrous acid under the action of sulphuric acid. Therefore it must possess the
nitroso (–NO) group joined either to oxygen (as in the metallic nitrites), or to
nitrogen (as in the nitrosoamines $R_2N.NO$, p. 158); if joined to carbon (as in
p-nitroso-dimethylaniline, p. 159) it will not usually give the Reaction (*p*-
nitroso-phenol itself is clearly an exception to the latter rule). (2) The phenol
used must have the *para* position to the OH group unsubstituted to enable the
p-nitroso-phenol to be formed.

phenols (except those containing acidic groups as substituents, *e.g.*, nitrophenols) give no reaction with Na_2CO_3 solution.

8. *Colorations with chloroform and alkali.* Dissolve about 0·2 gm. of the phenol in 1 c.c. of 30% NaOH solution, add 1 c.c. of chloroform, and heat *gently.* Characteristic colorations are produced in the aqueous layer as follows: α- and β-naphthol, deep blue fading to green; catechol, green; *o*-cresol, *m*-cresol and resorcinol, red with slight fluorescence; hydroquinone, brown; phenol and *p*-cresol, nil.

Section 11. Aldehydes. −CHO.

Formaldehyde, metaformaldehyde, acetaldehyde, paraldehyde, chloral hydrate, benzaldehyde, salicylaldehyde.

Physical Properties.

All colourless. Formaldehyde, HCHO, is a gas, and only its aqueous solution, which has a characteristic pungent odour, is considered:* metaformaldehyde or "trioxymethylene," $(CH_2O)_3$, is a solid polymer, insoluble in water and alcohol.

Acetaldehyde, CH_3CHO, is a liquid, b.p. 21°, generally used in aqueous solution, which has also a characteristic odour; paraldehyde $(CH_3CHO)_3$, is a liquid polymer, b.p. 124°, slightly soluble in water, odour similar to that of acetaldehyde, but less intense. Chloral, CCl_3CHO, a liquid, is almost invariably encountered as the stable solid "hydrate," $CCl_3CH(OH)_2$. Both have a characteristic odour: the hydrate is readily soluble in water.

Benzaldehyde, C_6H_5CHO, and salicylaldehyde, HOC_6H_4CHO, are both liquids insoluble in water. Benzaldehyde has a characteristic odour of bitter almonds: salicylaldehyde has a faint but also characteristic odour, resembling that of phenol. Salicylaldehyde stains the skin yellow.

GENERAL REACTIONS.

1. Usually form bisulphite addition compounds, $RCH(OH)SO_3Na$.
2. Usually restore the pink colour to Schiff's reagent.
3. Form oximes, phenylhydrazones and 2:4-dinitrophenylhydrazones.
4. Conc. NaOH solution reacts with:
   (*a*) aliphatic aldehydes (except formaldehyde) giving resins;
   (*b*) most aromatic aldehydes giving Cannizzaro's reaction.
5. Give silver mirror with ammoniacal silver nitrate.
6. Usually reduce Fehling's solution.
7. Oxidised by alkaline permanganate to corresponding acid.

* A 40% solution of formaldehyde in water containing about 15% of methyl alcohol is known as "formalin."

1. *Bisulphite addition compound.* Shake 1 c.c. of benzaldehyde with about 0·5 c.c. of saturated sodium bisulphite solution. The mixture becomes warm, and the white addition product separates (rapidly on cooling).

Aqueous solutions of formaldehyde and acetaldehyde give these addition products, but the latter are so soluble that they rarely crystallise: the reaction is therefore an unsatisfactory test for these two aldehydes.

2. *Schiff's reagent.** Add about 1 c.c. of Schiff's reagent to an equal volume of (a) formaldehyde, (b) acetaldehyde. A magenta colour rapidly develops in the cold. Benzaldehyde restores the colour very slowly.

3. (a) *Phenylhydrazones* of benzaldehyde and salicylaldehyde. To 5 c.c. of water add about 0·5 c.c. of glacial acetic acid and of phenyl-hydrazine: then add 3 drops of the aldehyde and shake the mixture. After 1–2 minutes, a flocculent precipitate of the phenylhydrazone RCH:NNHC$_6$H$_5$, is produced. Filter and recrystallise from alcohol, and take the m.p. Benzaldehyde phenylhydrazone, m.p. 157°; salicylaldehyde phenylhydrazone, m.p. 142°.

The phenylhydrazones of formaldehyde and acetaldehyde are difficult to isolate and are seldom prepared.

(b) *2:4-Dinitrophenylhydrazones.* To a few drops of formalin, add a few drops of 2:4-dinitrophenylhydrazine reagent: a yellow precipitate is produced in the cold. Acetaldehyde gives an orange-coloured precipitate. Dissolve a few drops of benzaldehyde or salicylaldehyde in 2 c.c. of methyl alcohol and then add a few drops of the reagent: an orange-coloured precipitate is obtained. In each case filter, recrystallise from alcohol. Take the m.p. of the product: dinitrophenylhydrazone of formaldehyde, m.p. 167°; acetaldehyde, m.p. 162°; benzaldehyde, m.p. 237°; salicylaldehyde, m.p. 252°.

4. *Action of sodium hydroxide.* (a) Warm 1 c.c. of acetaldehyde with a few c.c. of conc. NaOH solution. A yellow resin, having a characteristic odour of bad apples, is formed. Paraldehyde slowly gives a yellow resin.

(b) *Cannizaro's reaction* (cf. p. 179). Place 0·5 c.c. of benzaldehyde and 2 c.c. of 30% aqueous sodium hydroxide in a test-tube, warm very gently and stir the mixture *well* with a glass rod for 5 minutes. Then add sufficient water to dissolve the sodium benzoate which has been formed. Decant the solution from any unchanged benzaldehyde, and add concentrated hydrochloric acid: a white precipitate of benzoic acid is obtained on cooling.

---

* Schiff's reagent should never be warmed nor treated with alkaline substances, otherwise the pink colour will be restored even in the absence of aldehydes or ketones. The coloration of Schiff's reagent by an aldehyde or ketone is probably due to the formation of a compound (distinct from magenta) resulting from the combined action of SO$_2$ and the aldehyde or ketone upon magenta. Excess of mineral acid reduces the sensitivity of the reagent.

K

Salicylaldehyde gives a yellow coloration and forms salicylic acid very slowly. Cannizzaro's reaction is also given by formaldehyde but, owing to the difficulty in isolating the products, is not used as a test.

5. *Reduction of ammoniacal silver nitrate.* Place about 5 c.c. of silver nitrate solution in a *thoroughly* clean test-tube, and add 2–3 drops of dil. NaOH solution. Add dil. ammonia solution, drop by drop, until the precipitated silver oxide is *almost* redissolved, then add 2–3 drops of formaldehyde or acetaldehyde. A silver mirror is formed.

With paraldehyde and the aromatic aldehydes (being insoluble in water), it is advisable to warm the mixture gently in a water-bath, shaking the tube vigorously from time to time to break up the oily globules of the aldehyde.

6. *Fehling's solution.* Aqueous solutions of aliphatic aldehydes are almost invariably acidic owing to atmospheric oxidation, and therefore frequently fail to reduce Fehling's solution, since the alkali of the latter is neutralised by the acid present. On the other hand, an excess of Fehling's solution is not recommended, as the blue colour may then mask the ensuing reduction. Therefore proceed thus: To 1 c.c. of the aldehyde or aldehyde solution, add about 1 c.c. of 10% Na_2CO_3 solution and then a few drops of Fehling's solution, and boil the mixture *gently* for 1 minute: the solution usually turns green and on standing a fine yellow or red precipitate* of cuprous oxide slowly separates. A control experiment using Fehling's solution alone should always be carried out to ensure that no reduction takes place on boiling.

Aliphatic aldehydes reduce Fehling's solution rapidly, benzaldehyde very slowly and indecisively, salicylaldehyde does not reduce it.

7. *Oxidation to acids.* Warm together in a small conical flask on a water-bath for 10 minutes a mixture of 0·5 c.c. of benzaldehyde or salicylaldehyde, 15 c.c. of saturated potassium permanganate solution, and 0·5 gm. of Na_2CO_3. Then acidify with conc. HCl, and add 25% sodium sulphite solution until the precipitated manganese dioxide has redissolved. On cooling, benzoic or salicylic acid crystallises out.

SPECIAL REACTIONS.

Metaformaldehyde.

If boiled with water an aqueous solution is obtained which, owing to depolymerisation, gives the reactions for formaldehyde.

Acetaldehyde.

1. *Nitroprusside reaction.* Add 1 c.c. of a freshly prepared solution of sodium nitroprusside to the aldehyde or its solution. Add dil. NaOH solution in excess: a red coloration is produced.

---

* The colour of the precipitate depends upon the size of the cuprous oxide particles, and this in turn upon the rate of reduction, concentration of the solution, *etc.*

If a few drops of silver nitrate solution or nickel chloride solution are added to Fehling's solution, and then 1 c.c. of formalin added, a copper mirror is usually produced on warming.

2. *Iodoform reaction.* To 1 c.c. of the aldehyde solution, add 3 c.c. of 10% KI solution and 10 c.c. of freshly prepared sodium hypochlorite solution. Yellow crystals of iodoform, CHI_3, soon separate.

Paraldehyde.

Gives some of the tests for acetaldehyde, but more feebly: *e.g.*, it restores the colour to Schiff's reagent, gives a yellow resin with NaOH, and responds to the nitroprusside test. With ammoniacal silver nitrate, it gives a silver mirror only after 2–3 minutes' warming. It does not give the iodoform reaction.

To 1 c.c. of paraldehyde in a test-tube add 5 c.c. of dil. H_2SO_4 and distil gently into cold water contained in another test-tube (Fig. 52, p. 238). An aqueous solution of acetaldehyde is thus obtained.

Chloral hydrate.

1. *Action of sodium hydroxide.* Add a few c.c. of NaOH solution

$$CCl_3 \overline{CHO + NaO} H = CHCl_3 + HCOONa$$

to about 0·5 gm. of the hydrate and heat gently. Oily drops of chloroform are formed, recognised by characteristic odour.

2. *Bisulphite addition compound.* To 0·2 gm. of *powdered* chloral hydrate add 2 c.c. of *saturated* $NaHSO_3$ solution and stir. The hydrate dissolves and the white addition product separates. Stale or slightly diluted solutions of $NaHSO_3$ do not give this product.

3. Does not restore the pink colour to Schiff's reagent.

4. Gives a silver mirror with ammoniacal silver nitrate.

5. *Fehling's solution.* Reduces Fehling's solution on warming: an excess of the latter should be used. The odour of chloroform is also noticeable, due to the action of the alkali in Fehling's solution.

6. *Action of sulphuric acid.* To 0·5 gm. of powdered chloral hydrate add 2 c.c. of conc. H_2SO_4, shake well and allow to stand. Liquid chloral gradually separates out as an oil on the surface of the acid.

7. *Isocyanide reaction.* Since chloral hydrate is readily converted into chloroform by alkali, it will give the isocyanide reaction. To a few crystals of the solid add about 5 c.c. of alcoholic NaOH solution and a few drops of aniline, and heat: the disagreeable odour of phenyl isocyanide, C_6H_5NC, is rapidly detected.

Salicylaldehyde.

1. *Ferric chloride coloration.* Add a few drops of $FeCl_3$ solution to a few drops of the aldehyde: an intense violet coloration is produced.

2. *Bisulphite addition compound.* The formation of the bisulphite compound is delayed and appears only after 2–3 minutes' shaking.

3. Does not restore the colour to Schiff's reagent.

4. *Action of sodium hydroxide.* Does not undergo the Cannizzaro reaction. It dissolves in dil. NaOH solution, giving a yellow solution from which the aldehyde is precipitated unchanged on acidification.

If heated with conc. NaOH solution, salicylaldehyde slowly undergoes atmospheric oxidation to salicylic acid.

5. Does not reduce ammoniacal silver nitrate (except on long standing).

6. It does not reduce Fehling's solution, but turns it a pale green colour. (Note that salicylaldehyde turns ordinary copper sulphate solution a pale green.)

7. *Action of ammonia.* To 1 c.c. of aldehyde add 1 c.c. of aqueous ammonia: a precipitate of hydrosalicylamide, $(HOC_6H_4CH)_3N_2$, is rapidly produced.

Section 12. Ketones. >C:O.

Acetone, acetophenone, benzophenone.

Physical Properties.

All colourless.   Acetone, CH_3COCH_3, b.p. 56°, soluble in water, characteristic odour.   Acetophenone, $CH_3COC_6H_5$, m.p. 20° (therefore usually liquid), sparingly soluble in water.   Benzophenone, $C_6H_5COC_6H_5$, m.p. 48°, insoluble in water.

GENERAL REACTIONS.

1. Certain ketones form bisulphite compounds.
2. Aliphatic ketones containing the CH_3CO- group restore the colour very slowly to Schiff's reagent.
3. Form oximes, phenylhydrazones, and 2:4-dinitrophenyl-hydrazones.
4. Ketones containing the CH_3CO- group give the iodoform reaction. (For other substances which give this test, see p. 65.)
5. Do not reduce ammoniacal silver nitrate or Fehling's solution (distinction from aldehydes).
6. Ketones containing the CH_3CO- group give:
   (a) a red coloration with sodium nitroprusside and sodium hydroxide;
   (b) a violet coloration with *m*-dinitrobenzene and sodium hydroxide.

1. *Bisulphite addition compound.*   Shake 1 c.c. of acetone with 0·5 c.c. of a saturated solution of sodium bisulphite.   A white precipitate is formed, the mixture becoming warm and then, on cooling, almost solid. Acetophenone and benzophenone, having the >CO group directly joined to the benzene ring, do not respond to the test (p. 202).

2. *Schiff's reagent.*   Add about 1 c.c. of Schiff's reagent to about 1 c.c. of acetone and note the very slow formation of a magenta colour. Neither acetophenone nor benzophenone reacts in this way.

3. (a) *Phenylhydrazones.*   The phenylhydrazone of acetone has a low m.p. and is difficult to isolate.   The phenylhydrazones of acetophenone and benzophenone are readily obtained as follows: To 0·5 c.c. of water add about 1 c.c. of glacial acetic acid and 1 c.c. of phenylhydrazine.

Then add 3 drops of acetophenone (or about 0·3 gm. of powdered benzophenone dissolved in 1 c.c. of acetic acid) and shake the mixture. A precipitate of the phenylhydrazone is produced on scratching.

(b) 2:4-*Dinitrophenylhydrazones*. To a few drops of acetone, add a few drops of dinitrophenylhydrazine reagent: an orange-coloured precipitate is produced in the cold. Dissolve 0·5 gm. of acetophenone or benzophenone in 1 c.c. of methyl alcohol before adding the reagent: orange-coloured precipitates are again produced, although the one from benzophenone appears slowly. Filter and recrystallise. Derivative of acetone, m.p. 128° (from alcohol); acetophenone, m.p. 242° (from benzene); benzophenone, m.p. 239° (from benzene).

The preparation of acetoxime is given on p. 67; oximes, however, are not as useful for identification purposes as phenylhydrazones, because of their greater solubility.

4. *Iodoform reaction*. To 0·5 c.c. of acetone add 3 c.c. of 10% potassium iodide solution and 10 c.c. of freshly prepared sodium hypochlorite solution and mix well. A pale yellow precipitate of iodoform is rapidly formed without heating. Acetophenone similarly gives iodoform, but the mixture must be shaken vigorously on account of the limited solubility of acetophenone in water. Benzophenone does not give iodoform.

6. (a) *Nitroprusside reaction*. Add 1 c.c. of a freshly prepared solution of sodium nitroprusside to 0·5 c.c. of acetone or acetophenone. Add dil. NaOH solution in excess: a red coloration is produced. This is not given by benzophenone.

(b) *Dinitrobenzene test.** To 1 c.c. of acetone or acetophenone add about 0·1 gm. of finely powdered *m*-dinitrobenzene and then an excess of dil. NaOH solution and shake. A violet coloration is produced, but slowly fades. Not given by benzophenone.

NOTE. Reactions 6 (a) and 6 (b) are given only by those ketones which contain the – CH_2CO – group and which can thus by enolisation give the – CH:C(OH) – group.

SPECIAL REACTION.

Benzophenone. To 0·5 gm. of benzophenone add 1 gm. of naphthalene, and heat until completely molten. Add a small piece of sodium and heat again. The surface of the sodium becomes green, and the colour spreads throughout the molten mass on strong heating.

Section 13. Carboxylic Acids. –COOH.

Formic, acetic, oxalic, succinic, lactic, tartaric, citric, benzoic, salicylic, phthalic and cinnamic acids.

Physical properties. All are colourless crystalline solids except formic acid, acetic acid (m.p. 18° when glacial) and lactic acid

* This test is far more delicate if 3:5-dinitrobenzoic acid is used (owing to its solubility in sodium hydroxide), instead of the cheaper and more accessible *m*-dinitrobenzene.

(m.p. 18°, usually a syrup). Formic acid (b.p. 100°) and acetic acid (b.p. 118°) are the only members which are readily volatile: lactic acid can be distilled only under reduced pressure. Formic and acetic acids have characteristic pungent odours: cinnamic acid has a faint, pleasant and characteristic odour.

The aliphatic acids are all soluble in cold water. The aromatic acids are very sparingly soluble in cold water, but readily soluble in boiling water. Phthalic acid, having two carboxyl groups, is more soluble than the other aromatic acids in cold water.

GENERAL REACTIONS.

1. Soluble in NaOH solution.
2. Soluble in Na_2CO_3 solution with the evolution of CO_2.
3. Heating acids or their salts with soda-lime eliminates the carboxyl group, volatile products being often detectable.
4. With alcohol and sulphuric acid gives esters which frequently have characteristic odours.
5. The neutral salts of many acids treated with ferric chloride give colorations or precipitates.

1. *Solubility in sodium hydroxide solution.* See Section 4, p. 246. Note also that phenols dissolve in NaOH solution to give phenates.

2. *Solubility in sodium carbonate solution.* Note that phenols, when soluble in water, will also dissolve in Na_2CO_3 solution, but usually *without* evolution of CO_2, *i.e.*, without the formation of a sodium derivative. This reaction can therefore be used *to distinguish between carboxylic acids and most phenols.* See Section 5, p. 248.

NOTE. Some substituted phenols, particularly nitrophenols, are sufficiently acidic to liberate CO_2 from Na_2CO_3. Nitrophenols, however, all give yellow or red solutions with Na_2CO_3.

3. *Heating with soda-lime.* See Section 3, p. 245. Note that this test is particularly useful for providing evidence of:

(a) Benzoic Acid. Gives benzene, detected by odour and by burning with a very smoky flame.
(b) Salicylic Acid. Gives phenol, detected by odour and by violet coloration with ferric chloride solution (p. 254).
(c) Phthalic Acid. Also gives benzene, but requires longer heating than benzoic acid.
(d) Cinnamic Acid. Gives styrene, $C_6H_5CH:CH_2$ (characteristic odour) and usually benzene.

4. *Ester formation.* Heat gently 1 c.c. of ethyl alcohol with 0·5 gm. of the acid or one of its salts and a few drops of conc. H_2SO_4 for about 1 minute. Cool and pour into a few c.c. of water in a test-tube and note the odour. The test is particularly useful for identifying:

(a) Acetic Acid. Ester has strong odour of apples.
(b) Salicylic Acid. Ester has strong odour of oil of wintergreen.

The methyl ester formed by substituting methyl alcohol for ethyl alcohol in the above reaction has an even stronger odour and should be prepared if salicylic acid is suspected.

For detection of other esters, see Section 14, p. 268.

5. *Ferric chloride reaction.* For the success of this reaction it is important that the solution should be neutral. Excess of acid usually inhibits the production of colour or precipitate, and excess of alkali gives a reddish-brown precipitate of ferric hydroxide. A neutral solution may be made as follows:

Place about 0·5 gm. of the acid in a boiling-tube and add a slight excess of ammonia solution until just alkaline to litmus-paper. Add a piece of unglazed porcelain and boil until the colour of ammonia is completely removed. (See also p. 249.) To the cold neutral solution add a few drops of *neutral** ferric chloride solution.

(a) Formate and acetate give a deep red coloration which changes on boiling to a reddish-brown precipitate of the basic ferric salt.

(b) Succinate, benzoate, phthalate and cinnamate give buff or brownish coloured precipitates of the basic ferric salts in the cold. Add dil. H_2SO_4. The basic ferric succinate dissolves giving a clear solution: the other basic ferric salts also dissolve, but simultaneously a white precipitate of the free acid is also formed.

(c) A violet coloration denotes salicylate. Note however that a dilute solution of salicylic acid will give this coloration without any preliminary neutralisation. No colour is formed in the presence of mineral acid.

(d) If (a), (b) and (c) give negative results, take two test-tubes **A** and **B**: in **A** place about 5 c.c. of the neutral salt solution and in **B** place 5 c.c. of water. To each add 3–4 drops of ferric chloride solution. If **A** gives a marked yellow coloration compared with the control **B** (particularly when viewed down the length of the tube), then **A** contains the salt of an α-hydroxy-acid (lactic, tartaric or citric). If there is no difference in tint between **A** and **B**, then oxalate is indicated.

Isolation of the acid from its salt.

(i) If the salt is soluble in water, add conc. HCl to the solution. A precipitate indicates an aromatic acid: filter, wash with cold water, and drain. If no precipitate is obtained, the acid must be aliphatic.

(ii) If the salt is insoluble in water, boil with an excess of 10% aqueous Na_2CO_3 solution for several minutes and then filter. The residue contains the original metal as carbonate and should be examined in the usual way. The filtrate contains the sodium salt of the acid and an excess of Na_2CO_3. Add dil. HCl until distinctly acid to litmus-paper and note any precipitate as in (1).

The isolation of an aliphatic acid from its aqueous solution, particularly in the presence of metallic salts, is a difficult and tedious operation, although a

* See p. 249.

few such acids, *e.g.*, succinic acid, can be extracted with ether. Since, however, a solution of an acid or one of its salts is admirably suited for most of the tests in this series, the isolation of the free acid is rarely necessary, except as a means of distinguishing (as in (i)) between aliphatic and aromatic members.

SPECIAL REACTIONS.

Formic acid. HCOOH.

1. *Carbon monoxide test.* Warm together carefully 0·5 c.c. of formic acid (or 0·5 gm. of a formate) and 1 c.c. of conc. H_2SO_4. Identify the carbon monoxide by igniting the gas evolved and observing the pale blue flame travel down the test-tube. Note that dilute solutions of formic acid will not give this test. $HCOOH - H_2O = CO$.

2. *Mercuric chloride test.* Add mercuric chloride* solution to formic acid or a solution of formate and warm. A white precipitate of mercurous chloride, insoluble in dil. HCl, is produced. Sometimes the reduction proceeds as far as metallic mercury, which appears as a grey precipitate.

3. (*a*) *Reduction of acid permanganate.* Add a few c.c. of dil. H_2SO_4 to a solution of formic acid or of a formate: add a dilute solution of potassium permanganate drop by drop and note the decolorisation, which is hastened by warming.

(*b*) *Reduction of alkaline permanganate.* Dissolve about 0·1 gm. of a formate (or 2–3 drops of a formic acid solution) in 5 c.c. of a 10% Na_2CO_3 solution, add 1% aqueous potassium permanganate drop by drop: immediate decolorisation takes place in the cold with the simultaneous precipitation of manganese dioxide.

4. *Reduction of ammoniacal silver nitrate.* Add a few drops of a neutral solution of a formate to ammoniacal silver nitrate (see Test 5, p. 258). A silver mirror or *more usually* a grey precipitate of metallic silver is produced on boiling.

Acetic acid. CH_3COOH.

1. Does not reduce potassium permanganate, mercuric chloride or ammoniacal silver nitrate.

2. The odour of ethyl acetate is characteristic.

Oxalic acid. $(COOH)_2$.

1. *Calcium chloride test.*† Add calcium chloride solution to a neutral solution of an oxalate: a white precipitate of calcium oxalate is formed, insoluble in acetic acid, but soluble in dil. HCl.

2. *Reduction of acid permanganate.* Add a few c.c. of dil. H_2SO_4 to 1 c.c. of a solution of oxalic acid or of an oxalate. Warm gently and

---

* Salts of many organic acids give precipitates with mercuric chloride solution, but these are usually soluble in dil. HCl.

† It should be emphasised that the calcium chloride solution used in testing for acids is of Reagent strength (p. 425) throughout.

add a dilute solution of potassium permanganate drop by drop and note the decolorisation.

NOTE. Oxalates do not reduce alkaline permanganate in the cold (*cf.* Test 3 (*b*) for formic acid), and only extremely slowly on heating.

3. *Sulphuric acid test.* To 0·5 gm. of oxalic acid or of an oxalate add 1 c.c. of conc. H_2SO_4 and warm: CO and CO_2 are evolved (*cf.* formic acid). The former burns with a blue flame. Detect the latter by passing the mixed gases evolved into lime-water. It is essential to test for the CO_2 in a *separate* reaction, or (if the same test-tube is used) *before* testing for CO.

4. Does not reduce mercuric chloride or ammoniacal silver nitrate.

Succinic acid. $(CH_2COOH)_2$.

1. *Fluorescein test.* Fuse together carefully in a dry test-tube a few crystals of resorcinol and an equal quantity of succinic acid or a succinate, moistened with 2 drops of conc. H_2SO_4. Cool, dissolve in water and add NaOH solution in excess. A red solution is produced which exhibits an *intense* green fluorescence.*

2. *Calcium chloride test.* Add calcium chloride solution to a conc. neutral solution of a succinate. No precipitate is formed in the cold, but on boiling, white crystalline calcium succinate separates out, soluble in acetic acid.

Lactic acid. $CH_3CH(OH)COOH$.

1. *Sulphuric acid test.* To 0·5 c.c. of lactic acid or 0·5 gm. of a lactate add 1 c.c. of conc. H_2SO_4 and warm gently. A brisk effervescence takes place, CO being evolved together with varying amounts of CO_2 and SO_2. The mixture blackens considerably, but there is no marked charring.

2. *Iodoform reaction.* To 0·5 c.c. of lactic acid add 10% NaOH solution until alkaline to litmus. Then add 3 c.c. of 10% potassium iodide solution and 10 c.c. of freshly prepared sodium hypochlorite solution and mix well. A yellow precipitate of iodoform separates out almost immediately in the cold.

Tartaric acid. $[CH(OH)COOH]_2$.

1. *Sulphuric acid test.* Warm 0·5 gm. of tartaric acid or a tartrate with 1 c.c. of conc. H_2SO_4. Heavy charring takes place, CO and SO_2 being evolved.

* A similar *intense* green fluorescence is given by phthalic acid (p. 267). Very feeble fluorescences are sometimes given by other dibasic acids, but in general they are ill defined and not reliable in tests. A slight fluorescence is often given when resorcinol and conc. H_2SO_4 are heated together without an organic acid.

Certain salts of divalent metals (*e.g.*, lead and copper formate, calcium acetate) are exceptional in giving bright green fluorescences. In each case confirmatory tests must always be employed.

K*

2. *Reduction of ammoniacal silver nitrate.* Add 1 drop of dil. NaOH solution to about 5 c.c. of silver nitrate solution, and add dil. ammonia solution drop by drop until the silver oxide is almost redissolved. Add silver nitrate solution until a *faint* but permanent precipitate is obtained, see page 426. Then add 0·5 c.c. of a neutral tartrate solution. Place the tube in warm water: a silver mirror is formed in a few minutes.

3. *Fenton's reagent.* To a solution of tartaric acid or a tartrate add 1 drop of freshly prepared ferrous sulphate solution, 2 drops of hydrogen peroxide solution and then excess of NaOH solution: an intense violet coloration is produced, due to the ferric salt of dihydroxyfumaric acid, $HOOC \cdot C(OH):C(OH)COOH$.

4. *Calcium chloride test.* Add calcium chloride solution to a neutral concentrated solution of a tartrate: a white precipitate of calcium tartrate is produced in the cold.

Citric acid. $HOOC \cdot CH_2 \cdot C(OH)(COOH) \cdot CH_2COOH$.

1. *Sulphuric acid test.* Heat 0·5 gm. of citric acid or a citrate with 1 c.c. of H_2SO_4: carbon monoxide and carbon dioxide are evolved and the mixture turns yellow, but does *not* char. Acetone dicarboxylic acid, $OC(CH_2COOH)_2$, is also one of the products and is tested for after heating the mixture for 1 minute: cool, add a few c.c. of water and make alkaline with NaOH solution. Add a few c.c. of a freshly prepared solution of sodium nitroprusside and note the intense red coloration (see Test 6 (*a*) for ketones, p. 261).

2. Does not reduce ammoniacal silver nitrate solution (cf. tartaric acid).

3. No coloration with Fenton's reagent (cf. tartaric acid).

4. *Calcium chloride test.* Add calcium chloride solution to a neutral concentrated solution of a citrate. No precipitate is formed in the cold, but on boiling a white precipitate of calcium citrate is produced, insoluble in acetic acid.

Benzoic acid. C_6H_5COOH.

1. Does not give Unsaturation Test with alkaline potassium permanganate (distinction from cinnamic acid, see below).

2. Does not form a phthalein or fluorescein (distinction from phthalic acid).

Salicylic acid. HOC_6H_4COOH.

1. The odour of methyl or ethyl salicylate is characteristic.

2. *Acetylation.* Boil 1 gm. of salicylic acid with 4 c.c. of an acetic anhydride-acetic acid mixture (equal volumes) under reflux for 10 minutes. Pour into water. Filter off the aspirin (p. 83), wash with water and recrystallise from aqueous acetic acid (1:1): m.p. 136°.

3. *Phthalein formation.** Fuse together carefully in a dry test-tube a few crystals of salicylic acid or of a salicylate with an equal quantity of phthalic anhydride moistened with 2 drops of conc. H_2SO_4. Cool, dissolve in water and add NaOH solution in excess: a bright red coloration is developed.

4. *Azo-dye formation.** Prepare a cold diazonium chloride solution as described under Test 6 for phenols (p. 255), and pour it into a cold solution of salicylic acid (or of a soluble salicylate) in an *excess* of NaOH solution: a red coloration is produced and on making acid with dil. HCl a bulky yellowish-brown precipitate of the azo-dye is obtained.

Phthalic acid. $C_6H_4(COOH)_2$.

1. *Phthalein reaction.* Fuse together carefully in a dry test-tube a few crystals of phthalic acid or of a phthalate and an equal quantity of phenol moistened with 2 drops of conc. H_2SO_4. Cool, dissolve in water and add NaOH solution in excess: the bright red colour of phenolphthalein in alkaline solution is produced.

2. *Fluorescein reaction.†* Repeat Test 1, using however resorcinol instead of phenol. A reddish solution having an intense green fluorescence is produced.

Cinnamic acid. $C_6H_5CH:CHCOOH$

1. *Oxidation.* (a) *Unsaturation test.* Dissolve about 0·1 gm. of cinnamic acid or of a soluble cinnamate in about 5 c.c. of 10% Na_2CO_3 solution. To the *cold* solution add 1% aqueous potassium permanganate drop by drop. *Immediate* decolorisation denotes unsaturation. (Note. Many easily oxidisable substances, *e.g.*, formic acid, acetaldehyde, *etc.*, also rapidly decolorise alkaline permanganate. Cinnamates, however, do not reduce Fehling's solution.)

(b) *Formation of benzaldehyde.* Place 0·2 gm. of cinnamic acid (or a cinnamate) in a boiling-tube, add 5 c.c. of potassium permanganate solution and 5 c.c. of Na_2CO_3 solution, and boil: note the odour of benzaldehyde.

2. *Calcium chloride test.* Add calcium chloride solution to a neutral solution of a cinnamate: a white precipitate of calcium cinnamate is formed, soluble in acetic acid.

3. *Formation of bromo-styrene.* Dissolve 0·2 gm. of cinnamic acid (or a cinnamate) in about 5 c.c. of Na_2CO_3 solution. Add brominewater *drop by drop*, and note the rapid separation of bromo-styrene, $C_6H_5CH:CHBr$, as a colourless oil, having a pleasant characteristic odour.

4. *Fusion with potassium hydroxide.* This test definitely confirms cinnamic acid, but is rather long and tedious in operation. Warm together in a crucible 1 gm. of solid KOH and 0·5 c.c. of water until the mixture is completely

---

* It is important to note that in these reactions salicylic acid is functioning as a phenol.

† See footnote, p. 265.

molten. Then add about 0·5 gm. of cinnamic acid or a cinnamate and heat carefully until effervescence ceases and the mass nearly solidifies (this may

$$C_6H_5CH{:}CHCOOH + 2KOH = C_6H_5COOK + CH_3COOK + H_2$$

require several minutes and care must be taken to avoid charring). Boil the fused mass with about 20 c.c. of water and filter. Acidify the filtrate with dil. H_2SO_4, and then filter off and identify the white precipitate of benzoic acid. Place the filtrate in a small flask and distil to half bulk. Collect the distillate and identify the acetic acid.

Section 14. Esters. —COOR.

Methyl and ethyl esters of formic, acetic, oxalic, succinic, tartaric, benzoic, salicylic, phthalic, and cinnamic acids; benzyl acetate; phenyl esters of acetic, benzoic and salicylic acids.

Physical Properties. All colourless. All liquids, except the following, which are crystalline solids: methyl oxalate (m.p. 51°), methyl tartrate (m.p. 48°), methyl succinate (m.p. 18°, liquid in hot weather), methyl cinnamate (m.p. 36°), phenyl benzoate (m.p. 70°), phenyl salicylate or "salol" (m.p. 42°).

All very sparingly soluble in water, except methyl formate, methyl oxalate, methyl succinate, methyl tartrate, and ethyl tartrate, which are freely soluble.

GENERAL REACTIONS.

1. Many esters possess characteristic odours.
2. All esters are hydrolysed by sodium hydroxide to the alcohol (or sodium phenate) and the sodium salt of the acid from which they are derived.
3. Form amides with ammonia.

1. *Odours.* As it is impossible to describe the odours of esters in absolute terms, the student should familiarise himself with the odours of the above esters and decide for himself how much reliance he can place on this test.

As a general guide, however, it may be noted that the following have fairly easily recognisable odours: methyl and ethyl formate; methyl and ethyl acetate (apples); methyl and ethyl benzoate; methyl salicylate (oil of wintergreen) and ethyl salicylate; methyl and ethyl cinnamate. (It is however usually impracticable to distinguish by odour alone between the methyl and ethyl esters of a particular acid.) Methyl and ethyl oxalate, and methyl and ethyl phthalate are almost odourless. Succinic and tartaric esters have faint odours.

2. *Hydrolysis.* Place 3 c.c. of the ester in a 100 c.c. round-bottomed flask fitted with a reflux water-condenser. Add about 25 c.c. of 10% aqueous NaOH solution, and some fragments of unglazed porcelain, and reflux gently for 20–30 minutes. (Note that methyl oxalate is

hydrolysed rapidly by water alone. Phenyl esters on the other hand hydrolyse comparatively slowly even with hot NaOH solution, and should be refluxed for *at least* 30 minutes.* Phenyl esters when heated with soda-lime (Section 3) give an odour of phenol, and their identity will have already been suspected.) At the end of this time, all oily drops† of unchanged ester should have disappeared, and the solution now contains the free alcohol and the sodium salt‡ of the acid: in the case of the phenyl esters, the solution will contain sodium phenate and the sodium salt of the acid.

Now disconnect the condenser and re-attach it to the flask by a knee-tube for distillation (Fig. 43, p. 72). Distil off about 5 c.c. of the liquid.

(*a*) The aqueous distillate may be clear, and may contain methyl or ethyl alcohol. Test for each of these, as described on pp. 251, 253.

(*b*) If the distillate is clear and contains neither methyl nor ethyl alcohol, then only water has distilled over and the original substance is a phenyl ester (sodium phenoxide being non-volatile). Treat according to the special directions for phenyl esters given below.

(*c*) A cloudy distillate, separating later into two layers, may be obtained. This indicates benzyl alcohol which is insoluble in water: separate and apply special test (p. 252). (Obviously it is important that the ester should have been completely hydrolysed, otherwise unchanged ester will distil over, giving a cloudy distillate.)

Next cool the alkaline residue in the flask and add dil. H_2SO_4 until *definitely* acid.

(*a*) If a precipitate is formed, the acid is aromatic (benzoic, salicylic, cinnamic or phthalic). Cool, filter through a small Buchner funnel, wash thoroughly with water, drain well, and perform the tests for these acids (pp. 266, 267).

(*b*) If no precipitate is formed, the acid is soluble in water and is aliphatic. It may be volatile (formic and acetic acids), or non-volatile (oxalic, succinic and tartaric acids). Therefore reconnect the flask to the condenser and distil off about 8–10 c.c. Test the distillate for formic and acetic acids (p. 264). If a negative result is obtained, test the residue in the flask for the non-volatile acids (pp. 264-266), taking care to make an exactly neutral solution where required.

* See, however, footnote, p. 191.
† Any benzyl alcohol formed by hydrolysis of a benzyl ester will, however, remain as an oil.
‡ Some sodium salts (particularly sodium oxalate) may be precipitated, due to their low solubility in NaOH solution. The salt should be redissolved by the addition of water before the subsequent distillation.

Treatment of phenyl esters. (See also p. 191.) The alkaline solution containing phenate and the sodium salt of the acid should now be worked up by the following method.

Cool the solution in ice-water, and then add dil. H_2SO_4 with stirring until the solution is acidic to litmus-paper and the acid, if aromatic, begins to separate as a faint but *permanent* precipitate. Now add dil. Na_2CO_3 solution with *vigorous* stirring until the solution becomes definitely alkaline to litmus-paper and any precipitate entirely redissolves. Finally extract the clear solution twice with ether. Transfer the ethereal layer to an evaporating-basin, and evaporate on a previously heated water-bath. (*No flames must be near.*) Identify the phenol which remains in the basin (p. 253). Acidify the aqueous solution with dil. H_2SO_4 and investigate the organic acid as above.

3. *Amide formation.* The only esters which give insoluble amides *rapidly* with concentrated ammonia solution are methyl and ethyl oxalate.

Dissolve 0·2 gm. of methyl oxalate in 10 c.c. of water, add without delay 1 c.c. of ammonia (*d*, 0·880) and shake: a fine white precipitate of the insoluble oxamide is produced. A precipitate of oxamide is similarly produced when 2–3 drops of ammonia are added directly to 0·5 c.c. of ethyl oxalate.

Ethyl oxalate is the only *liquid* ester which gives this rapid separation of the amide, which is therefore characteristic. Methyl and ethyl formate react rapidly with ammonia, but the soluble formamide does not separate: methyl succinate gives crystalline succinamide after about 1 hour's standing, other esters only after a much longer time. The solid esters, other than methyl oxalate, are either soluble in water and remain so when treated with ammonia, or alternatively are insoluble in water and hence clearly not methyl oxalate.

Hydrolysis of methyl oxalate. The exceptionally rapid hydrolysis of methyl oxalate can be followed thus: Dissolve 0·2 gm. of finely powdered methyl oxalate in 10 c.c. of water, and add 1 drop of phenolphthalein. Then add very dil. NaOH solution (1%) drop by drop until the solution *just* turns pink: it will be noticed that the colour rapidly fades, but is restored on the further addition of 1–2 drops of NaOH solution. The colour fades again and the addition can be repeated until hydrolysis is complete. Oxalic acid (with which methyl oxalate may be confused) gives a precise end-point when treated with NaOH solution in this way.

NOTE. Many esters reduce Fehling's solution on warming. This reduction occurs rapidly with the alcohol esters of many aliphatic acids, but scarcely at all with similar esters of aromatic acids (*e.g.*, ethyl oxalate reduces, but ethyl benzoate does not). Note also that this is a property of the ester itself: thus both methyl and ethyl oxalate reduce Fehling's solution very rapidly, whereas neither oxalic acid, nor sodium oxalate, nor a mixture of the alcohol and oxalic acid (or sodium oxalate), reduces the solution.

Methyl and ethyl salicylate give a violet coloration with $FeCl_3$.

Section 15. Ammonium salts, amides, imides, and nitriles.

(A) AMMONIUM SALTS. R·COONH$_4$. *Ammonium salts of formic, acetic, oxalic, succinic, tartaric, citric, benzoic, salicylic, phthalic and cinnamic acids.*

(B) AMIDES. R·CONH$_2$. *Formamide, acetamide, oxamide, urea, benzamide, salicylamide.*

(C) IMIDES. R⟨ CO / CO ⟩NH. *Succinimide, phthalimide.*

(D) NITRILES. R·CN. *Acetonitrile, benzonitrile.*

Physical properties.

(A) *Ammonium salts.* All colourless solids readily soluble in cold water.

(B) *Amides.* All colourless solids except formamide, HCONH$_2$, a liquid which decomposes on boiling at atmospheric pressure. Formamide, acetamide, CH$_3$CONH$_2$, and urea, CO(NH$_2$)$_2$, are readily soluble in water; oxamide, (CONH$_2$)$_2$, benzamide, C$_6$H$_5$CONH$_2$, and salicylamide, HOC$_6$H$_4$CONH$_2$, are almost insoluble in cold water; salicylamide is readily soluble in cold NaOH solution. All are odourless: acetamide, however, has an odour of mice unless it has been purified by recrystallisation.

(C) *Imides.* Both colourless solids: succinimide is readily soluble, and phthalimide sparingly soluble, in cold water.

(D) *Nitriles.* Both liquids. Acetonitrile, CH$_3$CN, is miscible with water, but benzonitrile, C$_6$H$_5$CN, is insoluble. Acetonitrile, unless specially purified, retains the mouse-like odour of acetamide: benzonitrile has an odour resembling both that of benzaldehyde and of nitrobenzene (bitter almonds).

(A) GENERAL REACTIONS FOR AMMONIUM SALTS.

1. Give off ammonia freely when treated with aqueous NaOH solution *in the cold* (distinction from amides, imides and nitriles).

2. Aqueous solutions give with ferric chloride the characteristic reactions of the neutral salt of the acid (p. 249). Ammonium oxalate however gives no coloration with ferric chloride. Identify the carboxylic acids by the tests already given (Section 13, p. 261).

(B) GENERAL REACTIONS FOR AMIDES,* IMIDES AND NITRILES.

   1. *Boiled* with aqueous NaOH solution yield ammonia and the sodium salt of the corresponding acid.

   2. Aqueous solutions (when obtainable) give no reaction with ferric chloride. This is an important distinction from ammonium salts (see above). Salicylamide, being also a phenol, is however an exception (p. 274).

   1. *Hydrolysis by sodium hydroxide.* Classes (B), (C) and (D) hydrolyse thus:

$$(B) \quad RCONH_2 + NaOH = RCOONa + NH_3$$

$$(C) \quad R{<}\begin{matrix} CO \\ \\ CO \end{matrix}{>}NH + 2NaOH = R{<}\begin{matrix} COONa \\ \\ COONa \end{matrix} + NH_3$$

$$(D) \quad RCN + NaOH + H_2O = RCOONa + NH_3$$

Place together in a 100 c.c. conical flask about 2 gms. of the substance and 20 c.c. of 10% NaOH solution. Add a few pieces of unglazed porcelain, fit a reflux water-condenser, and boil gently for about 20 minutes. Nitriles require longer heating than amides, usually about 30 minutes. The completion of the hydrolysis of an insoluble nitrile (*e.g.*, benzonitrile) is indicated by the disappearance of oily drops in the liquid. Cool the flask, add an excess of dil. H_2SO_4 and cool thoroughly.

   (*a*) A white precipitate indicates an aromatic acid: filter off, wash well with water and carry out tests for benzoic, salicylic and phthalic acids (Section 13, p. 261). Phthalic acid is moderately soluble in cold water, and is therefore precipitated only if the volume of the liquid is kept small.

   (*b*) A brisk effervescence of CO_2 without the f rmation of a precipitate indicates urea (if the NaOH used is free from carbonate).

   (*c*) If no precipitate is obtained and there is no marked effervescence, connect a knee-tube and water-condenser to the flask (Fig. 43, p. 72) and distil off about 10 c.c. of the liquid. Test the distillate for formic and acetic acids (p. 264). If a negative result is obtained, cool the residue in the flask and carry out tests for oxalic and succinic acids (p. 264), taking care to neutralise the solution where necessary.

---

  * In addition to General Reactions 1 and 2, all amides react with nitrous acid evolving nitrogen:

$$CH_3CONH_2 + HNO_2 = CH_3COOH + N_2 + H_2O$$

The evolution of nitrogen is not always entirely satisfactory as a test owing to the possible evolution of gaseous decomposition products of nitrous acid itself. The test may be performed as follows. To 1 c.c. of chilled concentrated sodium nitrite solution add 1 c.c. of dilute acetic acid. Allow any preliminary evolution of gas to subside, and then add the mixed solution to a cold aqueous solution (or suspension) of the amide: note the *brisk* effervescence.

SPECIAL REACTIONS.

Formamide.

Boil 1 c.c. of formamide in a test-tube and note that ammonia is freely evolved. Carbon monoxide is also produced, but cannot usually be ignited in the presence of the ammonia.

Urea.

1. *Formation of Biuret, and Biuret reaction.* Place 0·2 gm. of urea in a dry test-tube, heat very gently just above the m.p. and note the production of ammonia. After 1–2 minutes the liquid suddenly solidifies with the formation of biuret:

$$2NH_2CONH_2 = NH_2CONHCONH_2 + NH_3$$

Dissolve the solid residue in a few c.c. of warm 10% NaOH solution, cool and add 1 drop of very dilute copper sulphate solution. A purple coloration is obtained.*

2. *Action of hypobromite.* To a solution of urea add sodium hypo-

$$NH_2CONH_2 + 3NaOBr = N_2 + CO_2 + 3NaBr + 2H_2O$$

bromite solution and note the brisk effervescence.

3. (*a*) *Urea nitrate.* Make a concentrated aqueous solution of urea and add a few drops of conc. HNO_3: a white crystalline precipitate of urea nitrate is produced.

(*b*) *Urea oxalate.* Add concentrated oxalic acid solution to concentrated urea solution and note the formation of white crystals of urea oxalate, particularly on scratching. The nitrate and oxalate redissolve in excess of water.

4. *Urease test.* The enzyme *urease* hydrolyses urea to ammonium carbonate (p. 418). The reaction is specific and is frequently used for solutions of urea to which the biuret test cannot be applied. Add about 5 drops of phenol-red to 0·2 gm. of urea dissolved in 5 c.c. of water. To this yellow solution, add 0·2 gm. of jack bean meal suspended in 2 c.c. of water containing also 5 drops of phenol-red. The colour changes to red as the solution becomes alkaline.

Oxamide.

1. *Biuret test.* Oxamide, having two ·$CONH_2$ groups, will give this test without any preliminary treatment (*cf.* urea). Shake 0·1 gm. of oxamide with 1 c.c. of 10% NaOH solution, add 1 drop of very dilute $CuSO_4$ solution and mix well. A rose-pink coloration is produced.

2. *Sulphuric acid test.* Heat 0·5 gm. of oxamide with conc. H_2SO_4. CO and CO_2 are evolved.

* A purple or rose-pink coloration is produced when sodium hydroxide and dilute copper sulphate solution are added to compounds containing two –CONH– groups attached *either* to one another, *or* to the same nitrogen atom, *or* to the same carbon atom. It is therefore also given by oxamide, $NH_2CO·CONH_2$, malonamide, $NH_2CO·CH_2·CONH_2$ and by proteins and peptides. In fact the –CONH– is often spoken of as the "peptide" linkage.

Salicylamide.

Ferric chloride coloration. To a trace of the solid add ferric chloride solution and shake: an intense violet coloration is produced, owing to the presence of the phenolic grouping.

Succinimide.

1. *Reduction.* Mix together intimately in a dry hard-glass test-tube 0·2 gm. of succinimide and an equal amount of zinc dust. Heat strongly, and in the mouth of the tube place a matchstick which has been soaked in conc. HCl. Note that the stick is turned red by the vapour of pyrrole which is formed by reduction.

$$\begin{array}{ccc} \mathrm{CH_2CO} & & \mathrm{CH{:}CH} \\ | \quad \Big\rangle \mathrm{NH} \longrightarrow & | \quad \Big\rangle \mathrm{NH} \\ \mathrm{CH_2{\cdot}CO} & & \mathrm{CH{:}CH} \end{array}$$

2. *Fluorescein reaction.* Fuse together in a dry test-tube 0·2 gm. of succinimide, 0·2 gm. of resorcinol and 4 drops of conc. H_2SO_4. Cool, add water and then NaOH solution in excess. A green fluorescent solution is obtained.

Phthalimide

1. *Phthalein reaction.* Fuse together very gently in a dry test-tube 0·2 gm. of phthalimide, 0·2 gm. of phenol and 4 drops of conc. H_2SO_4. Cool, add water and then NaOH solution in excess. A red coloration is produced which is decolorised by acids. (NOTE. Succinimide gives no definite coloration in these circumstances.)

2. *Fluorescein reaction.* Repeat the above test, but use resorcinol instead of phenol and fuse *very gently*. A green fluorescent solution is produced on the addition of NaOH solution.

Section 16. (A) Acid chlorides. R·COCl.
(B) Acid anhydrides. R·CO·O·CO·R

(A) ACID CHLORIDES. *Acetyl chloride, benzoyl chloride.*

(B) ACID ANHYDRIDES. *Acetic anhydride, succinic anhydride, phthalic anhydride.*

(A) ACID CHLORIDES.

Physical properties. Both colourless liquids when pure, benzoyl chloride, C_6H_5COCl, is frequently pale yellow. Acetyl chloride, CH_3COCl, has a pungent odour, fumes in moist air and is immediately hydrolysed by cold water. Benzoyl chloride also has a pungent odour, is lachrymatory, and is hydrolysed only slowly by cold water, in which it is insoluble.

(B) ACID ANHYDRIDES.

Physical properties. Acetic anhydride, $(CH_3CO)_2O$, is a colourless liquid with a sharp pungent odour, decomposed slowly by water, in which it is only slightly soluble.

Succinic anhydride and phthalic anhydride (of formulae

$$\begin{matrix} CH_2{\cdot}CO \\ | \qquad\qquad{\Large{>}}O \\ CH_2{\cdot}CO \end{matrix} \text{ and } C_6H_4{\Large{<}}\begin{matrix} CO \\ \\ CO \end{matrix}{\Large{>}}O$$ respectively) are both colourless

crystalline solids almost insoluble in cold water.

The chemical reactions of the acid chlorides and anhydrides are so closely parallel that they are considered together.

GENERAL REACTIONS.

1. Acid chlorides (but not acid anhydrides) precipitate silver chloride on treatment with aqueous silver nitrate acidified with HNO_3.
2. Hydrolysed by water or (more rapidly) by alkalis to corresponding carboxylic acid or salt.
3. Form esters with alcohols.
4. Acid chlorides, and some anhydrides, condense with aniline to give anilides.

    N.B. In all these reactions acetyl chloride reacts with much greater vigour than the other compounds, and accordingly tests with this substance must be carried out with extreme care.

1. *Action of Silver Nitrate.* Acidify 2 c.c. of aqueous silver nitrate solution with dil. HNO_3 and add the acid chloride drop by drop with shaking. Acetyl chloride and benzoyl chloride give a precipitate of silver chloride. Filter, wash with water, and then with methylated spirit to remove any benzoic acid: the silver chloride remains.

2. *Hydrolysis.* If the substance is a liquid, add 1 c.c. very carefully to 5 c.c. of distilled water:

(*a*) Acetyl chloride reacts almost immediately with the evolution of HCl and of heat. Cool, and to one portion of the solution add dil. HNO_3 and then aqueous silver nitrate solution: a copious precipitate of silver chloride is formed. Test the remainder of the solution for acetic acid (p. 262).

(*b*) Acetic anhydride is almost insoluble. Warm the solution gently and note that a completely homogeneous solution is rapidly obtained. No precipitate is obtained with dil. HNO_3 and silver nitrate. Carry out tests for acetic acid (p. 262).

(*c*) Benzoyl chloride does not dissolve even on warming. Transfer to a boiling-tube and add several c.c. of 10% aqueous NaOH solution and a few pieces of unglazed porcelain: boil *gently* until all the oil has dissolved. Cool and add conc. HCl carefully: a white precipitate is formed. Filter, wash with water and identify the benzoic acid (p. 262).

3. *Ester formation.* Add carefully 1 c.c. of the liquid to 1 c.c. of ethyl alcohol and then warm gently for 1 minute. Pour into water, make alkaline with aqueous Na_2CO_3 solution (to remove HCl and other acid fumes), and note the odour of ethyl acetate or ethyl benzoate.

$$CH_3COCl + HOC_2H_5 = CH_3COOC_2H_5 + HCl$$
$$CH_3 \cdot CO \cdot O \cdot CO \cdot CH_3 + HOC_2H_5 = CH_3COOC_2H_5 + CH_3COOH$$
$$C_6H_5COCl + HOC_2H_5 = C_6H_5COOC_2H_5 + HCl$$

4. *Anilides.* (*a*) To 1 c.c. of aniline in a small conical flask add very slowly and *carefully* about 1 c.c. of acetyl chloride. A vigorous reaction occurs and a solid mass is formed. Add just sufficient water (about 15 c.c.) to dissolve the solid completely on boiling. On cooling, crystals of acetanilide separate out: filter and determine the m.p. (113°).

(*b*) To 1 c.c. of aniline in a small conical flask add about 2 c.c. of acetic anhydride and heat on a boiling water-bath for 5 minutes. Now add just sufficient water to dissolve the product on boiling. On cooling, crystals of acetanilide separate out.

(*c*) Prepare benzanilide from benzoyl chloride and aniline according to the directions given on p. 191. The reaction can be carried out conveniently on a small scale using 1 c.c. aniline, 15 c.c. 10% aqueous NaOH solution and 1·5 c.c. of benzoyl chloride.

Succinic anhydride and phthalic anhydride.

These substances are not readily distinguished from the corresponding acids. Succinic anhydride (m.p. 120°) is however almost insoluble in cold water, whereas succinic acid (m.p. 185°) is readily soluble.

Phthalic anhydride has m.p. 130° and phthalic acid has m.p. 196–199° with decomposition. Each of these anhydrides when heated with water hydrolyses to the corresponding acids.

The fluorescein test for succinic acid (p. 265) and the phthalein and fluorescein tests for phthalic acid (p. 267) are obviously given also by succinic anhydride and phthalic anhydride, as these tests depend upon the initial formation of the anhydride in each case.

Section 17.   Carbohydrates. $C_x(H_2O)_y$.

Glucose and *fructose* ($C_6H_{12}O_6$, monosaccharides); *sucrose*, *maltose* and *lactose* ($C_{12}H_{22}O_{11}$, disaccharides); *starch*, $(C_6H_{10}O_5)_n$, a polysaccharide.

Before proceeding with this section the student should read pp. 106–109 very carefully in order to understand the nature of the reactions which substances of this type undergo.

Physical Properties.

All colourless solids, which decompose on heating and therefor have no definite m.p.s. All insoluble in ether (like most polyhydroxy-compounds). All except starch are soluble in water and have a sweet taste.* Starch as ordinarily supplied is insoluble in water. So-called "starch solution" or "starch paste" is prepared as follows: Place about 1 gm. of starch in a test-tube, add about 10 c.c. of water, and mix well. Pour this suspension with stirring into 100 c.c. of boiling water and continue to boil the mixture for 1 minute.

A soluble starch is obtainable which dissolves slightly in cold water and readily in hot water to give a clear solution. Concentrated solutions of both "soluble starch" and "ordinary starch" set to a jelly on cooling.

GENERAL REACTIONS.

1. Respond to Molisch's Test.
2. Blackening and effervescence when warmed with conc. H_2SO_4.
3. Certain carbohydrates give yellow colorations when boiled with NaOH solution.

1. *Molisch's Test.* Dissolve about 0·1 gm. of the carbohydrate in 2 c.c. of water (for starch use 2 c.c. of "starch solution"), add 2–3 drops of a 20% alcoholic solution of α-naphthol (ignoring traces of the latter precipitated by the water) and then carefully pour 2 c.c. of conc. H_2SO_4 down the side of the test-tube so that it forms a heavy layer at the bottom. A deep violet coloration is produced where the liquids meet. This coloration is due apparently to the formation of an unstable condensation product of α-naphthol with furfural (an aldehyde produced by the dehydration of the carbohydrate).

2. *Sulphuric Acid.* Warm about 0·2 gm. of the carbohydrate with 1 c.c. of conc. H_2SO_4, using a *small* flame. Observe the immediate blackening. As the temperature is raised, CO_2, CO and SO_2 are evolved.

3. *Action of sodium hydroxide.* Boil about 0·2 gm. of glucose with 5 c.c. of 10% NaOH solution: the mixture turns yellow, then brown, and emits the odour of caramel. Fructose, maltose, lactose and soluble starch behave similarly: sucrose and ordinary starch do not give colorations.

SPECIAL REACTIONS. A 1 % solution is suitable for most of the following reactions.

Glucose. (Dextrose or grape sugar.)

1. *Reduction of ammoniacal silver nitrate.* Place 2 c.c. of dilute silver nitrate solution in a clean test-tube. Add 1 drop of NaOH

---

* Students are strongly advised not to attempt identification of the soluble carbohydrates by taste—quite apart from the fact that other compounds (*e.g.*, saccharin) also have a sweet taste, the tasting of an imperfectly identified organic compound is too dangerous an operation.

solution and then add dil. ammonia drop by drop until the precipitate formed by the NaOH is *just* not redissolved. Now add 1–2 c.c. of glucose solution and place the test-tube in a water-bath at 50–60°: a silver mirror is produced in 1–2 minutes.

2. *Reduction of Fehling's solution.* Add 5 c.c. of the glucose solution to 5 c.c. of Fehling's solution and boil. Reduction takes place and a precipitate of cuprous oxide is formed; the latter is at first yellow but may become red on standing.

3. *Osazone formation.* The preparation of glucosazone has already been given (p. 109). It may be carried out on a small scale by either of the following methods, according as (*a*) the phenylhydrazine base, or (*b*) one of its salts, is used.

(*a*) Dissolve 1 gm. of the sugar in 20 c.c. of water in a boiling-tube, add 2·5 c.c. of phenylhydrazine and 3 c.c. of glacial acetic acid. Mix well, cork the tube loosely and place in a beaker of boiling water. Yellow crystals of the osazone appear after 10–15 minutes. Examine some of the crystals under the microscope as described on p. 110, and note the sheaves of fine needles (Fig. 47(A), p. 110). Filter off the remainder, wash well with water, dry and take the m.p. (204°).

(*b*) To 10 c.c. of a 1% solution of glucose, add about 0·2 gm. of phenylhydrazine hydrochloride, about 0·5 gm. of sodium acetate and a few drops of glacial acetic acid. Warm gently to dissolve and then filter if necessary through a small fluted filter-paper (to remove impurities) into a boiling-tube. Proceed as in (*a*) above. (Glucose can thus be identified in biological fluids.)

4. *"Rapid furfural test."* If in Molisch's test conc. HCl is used instead of H_2SO_4, the violet coloration is produced at different rates according to the carbohydrate used. Take 1 c.c. of a dilute solution of glucose, add 1 c.c. of a 1% alcoholic solution of α-naphthol and then 6–8 c.c. of conc. HCl and boil. In the case of fructose and sucrose a violet coloration is produced *immediately* the solution starts to boil: with glucose the coloration is delayed and may not be produced until after 1 minute's boiling. In this way glucose may be distinguished from fructose.

*Fructose.** (Laevulose or fruit sugar.)

* In an analytical laboratory, glucose (dextrorotatory) would be conclusively differentiated from fructose (laevorotatory) by using a polarimeter: in the present scheme, however, chemical tests are primarily considered. There are various other chemical tests for differentiating between glucose and fructose, but these are frequently vitiated by the fact that fructose as ordinarily supplied almost invariably contains traces of glucose. The student is recommended, when once the sugar is recognised as a monosaccharide, to base the final identification primarily on the Rapid Furfural test, and also on rate of osazone formation under parallel conditions.

Fructose can be distinguished from glucose, *if both sugars are pure*, by the Ammonium Molybdate test which is carried out as follows. To about 10 c.c. of a 1% solution of the sugar in a boiling-tube, add an equal volume of a freshly prepared 4% aqueous solution of ammonium molybdate, and then 4–5 drops of glacial acetic acid. Heat the boiling-tube in a beaker of boiling

1. *Reduction of ammoniacal silver nitrate.* As for glucose.

2. *Reduction of Fehling's solution.* As for glucose.

3. *Osazone formation.* Fructose forms an osazone identical with that obtained from glucose. It is, however, usually formed more quickly from fructose (about 5 minutes under above conditions) than from glucose, but little reliance can be placed on this difference unless the two reactions are carried out side by side under strictly parallel conditions.

4. *"Rapid furfural test."* Fructose gives an *immediate* violet coloration on boiling (see Test 4 for glucose).

Sucrose. (Cane sugar).

1. Does not reduce ammoniacal silver nitrate or Fehling's solution. If, however, the sucrose solution is warmed for some time with the reagent in question, slight hydrolysis to glucose and fructose does take place and reduction then occurs: occasionally samples of sucrose will rapidly give a silver mirror, presumably owing to impurities.

2. Does not form an osazone.

3. *"Rapid furfural test."* A violet coloration is produced *immediately* on boiling (as for fructose).

4. *Hydrolysis by acids.* Sucrose is readily hydrolysed by *dilute* acids. Dissolve 0·5 gm. of sucrose in 5 c.c. of water, add 2 c.c. of dil. H_2SO_4 and heat *in* a boiling water-bath for 5 minutes. Cool and perform tests for glucose and fructose. Note that the excess of acid must be neutralisd ebefore carrying out the reduction tests.

Maltose. (Malt sugar.)

1. Reduces ammoniacal silver nitrate, and Fehling's solution.

2. *Osazone formation.* Forms an osazone, m.p. 206° (see however footnote, p. 111); this osazone, unlike glucosazone, is soluble in hot water. See p. 111 for preparation. Examine the crystals under the microscope and note the sheaves of plates, not needles (Fig. 47(B), p. 110).

3. *"Rapid furfural test."* The violet coloration is produced only after boiling for about 1 minute (as for glucose).

Lactose. (Milk sugar.)

1. Reduces ammoniacal silver nitrate, and Fehling's solution.

2. *Osazone formation.* Forms a yellow osazone, m.p. 208°; soluble in hot water. See p. 111 for preparation. If examined under the microscope very characteristic clusters of "hedge-hog" crystals will be seen (Fig. 47(C), p. 110). The difference in the crystalline appearance of lactosazone and maltosazone should be very carefully noted, as this

---

water. Fructose gives a greenish-blue coloration within 3–4 minutes. *Pure* glucose gives only a very faint coloration after about 10 minutes, and other sugars give no coloration. All ordinary samples of glucose contain sufficient fructose, however, to give a coloration after about 4–5 minutes. Free mineral acids interfere with the test.

difference forms the chief and most reliable method of differentiating between these two sugars.

3. *"Rapid furfural test."* Violet coloration after about 1 minute's boiling, as for glucose and maltose.

Starch.

1. Does not reduce ammoniacal silver nitrate or Fehling's solution, and does not form an osazone.

2. *Starch Iodide coloration.* To a small volume of "starch solution" add 1–2 drops of dilute iodine solution. A deep blue colour is produced which disappears on boiling and reappears on cooling.

3. *Hydrolysis by acids.* Place 50 c.c. of starch solution in a boiling-tube, add 3 c.c. of conc. HCl, mix well and place in a boiling water-bath for 20 minutes. Cool and add 2 drops of iodine solution to 1 c.c. of the solution: no blue coloration is produced. On the remainder, perform tests for glucose: in particular show that glucosazone can be formed. Neutralise the excess of acid before carrying out these tests. (Note that a more concentrated acid is required to hydrolyse starch than to hydrolyse the disaccharides, such as sucrose.)

4. *Microscopic appearance.* Place a small amount of dry starch on a microscope slide, add a drop of water, cover with a slip and examine under the microscope. Characteristic oval grains are seen which have concentric rings round a hilum which is towards one end of the grain. Run a drop of *very* dilute iodine solution under the slip from a fine dropping-tube: the grains become blue.

5. *Hydrolysis with diastase and ptyalin.* See pp. 410, 411.

Section 18. Quinones. O:C< >C:O.

Benzoquinone, anthraquinone.

Physical properties. Both solids. Benzoquinone,

$O:C \Big< \begin{matrix} CH:CH \\ CH:CH \end{matrix} \Big> C:O$, deep yellow crystals, slightly soluble in cold water, readily soluble in hot water, and freely volatile in steam. Anthraquinone, $C_6H_4 \Big< \begin{matrix} CO \\ CO \end{matrix} \Big> C_6H_4$, pale yellow crystals, insoluble in cold and hot water, almost insoluble in alcohol, non-volatile in steam.

These quinones are best identified by their special reactions, benzoquinone being a very reactive substance, while anthraquinone is a very stable compound.

SPECIAL REACTIONS FOR BENZOQUINONE.

1. *Volatility in steam.* Add about 0·2 gm. of benzoquinone to 2–3 c.c. of water in a test-tube and boil gently. The benzoquinone readily

dissolves to give a yellow solution which rapidly darkens in colour. Note *cautiously* the irritating and characteristic odour of the benzoquinone which has volatilised in the steam.

2. *Oxidation.* Benzoquinone is readily oxidised in *alkaline* solution. This is shown by the following tests.

(*a*) *Sodium hydroxide.* Dissolve a few crystals of benzoquinone in 10% aqueous NaOH solution and shake gently. The solution turns rapidly brown, and then almost black, owing to atmospheric oxidation.

(*b*) *Ammoniacal silver nitrate.* To a few c.c. of ammoniacal silver nitrate solution (preparation, p. 426) add a few drops of cold aqueous benzoquinone solution: a silver mirror or (more generally) a dark precipitate of metallic silver is formed immediately in the cold.

3. *Reduction.* Benzoquinone is readily reduced (particularly in *acid* solution) ultimately to hydroquinone or quinol, $p\text{-}C_6H_4(OH)_2$. This is shown by the following reagents.

(*a*) *Sulphurous acid.* To a cold aqueous benzoquinone solution add 1 drop of sulphurous acid solution (SO_2–water): the solution turns brown owing to the intermediate formation of quinhydrone, $C_6H_4O_2,C_6H_4(OH)_2$. Now add an excess of sulphurous acid: the solution becomes colourless, owing to the formation of hydroquinone. Add a *few* drops of ferric chloride solution: the reaction is reversed and the deep brownish-yellow colour (quite distinct from that of the ferric chloride) is restored.

(*b*) *Acidified potassium iodide.* To an aqueous KI solution containing a few drops of dil. H_2SO_4, add 1 c.c. of aqueous benzoquinone solution: iodine is liberated, the quinone simultaneously undergoing reduction.

4. *Condensation with aniline.* Dissolve 0·2 gm. of benzoquinone in 1 c.c. of alcohol, add 2 drops of aniline and warm gently: a reddish precipitate, consisting mainly of 2:5-dianilinobenzoquinone, is produced.

5. *Iodoform reaction.* To 5 c.c. of an aqueous solution of benzoquinone add 3 c.c. of 10% KI solution and 10 c.c. of sodium hypochlorite solution. Yellow crystals of iodoform soon separate.

SPECIAL REACTIONS OF ANTHRAQUINONE.

1. *Differences from Benzoquinone.*

(*a*) Unaffected by NaOH solution.
(*b*) Does not reduce ammoniacal silver nitrate.
(*c*) Unaffected by sulphurous acid.
(*d*) Does not liberate iodine from acidified KI solution.
(*e*) Does not give the iodoform reaction.

2. *Reduction. Formation of Oxanthranol.* Heat 0·2 gm. of anthraquinone with about 5 c.c. of 10% NaOH solution, and add a small

quantity of zinc dust: an intense red coloration is produced. On shaking in contact with air (after the zinc has dissolved) the solution is slowly decolorised and the anthraquinone reappears as an almost colourless flocculent precipitate.

The red coloration is due to oxanthranol, C_6H_4——CO——C_6H_4, which is red in alkaline solution. $\diagdown CH(OH)\diagup$

Section 19. Amines.

(A) PRIMARY AROMATIC AMINES.* RNH_2. *Aniline, o-, m- and p-toluidine, α and β-naphthylamine.*

(B) SECONDARY AROMATIC AMINES. R_2NH. *Monomethylaniline, diphenylamine.*

(C) TERTIARY AROMATIC AMINES. R_3N. *Dimethylaniline, triphenylamine.*

(D) HETEROCYCLIC AMINES. *Hexamethylene-tetramine* (urotropine), *pyridine, quinoline.*

The aliphatic amines are rarely encountered in elementary work owing to their high cost, and they are consequently not considered here.

(A) PRIMARY AMINES.

Physical properties. All are liquids except *p*-toluidine and α- and β-naphthylamine. All are colourless when pure, but rapidly darken on exposure to air and light. All are very sparingly soluble in water, but dissolve readily in dilute mineral acids (except the naphthylamines, which are only moderately soluble in acids). They form colourless crystalline salts (*e.g.*, $C_6H_5NH_2,HCl$) which are soluble in water; such aqueous solutions usually have an acid reaction owing to hydrolysis, and give the reactions of both the amine and the acid from which they are derived. Addition of alkali to the acid solution liberates the amine.

GENERAL REACTIONS.†

* Only the mono-amines are described here. The diamines are more frequently encountered as reduction products of dinitrobenzenes and nitro-anilines, and the chief reactions of the phenylene diamines are therefore given in Section 22, pp. 293, 295.

† All the classes of amines mentioned above (except diphenylamine, triphenylamine and hexamethylene-tetramine) readily form picrates, which may be prepared by mixing cold benzene solutions of the amine and of dry picric acid. Some picrates are too soluble in alcohol for the latter to be used as a solvent (p. 134).

Members of classes (A), (B) and (C) also reduce ammoniacal silver nitrate to silver or a silver mirror, the reduction by primary amines being usually rapid, by secondary amines rather slower, and that by tertiary amines occurring only with difficulty.

1. Give the isocyanide (or carbylamine) reaction.
2. Form diazonium compounds which couple with alkaline β-naphthol to give red dyes (p. 255).
3. Give acetyl derivatives.
4. Give benzoyl derivatives (Schotten-Baumann reaction).
5. Oxidised to coloured substances, the product depending upon the amine and the oxidising agent used.

For the following experiments the amine or one of its salts may be used.

1. *Isocyanide reaction.* Add a few drops of chloroform to about 0·2 gm. of the substance, and then 2–3 c.c. of alcoholic NaOH solution. Mix well and warm gently: the foul odour of isocyanide (carbylamine) is produced. *Immediately* the odour of isocyanide is detected, cool the tube and add carefully an excess of conc. HCl: the isocyanide is thus hydrolysed to the odourless amine. Note: when this test is applied to amino-acids, *e.g.*, glycine, anthranilic acid, sulphanilic acid, no odour is detected owing to the non-volatility of the acidic isocyanide in the alkaline solution.

2. *Diazotisation.* Dissolve 0·2 gm. of the substance in 1 c.c. of conc. HCl: dilute with about 3 c.c. of water, cool in ice, and add a few drops of sodium nitrite solution. Now add this cold diazonium solution slowly to a cold solution of β-naphthol in a considerable excess of 10% NaOH solution: a brilliant red dye is produced.

3. *Acetylation.* Place 1 c.c. of the substance (or, if solid, 1 gm. of the *powdered* amine) in a small flask fitted with a reflux condenser (or in a test-tube fitted with a "cold-finger", as in Fig. 25, p. 43), add 5 c.c. of an acetic anhydride-acetic acid mixture (equal volumes) and reflux gently for 15 minutes. Pour into water: the solid anilide separates. Filter off, wash with water, and recrystallise from water or dilute methylated spirit. Note the m.p.: acetanilide, m.p. 113°; aceto-*o*-toluidide, m.p. 112°; aceto-*m*-toluidide, m.p. 65°; aceto-*p*-toluidide, m.p. 148°; aceto-α-naphthalide, m.p. 159°; aceto-β-naphthalide, m.p. 132°.

4. *Benzoylation* (Schotten-Baumann reaction). Mix together in a strong boiling-tube 2 c.c. (or 2 gms.) of the substance and 20 c.c. of 10% NaOH solution. Add 2–3 c.c. of benzoyl chloride (0·5 c.c. at a time) until shaking the mixture vigorously in the securely corked boiling-tube gives no further separation of the semi-solid benzoyl derivative. Then continue the shaking for 5 minutes to complete the reaction, and finally filter off the solid, wash well with water, and recrystallise from methylated spirit. Take the m.p.: benzanilide, m.p. 163°; benz-*o*-toluidide, m.p. 143°; benz-*m*-toluidide, m.p. 125°; benz-*p*-toluidide, m.p. 158°; benz-α-naphthalide, m.p. 160°; benz-β-naphthalide, m.p. 162°.

5. (*a*) *Action of bleaching powder.* Shake 1–2 drops of aniline with 10 c.c. of water and add a few drops of bleaching powder solution. A transient purple coloration is produced which soon turns brown. *o*- and *m*-Toluidine give a brown coloration immediately, *p*-toluidine gives a

yellow-brown colour, α-naphthylamine gives a pale purple coloration and β-naphthylamine is unaffected.

(b) *Action of H_2O_2 and ferrous sulphate in conc. HCl solution.* To 1 c.c. of aniline add 5 c.c. of conc. HCl and then add 1 c.c. of water. Shake to dissolve all the hydrochloride which has been precipitated, cool, and add about 2 c.c. of H_2O_2 solution and then 2–3 drops of freshly prepared ferrous sulphate solution. A bright green coloration is first produced and then a deep green precipitate of the dye emeraldine gradually separates.

o-Toluidine and *m*-toluidine similarly give deep green precipitates: *p*-toluidine is distinguished by giving a yellow-brown or yellow-red coloration. α-Naphthylamine gives a green precipitate, β-naphthylamine gives no definite coloration.

(c) *Colorations with ferric chloride.* Dissolve a few drops (or crystals) of the amine in dil. HCl, and then add 2–3 drops of ferric chloride solution. Aniline gives a pale green coloration, deepened by warming. *o*-Toluidine gives a green coloration, which is slowly replaced by a deep green or blue precipitate: solid α-naphthylamine gives a blue precipitate: *p*-toluidine gives a reddish-brown coloration slowly. The remainder are practically unaffected in the cold.

(d) The colour reactions with the enzyme *peroxidase* and H_2O_2 permit all the above amines to be distinguished from one another in very dilute solution (p. 421).

NOTE.—All but the purest samples of monomethylaniline contain sufficient aniline to give positive (although possibly weak) reactions to certain tests for aniline (particularly Tests 1 and 2). If it is suspected that aniline is present solely as an impurity, the positive tests for monomethylaniline (particularly Test 2, below) should be applied.

B. SECONDARY AMINES.

Physical Properties. Colourless when freshly prepared, but usually brown. Monomethylaniline, $C_6H_5NHCH_3$, b.p. 193°; diphenylamine, $(C_6H_5)_2NH$, m.p. 54°; both insoluble in water: the former has well-marked basic properties, the latter is only feebly basic and is insoluble in dilute mineral acids.

GENERAL REACTIONS.

1. Do not give the isocyanide reaction.
2. With nitrous acid give nitrosamines which respond to Liebermann's nitroso reaction.
3. Give acetyl and benzoyl derivatives, but the latter are usually more difficult to prepare than those of primary amines, and consequently are not so often used for identification purposes.
4. Give coloured products with oxidising agents.

2. *Formation of nitrosoamine, R_2NNO. (a) From monomethylaniline.* Dissolve 1 c.c. of monomethylaniline in about 3 c.c. of dil. HCl and add sodium nitrite solution gradually with shaking until the yellow oil separates out at the bottom of the solution. Transfer completely to a small separating-funnel, add about 20 c.c. of ether and shake.

Run off the lower layer and wash the ethereal extract first with water, then with dil. NaOH solution, and finally with water to free it *completely* from nitrous acid. Evaporate the ether in a basin over a previously warmed water-bath, *in a fume-cupboard with no flames near.* Apply Liebermann's reaction (p. 255) to the residual oil thus: Place 1 drop of the oily nitroso-compound in a dry test-tube, add 0·5 gm. phenol and warm gently for 20 seconds. Cool and add 1 c.c. of conc. H_2SO_4: a greenish-blue coloration is produced which turns red when the solution is diluted with water. Then add an excess of NaOH solution: the greenish-blue coloration is restored.

(b) *From diphenylamine* (p. 158). Dissolve 1 gm. of diphenylamine in about 8 c.c. of warm alcohol and dissolve also 0·5 gm. of sodium nitrite in 1 c.c. of water. Cool each solution in ice-water and then add 1 c.c. of conc. HCl to the diphenylamine solution, mix thoroughly and immediately add the sodium nitrite solution. Allow the mixture to stand in ice-water for a few minutes and then filter off the yellow crystals which have separated. Wash thoroughly with water to remove the sodium nitrite. Carry out Liebermann's reaction on the product as described above, using about 0·05 gm. of the nitrosoamine. The crystals of diphenylnitrosoamine may be recrystallised from methylated spirit and then have m.p. 68°.

3. *Acetylation.* Boil gently 2 c.c. of monomethylaniline and 5 c.c. of 1:1 acetic anhydride-acetic acid mixture for 30 minutes in a small flask fitted with a reflux condenser. Pour into 10 c.c. of water and add 10% NaOH solution, with stirring, until no more anilide is precipitated (acetyl-monomethylaniline is very soluble even in dil. acetic acid). Filter, wash with water, and recrystallise from boiling water: m.p. 102°.

Repeat using 2 gms. of diphenylamine in place of monomethylaniline: it is unnecessary in this case to add NaOH solution. Recrystallise from 50% aqueous methylated spirit: m.p. 101°.

4. *Coloured products with oxidising agents.* (a) Dissolve a few small crystals of diphenylamine in 1 c.c. of conc. H_2SO_4.* Add 2 drops of conc. HNO_3 to about 10 c.c. of water, shake, and add 1 drop of this diluted HNO_3 to the diphenylamine solution: an intense purple-blue coloration is produced. Monomethylaniline merely turns a dirty brown when treated in this way.

(b) Neither monomethylaniline nor diphenylamine when pure gives colorations with bleaching powder. The former, however, almost invariably contains aniline and so gives a purple-brown coloration.

(c) Dissolve 0·5 gm. of diphenylamine in 1 c.c. of conc. HCl and add 1 c.c. of water. Shake to dissolve, cool, and add a few drops of hydrogen peroxide solution and then 1 drop of ferrous sulphate solution. An intense green coloration is produced which changes to a green-violet fluorescence on dilution. Monomethylaniline gives a green coloration.

---

* A slight green coloration is usually noticed at this stage, due presumably to traces of impurities.

(C) TERTIARY AMINES.

Physical Properties. Dimethylaniline, $C_6H_5N(CH_3)_2$, b.p. 193°. Colourless when pure, but rapidly darkens in air; characteristic odour: insoluble in water. It is a strong base and dissolves in dilute as well as concentrated mineral acids. Addition of alkali to the acid solution liberates the amine. Triphenylamine, $(C_6H_5)_3N$, m.p. 127°, colourless when pure, but usually pale brown: insoluble in water. Non-basic, does not dissolve in conc. HCl, but dissolves in conc. H_2SO_4.

GENERAL REACTIONS.

1. Do not give the isocyanide reaction.
2. Do not give acetyl or benzoyl derivatives.
3. The dialkylanilines give bright green *p*-nitroso compounds with nitrous acid (p. 159).
4. Give coloured products with oxidising agents.

3. *p-Nitroso derivative*. Dissolve 0·5 c.c. of dimethylaniline in about 4 c.c. of dil. HCl, chill in ice and then add carefully drop by drop about 2 c.c. of a 20% sodium nitrite solution. A reddish solution is obtained, but no oil separates (*cf.* methylaniline). Allow to stand for 5 minutes in the cold and then add dil. NaOH solution. A green precipitate of *p*-nitrosodimethylaniline is obtained. Shake with a few c.c. of ether and note that the ethereal layer becomes deep green in colour.

4. *Coloured products with oxidising agents*. (*a*) Dissolve a few small crystals of triphenylamine in 1 c.c. of conc. H_2SO_4.* Add 2 drops of conc. HNO_3 to about 10 c.c. of water, mix, and add 1 drop of this diluted HNO_3 to the triphenylamine solution: an intense greenish-blue coloration is produced. Dimethylaniline when treated in this way turns a deep dichromate colour.

(*b*) Neither dimethylaniline nor triphenylamine gives colorations with bleaching powder.

SPECIAL REACTION FOR DIMETHYLANILINE.

Picrate. To 0·5 c.c. of dimethylaniline dissolved in acetone add about 2 c.c. of a cold concentrated solution of picric acid in acetone. Shake well: a yellow precipitate of dimethylaniline picrate soon separates. Filter, wash with cold acetone, and recrystallise from alcohol, m.p. 162°.

D. HETEROCYCLIC BASES.

Physical Properties. Hexamethylene-tetramine, $(CH_2)_6N_4$, colourless crystalline solid, m.p. 280°, readily soluble in cold water. Pyridine, C_5H_5N, b.p. 115°, and quinoline, C_9H_7N, b.p. 236°, are colourless liquids when pure, having characteristic penetrating odours. Pyridine is completely miscible with water,

* See footnote on p. 285.

but quinoline is only slightly soluble. Pyridine and quinoline are both comparatively strong bases.

SPECIAL REACTIONS FOR HEXAMETHYLENE-TETRA-MINE.

1. *Hydrolysis.* Warm 0·5 gm. with a few c.c. of dil. HCl. The pungent odour of formaldehyde, produced by the hydrolysis of the tetramine, is readily detected:

$$(CH_2)_6N_4 + 6H_2O + 4HCl = 6CH_2O + 4NH_4Cl.$$

2. *Action of nitrous acid.* Dissolve 0·5 gm. in a few c.c. of dil. HCl. Add slowly in the cold 2 c.c. of a 20% solution of sodium nitrite. A brisk effervescence takes place and almost colourless crystals of trimethylenetrinitrosamine, m.p. 105°, separate out.

PYRIDINE AND QUINOLINE.

General Reactions.

1. Do not give the isocyanide reaction.
2. Do not give acetyl or benzoyl derivatives.
3. Do not give coloured products on treatment with oxidising agents.
4. Form methiodides with methyl iodide.
5. Form picrates which separate readily from alcoholic solutions.

4. *Methiodides.* Place 2 drops of dry pyridine in a dry test-tube, add 2 drops of methyl iodide, and mix. A vigorous action takes place and on cooling a colourless crystalline mass of pyridine methiodide, C_5H_5N,MeI, m.p. 117°, is formed. Quinoline similarly gives a yellow crystalline mass of quinoline methiodide, m.p. 134° (monohydrate, m.p. 72°), but the reaction is much less vigorous.

5. *Picrates.* To a few drops of pyridine or quinoline dissolved in alcohol add 1 c.c. of an alcoholic solution of picric acid. A yellow crystalline precipitate of the picrate is formed immediately. Pyridine picrate, m.p. 167°; quinoline picrate, m.p. 203°.

SPECIAL REACTION FOR QUINOLINE.

Dissolve 1 drop of quinoline in 1 c.c. of dil. HCl and add a few drops of a saturated solution of potassium dichromate. A copious orange-yellow precipitate of quinoline dichromate, $(C_9H_7N)_2,H_2Cr_2O_7$, is formed; pyridine does not give a crystalline dichromate under these conditions.

Section 20. Anilides. $R \cdot CONHC_6H_5$.

Acetanilide, benzanilide.

Physical properties. Both colourless odourless crystalline solids. Acetanilide, $CH_3CONHC_6H_5$, is soluble in boiling water, sparingly soluble in cold water. Benzanilide, $C_6H_5CONHC_6H_5$, is sparingly soluble in both hot and cold water, soluble in alcohol.

GENERAL REACTIONS.

1. Give the isocyanide (carbylamine) reaction.
2. Hydrolyse readily with 70% H_2SO_4.

1. *Isocyanide reaction.* Heat together *gently* 0·2 gm. of the anilide, 3 c.c. of alcoholic NaOH solution and 1 c.c. of chloroform: hydrolysis of the anilide occurs, and the odour of the isocyanide can be detected after about 1 minute's heating.

2. *Hydrolysis with* 70% H_2SO_4. The acid hydrolysis of acetanilide and of benzanilide are fully described on pp. 80, 192 respectively. Hydrolyse about 2 gms. of the substance by boiling with 70% H_2SO_4 under reflux as there described. As the reaction proceeds, it will be obvious which method for the identification of the organic acid is to be followed in the final stages.

Section 21. Amino-acids. NH_2RCOOH and NH_2RSO_3H.

(A) AMINO-ALIPHATIC CARBOXYLIC ACIDS.*
   Glycine or *amino-acetic acid*, NH_2CH_2COOH;
   tyrosine, $p\text{-}HOC_6H_4CH_2CH(NH_2)COOH$;
   cystine, $[SCH_2CH(NH_2)COOH]_2$.

(B) AMINO-AROMATIC CARBOXYLIC ACIDS. *Anthranilic* or *o-amino-benzoic acid*, $NH_2C_6H_4COOH$.

(C) AMINO-AROMATIC SULPHONIC ACIDS. *Sulphanilic* or *p-amino-benzene sulphonic acid*, $NH_2C_6H_4SO_3H$.

(A) AMINO-ALIPHATIC CARBOXYLIC ACIDS. *Glycine, tyrosine, cystine.*

Physical Properties. Glycine is a colourless crystalline solid soluble in water. Owing to the almost equal opposing effects of the amino and the carboxylic groups, its aqueous solution is almost neutral (actually, slightly acidic to phenolphthalein) and glycine is therefore known as a "neutral ampholyte."† It exhibits both acidic and basic properties.

* All the amino-acids of physiological importance are α-amino-acids, *e.g'* (in addition to the above compounds), alanine or α-amino-propionic acid' $CH_3CH(NH_2)COOH$, and leucine or α-amino-γ-dimethyl-*n*-butyric acid, $(CH_3)_2CHCH_2CH(NH_2)COOH$, and naturally occurring samples (except glycine) are therefore optically active.

† Some amino-acids, *e.g.*, aspartic acid, $HOOC·CH_2·CH(NH_2)COOH$, also exhibit acidic and basic properties, but the acidic properties predominate owing to the presence of the two carboxylic groups. These are known as "acid ampholytes." A third class of amino-acids contain more basic than carboxylic groups and are consequently known as "basic ampholytes."

Tyrosine and cystine are colourless solids almost insoluble in water and in alcohol (tyrosine dissolves in hot water). They are readily soluble in dilute caustic alkali solution, in ammonia and mineral acids, but not in acetic acid. They are also classed as "neutral ampholytes."

GENERAL REACTIONS.

1. Soluble in Na_2CO_3 solution with evolution of CO_2.
2. React with nitrous acid to give nitrogen and the corresponding hydroxy-carboxylic acid.
3. Formaldehyde converts the basic NH_2 group into the neutral CH_2:N group (Sørenson's reaction).
4. Form derivatives with benzoyl chloride and (more rapidly and conveniently) with 3:5-dinitrobenzoyl chloride.
5. Form deep blue copper salts usually sparingly soluble in water.

1. *Solubility in Na_2CO_3 solution.* See Section 5 (p. 248), and also Test 2 for carboxylic acids (p. 262).

2. *Action of nitrous acid.* To a few c.c. of 20% sodium nitrite solution add a few drops of cold dil. acetic acid. Pour the mixture into a cold aqueous solution of glycine, and note the brisk evolution of nitrogen. $NH_2CH_2COOH + HNO_2 = HO.CH_2COOH + N_2 + H_2O$. Owing to the insolubility of cystine in acetic acid use a suspension in dil. acetic acid for this test. In each case care must be taken not to confuse the evolution of nitrogen with any possible thermal decomposition of the nitrous acid (*cf.* footnote, p. 272).

3. *Sørensen's reaction.* First read carefully the "Estimation of Glycine," p. 367. Dissolve 0·2 gm. of glycine in a few c.c. of water in a test-tube **A**, add 2 drops of phenolphthalein and then *very dilute* NaOH solution drop by drop until the solution *just* turns pink. In a second test-tube **B** place 2 c.c. of 40% formalin solution, add 2 drops of phenolphthalein solution and then the dil. NaOH solution until the solution *just* turns pink. Pour the contents of **B** into **A** and note the immediate decolorisation of the phenolphthalein, the solution now being acid. Observe also that several drops of dil. NaOH solution can now be added before the pink colour is restored.

Tyrosine and cystine are insoluble in water: therefore place about 0·2 gm. in the test-tube **A**, dissolve in the dil. NaOH solution, add phenolphthalein as before and then add dil. HCl until pink colour is *just* not discharged: then proceed as above.

4. 3:5-*Dinitrobenzoyl-glycine.** Dissolve 0·4 gm. of glycine in 10 c.c. of *N*.NaOH solution in a small stoppered bottle. And 1·1 gms. of finely powdered 3:5-dinitrobenzoyl chloride and shake vigorously for about 1 minute. Filter if necessary and acidify with dil. HCl. The

---

* Many amino-acids are easily identified as their 3:5-dinitrobenzoyl derivatives (Saunders, *Biochem. Jour.*, 1934, **28**, 580; 1942, **36**, 368). Cystine, however, forms a gelatinous derivative, but is readily identified by special tests. Tyrosine does not form a derivative under these conditions.

L

derivative crystallises out immediately: filter off, wash with cold water and recrystallise from boiling water. Long colourless silky needles, m.p. 179°.

5. *Copper salt.* (a) Add aqueous copper acetate solution to an aqueous solution of glycine. Note the formation of a blue colour which is considerably deeper than the colour of the original copper acetate solution. On heating the solution, blue needles of the copper salt usually separate.

(b) Dissolve about 0·5 gm. of glycine in about 40 c.c. of water and add an excess of freshly precipitated well-washed cupric hydroxide. Boil for 5 minutes and filter while hot into a small evaporating-basin. Concentrate to about half-bulk on a boiling water-bath and then allow to cool: fine blue needles of the copper salt, $(NH_2CH_2COO)_2Cu$, crystallise out (*cf.* p. 101).

Prepare the cupric hydroxide by dissolving 2 gms. of copper sulphate in about 100 c.c. of water, and adding with stirring 16 c.c. of N.NaOH solution. Filter off the precipitate and wash thoroughly with water.

SPECIAL REACTIONS FOR TYROSINE.

1. *Mercuric nitrite reaction* (*Millon's reaction*). Dissolve a very small crystal of tyrosine in 1 c.c. of water, add 1–2 drops of mercuric nitrate* solution, and 1 drop of dil. H_2SO_4, and then boil. Cool, add 1 drop of sodium nitrite solution and warm again: a red coloration is obtained.

2. *Formalin coloration.* To a small crystal of tyrosine, add 1 drop of 40% formalin, 1 c.c. of water, and 1 c.c. of conc. H_2SO_4. Boil gently: a deep green coloration is developed.

SPECIAL REACTIONS FOR CYSTINE.

1. *Removal of sulphur as sodium sulphide.* Dissolve about 0·1 gm. of cystine in a few c.c. of 10% NaOH solution. Add a few drops of lead acetate solution and boil for 1 minute. The solution darkens owing to the formation of lead sulphide.

2. *Nitroprusside test.* Dissolve about 0·1 gm. of cystine in a few c.c. of dilute ammonia and then add a few drops of potassium cyanide solution. This reduces cystine to cysteine.

$$S \cdot CH_2CH(NH_2)COOH + 2H = 2HS \cdot CH_2CH(NH_2)COOH$$
$$\qquad\qquad\qquad\qquad\qquad\qquad\qquad\qquad (Cysteine)$$
$$S \cdot CH_2CH(NH_2)COOH$$
$$\qquad\quad (Cystine)$$

Now add a few drops of a freshly prepared solution of sodium nitroprusside. A purple coloration is obtained (test for $-SH$ Group).

(B) AMINO-AROMATIC CARBOXYLIC ACIDS. *Anthranilic acid.*

Physical Properties. Colourless solid when pure, usually pale

---

* Mercuric sulphate may be used instead of the nitrate: mercuric chloride must not be used, however, as chlorides interfere with the formation of the red coloration.

brown. Sparingly soluble in cold water, soluble in hot water: soluble also in cold mineral acids and caustic alkalis. Dissolves readily in cold alcohol, and solution possesses a marked blue fluorescence.

REACTIONS.
1. Soluble in Na_2CO_3 solution with evolution of CO_2.
2. Gives aniline on heating with soda-lime.
3. Gives diazo derivative which:
   (a) couples with alkaline β-naphthol to give an azo-dye;
   (b) decomposes on heating to give a phenolic derivative.

1. *Solubility in Na_2CO_3 solution.* See Section 5 (p. 248), and also Test 2 for carboxylic acids (p. 262).
2. *Heating with soda-lime.* See Section 3, p. 245. Condense the aniline which distils over in a test-tube, dilute with water and add bleaching powder (or NaClO) solution. Note the violet coloration.
3. *Diazotisation.* Dissolve 0·2 gm. of anthranilic acid in about 4 c.c. of dil. HCl and cool in ice-water. To this solution, add slowly about 1 c.c. of cold 20% sodium nitrite solution and divide the cold diazonium solution thus prepared into two portions A and B.

(a) Pour A into a cold alkaline solution of β-naphthol and note the formation of a brilliant red dye.

(b) Boil B until the evolution of nitrogen ceases, cool the solution and shake. Note the separation of salicylic acid.

$$NH_2C_6H_4COOH \longrightarrow ClN_2C_6H_4COOH \longrightarrow HOC_6H_4COOH$$

To the contents of the test-tube, add about 1 c.c. of methyl alcohol and 1 c.c. of conc. H_2SO_4, and heat for 1 minute. Pour the solution into cold water in a boiling-tube and note the characteristic odour of methyl salicylate (oil of wintergreen).

(C) AMINO-AROMATIC SULPHONIC ACIDS. *Sulphanilic acid.*

Physical Properties. Colourless crystalline solid, soluble in boiling water, very sparingly soluble in cold water: crystallises $+2H_2O$. The strongly acidic $-SO_3H$ group suppresses the normal basic properties of the $-NH_2$ group: the acid therefore dissolves readily in alkalis, but not in dilute mineral acids.

REACTIONS.
1. Soluble in Na_2CO_3 solution with the evolution of CO_2.
2. Gives aniline when heated with soda-lime.
3. Forms diazo derivative which can be coupled with β-naphthol or with dimethylaniline to form azo-dyes.

1. *Solubility in sodium carbonate solution.* See Section 5 (p. 248), and also Test 2 for carboxylic acids (p. 262).

2. *Heating with soda-lime.* See Test 2 for anthranilic acid (p. 291) and also Section 3, p. 245.

3. *Formation of Methyl-orange (cf.* p. 169). Dissolve about 0·3 gm. of sulphanilic acid in 2 c.c. of 10% aqueous Na_2CO_3 solution. Cool in ice-water and add 2–3 drops of 20% sodium nitrite solution. Now add about 1 c.c. of cold dil. HCl, shake and leave for 2–3 minutes. Meanwhile dissolve 1 drop of dimethylaniline in a few drops of dil. HCl, cool thoroughly in ice-water and then add to the cold diazo solution. Shake well and make alkaline with aqueous NaOH solution: note the formation of a deep orange-yellow coloration or precipitate. On the addition of HCl, a bright red coloration is produced.

Section 22. Nitro-compounds.* $R \cdot NO_2$.

(A) NITRO-HYDROCARBONS. *Nitrobenzene,* p-*nitrotoluene,* m-*dinitrobenzene.*

(B) NITRO-PHENOLS. o- and p-*Nitrophenols.*

(C) NITRO-ANILINES. o-, m- and p-*Nitro-anilines.*

(A) NITRO-HYDROCARBONS.

Physical properties. Nitrobenzene, $C_6H_5NO_2$, pale yellow liquid, insoluble in and heavier than water, characteristic odour of bitter almonds (similar to that of benzaldehyde and benzo-nitrile). p-Nitrotoluene, $C_6H_4(CH_3)NO_2$, usually pale yellow solid, insoluble in water. m-Dinitrobenzene, $C_6H_4(NO_2)_2$, colourless solid when pure, but often pale yellow; insoluble in water.

GENERAL REACTION.

Reduced in acid solutions to primary amines.

Place about 1 gm. of the nitro-hydrocarbon in a boiling-tube and add 5 c.c. of conc. HCl and several pieces of granulated tin. Warm the mixture and shake continuously to break up the oily drops of the nitro-compound. When all the oil has disappeared (about 3 minutes' heating) pour off the liquid from any undissolved tin into a 100 c.c. conical flask. Cool and add cautiously 30% aqueous NaOH solution until the precipitate formed redissolves to give a dark-coloured solution. Cool the latter thoroughly and shake well with about 15 c.c. of ether. Separate the ethereal layer in a separating-funnel, wash with water and evaporate the ether in a basin on a previously heated water-bath in a fume-cupboard *away from all flames.* The residue is either (*a*) aniline (from nitrobenzene), p-toluidine (from p-nitrotoluene), or (*b*) m-phenylene diamine, $C_6H_4(NH_2)_2$, (from m-dinitrobenzene).

(*a*) Carry out tests for aniline and p-toluidine (p. 283).

* Most nitro-compounds react vigorously with metallic sodium during the tests for elements present (p. 239).

(*b*) Carry out the following tests for *m*-phenylene diamine. Usually dark coloured, sticky solid, soluble in hot water, slightly soluble in cold water.

(i) Dissolve a small quantity of the substance in about 1 c.c. of dil. HCl. Cool and add a few drops of sodium nitrite solution. A deep brown solution is produced, and a brown precipitate of the dye Bismarck Brown separates out: the latter is best observed by pouring the mixture into a small porcelain basin and stirring it around.

(ii) To a very dilute aqueous solution of the substance, add a few drops of ferric chloride solution. A reddish coloration is produced.

SPECIAL TEST FOR NITROBENZENE.

Nitration. Mix together in a boiling-tube 2 c.c. of conc. HNO_3 and 2 c.c. of conc. H_2SO_4. Add 1 c.c. of nitrobenzene with shaking and then heat the mixture with constant shaking in a fume-cupboard for a few minutes. Pour into cold water and note the separation of solid *m*-dinitrobenzene.

SPECIAL TEST FOR *m*-DINITROBENZENE.

Acetone-Alkali coloration. Dissolve a few crystals in 1–2 c.c. of acetone and add a few drops of aqueous NaOH solution. A deep violet coloration is produced, and is turned red by acetic acid but destroyed by mineral acids (see Test 6(*b*) for Ketones, p. 261, and also Test 2(*a*) p. 215).

(B) NITROPHENOLS.

Physical Properties. Both solids, freely soluble in hot water, sparingly in cold water. *o*-Nitrophenol, bright yellow, volatile in steam,* odour resembling both that of phenol and of nitrobenzene: *p*-nitrophenol, colourless when pure, non-volatile in steam, odourless.

GENERAL REACTIONS.

1. Soluble in aqueous NaOH solution, giving yellow or red solutions.
2. Sufficiently strongly acidic to liberate CO_2 from Na_2CO_3 solution.
3. Reduced to primary amino-phenols.
4. Some nitrophenols give colorations with ferric chloride.
5. Do not give the Liebermann reaction (p. 255).
6. Give acetyl derivatives, but that from *o*-nitrophenol is not so readily obtained.

* Volatility in steam is readily observed by boiling a small quantity of the substance with water in a test-tube, and noting the appearance of drops of condensed yellow oil on the upper and cooler portions of the tube.

1. *Coloured salts with alkalis.* Dissolve a few crystals of *o*-nitro-phenol in a few c.c. of 10% NaOH solution. An orange-coloured solution is produced, and becomes almost colourless on the addition of acids. Alkali restores the orange coloration, and so the solution exhibits the properties of an indicator.

p-Nitrophenol gives similarly a bright yellow coloration with NaOH solution.

2. *Reaction with sodium carbonate.* Boil about 0·5 gm. of *o*- and of *p*-nitrophenol in turn with Na_2CO_3 solution, using the method described in Section 5, p. 248, and note the evolution of CO_2.

3. *Reduction to amino-phenol.* Place about 0·5 gm. of *o*-nitro-phenol in a boiling-tube and add 5 c.c. of conc. HCl and several pieces of granulated tin. Warm the mixture and shake. After a few minutes the yellow molten *o*-nitrophenol disappears completely, the solution becoming homogeneous and colourless due to the formation of *o*-aminophenol (which is soluble in HCl). Cool and add 30% aqueous NaOH solution: note that a white precipitate is first formed and then redissolves in an excess of NaOH, and that the solution does not develop an orange coloration, indicating that the nitro-group has been reduced.

p-Nitrophenol is reduced similarly and the product does not give a yellow coloration with alkali.

4. *Ferric chloride coloration.* Add ferric chloride solution to a few crystals (or to an aqueous solution) of *p*-nitrophenol: a violet-red coloration is produced. *o*-Nitrophenol does not give a coloration.

6. *Acetylation.* Heat 1 gm. of *p*-nitrophenol with 5 c.c. of an acetic acid-acetic anhydride mixture under reflux for 15 minutes. Pour into water: the solid acetate separates. Filter, wash with water and re-crystallise from alcohol: m.p. 77·5°. This treatment usually leaves *o*-nitrophenol unchanged. The addition, however, of about 0·5 c.c. of conc. H_2SO_4 to the acetylating mixture gives the *o*-derivative, m.p. 40°.

(C) NITRO-ANILINES.

Physical Properties. All solid, sparingly soluble in cold water, freely soluble in hot water. *o*-Nitro-aniline, $NO_2C_6H_4NH_2$, orange, volatile in steam; *m*-nitro-aniline, yellow, also volatile in steam; *p*-nitro-aniline, yellow, non-volatile in steam.

GENERAL REACTIONS.

1. Form colourless diazonium compounds which couple with alkaline β-naphthol to give red dyes.
2. Reduced to colourless diamines.
3. Give (*a*) acetyl derivatives, (*b*) benzoyl derivatives.
4. No odour is detectable in the isocyanide reaction.
5. No colour reaction with bleaching powder (*cf.* amines).

1. *Diazotisation.* Dissolve 0·2 gm. of the substance in about 5 c.c.

of dil. HCl, warming if necessary. Cool in ice-water* and add sodium nitrite solution drop by drop: the end of the diazotisation is marked by the complete decolorisation of the solution. Pour the diazonium solution into a cold solution of β-naphthol in a considerable excess of NaOH solution: a brilliant red dye is produced.

2. *Reduction.* Place 0·5 gm. of the nitro-aniline in a boiling-tube, add 5 c.c. of conc. HCl and several pieces of granulated tin. Warm the mixture and shake, and note after a few minutes that the original yellow colour has entirely disappeared. Cool and add 30% aqueous NaOH solution: a white precipitate is formed which redissolves to give a dark-coloured solution. Cool and extract with about 15 c.c. of ether. Separate the ethereal layer, wash with water and evaporate the ether in a basin on a previously heated water-bath in a fume-cupboard *away from all flames*.

The residue may be:

(a) *o*-Phenylene diamine from *o*-nitro-aniline. Colourless crystals. Dissolve in a *small* quantity of dil. HCl and add several drops of ferric chloride solution: a deep red coloration is produced and increases in intensity on standing.

(b) *m*-Phenylene diamine from *m*-nitro-aniline. Usually dark-coloured, semi-solid mass. Carry out the two tests described on p. 293. Note that although both *o*- and *m*-phenylene diamines give reddish colorations with ferric chloride, only the *m*-phenylene diamine on diazotisation gives a *deep* brown solution with separation of the solid Bismarck Brown. *o*-Phenylene diamine similarly treated gives a very pale brown (almost colourless) solution with only a trace of solid matter separating, while *p*-phenylene diamine is unchanged.

(c) *p*-Phenylene diamine from *p*-nitro-aniline. Colourless solid, but soon becomes coloured on exposure to air. Dissolve in cold water and add 1 drop of ferric chloride solution: a deep green coloration is produced and rapidly turns brown.

3. (a) *Acetylation.* Proceed exactly as for the acetylation of amines, (Test 3, p. 283). *o*-Nitro-acetanilide, pale yellow crystals from water, m.p. 92°; *m*- and *p*-nitro-acetanilides, colourless crystals from methylated spirit, m.p. 155° and 212° respectively.

(b) *Benzoylation.* Proceed exactly as for benzoylation of amines (Test 4, p.283), but use a suspension of the finely ground nitro-aniline in the 10% NaOH solution. This preparation of the benzoyl derivatives is rarely necessary, however, as the above acetylation proceeds very satisfactorily. The benzoyl derivatives of *o*-, *m*-, and *p*-nitro-anilines have m.p. 94°, 155° and 199° respectively.

---

* The hydrochloride of the nitro-aniline may separate out at this stage, but this does not interfere with the reaction as the hydrochloride separates in fine, feathery crystals which readily redissolve and hence are very reactive.

Section 23. Purines.

Uric acid or 2:6:8-*trihydroxypurine*, $C_5H_4N_4O_3$.

$$
\begin{array}{cc}
\begin{array}{l}
\text{HN}\text{---}\text{C:O} \\
\;|\qquad\;| \\
\text{O:C}\quad\text{C}\text{---}\text{NH} \\
\;|\qquad\;\|\qquad\;\rangle\text{C:O} \\
\text{HN}\text{---}\text{C}\text{---}\text{NH}
\end{array}
&
\begin{array}{l}
\text{N}\!\!=\!\!=\!\!\text{C·OH} \\
\;|\qquad\;| \\
\text{HO.C}\text{---}\text{C}\text{---}\text{N} \\
\;\|\qquad\;\|\qquad\rangle\text{C·OH} \\
\text{N}\text{---}\text{C}\text{---}\text{NH}
\end{array}
\end{array}
$$

(A) *Keto* or *lactam* form.   (B) *Enol* or *lactim* form.

Physical Properties. White solid almost insoluble in water and in alcohol. It is a weak acid and exists in the tautomeric forms (A) and (B) above. It dissolves in alkali hydroxide solutions, giving salts of the type $C_5H_2Na_2N_4O_3$, the free acid being reprecipitated from such solutions on the addition of HCl or acetic acid: it is also soluble in solutions of borates, phosphates, carbonates and acetates of the alkali metals. It dissolves in conc. H_2SO_4, and is reprecipitated on addition of water.

REACTIONS.

1. Chars on being heated.
2. Gives murexide on treatment with conc. HNO_3 and then ammonia.
3. Solution in aqueous Na_2CO_3 reduces silver nitrate (Schiff's test).
4. Reduces Fehling's solution.
5. Reduces alkaline $KMnO_4$ in the cold.

1. *Action of heat.* Heat about 0·2 gm. of uric acid in a hard-glass test-tube. Note the charring and also the formation of a white sublimate on the cooler parts of the tube.

2. *Murexide test.* Place about 0·1 gm. of uric acid in a small evaporating-basin and moisten with 2–3 drops of conc. HNO_3. Heat *very gently* to dryness, and then add 1 drop of aqueous ammonia from a glass rod: a purple coloration is produced due to the formation of ammonium purpurate or murexide.* Now add a drop of NaOH solution: the coloration changes to blue.

3. *Schiff's test.* Dissolve about 0·1 gm. of uric acid in Na_2CO_3 solution and pour some of this solution on to a filter-paper which has been moistened with silver nitrate solution: a black stain of metallic silver results.

4. *Reduction of Fehling's solution.* Dissolve 0·1 gm. of uric acid in Na_2CO_3 solution, and to the clear solution add Fehling's solution

* Murexide is probably
$$
\begin{array}{ccccc}
\text{NH}\text{---}\text{CO} & & \text{CO}\text{---}\text{NH} \\
\;|\qquad\;| & & \;|\qquad\;| \\
\text{CO}\quad\text{C}\text{---}\text{N} & = & \text{CH}\quad\text{CO} \\
\;|\qquad\;| & & \;|\qquad\;| \\
\text{NH}\text{---}\text{C(ONH}_4\text{)} & & \text{CO}\text{---}\text{NH}
\end{array}
$$

drop by drop. Note the formation of a white precipitate of copper urate. Now add a slight excess of Fehling's solution and boil for several minutes: reduction occurs with the precipitation of cuprous oxide.

5. *Reduction of potassium permanganate.* To a solution of uric acid in aqueous Na_2CO_3 add potassium permanganate solution drop by drop: a brown precipitate of manganese dioxide is produced immediately in the cold.

Section 24. Halogeno-hydrocarbons.

Methyl iodide, ethyl bromide, ethyl iodide, chloroform, iodoform, carbon tetrachloride, chlorobenzene (phenyl chloride), bromobenzene (phenyl bromide), iodobenzene (phenyl iodide), benzyl chloride.

Physical Properties. All heavier than, and insoluble in, water. All liquids, except iodoform, CHI_3, which is a yellow crystalline solid with a characteristic odour. The remainder are colourless liquids when pure: ethyl iodide, C_2H_5I, and iodobenzene, C_6H_5I, are, however, usually yellow or even brown in colour. Methyl iodide, CH_3I, ethyl bromide, C_2H_5Br, ethyl iodide, chloroform,* $CHCl_3$, and carbon tetrachloride,† CCl_4, have sweetish odours, that of chloroform being particularly characteristic.

Chlorobenzene, C_6H_5Cl, bromobenzene, C_6H_5Br, and iodobenzene possess aromatic odours. Benzyl chloride, $C_6H_5CH_2Cl$, has a sharp irritating odour and is lachrymatory.

GENERAL REACTIONS.

1. Aliphatic mono-halides, and aromatic hydrocarbons with halogen in side-chain, precipitate silver halide on treatment with cold aqueous silver nitrate solution.

2. Aliphatic halides, and aromatic hydrocarbons with halogen in side-chain, are readily hydrolysed by boiling with alcoholic NaOH solution.

3. Aromatic halides can, in virtue of their aromatic character, be nitrated, *etc.*

1. *Reaction with cold silver nitrate solution.* Add 2 c.c. of 10% aqueous silver nitrate solution to 1 c.c. of methyl iodide and shake vigorously: a yellow precipitate of silver iodide is formed in the cold. Add an excess of dil. HNO_3 to show that the precipitate does not dissolve.†

* Chloroform and carbon tetrachloride must not be heated with metallic sodium as an explosive reaction is likely to take place (see footnote, p. 239).

† The identity of the silver *iodide* may be confirmed in the usual way, but this is unnecessary at this stage as the halide should already have been identified during the Preliminary Tests, p. 242.

L*

Ethyl bromide and ethyl iodide behave similarly. Benzyl chloride gives a faint precipitate in the cold, but the precipitation is complete on gentle warming.

Chloroform, carbon tetrachloride, iodoform and the halogeno-benzenes do not give precipitates with cold aqueous silver nitrate solution.

2. *Hydrolysis with alcoholic NaOH solution.* Boil together in a small conical flask, fitted with a reflux water-condenser, 1 c.c. of chloroform and 10 c.c. of alcoholic NaOH solution for 10 minutes. Then dilute with water to dissolve any sodium chloride which may have separated, add dil. HNO_3 until acid and then silver nitrate solution. A copious precipitate of silver chloride is produced.

Similar results are obtained with methyl iodide, ethyl bromide, ethyl iodide, iodoform, carbon tetrachloride, and benzyl chloride.

Chloroform and iodoform give also sodium formate in this reaction: $CHCl_3 + 4NaOH = HCOONa + 3NaCl + 2H_2O$. A portion of the solution, before the addition of the HNO_3, should therefore be tested for formic acid (Tests, p. 264): ensure however that the solution is neutralised where necessary during these tests.

Methyl iodide, ethyl bromide and ethyl iodide also evolve ethylene when treated as above. If this is suspected, a small quantity of the substance should be heated with alcoholic NaOH solution in a small flask, fitted with a "knee" delivery-tube. Pass the gas evolved through a very dilute solution of potassium permanganate which has been made alkaline with aqueous Na_2CO_3 solution. If ethylene has been formed, a brown precipitate of manganese dioxide will be produced (a transient green colour may appear).

3. *Nitration.* Place 1 c.c. of chlorobenzene in a boiling-tube and add 2 c.c. of conc. HNO_3 and then 2 c.c. of conc. H_2SO_4. Warm *gently** with continuous shaking for about 4 minutes. Pour into about 50 c.c. of water; an oil separates and, on cooling and scratching with a glass rod, solidifies to a pale yellow crystalline mass: the characteristic odour of "bitter almonds" also becomes noticeable.

Bromobenzene, iodobenzene and benzyl chloride behave somewhat similarly. The *p*-nitro-derivatives of the first two compounds frequently crystallise out even before pouring into water: *p*-nitro-benzyl chloride usually remains as an oil for several minutes before solidifying.

SPECIAL REACTIONS.

Methyl iodide and ethyl iodide.

Pyridine methiodide and ethiodide. Place 2 drops of dry pyridine in a test-tube, add 2 drops of methyl iodide and mix. A vigorous reaction

---

* Although these nitrations proceed smoothly, attempted nitration of an unidentified substance should always be carried out *with extreme care*, *e.g.*, by working in a fume-cupboard and pointing the boiling-tube *away* from the operator. Many organic substances (*e.g.*, alcohols and phenols) react with great violence with a mixture of nitric and sulphuric acids.

occurs and on cooling, a colourless crystalline mass of pyridine methiodide, C_6H_5N,MeI, is formed (*cf.* p. 287): when recrystallised from methylated spirit, the methiodide has m.p. 117°.

The reaction with ethyl iodide is less rapid and it is necessary to warm the mixture *gently* until cloudy. On cooling, crystals of the ethiodide are formed, and after recrystallisation from methylated spirit have m.p. 84°.

Chloroform.

1. *Isocyanide (or carbylamine) reaction.* Dissolve 1 c.c. of chloroform in 2–3 c.c. of alcoholic NaOH solution, add a few drops of aniline, mix well and warm *gently*: the foul odour of isocyanide is produced.

$$CHCl_3 + C_6H_5NH_2 + 3NaOH = C_6H_5NC + 3NaCl + 3H_2O$$

Immediately the odour is detected, cool the tube and add carefully an excess of conc. HCl: the isocyanide is thus hydrolysed to the odourless amine.

2. *Colorations with resorcinol and naphthol.* Dissolve about 0·2 gm. of resorcinol in 1 c.c. of 30% aqueous NaOH solution, add 1 c.c. of chloroform and warm gently: the aqueous layer turns red and shows a slight fluorescence.

Repeat using α- or β-naphthol in place of resorcinol: the aqueous layer becomes deep blue, fading to green.

3. *Reduction of Fehling's solution.* Boil 1 c.c. of chloroform *gently* with 3 c.c. of Fehling's solution with constant shaking for 3–4 minutes. Reduction occurs and reddish cuprous oxide slowly separates.

Iodoform.

1. *Liberation of iodine on heating.* On heating in a dry tube, iodoform gives off copious violet vapours of iodine. This will have been observed during the Preliminary Tests, p. 237.

2. *Isocyanide reaction.* Repeat Test 1 for chloroform (above) using 0·5 gm. of iodoform instead of 1 c.c. of chloroform: the foul odour of isocyanide is produced as before.

Carbon tetrachloride.

1. *Isocyanide reaction.* Repeat Test 1 for chloroform using 1 c.c. of carbon tetrachloride in place of the chloroform. The odour of isocyanide can be detected only after heating gently for several minutes.

2. Does not give a coloration with alkaline solutions of resorcinol or naphthol (difference from chloroform).

Benzyl chloride.

1. *Oxidation to benzoic acid.* Boil a mixture of 1 c.c. of benzyl chloride, 50 c.c. of saturated aqueous potassium permanganate solution and 2 gms. of anhydrous Na_2CO_3 under reflux for 30 minutes. Acidify with conc. HCl and then add 25% sodium sulphite solution until the brown precipitate of manganese dioxide has dissolved. On cooling,

benzoic acid crystallises out. Filter through a small Buchner funnel, wash with water and identify (p. 261). When recrystallised from water, benzoic acid has m.p. 121°.

Section 25. Hydrocarbons. C_xH_y.

Benzene, toluene, naphthalene, anthracene, petrol.

Physical Properties. Benzene, C_6H_6, toluene, $C_6H_5 \cdot CH_3$, and petrol (a mixture of aliphatic hydrocarbons, *e.g.*, pentane, hexane, *etc.*) are colourless liquids, insoluble in and lighter than water. Benzene and toluene, which have similar odours, are not readily distinguishable chemically, and their physical constants should therefore be carefully noted: benzene, m.p. 5° (solidifies when a few c.c. in a dry test-tube are chilled in ice-water), b.p. 81°; toluene, m.p. $-93°$, b.p. 110°. Petrol* has a characteristic odour.

Naphthalene, $C_{10}H_8$, colourless solid, insoluble in water, soluble in alcohol, characteristic odour. Anthracene, $C_6H_4:C_2H_2:C_6H_4$, white crystals when pure, with a faint blue fluorescence, but usually very pale yellow crystals; insoluble in water, slightly soluble in alcohol.

The aliphatic hydrocarbons are extremely unreactive and do not respond to any of the following tests for aromatic hydrocarbons.

GENERAL REACTIONS FOR AROMATIC HYDROCARBONS.

1. Can be nitrated.
2. Can be sulphonated.
3. Form picrates: those of naphthalene and anthracene can be readily isolated.

1. *Nitration.* (*a*) To 5 c.c. of a mixture of equal volumes of conc. HNO_3 and conc. H_2SO_4, add gradually 1 c.c. of benzene or toluene with shaking; cool if the reaction tends to become too violent. After shaking the mixture well for about 2 minutes, pour into cold water: the nitro-compound will separate out as a yellow oil or solid. Separate the product, wash once with water, and then prove the presence of the nitro-group by reduction with tin and conc. HCl as described for nitro-benzene (p. 292).

(*b*) To nitrate naphthalene: dissolve 1 gm. in 5 c.c. of glacial acetic acid by gentle warming, cool, add 1 c.c. of conc. HNO_3 and warm gently for 1 minute, a clear yellow solution being obtained. Pour into water: the yellow nitro-compound solidifies.

* Petroleums or "petrols" are used as solvents and are usually supplied as fractions boiling over the following ranges: 40–60°, 60–80°, 80–100°, 100–120°.

The nitration of anthracene is more difficult to perform and is not recommended as a test.

2. *Sulphonation.* To 1 c.c. of benzene or toluene, add slowly 1 c.c. of 20% fuming H_2SO_4. Shake well and note that a homogeneous solution is obtained. [If this is repeated using petrol, the latter does not react, but merely floats unchanged on the surface of the H_2SO_4 (a slight darkening may take place due to traces of impurities).] Now pour the reaction mixture carefully with stirring into about 20 c.c. of cold water: a clear solution of the sulphonic acid is obtained. Usually, however, a small amount of the corresponding sulphone, R_2SO_2, separates as fine colourless crystals.

Naphthalene and anthracene can also be sulphonated, but the reaction has little value as a test.

3. *Picrates.* The picrates of benzene and toluene are isolated only with extreme difficulty and are not used for purposes of identification.

(*a*) *Naphthalene picrate.* Make a concentrated solution of picric acid in cold acetone,* and add about 2 c.c. of this solution to 2 c.c. of a cold concentrated solution of naphthalene also in acetone. Shake well: on standing for about 1 minute long yellow needles of naphthalene picrate crystallise out. After recrystallisation from alcohol the picrate has m.p. 152°.

(*b*) *Anthracene picrate.* This picrate has a characteristic red colour. It is, however, far more soluble than that of naphthalene: therefore proceed thus:

Make a concentrated solution of anthracene in hot acetone. To about 2 c.c. of this solution add a cold concentrated acetone solution of picric acid drop by drop, and note the formation of a red coloration which becomes deeper on further addition of the acid. If excess of picric acid is added, however, the solution becomes paler in colour, and this is to be avoided if possible. Boil to ensure that both components are in solution and then transfer to a small porcelain basin or watch-glass: ruby-red crystals of anthracene picrate separate out on cooling. The product, however, is often contaminated with an excess of either anthracene or of picric acid, which appear as yellowish crystals.

Toluene may be distinguished from benzene in that it gives benzoic acid on oxidation. The reaction however takes several hours for completion and hence is of little practical value as a test. Anthracene may also be distinguished from naphthalene by its oxidation to the characteristic anthraquinone (p. 204). Here again the process is long and its application is seldom necessary.

SCHEME FOR THE SEPARATION OF SIMPLE BINARY MIXTURES OF ORGANIC COMPOUNDS.

The successful separation of a mixture of the two organic substances will depend largely upon the student's general know-

* Picric acid is usually stored damp for safety, and acetone is therefore a better solvent than benzene for this test: the solutions *must* be almost saturated, however.

ledge of organic chemistry and in particular upon his acquaintance with the reactions of the substances given in the previous sections. It is impossible to give more than an outline of the methods employed, as the mode of separation depends upon the actual substances present as well as the classes to which they belong.

Three types of mixtures will be considered:

(1) *Two neutral substances.*
(2) *A neutral and an acidic substance.*
(3) *A neutral and a basic substance.*

(1) **Two neutral substances.** The separation is usually based upon one of the following:

(a) difference in volatility (*i.e.*, fractional distillation);
(b) difference in solubility;
(c) the formation of a crystalline derivative of one or of both the substances.

(a) Two liquids may be separated by fractional distillation provided that they do not form a constant-boiling mixture and that their boiling-points are sufficiently far apart. For instance, carbon tetrachloride (b.p. 77°) and toluene (b.p. 110°) can be separated in this way, but difficulty may be experienced in separating substances with much closer boiling-points, unless an efficient fractionating column is used.

Solutions of solids in liquids can sometimes be separated by distilling off the liquid and leaving a residue of the solid, *e.g.*, acetone and acetamide.

(b) This depends entirely upon the nature of the particular compounds present, and no general rule can be given. The method of separation ultimately adopted must be based solely on experimental tests, *e.g.*, a mixture of starch and cane sugar can be separated by making use of the fact that the latter is soluble in cold water whereas the former is completely insoluble. The components of other mixtures can sometimes be separated by fractional crystallisation: this is often a long process, as it must be repeated until each component is pure, *i.e.*, entirely free from the other component.

(c) In a mixture of toluene and benzaldehyde, for example, the latter may be separated as the bisulphite compound. It must be pointed out, however, that a derivative of one component may prove to be very soluble in the other component. In such a case it may be necessary to make some less soluble derivative.

(2) A neutral and an acidic substance.

Only those mixtures in which the neutral substance is insoluble in water will be considered. The method of separation consists in extracting the mixture with aqueous sodium hydroxide solution, whereby the acidic component dissolves in the form of its sodium salt, while the neutral component remains undissolved and can thus be separated.

First carry out a small-scale test, placing about 0·5 gm. of the mixture in a test-tube, adding about 5 c.c. of 10% aqueous NaOH solution, and shaking the mixture well. It will be readily seen whether the neutral substance (which remains undissolved) is solid or liquid. Then repeat the extraction on a larger scale as follows:

(a) *Neutral Component is solid.* Place about 5 gms. of the original mixture (if solid) or 10–15 c.c. (if liquid) in a small conical flask, add excess of NaOH solution as before, and thoroughly shake the securely corked flask. Then dilute somewhat with water, and filter off the solid neutral component at the pump. Reserve the filtrate for subsequent identification of the acidic component (see below). Wash the solid residue on the filter thoroughly with very dilute NaOH solution to ensure complete extraction of the acidic component, then wash with water, drain, and dry by pressing between sheets of drying-paper as usual. Then identify.

(b) *Neutral Component is liquid.* Place the above quantities of the original mixture in a separating-funnel, add excess of the NaOH solution and shake thoroughly. Run off the aqueous layer and reserve as before for the identification of the acidic component. Then again extract the neutral liquid remaining in the funnel with more NaOH solution. Run off and reject the latter, and extract the neutral liquid finally with water. Separate the liquid, dry it with anhydrous sodium sulphate, and distil if considered necessary. Alternatively, if the volume is very small, extract with ether, dry the ethereal extract, filter, and then evaporate the solvent. Then identify the pure neutral component.

Acidic Component. The filtrate from (a) or the first alkali extract from (b) will contain the acidic component, which will be either an acid or a phenol. Continue as follows:

Add dil. H_2SO_4 until the solution is acid to litmus. Cool, and scratch the sides of the vessel with a glass rod: a white precipitate indicates an aromatic carboxylic acid* or uric acid, or a solid phenol insoluble in water (e.g., α- or β-naphthol). If a precipitate is obtained, filter off through a Buchner funnel, wash with water, recrystallise if necessary and identify.

If no solid precipitate is obtained but the solution becomes cloudy, a low-melting or liquid phenol is indicated: this will, of course, be revealed also by the characteristic phenolic odour. Transfer to a separating-funnel and extract with an equal volume of ether. Separate and dry with anhydrous sodium sulphate. Distil off the ether and identify the residue.

---

* An amino-acid, although insoluble in water (e.g., anthranilic acid), is usually soluble in excess of mineral acid: in such a case it is important to make the solution only very slightly acid. This applies also to a mixture of a neutral and a basic substance, from which dil. HCl will extract an amino-acid: the solution must then be carefully treated with NaOH to precipitate the amino-acid.

If a phenol is not indicated, the solution may contain an aliphatic acid. Transfer to a distilling-flask, make definitely acid with dil. H_2SO_4, and distil: the volatile formic and acetic acids if present will distil over. If the distillation gives negative reactions, test the residual solution in the flask for oxalic, succinic, lactic, tartaric and citric acids and glycine, remembering that the solution is strongly acid.

(3) A neutral and a basic substance.

It is again assumed that the neutral substance is insoluble in water. The separation now consists in extracting the mixture with dil. HCl, which dissolves the basic component, leaving the undissolved neutral component.

Again, first carry out a small-scale test, extracting about 0·5 gm. of the mixture with about 5 c.c. of dil. HCl in a test-tube, in order to determine whether the neutral component is solid or liquid.

(a) *Neutral Component is solid.* Continue precisely as in 2(a) above, except that the mixture must now be extracted with an excess of dil. HCl instead of NaOH. Filter at the pump, reserve the filtrate, and then wash the residue on the filter thoroughly with dil. HCl, then wash with water, and finally drain, dry and identify as before.

(b) *Neutral Component is liquid.* Proceed as in 2(b) above, extracting the mixture with dil. HCl: reserve the HCl extract, and then wash the neutral insoluble liquid with dil. HCl, then with water. Continue as in 2(b) to identify the neutral component.

Basic Component. The filtrate from (a), or the HCl extract from (b), now contains the basic component in the form of its hydrochloride. Add 30% aqueous NaOH solution until alkaline to litmus. Cool, and scratch the sides of the vessel with a glass rod: a white precipitate indicates a solid amine, *e.g.*, *p*-toluidine or a naphthylamine. Dilute, filter off, wash well with water (recrystallise if necessary), dry and identify.

If no solid precipitate is obtained, an oil or an oily suspension, may be produced. Allow to stand, and then, if possible, separate the oil directly in a separating-funnel and dry with solid KOH. If the volume of the oil is too small for such separation, extract with ether* and then separate the ethereal solution, dry as before, filter, and distil off the ether. Distil the amine (if considered necessary) and identify.

In the separations (2) and (3) above, it is often advisable to dissolve the original mixture in a water-insoluble solvent. Select a solvent which will dissolve the *entire* mixture, and then shake the solution with either (i) dil. NaOH or (ii) dil. HCl. Separate the aqueous layer, and to it add either (i) dil. HCl or (ii) dil. NaOH to liberate the organic acid or the organic base, as the case

---

* Or alternatively stir in powdered sodium chloride in order to "salt out" the amine, and then run off the lower aqueous layer.

may be. The non-aqueous layer now contains the neutral component. Re-extract this layer with either (i) dil. NaOH or (ii) dil. HCl to ensure removal of traces of the non-neutral component.

SCHEME FOR THE IDENTIFICATION OF AN ORGANIC COMPOUND.

General Remarks. In the following pages an account is given of the results which may be observed when an unknown organic compound is subjected to the following tests:

A. Physical characteristics.
B. Heating on a crucible lid.
C. Identification of the elements present.
D. Heating with soda-lime.
E. Treatment with 30% aqueous NaOH solution.
F.   ,,   dil. Na_2CO_3 solution.
G.   ,,   conc. H_2SO_4.
H.   ,,   dil. HCl.
I (i)   ,,   Fehling's solution.
  (ii)   ,,   Ammoniacal silver nitrate solution.
J. Reactions and colorations with ferric chloride.
K. Treatment with 2:4-dinitrophenylhydrazine.

Proceed through Tests A, B and C. Carry out Test C (identification of the elements present) *with great care*, as a mistake at this stage will invalidate much of the subsequent analysis. Then proceed, in general, through Tests D—K, keeping in mind the results obtained in Test C. (If, for example, the substance is found not to contain nitrogen, then it is obvious that neither ammonia nor aniline can be produced when treating the substance with sodium hydroxide in Test E. In such a case the student should keep a sharp lookout for a positive reaction characteristic of a non-nitrogenous substance.)

From the cumulative evidence given by Tests A—K, the student will probably have a strong indication of the type of compound which he is investigating. He should then refer back to the table given under Test C (p. 308), and with the information that he has gained (and in particular with the knowledge of the elements present) he should select the most likely class to which the compound belongs. He should then consult the appropriate section giving the reactions of this class of compound, and carry out the tests there mentioned, when it should soon become apparent whether he has selected the correct class to which the compound belongs. If the results obtained are conflicting, the student should then select the next likely class of compounds, and then proceed in this way until the behaviour of the substance investigated agrees closely with those given in a particular section.

After some experience, an able student will find that it is frequently unnecessary to carry out all the Tests A—K. If, for example, the substance is found to contain only carbon and hydrogen, and chars on ignition giving a smell of burnt sugar, then confirmatory tests (given in the appropriate section) can be carried out immediately for carbohydrates and aliphatic hydroxy-acids.

Derivatives. The precise identification of a compound normally depends upon the preparation of a derivative and the determination of physical constants such as m.p. in the case of a solid. Many simple compounds can, however, be identified with a fair degree of certainty by intelligently-selected qualitative tests alone, e.g., formates, oxalates, succinates, lactates, tartrates, chloral hydrate.

In general, derivatives should be easily-prepared crystalline solids with sharp m.p.'s. In this book no attempt has been made to describe derivatives which go beyond the theoretical knowledge that a student of this standard might be expected to possess. Useful derivatives are as follows:

Alcohols. 3:5-Dinitrobenzoates (pp. 193 and 251).

Phenols. Benzoates (p. 254), 3:5-dinitrobenzoates (p. 255), toluene *p*-sulphonates (p. 193).

Aldehydes and Ketones. Phenylhydrazones (pp. 257, 260), 2:4-dinitrophenylhydrazones (pp. 257, 261), semicarbazones (p. 203), benzylidine derivatives (p. 178).

Acid Chlorides. Anilides (p. 276).

Acid Anhydrides. Anilides (p. 276).

Carbohydrates. Osazones (crystalline structure, pp. 108–111).

Primary and Secondary Amines. Acetyl derivatives (pp. 283–285), benzoyl derivatives (pp. 283–284), 3:5-dinitrobenzoyl derivatives (p. 193), picrates (p. 134).

Tertiary Amines. Picrates (pp. 134, 287), methiodides (p. 287).

Heterocyclic Bases. Picrates (p. 287), methiodides (p. 287).

Amino-acids. 3:5-Dinitrobenzoyl derivatives (p. 289).

Nitrophenols. Acetates (p. 294).

Nitro-anilines. Acetyl, benzoyl derivatives (p. 295).

Certain Aromatic Hydrocarbons. Picrates (p. 301).

A more complete list of derivatives and their melting-points are given on pp. 434–447.

A. Physical characteristics.

Note the obvious physical properties: appearance, colour, state, odour, solubility in (or reaction with) water, whether aqueous solution is neutral or otherwise.

Colour.

    Yellow. Benzoquinone, *m*- and *p*-nitro-aniline, anthraquinone, *o*-nitro-phenol, iodoform.

    Orange. *o*-Nitro-aniline.

    Blue. Copper salts.

Odour.

    Pleasant (often fruity) odour. Esters, ethers.

    Pungent odour. Formic acid, acetic acid, acetyl chloride, acetic anhydride, benzoyl chloride, benzyl chloride, pyridine. Benzoquinone (when warmed with water).

Phenolic (carbolic) odour. Many phenols, some derivatives of salicylic acid (*e.g.*, salicylaldehyde).

Odour of almonds. Benzaldehyde, benzonitrile, nitrobenzene.

The following substances possess odours which, although not necessarily characteristic, often aid identification considerably:

Monohydric alcohols, aldehydes (including chloral hydrate), ketones, cinnamic acid, amines (β-naphthylamine is odourless), nitrophenols (resemble both phenol and nitro-compound), halogeno-hydrocarbons, aliphatic hydrocarbons, liquid aromatic hydrocarbons, naphthalene.

Acetamide and acetonitrile, unless specially purified, possess a mouse-like odour.

Solubility in water and action of solution on litmus-paper.

(*a*) *Soluble in cold water.* Lower aliphatic alcohols (including glycerol), some phenols, lower aliphatic aldehydes (including chloral hydrate), lower aliphatic ketones, aliphatic acids, ammonium salts and alkali salts of all acids, methyl esters of certain acids (*e.g.*, formic, oxalic, succinic, tartaric), ethyl tartrate, some aliphatic amides (including urea) and imides (*e.g.*, succinimide), lower aliphatic nitriles, lower aliphatic acid chlorides (with hydrolysis), mono- and di-saccharides, hexamethylene-tetramine, pyridine, salts of amines, glycine.

(*b*) *Almost insoluble in cold water.* Higher alcohols (including benzyl alcohol), higher phenols (*e.g.*, naphthols), metaformaldehyde, paraldehyde, aromatic aldehydes, higher ketones (including acetophenone), aromatic acids, most esters, ethers, oxamide and aromatic amides, aromatic imides, aromatic nitriles, aromatic acid anhydrides, aromatic acid chlorides, starch, aromatic amines, anilides, tyrosine, cystine, nitro-compounds, uric acid, halogeno-hydrocarbons, hydrocarbons.

(*c*) *Acid reaction in aqueous solution*, or when hydrolysed with water. Acids, esters which hydrolyse easily (*e.g.*, methyl oxalate), acid chlorides, acid anhydrides, salts of amines, nitrophenols.

(*d*) *Weakly acidic.* Phenols.

Note. Phenols (unless nitrated) do not liberate CO_2 from Na_2CO_3 solution.

(*e*) *Weakly alkaline.* Alkali salts of some weak acids, pyridine.

B. Heating on a crucible lid (p. 236).

(*a*) *Almost non-luminous flame.* Aliphatic compounds containing a low percentage of carbon.

(*b*) *Smoky flame.* Aromatic compounds.

(*c*) *Non-inflammable.* Compounds rich in halogen or containing a metal.

(*d*) *Residual ash.* Compounds containing a metal.

(i) Metallic salts of carboxylic acids give carbonate, oxide or metal. Apply usual tests of qualitative inorganic analysis to this residue.

Note that some of the metals frequently encountered in simple organic compounds give characteristic flame colorations: Na, yellow; K, lilac through blue glass; Ca, brick-red; Ba, apple-green; Cu, bright blue-green. Ag and Pb, no characteristic flame.

(ii) The bisulphite compounds of aldehydes or ketones leave sodium sulphite and sodium sulphate.

(iii) The alkali salts of sulphanilic acid leave alkali sulphide.

(*e*) *Charring.* Many organic compounds char, more particularly the following: carbohydrates (odour of burnt sugar); tartaric acid and its salts, citric acid and its salts (odour somewhat resembling burnt sugar); uric acid. (Salts of some acids char, although the free acids do not, *e.g.*, sodium succinate, lactate, and salicylate.)

(*f*) *Violet vapours.* Iodoform.

C. Identification of elements present.

(i) *Beilstein's Test* (p. 241). Note that this test is of negative value only, and the *absence* of a green colour proves that the compound does *not* contain halogen.

(ii) *Lassaigne's Test for nitrogen, halogens and sulphur* (pp. 238–243). Perform with great care. If only a faint indication of a particular element is obtained, repeat, using a slightly larger amount of material and longer heating.

Elements present	Substances	Section	Page
C.H.[O]	Alcohols	9	251
	Phenols	10	253
	Aldehydes	11	256
	Ketones	12	260
	Carboxylic acids (and metallic salts)	13	261
	Esters	14	268
	Acid anhydrides	16(B)	274
	Carbohydrates	17	276
	Quinones	18	280
	Hydrocarbons	25	300
C.H.[O].Halogen	Chloral hydrate	11	256
	Acid halides	16(A)	274
	Halogeno-hydrocarbons	24	297
C.H.[O].N	Ammonium salts ⎫ Amides, imides ⎬ Nitriles ⎭	15	271
	Amines	19	282
	Anilides	20	287

Elements present	*Substances*	*Section*	*Page*
C.H.[O].N	Amino-carboxylic acids	21	288
	Nitro-compounds	22	292
	(a) Nitro-hydrocarbons		
	(b) Nitro-phenols		
	(c) Nitro-anilines		
	Uric Acid	23	296
C.H.[O].N.Halogen	Salts of amines, nitro-amines	19, 22(C)	282, 294
	and amino-carboxylic acids with	21	288
	halogen acids (HCl, *etc.*). (*Note.*		
	The halogen is ionic and can be		
	tested for directly with $AgNO_3$+		
	HNO_3).		
C.H.[O].S	Alkali bisulphite compound of	11, 12	256, 260
	(a) aldehyde, (b) ketone		
C.H.[O].N.S	Salts of amines and nitro-	19, 22(C)	282, 294
	amines with H_2SO_4. (*Note.* The		
	SO_4 radical can be tested for di-		
	rectly in solution).		
	Amino-aromatic sulphonic acid	21(C)	291
	(sulphanilic acid)		
	Cystine	21(A)	290

NOTE.—1. If C and H only have been detected and the substance is soluble in water, then O must also be present.

2. If C, H, and a halogen (but no nitrogen) have been detected, and the substance is *freely* soluble in (or readily hydrolysed by) cold water, then O must also be present.

D. Heat with an excess of soda-lime (p. 245).

(a) *Ammonia or ammoniacal vapours evolved.* Ammonium salts, amides, imides; amino-aliphatic acids, uric acid. (Certain polynitro-compounds, *e.g.*, *m*-dinitrobenzene, sometimes give ammonia on strong heating.)

(b) *Hydrogen evolved.* Formate, oxalate.

(c) *Hydrocarbon evolved.* Carboxylic acid or salt of carboxylic acid:

methane from acetate;
ethane from succinate;
benzene from benzoate or phthalate;
styrene and benzene from cinnamate.

(d) *Phenol produced.* Salicylic acid and salts; phenyl esters of carboxylic acids; tyrosine also produces a phenolic odour.

Note. Phenols distil unchanged.

(e) *Odour of burnt sugar.* Carbohydrates; some aliphatic hydroxy-acids (*e.g.*, tartaric acid) and their salts.

(f) *Aromatic amine produced.* Amine salts; anilides; aromatic amino-carboxylic acids.

(g) *Chloroform produced.* Chloral hydrate.

Note. A compound may yield more than one product, *e.g.*, salicylamide, $HO \cdot C_6H_4CONH_2$, will give ammonia and phenol.

E. Treat with 30% aqueous NaOH solution, then heat (p. 246).

(a) *Dissolves easily in cold NaOH solution although insoluble in cold water.* Some phenols*; aromatic carboxylic acids; some amino-acids; uric acid.

(b) *Dissolves easily in cold NaOH solution (although only slightly soluble in cold water), at the same time forming deep yellow or orange alkaline solution.* Nitrophenols. (Salicylaldehyde gives a yellow coloration in the cold: *m*-dinitrobenzene gives a reddish-brown coloration on warming.)

(c) *Dissolves easily, giving yellow solution which rapidly darkens on shaking.* Benzoquinone. Polyhydric phenols, *e.g.*, resorcinol, rapidly darken.

(d) *Ammonia evolved in the cold.*† Ammonium salts.

(e) *Ammonia evolved on heating.* Amides, imides, nitriles (slowly).

(f) *Brown resinous product formed.* Aliphatic aldehydes (except formaldehyde); carbohydrates and soluble starch (sucrose and ordinary starch only faintly coloured).

(g) *Reacts slowly on heating without evolution of gas.* Esters; some acid chlorides and anhydrides; benzaldehyde (undergoes Cannizzaro's reaction, p. 257).

(h) *Chloroform produced.* Chloral and chloral hydrate.

(i) *Aromatic amine liberated rapidly* (as an oil, if liquid or of low m.p.). Salts of amines.

(j) *Aromatic amine liberated slowly* on prolonged heating. Anilides.

(k) *Hydrogen sulphide evolved.* Cystine.

F. Treat with dil. Na₂CO₃ solution and boil (p. 248).

CO_2 *liberated.* All acids; esters which hydrolyse easily, *e.g.*, methyl oxalate (p. 270); salts of amines; nitrophenols.

G. Treat with conc. H₂SO₄, then heat (p. 248).

(a) *Gives a clear solution on gentle heating, dilution then precipitating the unchanged substance.* Uric acid.

(b) *No blackening, CO evolved.* Formates.

(c) *No blackening, CO + CO₂ evolved.* Oxalates.

(d) *Turns yellow, no charring, evolution of CO and CO₂.* Citrates.

(e) *No blackening, no marked effervescence, pungent vapour*

---

* Many phenols are of course freely soluble in cold water as well as in NaOH solution.

† This distinction is not absolute, as some amides decompose slightly even in cold 30% NaOH solution.

evolved. Certain acids and their salts, *e.g.*, acetic, succinic, and benzoic acid.

(*f*) *Blackening with effervescence.* Carbohydrates; tartrates and lactates.

(*g*) *Blackening without effervescence.* Certain polyhydric phenols. Succinates (strong heating).

(*h*) *Gelatinous polymeric product.* Benzyl alcohol.

Note. A large variety of organic compounds darken to some extent (without actual blackening) when heated with conc. H_2SO_4.

H. Treat with dil. HCl, then warm.

Substance insoluble in cold water, readily soluble in warm dil. HCl. Various basic substances, such as aromatic amines (naphthyl-amines dissolve with difficulty in dil. HCl, diphenylamine only in conc. HCl, triphenylamine insoluble); nitro-anilines; some amino-carboxylic acids.

I. (*a*) Heat with Fehling's solution.

Disappearance of the deep blue colour and precipitation of cuprous oxide indicates reducing agents such as:
Aldehydes (including chloral hydrate); formates and lactates; some esters; chloroform and iodoform; reducing sugars; some phenols.
Uric acid first gives white precipitate of copper urate and then reduces.

(*b*) Treat with ammoniacal silver nitrate solution and warm.

Formation of silver mirror or precipitate of silver indicates reducing agent. (This is often a more sensitive test than I (*a*) above, and some compounds reduce ammoniacal silver nitrate but are without effect on Fehling's solution.) Given by aldehydes and chloral hydrate; formates, lactates and tartrates; reducing sugars; benzoquinone; many amines; uric acid.

J. Treat with neutral ferric chloride solution (p. 249).

Colorations or precipitates given by phenols and many derivatives of phenols; by neutral salts of acids; by some amines. (The $FeCl_3$ solution can be added directly to a *small quantity* of the phenol or to its aqueous solution: free acids must first be neutralised.)

(*a*) *Red coloration.* Formate and acetate.

(*b*) *Yellow coloration.* Lactates, tartrates and citrates.

(*c*) *Violet coloration.* Phenol, resorcinol, *o*-, *m*-, and *p*-cresol; salicylates; methyl and ethyl salicylate; salicylamide; salicyl-aldehyde.

(*d*) *Violet-red coloration.* *p*-Nitrophenol.

(*e*) *Buff or pale-brown precipitate.* Succinate, benzoate, phthalate and cinnamate. (Add dil. H_2SO_4: basic ferric succinate dissolves giving a clear solution; the others dissolve but are rapidly replaced by white precipitate of free acid.)

(*f*) *Green coloration.* Catechol (colour rapidly darkens). [Aniline (pale green), *o*-toluidine (pale green initially), monomethylaniline, and diphenylamine, each in dil. HCl.]

(*g*) *Bluish precipitate.* α-Naphthylamine.

K. Treat with 2:4-dinitrophenylhydrazine reagent (pp. 257, 261).

Yellow or orange-yellow precipitates given by most aldehydes and ketones.

Below are tabulated the reactions of certain of the most important classes of organic compounds. It must be emphasised that these tables serve solely to summarise the detailed descriptions given in the foregoing sections, and should be used only after these sections have been carefully worked through in the laboratory.

Section 10. Phenols (pp. 253, 435)

TEST	Phenol	Resorcinol	Catechol	Hydroquinone	o-Cresol	m-Cresol	p-Cresol	α-Naphthol	β-Naphthol
FeCl$_3$ (coloration)	violet →	violet	green	red, green crystals then yellow	violet →	violet	violet	—	—
Liebermann (NaNO$_2$ + H$_2$SO$_4$)	+	+	green with H$_2$SO$_4$ only	indefinite	+	green with H$_2$SO$_4$ only	—	green with H$_2$SO$_4$ only	—
Azo dyes	+	+	usually decomposes	—	+	+	+	+	+
Phthaleins (Phthalic anhydride + H$_2$SO$_4$)	red	green fluorescence	usually blue	purple	red	bluish purple	—	very faint green fluorescence	green
Chloroform + NaOH (coloration)	—	red	green	brown	red →	red	—	deep blue →	deep blue
Benzoyl chloride + NaOH m.p. of deriv.	69°	117°	84°	204°	liquid	54°	71°	56°	107°

Section 11. Aldehydes (pp. 256, 436)

TEST	Formaldehyde (solution)	Acetaldehyde (solution)	Paraldehyde	Chloral hydrate	Benzaldehyde	Salicylaldehyde
Ammoniacal AgNO₃ (reduction)	+	+	+	+	+	—
Fehling's solution (reduction)	+	+	+	+	(very faint reduction)	—
Na Bisulphite (addition)	—	—	—	+	+	on standing
NaOH	Cannizzaro's reaction	←——— resin ———→		chloroform on heating	Cannizzaro's reaction	yellow coloration
Schiff's reagent (pink)	+	+	+	—	+	—
Na Nitroprusside +NaOH (coloration)	—	+	+	—	—	—
Iodoform (KI + NaClO)	—	+	—	—	—	—
FeCl₃ (coloration)	—	—	—	—	—	violet

Section 12. Ketones (pp. 260, 436)

TEST	Acetone	Acetophenone	Benzophenone
Na Bisulphite (addition)	+	—	—
Phenylhydrazone	—	+	+
Na Nitroprusside + NaOH (coloration)	+	+	—
m-Dinitrobenzene + NaOH (coloration)	+	+	—
Iodoform (KI + NaClO)	+	+	—

Section 13. Carboxylic Acids (pp. 261, 437, 438)

NOTE. The tests marked * must be performed with a neutral salt of the acid.

TEST	Formic	Acetic	Oxalic	Succinic	Lactic	Tartaric	Citric	Benzoic	Salicylic	Phthalic	Cinnamic
Soda-lime	H_2	CH_4	H_2	C_2H_6	← odour of burnt sugar →			benzene	phenol	benzene	styrene, benzene
Conc. H_2SO_4	CO	—	$CO + CO_2$	slight darkening on strong heating	blackening with effervescence	heavy charring with effervescence	yellow with effervescence	—	slight darkening	—	—
FeCl$_3$*	← red →		—	buff ppt.	← yellow →			buff ppt.	violet	← buff ppt. →	
KMnO$_4$ + dil. Na$_2$CO$_3$	immediate decolorisation in the cold	—	slight fading	—	← rapid reduction on heating →			—	immediate decolorisation in the cold	—	immediate decolorisation in the cold
CaCl$_2$*	—	—	ppt. in the cold, insol. in acetic acid	ppt. on boiling, sol. in acetic acid	—	ppt. in the cold, sol. in NaOH	ppt. on boiling, insol. in acetic acid	—		—	ppt. in the cold, sol. in acetic acid
Ammoniacal* AgNO$_3$ (reduction)	+	—	—	—	+	+	—	—	—	—	reduction on boiling
Iodoform* (KI + NaClO)	—	—	—	—	+	—	—	—	—	—	—
Phthaleins (Phenol + H$_2$SO$_4$)	—	—			—	—	—	—	—	+	—
Fluoresceins (Resorcinol + H$_2$SO$_4$)	—	—	—	+	—	—	—	—	—	+	—
FeSO$_4$ + H$_2$O$_2$ + NaOH	—	—	—	—	—	violet	—	—	—	—	—

Section 14. Esters (pp. 268–270). *Summary of Hydrolysis.*

Hydrolyse by boiling with 10% aqueous NaOH solution for about 30 minutes:

Substance.	Products.	
Ester of an alcohol	Alcohol (volatile)	Na salt of a carboxylic acid (non-volatile).
Ester of a phenol	a Na phenoxide (non-volatile)	,,

Distil.

(A) (i) *Distillate.* Test for methyl, ethyl, or benzyl alcohol.

(ii) *Residual solution.* If test in (A) (i) is *positive*, proceed with tests for organic acid in residual solution: acidify with dil. H_2SO_4.

    (*a*) white ppt.: aromatic acid.

    (*b*) no ppt.: aliphatic acid. Distil off 5 c.c. and test distillate for formic and acetic acids. If negative results are obtained, test residual solution for oxalic, succinic and tartaric acids.

(B) If test in (A) (i) is *negative*, an alcohol is absent and the residual solution must contain a Na phenoxide as well as the Na salt of a carboxylic acid.

    Residual solution. Make just acid with dil. H_2SO_4, and then just alkaline to litmus-paper with Na_2CO_3 solution. Extract phenol with ether, distil off latter and identify the residue. Identify the organic acid in the aqueous layer, as in (A) (ii).

Section 17. Carbohydrates (water-soluble) (pp. 276-280)

TEST	Glucose	Fructose	Sucrose	Maltose	Lactose
Molisch's (α-naphthol + H_2SO_4)	← violet coloration →				
Rapid furfural (α-naphthol + HCl)	← delayed →	← immediate →		← delayed →	
NaOH (Conc.)	← yellow resin →			← yellow resin →	
Ammoniacal $AgNO_3$ (reduction)	+	+	−	+	+
Fehling's solution (reduction)	+	+	−	+	+
Osazone	+	+	−	+	+

Osazone: Glucose–Fructose ← (identical, insol. in hot water) → ; Maltose (freely sol. in hot water); Lactose (moderately sol. in hot water)

Section 19. Aromatic (mono)amines (p. 282, 440)

TEST	Aniline	o-toluidine	m-toluidine	p-toluidine	α-naphthyl-amine	β-naphthyl-amine	mono-methyl-aniline	diphenyl-amine	dimethyl-aniline	triphenyl-amine
Isocyanide (carbylamine)	+	+	+	+	+	+	—	—	—	—
Nitrous acid (NaNO₂ + HCl)	diazotises →						← yellow → nitrosamine →		green nitroso compound (on adding NaOH)	—
Acetylation m.p. of deriv.	+113°	+112°	+65°	+148°	+159°	+132°	+102°	+101°	No deriv.	No deriv.
NaClO or Bleaching powder	purple then brown	← brown →		yellow						
Conc. HCl+H₂O₂ +FeSO₄	← green →			yellow-brown	green ppt.		green	green, violet on dilution	dichromate colour	
FeCl₃ + dil. HCl	pale green, develops slowly	green-ish blue ppt.	—	reddish-brown	blue ppt.	—	green	green	—	—
Benzoylation m.p. of deriv.	+163°	+143°	+125°	+158°	+160°	+162°	+63°	+180°	No deriv.	No deriv.

PART IV

QUANTITATIVE ANALYSIS

THE analyses which follow are arranged in the order in which they would be applied to a newly discovered substance, the estimation of the elements present and molecular weight determinations (*i.e.*, determination of empirical and molecular formulae respectively) coming first, then the estimation of particular groups in the molecule, and finally the estimation of special classes of organic compounds. It should be noted, however, that this systematic order differs considerably from the order of experimental difficulty of the individual analyses. Consequently many of the later macro-analyses, such as the estimation of hydroxyl groups, acetyl groups, urea, *etc.*, may well be undertaken by elementary students, while the earlier analyses, such as estimation of elements present in the molecule, should be reserved for more senior students.

The estimation of carbon and hydrogen, of nitrogen and of methoxy groups has now however been transferred to Section B (Semi-microanalysis) (p. 369). In this connection it should be noted that the macro-estimation of nitrogen in foodstuffs, *etc.*, by the Kjeldahl method is still often employed because of the low nitrogen content and the non-homogeneous nature of the material. Full details of this method on the macro-scale will be found in *An Introduction to Practical Organic Chemistry* by Mann and Saunders, p. 148 (Longmans, Green & Co. Ltd.).

SECTION A

MACROANALYSIS

Estimation of Halogens. Carius's Method.

Principle. A known weight of the substance is heated with fuming nitric acid and silver nitrate in a sealed tube. The organic material is thus oxidised to carbon dioxide and water, whilst the halogen is converted quantitatively into the corresponding silver halide. The latter is subsequently washed out of the tube, filtered and weighed.

The method is general for all organic halogen compounds and is the standard method for almost all such compounds, except of course those water-soluble compounds (*e.g.*, halide salts) in which the halogen is ionic. The method, although long, is simple, the main difficulty for students being the preparation and sealing of the glass tube.

Carius tubing is normally supplied in lengths of about 15 dcm. (5 ft.), sufficient for two tubes: the tubing is usually of about 2 cm. external diameter, whilst the thickness of the wall is about 3 mm. Carius tubing of good quality soft glass, if carefully prepared and sealed, is amply strong enough and has the great advantage of being easily worked in the ordinary air-gas blowpipe flame. Hard-glass tubing gives a much stronger sealed tube, but the latter has to be worked in an oxygen-gas blowpipe flame.

For the actual estimation, heat the middle portion of a double length* of Carius tubing cautiously in the blowpipe flame, starting first with a smoky flame and then increasing the proportion of air until a flame of maximum temperature is obtained, meanwhile rotating the horizontal tube (using both hands simultaneously, and not each hand in turn, for the rotation) in order to secure uniform heating. When the middle portion of the tube is quite soft, draw the two portions of the tube apart, so that two tubes similar to **A** (Fig. 56) are obtained, each being open at one end and drawn out to a fine tail at the other. Two Carius tubes can thus be made, although only one will be

* A practical demonstration of the preparation and sealing of Carius tubes is of vastly greater value than any written description.

FIG. 56.

considered further. The tube, throughout the whole of its subsequent manipulation in the blowpipe flame, *must* be kept steadily and regularly rotated in order to ensure uniform heating and treatment: this point will not therefore be further emphasised. Now heat the tube in a small hot flame about the portion *aa* until the pointed tail, which has hitherto been used as a handle, can be drawn off, leaving the tube closed as shown in **B**. By using this method, the formation of a heavy blob or button of glass at the extreme end of the tube (a source of great subsequent weakness) can easily be avoided. Now heat the closed end of the tube in a rather larger flame until the end is uniformly soft, and then carefully blow down the tube, keeping the latter rotated gently in the mouth whilst the pressure is applied. By these means, a rounded end of uniform thickness, as in **C**, is obtained. The heating and subsequent blowing down the rotating tube should be repeated until a really satisfactory seal has been obtained. Allow the tube to cool (away from draughts) for at least 45 minutes. Then ensure that the interior of the tube is quite clean and free from dust, *etc.* For this purpose, pour a few c.c. of concentrated nitric acid into the tube, cork securely and then invert several times: finally wash the tube out thoroughly with distilled water, and then in turn with methylated spirit and dry ether. Remove the last traces of ether by blowing air right down to the closed end of the Carius tube by means of a length of clean glass quill-tubing temporarily attached to the blowpipe bellows.

It is now necessary to place about 1 gm. of finely powdered pure silver nitrate in the closed end of the tube: at the same time, care should be taken to avoid dusting the internal walls of the tube with silver nitrate, as it is a great advantage to have the silver halide subsequently collected at the extreme end of the tube, and not scattered in specks over the walls. Therefore roll a narrow strip of clean glazed paper around the quill-tubing originally used for drying the tube and then insert the roll of paper and the quill-tube into the Carius tube (which has been clamped in a vertical position) until the paper roll reaches within about 5 cm. of the bottom of the Carius tube. Now remove the central quill-tube, when the paper will tend to unroll slightly and so grip the Carius tube securely. Add about 1 gm. of the powdered silver nitrate, tap the tube to shake down the last fragments of the nitrate, and then withdraw the paper roll. Insert into the tube a clean thistle-funnel, the stem of which has been extended until it reaches to about 10 cm. from the bottom of the tube. Add 1·5–2·0 c.c. (*not more*) of fuming nitric acid (*d*, 1·5): for this and the next estimation, a sample of fuming nitric acid free from halogen and sulphur should be used. If there is any doubt with regard to the purity of the acid, the latter should be well shaken with a small quantity of powdered silver nitrate, and the mixture allowed to stand (preferably overnight) until all the solid matter has collected at the bottom, the acid being subsequently withdrawn for the analysis by means of a short dropping-tube. When the nitric acid has thoroughly drained from the thistle-funnel, the latter should be cautiously withdrawn so that the upper portion of the Carius tube is not wetted.

M

Meanwhile, the organic compound can be prepared for analysis whilst the sealed end **C** (Fig. 56) of the Carius tube has been cooling down. For this purpose, thoroughly clean and dry a small tube, which is about 6 cm. long and 8–10 mm. wide. Weigh it carefully, supporting it on the balance pan either by means of a small stand of aluminium foil, or by a short section of a perforated rubber stopper (Fig. 57 (A) and (B)

(A)   (B)

FIG. 57.

respectively): alternatively the tube may be placed in a small beaker on the balance pan, or suspended above the pan by a small hooked wire girdle. Place in the tube sufficient organic compound to give subsequently about 0·3 gm. of the silver halide, and weigh again. Now allow the small tube to slide carefully down the inclined Carius tube until it finally adopts the position shown in **D** (Fig. 56). If the compound readily loses halogen in the presence of nitric fumes, the Carius tube should first be rotated in an oblique position to wet the tube for about 10 cm. from the bottom: the small tube, if cautiously inserted into the Carius tube, will now come to rest when it first reaches the wet portion of the tube and will thus be held above the main bulk of the acid until the tube is sealed.

Before sealing the Carius tube, the length desired for the final sealed tube should first be decided. The tube has to be placed in a heavy iron tube, and its length should be roughly adjusted so that the final capillary end of the sealed tube will project about 2 cm. beyond the mouth of the iron tube. Now heat the upper portion of the Carius tube at a suitable place to obtain this length, holding the rotated tube in an oblique position meanwhile. When the glass is soft, draw off the unrequired end, leaving the top of the tube drawn out into a long tail as in **E** (Fig. 56): break off this tail so that it is about 15 cm. long and can thus serve as a handle, and ensure that the end is open. (If the tube is not sufficiently long to enable the extreme top to be held in the hand whilst it is being drawn off, first fuse a piece of stout rod on to the extreme end, taking care that the end of the tube is not closed thereby.) Now heat the tapering portion of the tube, approximately between *ee* and *e'e'* (**E**, Fig. 56) in a rather small and not too hot flame until the walls have thickened uniformly and very considerably, and can be slowly drawn out into a thick-walled capillary, as in **F**. Allow to cool slightly and then with a very small hot flame close the capillary, as shown in **G**: rotate the closed tip rapidly for a few seconds in the flame until the sealed end is of uniform thickness, and then place in a smoky, air-free blowpipe flame for a few seconds to ensure an even temperature-distribution over the heated end. Finally allow the tube to cool slowly in a vertical position in a place free from draughts: as a further precaution, a handful of cotton-wool may be loosely tied around the upper

end of the tube as it cools. The tube whenever possible should be left overnight before being heated in the furnace: failing this, at least 3 hours should
elapse between sealing and heating in the furnace.

Now roll up the Carius tube (while still in a vertical position) in a
strip of ordinary thick drying-paper, and then place it in the heavy iron
protector tube: if the Carius tube is too short and tends to disappear
within the iron tube, a short section of old glass tubing should first be
placed in the iron tube so that the capillary of the Carius tube just
projects. The function of the paper is to protect the Carius tubing from
being scratched, and also (more important) to prevent the local overheating which would otherwise occur at places where the Carius tube is in
direct contact with the iron tube. The sealed tube, throughout its
manipulation, should be left as nearly vertical as possible, so that the
contents do not leave the rounded end.

The furnace (Fig. 58) consists primarily of an iron box **A**, having
3 or 4 tubes (*e.g.*, **B**) arranged in a horizontal row, and dipping slightly
from the open (left-hand) to the closed (right-hand) end. The top,
which usually forms a loose lid to the rest of **A**, carries a thermometer
T, and care should be taken to ensure that the bulb of the thermometer
is not touching any part of the metal box. The Carius tube encased in
its iron protector tube is
then placed as shown in
one of the wide tubes **B** of
the box, and the latter can
then be heated either by
the burners below, or in a
suitable electric furnace.
The box **A** is usually per-
manently fitted inside a
much larger iron or brick-
work oven having sliding
doors on one of the longer
sides: this oven and its
doors have necessarily to

FIG. 58.

be large enough to allow the introduction of the Carius tube into the
box **A** without moving the latter. Occasionally no oven is used, and
instead the ends of the box **A** are covered with heavy iron flaps hinged
horizontally along the top: in the event of a tube bursting during the
heating, these flaps lift sufficiently to allow immediate release of the
gases, but not sufficiently to permit fragments of glass being blown away
from the apparatus.

Now heat the furnace, so that the temperature rises slowly in the
course of about 2 hours to 260–270°, and then maintain this temperature for at least another 4 hours. Then turn off the heating, and allow
the furnace to cool and remain untouched overnight. A considerable
pressure will now exist in the cold tube, and must be released *before* the
tube is removed from the box **A**: *on no account* must the unopened

tube be removed from the furnace, nor must any attempt be made to crack open the capillary end by means of a file, *etc.*, even when the tube is still in position. To release the pressure, first gently warm the capillary end of the Carius tube (which projects just beyond the mouth of the iron tube) with a small smoky Bunsen flame. The extreme end of the cold capillary will always contain some condensed liquid, which under the influence of this preliminary warming will be forced back into the wider portion of the tube: this step is particularly necessary in the estimation of sulphur (p. 326). Finally increase the heating of the extreme tip of the capillary until softening of the glass finally allows the compressed gases to blow out.

Now remove the tube from the furnace and make a deep file-mark completely round the tube about 15 cm. from the bottom: then wash the outside of the tube to remove any powdered glass from the file-mark, and also all traces of charred paper, *etc.* Then, whilst holding the tube securely in a vertical position, press the molten end of a fine glass rod on to the file-mark, when the tube should crack cleanly around the scratch: finally pull the two portions of the tube *away* from one another, so that the two ends have no opportunity of grating against one another and so causing fine splinters of glass to fall into the tube. Then wipe the two cut ends of the tube carefully in an outwards direction to remove any splinters which, in spite of these precautions, may have formed. (Cutting the tube in this way about 15 cm. from the bottom has the advantage that the silver halide is now readily accessible, but has the disadvantage that the tube is usually too short to be used again. It is not advisable, however, to use soft-glass tubing a second time, as it often devitrifies on further heating and in any case usually gives an unsatisfactory sealed tube. Hard-glass tubing can sometimes be used for several consecutive estimations, and if this is intended the tube should be cut across *gg* (Fig. 56): the silver halide is now, however, not so readily removed from the tube.) Now smear a trace of vaseline around the outside portion of the cut ends of the two portions of the tube (to prevent drops of the liquid from subsequently running down the outside of the tube). Pour some distilled water into the portion of the tube containing the silver halide, loosen the contents by stirring them gently with a rod, and then tip the contents carefully into a beaker. If any fragments of silver halide still adhere to the Carius tube, loosen them further by means of a glass rod the end of which is covered with a short length of rubber tubing, and then finally wash out the inside of the tube (whilst the latter is inclined downwards over the beaker) with a fine jet of water from a wash-bottle. Now remove the small tube from the beaker (preferably with a pair of forceps), again loosen any adhering particles of silver halide, and wash the tube thoroughly whilst it is held over the beaker. Similarly wash the longer portion of the Carius tube, which however should not contain any particles of silver halide. Then boil the liquid in the covered beaker until the silver halide has thoroughly coagulated, and formed a heavy amorphous mass at the bottom of the beaker: for silver chloride and bromide 20–30 minutes' boiling is usually sufficient for this purpose, but for silver iodide at least $2\frac{1}{2}$ hours' boiling (with occasional addition of more water) is required to ensure complete decomposition of a stable addition product of silver iodide and nitrate.

Then cool the solution, and filter, wash and weigh the silver halide by any of the standard methods of gravimetric analysis: the most usual method is to filter the solution through a weighed Gooch crucible, wash the contents thoroughly with *very* dilute nitric acid, and then dry the crucible in an oven at 130°. The value obtained for the percentage of halogen should be within $\pm$ 0·2 of the theoretical value.

ESTIMATION OF HALOGENS IN LIQUID ORGANIC COMPOUNDS. If the liquid is of high boiling-point and not deliquescent, it may be weighed in the small tube precisely as for solid compounds. The tube may be corked during the two weighings, but in this case great care should be taken to place the liquid in the tube so that the neck is not moistened: the use of a fine dropping-tube is of particular value for this purpose.

Volatile, deliquescent, or unstable liquids should be weighed in a small, thin-walled sealed bulb-tube **T** (Fig. 59). This is made by blowing a delicate bulb of about 1–2 ml. capacity on the end of a piece of fine, thin-walled quill tubing, the neck of which is then drawn out into a long thin taper. For use, first weigh the clean dry tube, then place it upside-down as shown in a small beaker or bottle containing the organic liquid. Now place the beaker in a vacuum desiccator, and gently evacuate. After a few minutes, remove the desiccator from the pump and slowly admit air, dried if necessary beforehand by passage through a calcium chloride tube. The liquid will now rise in the tube **T**. If the amount which enters is insufficient, repeat the evacuation in the desiccator for a longer period. Then reverse the tube, carefully dry the tapered neck, and seal the extreme tip in a small flame.

FIG. 59.

Weigh the tube, place it in the Carius tube and seal the latter as before. The weighed tube must now be broken in the Carius tube *before* the latter is heated—on no account should the fracture of the small tube be left to the expansion of its contents during the heating. The bulb-tube can usually be broken by holding the Carius tube in a vertical position, and then vigorously jerking the bottom of the tube to one side: it should not be fractured by shaking the Carius tube up and down its long axis, as this will fling both silver nitrate and glass into the capillary end. If the organic material is readily oxidised, wrap the Carius tube in several thicknesses of iron gauze and then in a duster before shaking, in case the vigorous oxidation which will occur on fracture of the bulb-tube also causes the Carius tube to burst. After heating the Carius tube in the furnace, transfer the contents as before to a beaker, and with a pair of forceps pick out the larger pieces of broken glass, wash them carefully free from silver halide, dry in an oven and weigh when cold. The weight of the remaining smaller pieces of glass, which will be subsequently weighed with the silver halide in the crucible, is thus known.

Example of Calculation.

Estimation of Cl in chloral hydrate.

0·1872 gm. chloral hydrate gave 0·4856 gm. silver chloride
Factor for Cl in AgCl, 0·2474. (Table III, p. 433.)
∴ 0·1872 gm. chloral hydrate contains 0·4856 × 0·2474 gm. chlorine

∴ 100 gms. chloral hydrate contain $\dfrac{0\cdot4856 \times 0\cdot2474 \times 100}{0\cdot1872}$ gms. chlorine

$$= 64\cdot16\%$$

Theoretical for $C_2H_3O_2Cl_3$; 64·33% chlorine.

Estimation of Sulphur. Carius's Method.

Principle. A known weight of the substance is heated with fuming nitric acid in a sealed tube, the organic material being oxidised to carbon dioxide and water, and the sulphur to sulphuric acid. The latter is subsequently washed out of the tube, precipitated as barium sulphate, and estimated as such.

The method is general for all organic compounds, although some require prolonged heating to ensure complete oxidation (see later).

Proceed precisely as in the estimation of halogen, but omitting the silver nitrate: take sufficient of the organic compound to give 0·2–0·3 gm. of barium sulphate. Before opening the cold Carius tube, pay particular attention to the initial gentle warming of the capillary end of the tube to ensure that the liquid which has condensed in the capillary is driven back well into the wide portion of the tube, otherwise it will be lost with the escaping gases. Then cut open the tube as already described, wash out the contents into a beaker and, should any trace of glass splinters be observed, filter carefully, finally washing the filter thoroughly with water.

The precipitation of the barium sulphate must be performed with care, otherwise high results are obtained owing to occlusion of barium chloride in the barium sulphate. This is avoided by the following method, which has the further advantage that the tedious initial removal of the excess of nitric acid by evaporation is unnecessary.

Dilute the solution (if necessary) to about 150 ml., add 1 ml. of concentrated hydrochloric acid, and then heat in a covered beaker almost to boiling. Meanwhile dissolve a small excess (0·4–0·5 gm.) of barium chloride in about 50 ml. of water, bring to the boil, and then transfer to a clean 50 ml. burette. Now run this solution slowly *drop by drop* into the sulphuric acid solution, keeping the latter steadily stirred throughout the addition. Then boil the solution *gently* in the covered beaker for about 1 hour in order to increase the size of the barium sulphate particles: if the solution tends to "bump," transfer it to a hot plate and keep it just below the boiling-point for about 2 hours.

Then cool, filter and estimate the barium sulphate by any of the standard methods, *e.g.*, by filtering the liquid through a weighed Gooch crucible, washing the barium sulphate thoroughly with water, and then drying in an oven at about 130°. The value obtained for the percentage of sulphur should be within $\pm$ 0·2 of the theoretical value.

NOTE. (1) Most sulphur compounds are completely oxidised if the tube is heated under the conditions described for the estimation of halogens. Sulphonic acids and sulphones are more difficult to oxidise completely and the tube should be slowly heated to 300° and maintained at this temperature for at least 6 hours. The oxidation may be facilitated by adding a few crystals of sodium or potassium bromide to the organic material in the small tube, so that bromine shall be present to intensify the oxidation during the heating.

(2) Liquid sulphur compounds should be weighed and introduced into the Carius tube by precisely the same methods as those described for liquid halogen compounds (p. 325).

Example of Calculation.

Estimation of S in thiocarbanilide.

0·2563 gm. of thiocarbanilide gave 0·2655 gm. barium sulphate.

Factor for S in $BaSO_4$ = 0·1374 (Table III, p. 433).

∴ 0·2563 gm. of thiocarbanilide contains 0·2655 × 0·1374 gm. sulphur

∴ 100 gms. of thiocarbanilide contain $\dfrac{0\cdot2655 \times 0\cdot1374 \times 100}{0\cdot2563}$ gms. sulphur

$$= \underline{14\cdot23\%.}$$

Theoretical for $C_{13}H_{12}N_2S$, 14·05%.

Determination of Molecular Weights.

The chief methods available for the determination of the molecular weight of organic compounds are:

A. *Physical Methods.*

    I.   Determination of Vapour Density.
         (*a*) Dumas' Method.
         (*b*) Victor Meyer's Method.
         (*c*) Hofmann's Method.

    II. Depression of the Freezing-point (Cryoscopic Method).
    III. Depression of the Freezing-point of Camphor (Rast's Method).
    IV. Elevation of the Boiling-point (Ebullioscopic Method).
    V. Elevation of the Boiling-point by Landsberger-Walker Method.

B. *Chemical Methods.*

    I.   Molecular Weight of Acids by Analysis of Silver Salts.
    II. Molecular Weight of Acids by Titration with Standard Alkali.
    III. Molecular Weight of Bases by Analysis of Chloroplatinates.

The practical limitations of the above methods are indicated in their detailed description.

Although certain of the above methods give results of high accuracy, it should be emphasised that very accurate determinations of molecular weights are not *usually* required in organic chemistry, where the chief purpose of such determinations is to fix the molecular formula of a compound. Thus the quantitative estimation of the elements in a particular compound may show that the empirical formula is $(C_3H_5Cl)_n$, and the molecular weight is then required in order to fix the value of n and hence the molecular formula.

Molecular Weight Determinations by Physical Methods. Vapour Density. (a) Dumas' Method.

In Dumas' method for vapour density determinations the amount of the compound which as vapour fills a large glass bulb is determined by direct weighing. The method can, however, be conveniently applied only to readily volatile and non-inflammable liquids, of which a comparatively large quantity is required. Since, moreover, the accuracy of the results is not high, the method has been largely superseded by Victor Meyer's method (see below). Full details of Dumas' method are to be found in *An Introduction to Practical Organic Chemistry* by Mann and Saunders, p. 152 (Longmans, Green & Co., Ltd.).

Vapour Density. (b) Victor Meyer's Method.

Victor Meyer's method is almost universally employed for the determination of the vapour density of organic compounds. It has the advantages of requiring a very small quantity of the organic material, giving accurate results, and of being applicable to compounds the boiling-points of which lie over a wide range. It cannot however be applied to compounds which decompose on attempted volatilisation at atmospheric pressure: for these compounds Hofmann's method (see later) must be employed. In principle, Victor Meyer's method consists in volatilising a known weight of the organic compound at the lower closed end of a hot tube: an equivalent volume of hot air is therefore displaced from the upper portion of the tube through a side delivery-tube (where it cools to room temperature) into a calibrated vessel, in which its volume is measured under known conditions of temperature and pressure. The volume of this cold air is clearly equal to the volume of vapour which the known weight of the organic liquid would evolve, assuming that this vapour could exist without condensation under the same conditions of temperature and pressure as those of the cold air.

The apparatus consists of a tube **T** (Fig. 60) usually of total height about 75 cm.: the upper portion of the tube has an internal diameter of about 1 cm., whilst the lower portion is blown out as shown into a bulb of about 100 c.c. capacity. Near the top of **T** is the delivery-tube **D** of coarse-bored capillary, bent as shown. The tube **T** is suspended in an outer glass jacket **J** which contains the heating liquid: this jacket is fitted around **T** by a split cork **F** which has a vertical groove cut or filed in the side to allow the subsequent expansion of the air in **J**. The open end of the side-arm **D** can be placed in a trough **W** containing water, and a tube **C**, calibrated in ml. from the top downwards, can be secured as shown over the open end of **D**.

FIG. 60.

For an actual determination, first place in **J** some stable liquid the boiling-point of which is at least 50° above that of the organic liquid the vapour density of which is to be measured. This difference in boiling-point is important, because it is essential that the organic liquid, when subsequently dropped into the bottom of **T**, should volatilise rapidly and so push out an equivalent volume of air before the organic vapour itself can diffuse up the tube **T** and possibly condense in the cooler upper portion of the tube. Suitable liquids for use in the jacket are water, chlorobenzene (132°), *sym*-tetrachloro-ethane (147°), *p*-chlorotoluene (156°), aniline (184°), nitrobenzene (210°), α-chloro-naphthalene (260°) and α-bromonaphthalene (281°). Finally add a few fragments of unglazed porcelain to the liquid in **J** to ensure smooth steady boiling.

Thoroughly clean and dry the tube **T**, blowing air through a long piece of quill tubing to the lower end of **T** to ensure complete removal of any organic liquid remaining from a previous determination. Place a small quantity of clean *dry* sand at the bottom of **T**, and adjust the tube in position within the jacket **J**. Close the top of **T** securely with a rubber stopper **S**, and place the end of the tube **D** in the trough of water **W**, omitting at this stage the tube **C**. Now boil the liquid in **J** until it is refluxing up to a level *aa*. The air in **T** expands and escapes through **D**:

M*

allow the boiling to continue steadily so that eventually the expansion of the air is complete and no more bubbles escape from the end of **D**.

Meanwhile clean, dry and weigh a small bottle **B** made specially for this purpose: it has a ground-glass stopper, and a capacity of about 0·5 ml. Then by means of a fine dropping-tube, place about 0·2 ml. of the organic liquid in the bottle and weigh again. Fill the calibrated tube **C** with water and invert it in the trough **W** over the end of **D**. After loosening the stopper, quickly drop the bottle **B** down the tube **T**, where its fall is broken by the sand below: *at once* replace firmly the rubber stopper **S** at the top of **T**.

The liquid in **B** rapidly volatilises at the bottom of the tube **T**, the stopper being thrown off, and bubbles of air escape from **D** into the tube **C**. Continue boiling the liquid in **J** steadily until no more bubbles escape into **C**. Then carefully slip the end of **D** from under the tube **C**, close the end of **C** securely with the finger, and then transfer the tube to a gas-jar of water, so that the level of the water inside and outside **C** can be equalised. Measure the volume of air in **C**, and note the room temperature and the barometric pressure. The vapour density can now be calculated (see opposite page).

NOTE. The above represents the simplest form of Victor Meyer's apparatus. The following modifications may however be applied:

(1) A small error is introduced in the above method of working when the stopper **S** is removed from **T** in order to admit the bottle **B**, because water at once enters the lower end of the delivery-tube **D** and rises slightly above the normal level (*b*) of the water in the trough **W**. When **S** is replaced and the organic liquid volatilises, this water has to be expelled before any air can escape into **C**. The tube **D** is made of coarse capillary tubing so that this error is reduced to a minimum, and so that the air can escape readily through **D**. The error may be overcome by storing the bottle **B** (when filled and weighed) in the upper cold portion of **T**, and allowing it to fall when required into the lower portion. Various devices are available for this purpose. One of the simplest consists of a short wide tube **A** (Fig. 60) fused at an angle to the tube **T**, as shown, a few cm. above the delivery-tube **D**. **A** is closed by a rubber stopper containing a short thick glass rod, the upper end of which is flattened to allow ready rotation. The central hole of the rubber stopper is well lubricated with vaseline or some other non-volatile grease, so that the rod can be readily pushed up and down, at the same time making a satisfactorily air-tight fit in the stopper. Before starting the experiment, the rod is pushed down (as shown) so that the tube **T** is partly obstructed and the bottle **D** containing the organic liquid is placed so that it is held loosely in position by the end of the rod. The stopper **S** is replaced, the liquid in **J** boiled as before, and the tube **C** placed in position. The rod in **A** is then partly withdrawn until the bottle **B** falls, and is then replaced in its former position.

(2) The air may be collected directly into a Hempel gas-burette (Fig. 60) and there measured. This burette consists of a glass tube **H** calibrated in ml. from the tap **E** downwards, and connected by a piece of rubber tubing to the reservoir **R**, the height of which can be adjusted. The tap **E** is a 3-way tap, by which the

tube **H** can be connected directly through to the capillary tube above, or either tube can be connected through the left-hand end of the tap to the atmosphere.

In use, the burette **H** and the reservoir **R** are partly filled with water. The delivery-tube **D** of the Victor Meyer apparatus is now horizontal, and is connected by a further piece of coarse capillary tubing at least 30 cm. long to the burette **H** as shown. The tubing is made of this length partly to ensure that the warm air passing along **D** becomes cooled to room temperature before being collected and partly to ensure that the burette itself is not heated by the boiling liquid in **J**: for the latter purpose it is advisable in addition to place a metal or asbestos screen vertically between **J** and **H** during the experiment.

In the actual determination, the tap **E** is adjusted to give direct access from **D** to the open air during the initial boiling of the liquid in **J**, so that the expanding air in **T** can readily escape. To determine when the air in **T** has been heated until no further expansion occurs, equalise the water levels in **H** and **R** (**H** containing a few ml. of air) and then adjust **E** to give access between the capillary **D** and the tube **H**: no change in the level of the water should occur. Now rotate **E** so that **H** is open to the air, and raise **R** so that the water completely fills the tube **H** up to **E**. Drop the bottle **B** containing the weighed liquid into **T**, and *at once* replace **S** and rotate **E** to give access again from **D** to **H**. As the air passes into **H**, drop **R** steadily so that the levels remain approximately equal. When no more air passes into **H**, close **H** (by rotating **E** so that **D** is open to the air) and allow the air in **H** to stand for about 10 minutes to attain a uniform temperature. Meanwhile suspend a thermometer from the tap **E**. Then readjust the two water levels accurately, and note the volume of air in **H**, the temperature, and also the barometic pressure.

Example of Calculation.

Vapour Density of Carbon Tetrachloride, chlorobenzene being used as the heating liquid.

Weight of carbon tetrachloride taken . . . . . 0·2120 gm.
Volume of air collected . . . . 32·8 ml.

Temperature, 14·5°. Barometic Pressure, 744·5 mm.

Vapour Pressure of water at 14·5°, 12·3 mm. (Table II, p. 433.)

$$\text{Therefore volume of air at N.T.P.} = 32\cdot8 \times \frac{273}{287\cdot5} \times \frac{(744\cdot5 - 12\cdot3)}{760}$$
$$= 30\cdot00 \text{ ml.}$$

30·00 ml. of vapour weigh 0·2120 gm.

$$\therefore 11{,}210 \text{ ml.* of vapour weigh } \frac{0\cdot2120 \times 11{,}210}{30\cdot00} = 79\cdot2 \text{ gms.}$$

Therefore Vapour Density = 79
and Molecular Weight = 158

Theoretical for CCl₄; 154.

* NOTE. (1) 1 Gm. of hydrogen (taken as standard) occupies 11,210 ml. at N.T.P., therefore the density of any gas is that weight of it which occupies 11,210 ml. at N.T.P. (2) By Avogadro's hypothesis, the Molecular Weight of any gas = 2 × Vapour Density. Therefore the molecular weight of any gas is that weight which occupies 22,420 ml. at N.T.P. It is usual, therefore, to ignore the actual vapour density in organic chemistry and calculate the molecular weight directly on the 22,420 ml. basis.

Vapour Density. (c) Hofmann's Method.

Victor Meyer's method of vapour density determination can clearly be applied only to those liquids which volatilise at atmospheric pressure without decomposition. In Hofmann's method, the liquid is volatilised in a vacuum, and consequently a much lower temperature (at which decomposition does not occur) can be employed.

The apparatus employed (Fig. 61) consists of a stout-walled barometer tube **T** about 1 metre long, and calibrated in c.c. from the top downwards. The tube **T** is fitted by a rubber stopper **S** into the glass

jacket **J**, the top of which is drawn out to a stout-walled delivery-tube **D**, the internal diameter of which should be not less than 1 cm. At the bottom of **J** is an outlet tube **O** which should be just above the top of rubber stopper **S**. Near the top of the barometer tube **T**, a wire loop is fitted from which the thermometer **A** can be suspended in the annular space between the two tubes. The bottom of the tube **T** dips into a trough **M** containing clean dry mercury: this trough must be large enough to allow free access with the fingers to the open end of **T**. Finally the delivery-tube **D** is connected to a copper can **C** (or alternatively a strong hard-glass flask) containing the liquid the vapour of which heats the tube **T**: the can **C** is heated by means of a powerful Bunsen burner (or small gas-ring) **B**. It is important that the delivery-tube leading up from **C** and the tube **D** are connected by stout-

FIG. 61.

walled rubber tubing capable of successfully withstanding the passage of the hot vapour: this tubing should be securely wired on to the two glass tubes.

Before starting an actual determination, great care must be taken to ensure that the inside of the tube **T** is clean, dry, and free from air. For this purpose, detach the jacket **J** (retaining the stopper **S** in position on the tube **T**) and then thoroughly wash out the inside of **T** first with dilute nitric acid, then with water, and lastly with methylated spirit and ether in turn: finally blow air from bellows through a long piece of quill tubing which reaches to the closed end of **T**. When **T** is free from ether vapour, warm it gently for 1–2 minutes whilst the air is still being blown through. Now pour clean dry mercury into the inverted tube until it is almost completely full. To ensure the absence of air bubbles adhering to the glass walls, connect the end of **T** to an ordinary water-pump, and warm the mercury *gently* for a few minutes until no more bubbles rise to the surface of the mercury. Then fill the tube completely with mercury, close the end securely with the finger-tip, re-invert the tube into position in the trough **M**, suspend the thermometer **A** as shown, and replace the outer jacket **J**. Owing to the height of the tube, the mercury now falls to a position *a*, the exact level of which is ignored.

The boiling-point under reduced pressure of the liquid the vapour density of which is required is probably already known, as this liquid will have been purified by distillation under reduced pressure, *i.e.*, usually at about 15 mm. pressure. Now select for heating purposes a liquid the boiling-point of which at atmospheric pressure is about 60–70° above this temperature. The liquids used for heating the Victor Meyer apparatus (p. 329) in the previous determination are equally suitable for Hofmann's apparatus, but it should be noted that when the chloro-compounds are used, stout-walled rubber tubing is particularly required for the connection between the two tubes.

Fill the can **C** about three-quarters full with this liquid and boil the latter so that a vigorous stream of vapour passes through **D** into the jacket **J**, and ultimately passes through the outlet **O** to the air-condenser, from which the condensed liquid is collected. Allow this stream of vapour to flow unchecked for at least 5 minutes before proceeding with the determination, in order to ensure that the portion of the tube **T** and its contents within the jacket **J** have reached the maximum temperature possible.

Meanwhile clean, dry and weigh a very small bottle similar to that used in the previous Victor Meyer method. (The size of this bottle is important: it must always be completely full when weighed, but must contain no more liquid than is sufficient subsequently to fill the tube **T** about three-quarters full of vapour.) Fill the bottle completely with the pure *dry* liquid the vapour density of which is to be determined, and then insert the stopper firmly so that some of the liquid is displaced and no air remains: dry the outside of the bottle, stopper thoroughly and reweigh.

Now, while holding the bottle between the finger and thumb so that the stopper cannot be displaced, insert the bottle under the end of **T** so that when released it at once floats up to the surface of the mercury in **T**. The stopper is ejected as the liquid vaporises, and the mercury surface sinks to *b*. Continue the passage of the vapour from **C** for several minutes until steady readings are obtained both for the volume of vapour in **T** (*i.e.*, the level of *b*) and the temperature of the thermometer **A**. Finally measure carefully the vertical distance between *b* and the level *b*^{1} of the mercury in the trough **M**. Note also the barometric pressure.

NOTE. Results of high accuracy cannot be expected by Hofmann's method, as a number of errors are necessarily incurred. The main errors are:

(1) The tube **T** is calibrated in ml. at room temperature, and its expansion on heating is ignored.

(2) At the temperature of the determination, the vapour pressure of the mercury may become appreciable. This may be ignored below 120°: at higher temperatures the vapour pressure of mercury has the following values (in mm. of mercury; to the nearest whole number):

Temp.	120°	130	140	150	160	170	180	190	200
Vapour Press.	1·5	2	3	4	5	7	11	15	20
Temp.	210°	220	230	240	250	260	270	280	
Vapour Press.	27	35	44	59	72	97	119	155	

(3) The liquid mercury below b in the tube **T**, being hot, has of course a lower density than that assumed in measuring the pressure represented by the height bb^1. Moreover, this column of mercury acts as a very efficient condenser for the heating vapour from **C** and hence the necessity for boiling the liquid in **C** *vigorously* throughout the determination.

Example of Calculation.

Vapour Density of ethyl malonate, aniline being used as the heating liquid.

Weight of ethyl malonate used	0·1076 gm.
Volume of vapour obtained	56·7 ml.
Temperature of vapour	185°
Height of mercury below the vapour (*i.e.*, bb^1) . .	397 mm.
Barometric pressure	742 mm.
Vapour pressure of mercury at 185° (see above) .	13 mm.

∴ Pressure on vapour = 742 − 397 − 13 mm. = 332 mm.

Volume of vapour at N.T.P. $= 56 \cdot 7 \times \dfrac{273}{458} \times \dfrac{332}{760}$

$$= 14 \cdot 77 \text{ ml.}$$

14·77 ml. of vapour at N.T.P. weigh 0·1076 gm.

∴ 11,210 ml. of vapour at N.T.P. weigh $\dfrac{0 \cdot 1076 \times 11{,}210}{14 \cdot 77} = 81 \cdot 7$ gms.

Therefore Vapour Density = 82
and Molecular Weight = **164**

Theoretical for $C_7H_{12}O_4$, 160.

Molecular Weight Determinations in Solution.

Before describing the chief methods by which the molecular weight of an organic compound in solution may be determined, a description is given of the Beckmann thermometer, and of the Tabloid Press, both of which are frequently used in the above determinations.

The Beckmann Thermometer.

For determining the depression of the freezing-point, or elevation of the boiling-point, of a solvent when a solute is added, a thermometer is required which measures accurately a small change in temperature, the absolute value in degrees Centigrade of the limits of this change being immaterial. The Beckmann thermometer (Fig. 62(A)) is therefore constructed with a very large mercury bulb so that a change in temperature of a few degrees causes a considerable movement of the mercury in the capillary: consequently the scale **S** can be so large that readings to 0·01° can easily be made with

the unaided eye. Since this scale **S** usually covers only 5–6°, it is necessary that the amount of mercury in the bulb should be capable of adjustment, so that, irrespective of the *actual* temperature at which the thermometer is being used, the readings will come conveniently on the scale. For this purpose the thermometer has a reserve supply of mercury in the reservoir **R**. For working at low temperatures, more mercury is required in the bulb, and an extra supply is brought down from **R**: for working at higher temperatures, less mercury is required in the bulb to enable readings to be made on the scale **S**, and therefore a suitable quantity of mercury is detached from that in the bulb and deposited in the reservoir.

Therefore before the thermometer can be used in a particular experiment, it must be "set," *i.e.*, the amount of mercury must be adjusted so that the readings fall conveniently upon the scale **S**. As an example of this process, suppose the thermometer is required for determining the depression of the freezing-point of benzene (m.p. 5·5°), on the addition of a particular solute. First place the bulb of the thermometer in a beaker of water the temperature of which has been adjusted by the careful addition of ice to 7–8°C., this temperature being registered of course by an independent thermometer: this difference of 2–3° (above the true freezing-point of the solvent) corresponds to rather more than the length of the capillary between *c* (the highest calibrated point on the scale **S**) and the point *a*, where the capillary widens out into the reservoir **R**. If the thermometer has

(B)

(A)   FIG. 62.

previously been used at some higher temperature, the mercury will now fall well below the scale **S**. Now momentarily invert the thermometer and tap it gently, so that the mercury in the reservoir **R** falls to *a*, where it remains when the thermometer is again carefully restored to its normal position. Place the bulb of the thermometer in a *warm* water-bath (avoid if possible the use of *hot* water) so that the mercury in the bulb rises up beyond the scale **S** and joins up with the mercury at *a*. Now replace the thermometer in the beaker of water at 7–8°C., and when the contraction of the mercury is complete, tap the thermometer sharply at **R** so that the mercury remaining in the upper part of **R** breaks sharply at the constriction *a* and falls to *b*. Finally place the dry thermometer in a boiling-tube containing about 25 c.c. of the benzene to be used, and chill the tube in ice-water so that the benzene when stirred with the thermometer undergoes partial crystallisation to a semi-solid mass. The temperature recorded by the Beckmann thermometer should now be about 1° below the highest point *c* on the scale **S**: consequently subsequent depressions of the freezing-point of the benzene on the addition of the solute can now be conveniently read on the scale **S**.

If, on the other hand, the thermometer has previously been used at some temperature below the freezing-point of benzene, when the bulb is originally placed in the beaker of water at 7–8°C., the mercury will rise in the capillary and ultimately collect in the upper part of the reservoir at *a*. When the expansion is complete, again tap the thermometer sharply at **R** so that this excess of mercury drops down into *b*, and then as before check the success of the "setting" by placing the thermometer in some partly frozen benzene. In either case, if the adjustment is not complete, repeat the operations, making a further small adjustment, until a satisfactory result is obtained.

If the thermometer is to be used to determine the elevation of the boiling-point of a liquid on the addition of a solute, it must be remembered that at the boiling-point of the pure solvent the mercury must now be about 1–2° *above the bottom* of the scale **S**, and hence for adjustment purposes the temperature of the beaker of water should be 6–7° above the boiling-point of the liquid itself, instead of 1–2° as before.

The "setting" of modern Beckmann thermometers has been made much more simple and rapid by having the reservoir itself calibrated in degrees Centigrade as shown (much enlarged) in Fig. 62(B). Owing to the position of the scale **D**, the readings are necessarily inverted: readings at the top of the scale **D** above the zero mark represent degrees *below* 0°C., and *vice-versa*. Its use is best illustrated by a particular example. Suppose the thermometer is again to be used to determine the depression of the freezing-point of benzene: it is required therefore that at 5°C., the thermometer itself should give a reading about 1° below the top point *c* on the major scale **S**, *i.e.*, a reading near the 0° mark on this scale. All the mercury in the reservoir at *b* is transferred to *a* as before, and the bulb of the thermometer again gently warmed until the mercury in the bulb joins up with that at *a*. The bulb of the thermometer is now cooled so that the mercury at *a* contracts and the meniscus in the reservoir **R** rises. When this meniscus reaches the +5° mark on the small scale **D**, the top of the thermometer is tapped as before to break the mercury thread at *a* so that the remainder of the mercury in *a* falls to *b*: it will now be found that if the bulb is cooled to 5°C. (*e.g.*, by immersion in crystalline benzene as before) the thermometer will give a reading at the 0° mark on the major scale **S**. Stated in general terms, therefore, to "set" this type of Beckmann thermometer for use at a particular temperature, it is necessary merely to join the mercury in the bulb to the whole of the reservoir-mercury collected at *a*, and then to cool or warm the bulb until the reservoir-mercury reads the required temperature on the small scale **D**. The mercury thread is then broken at *a*, and at the desired temperature, the thermometer will then read 0° on the major scale **S**.

When actually taking a reading on the scale **S** during an experiment, a small lens is used, and the usual precautions must be taken to avoid an error by "parallax."

It is always advisable to use a particular Beckmann thermometer either solely for freezing-point determinations or solely for boiling-point determinations. If a thermometer which has been used at low temperatures for some time is reset for boiling-point determinations, it will be found that the glass bulb of the thermometer (as distinct from the mercury) does not adjust itself at once to the higher temperature: a slow "settling-down" process occurs, during which the reading of the thermometer steadily changes. This effect is of course negligible when the thermometer is reset over a range of only a few degrees.

The Tabloid or Pellet Press. When determining the molecular weight of a solid substance in solution, it is often most convenient to add a weighed pellet or tabloid of the substance to the solvent. A tabloid press is therefore used to compress the powdered substance into a pellet of suitable weight. The press consists essentially of a cylinder **C** (Fig. 63), having a circular bore through its long axis. The cylinder **C** fits over a metal base **B**, and a plunger **P** fits closely into the circular bore: the plunger **P** and the cylinder **C** have side-arms to limit rotation in the frame **F**.

FIG. 63.

In use, the cylinder **C** is fitted over the base **B**, and the powdered compound is placed in **C** in small quantities at a time, and pressed firmly down (by hand) with the plunger **P**. When sufficient material has been placed in **C**, the whole unit is fitted into the frame **F** as shown, and the screw-plunger **S** screwed down first until **P** is held in position, and then more firmly until the material in **C** has formed a compact pellet. The cylinder **C** is then removed from **F**, and the pellet ejected from the lower end by thrusting **P** completely down the circular bore.

NOTE. For most compounds, the circular bore in C should have a diameter of not less than 1 cm.: otherwise the final ejection of the pellet may prove very difficult. Some powdered substances do not "bind" well in the press however, and for these compounds a cylinder having a narrower bore (3-5 mm.) is desirable.

It is of great advantage, however, to have available a second cylinder similar to, but much shorter than, C, and of wider internal bore. When the pellet has been formed inside C, the plunger S is released and the shorter cylinder inserted between C and the base B. The plunger S is again screwed down, and the pellet is thus slowly forced out of C into the shorter cylinder below. In this way the pellet, even if originally firmly fixed in C, can be removed without risk of fracture.

Molecular Weight by Depression of the Freezing-point.

When a substance is dissolved in a solvent, the freezing-point of the latter is depressed, this depression (for dilute solutions) being directly proportional to the number of molecules of the solute in unit weight of the solvent. It follows therefore that for a particular solute, the depression of the freezing-point will be directly proportional to the concentration of the solute in the solution: and also equimolecular quantities of different solutes, each dissolved separately in the same weight of the solvent, will cause equal depressions of the freezing-point. The **Molecular Depression Constant** (K) of a solvent is the depression of the freezing-point produced when 1 gram-molecule of a substance is dissolved in 100 grams of the solvent. This Constant may be calculated thermodynamically, but is more usually determined experimentally, using in turn a number of solutes of known molecular weight, the solutes being selected from those compounds which show neither ionisation nor association in the particular solvent. It should be borne in mind that in the majority of cases the conditions defined for the Molecular Depression Constant are not physically realisable, because 1 gram-molecule of a compound is rarely soluble in 100 grams of a solvent, and moreover when soluble, would give far too concentrated a solution for the physical laws underlying the process to apply accurately. In the experimental determination of the constant, however, only very dilute solutions (rarely exceeding 5%) are used, and the Constant calculated by simple proportion: in using this Constant in turn to determine the molecular weight of a new solute, the depression of the freezing-point once again of a very dilute solution is measured, and the weight of the solute, which when dissolved in 100 grams of the solvent would give a depression equal to the Constant, is then calculated. Therefore only dilute solutions are used both in the determination and in the subsequent application of the Molecular Depression Constant.

Since ice-water is the cheapest and most convenient cooling agent available in the laboratory it is best to use for Freezing-point determinations the following solvents, which freeze a few degrees above 0°C.

SOLVENT	FREEZING-POINT	MOLECULAR DEPRESSION CONSTANT (K)
Benzene	5·5°	50
Nitrobenzene	5·0	69
*Cyclo*hexane	6·5	201
Bromoform	7·8	144
Ethylene dibromide	8·0	118
Water	0°	18·6
Acetic acid	17	39·0

Certain practical points concerning the use of these solvents are discussed after the description of the experimental method: water and acetic acid are also included, although the former is rarely used in organic work, and the latter presents certain experimental difficulties which are also discussed later.

The apparatus (Fig. 64) used consists of a glass tube **T** (usually about 18 cm. in length and 2·5–3·0 cms. in diameter), having a short side-arm **A**, as shown. Into the top of **T** are fitted through a cork the Beckmann thermometer **B** (already "set" for the required solvent) and the stirrer **S** made of thin glass rod. It is advisable for the hole in the cork carrying the stirrer **S** to be protected by a short collar **C** of glass tubing, the handle of the stirrer being bent after threading through the collar. The tube **T** fits into an outer tube **J**, which acts as an air-jacket to prevent too rapid cooling of the contents of **T**. **J** in turn is held in a metal lid covering a large glass jar of ice-water: a much heavier and stronger stirrer **D** passes through this lid to enable the ice-water mixture to be thoroughly stirred from time to time.

Weigh the clean dry tube **T**, then add about 25 ml. of the pure solvent (*i.e.*, sufficient to ensure that the bulb of the thermometer

Fig. 64.

is subsequently well covered) and weigh again. Place the thermometer and stirrer in position, and, to save time, dip **T** directly into some ice-water: stir the solvent occasionally, when crystallisation will soon occur.

Remove **T** from the ice-water, dry it thoroughly, and then stir the semi-solid solvent whilst holding the bottom of **T** in the hand: directly the last trace of crystals disappears, fit **T** into the jacket **J** and assemble the apparatus as shown in Fig. 64. Now stir the solvent in **T** by moving **S** up and down *slowly and at uniform speed.* The temperature of the solvent falls steadily, and ultimately drops slightly below its freezing-point: crystallisation then occurs and the latent heat causes the temperature to rise a few degrees, when it then becomes stationary for several minutes. Note the highest temperature reached, maintaining a steady stirring throughout this process. Now remove **T** and warm it in the hand until all crystals disappear. Repeat the process until *three consistent* readings of the freezing-point have been obtained.

Then again remove **T**, and drop a weighed pellet of the solute through the side-arm **A**. Stir the mixture until a clear solution is obtained, and then repeat the above process until three consistent readings of the freezing-point of the solution have been obtained. Then add a second weighed pellet of the solute, and determine the freezing-point of this more concentrated solution in the same way.

Then if:

g gms. of solute in G gms. of solvent depress F.P. by T°C.

$$\frac{g \times 100 \times K}{G \times T}$$ gms. of solute in 100 gms. of solvent depress F.P. by K°C.

= Molecular Weight of the solute.

NOTE. (1) It is often found on determining the freezing-point of a solution that considerable super-cooling occurs, with the result that crystallisation, when it does take place, is considerable, and the temperature of the solution rises possibly several degrees. This is always to be avoided, because the freezing-point now measured is that of the more concentrated solution remaining after the crystallisation of a large proportion of the solvent, and a marked error may be thus incurred. If the solution shows signs of super-cooling, chill 1–2 ml. of the pure solvent in a test-tube in ice-water, and stir with a glass rod until crystallisation occurs. Now, when the solution is only slightly super-cooled, lift the stirrer **S** until its base is opposite the side-arm **A**, and then quickly transfer some of the crystals from the test-tube by means of the rod on to the stirrer. At once lower the stirrer into the solution and continue stirring, when crystallisation should occur within a few seconds.

(2) This method of Molecular Weight determination should be used only with solvents in which the particular substance is freely soluble, since it is essential that, on cooling, the *solvent*, and not the solute, should crystallise out.

FIG. 65.

(3) If the solute is a liquid,

introduce it into the apparatus from an ordinary pyknometer tube (Fig. 65), weighing the tube before and after. For this purpose, insert the delivery-tube of the pyknometer carefully down the side-arm **A** (Fig. 64) so that the liquid falls well into the body of **T**. Force the liquid out of the pyknometer by blowing gently down the right-hand inlet tube by means of a piece of rubber tubing carrying a short calcium chloride tube.

(4) Molecular weight determinations by depression of the freezing-point are more accurate and far less troublesome than those by the elevation of the boiling-point (p. 345), and the former method should always be preferentially employed if the solubility of the organic compound in the solvent is sufficiently high.

(5) Certain solvents, particularly benzene, cause many organic compounds to form bi-molecular associates in solution, with the result that the experimental molecular weight is twice the true value. If association is suspected, the determination should be repeated in one or more other solvents, in order to ascertain whether consistent results are obtained.

The following practical points in the choice and use of the solvents mentioned in the above table should be noted:

Benzene. Pure benzene (free in particular from toluene) must be used, otherwise the freezing-point is too low, and crystallisation may not occur with ice-water cooling alone. On the other hand, this benzene should not be specially dried immediately before use, as it then becomes slightly hygroscopic and does not give a steady freezing-point until it has been exposed to the air for 2–3 hours. Many compounds (particularly the carboxylic acids) associate in benzene, and molecular weights determined in this solvent should therefore be otherwise confirmed.

Nitrobenzene. Usually rather a troublesome solvent, as it is markedly hygroscopic and the freezing-point of the solvent itself tends to fall steadily: moreover it is, like benzene, an associating solvent. For a modification of the above freezing-point apparatus, by which the determination may be made in the absence of water-vapour, the student should consult an advanced text-book of practical physical chemistry.

Cyclohexane. An excellent solvent for many determinations, particularly as, owing to the high value of K, a large fall in the freezing-point is obtained, and the accuracy of the determination is therefore correspondingly increased. Care should be taken to avoid super-cooling, however, as it has a marked effect on the true freezing-point of cyclohexane solutions.

Bromoform. Commercial bromoform should be shaken thoroughly with water, separated, dried over powdered anhydrous sodium sulphate and then fractionally distilled under reduced pressure using a water-condenser. It should be stored in a dark cupboard. It is an excellent solvent, has the advantage of a high Constant, and very seldom causes association of the solute.

Ethylene dibromide. Also has a very high Constant, but sometimes causes association of the solute. It usually gives excellent consistent results.

Water. When water is used as a solvent, an ice-salt mixture should be employed for cooling purposes.

Glacial Acetic Acid. Acetic acid is very hygroscopic, and its freezing-point is considerably affected by the water absorbed. Satisfactory results cannot be obtained with the apparatus shown in Fig. 64, p. 339, and a specially modified apparatus must be employed (see Nitrobenzene).

Example of Calculation.

Molecular Weight of Naphthalene in Benzene.

Weight of benzene used . . . . . . 19·40 gms.

F.P. of benzene . . 5·056, 5·057, 5·057. Mean, 5·057°

(i) Weight of first pellet of Naphthalene added, 0·2107 gm.

F.P. of solution . . 5·496,* 5·497, 5·497. Mean, 5·497°

Depression of F.P. = 0·440°

$$\therefore \text{ Molecular Weight of naphthalene} = \frac{0·2107 \times 100 \times 50}{19·40 \times 0·440} = 123$$

(ii) Weight of second pellet of naphthalene added, 0·1385 gm.

Total weight of naphthalene present, 0·3942 gm.

F.P. of solution . . 5·776, 5·775, 5·776. Mean, 5·776°

Depression of F.P. = 0·719°

$$\therefore \text{ Molecular Weight of naphthalene} = \frac{0·3492 \times 100 \times 50}{19·40 \times 0·719} = 125$$

Theoretical for $C_{10}H_8$; 128.

Molecular Weight by Depression of the Freezing-point of Camphor. (Rast's Method.)

Camphor possesses the very high Molecular Depression Constant of 400, and therefore a given weight of a particular solute will give a much greater depression in camphor solution than in solutions of the usual organic solvents at the same concentration. Consequently the chief advantages arising from the use of camphor as a solvent, compared with the usual liquid solvents, are (1) much smaller quantities of the solute and of the solvent are required, so that the method amounts almost to a micro-determination, (2) an ordinary thermometer can be used instead of a Beckmann thermometer, (3) because of the high melting-point of camphor, no special apparatus is required, the ordinary melting-point apparatus (Figs. 1(A) and 1(B), p. 3) giving excellent results, (4) the method is much more rapid, particularly in the hands of an experienced worker.

On the other hand, molten camphor can exist as either the *keto* or the *enol* form, and it is essential that the substance the molecular weight of which is required should (a) dissolve freely in molten camphor, and (b) not react chemically with either form of the solvent.

$$C_8H_{14} \begin{matrix} CH_2 \\ | \\ CO \end{matrix} \rightleftharpoons C_8H_{14} \begin{matrix} CH \\ \| \\ C(OH) \end{matrix}$$

keto   *enol*

Moreover, it is important that a determination of the Molecular Depression Constant of the camphor should always precede that of the molecular weight of a particular solute: the precise

* The degrees of the thermometer are numbered from the top downwards; hence the apparent rise in the F.P.

value of the constant depends largely on the "personal equation" of the observer,* and the two determinations should therefore always be made by the same observer to ensure identical conditions of manipulation.

The capillary tubes used for the melting-point determinations should be both longer and wider than those normally used: they should be at least 10 cm. long (to decrease the chance of slipping off the thermometer during the determination) and 2–3 mm. in diameter (in order to have sufficient semi-molten material in the tube to observe accurately the process of melting).

(1) DETERMINATION OF THE MELTING-POINT OF THE PURE CAMPHOR.

Pulverise some pure camphor on a piece of unglazed porcelain, using a clean spatula: transfer some of this camphor to a capillary tube, and press it firmly down by means of a second capillary tube sealed at the end and fitting snugly into the larger tube. Sufficient camphor should be taken to give a column of pressed material about 15 mm. in height. Place the capillary in the usual melting-point apparatus and raise the temperature fairly rapidly until the camphor melts to a clear liquid (about 180°). Now allow the temperature to fall until the camphor resolidifies, and then increase the temperature *very slowly* again. The camphor slowly remelts: take as the melting-point of the camphor that temperature at which the last trace of crystalline material *just* disappears. Allow to cool and redetermine the melting-point of the solidified camphor. Three *consistent* determinations should be made in this way: an accurate determination cannot be obtained unless the temperature rises very slowly (not more than 1 degree in 1 minute), therefore use a *very* small flame protected from draughts by a windscreen.

(2) DETERMINATION OF MOLECULAR DEPRESSION CONSTANT OF CAMPHOR, using Solute of Known Molecular Weight (Naphthalene, $C_{10}H_8$).

Weigh accurately a small clean specimen-tube directly on the balance. Add about 0·2 gm. of pure naphthalene and reweigh: finally add about 2·0 gms. of finely divided camphor and weigh again. The two substances have now to be melted together to obtain a clear homogeneous solution, and for this purpose the tube should be sealed to prevent loss of either substance by volatilisation. It is sufficiently accurate, however, to cork the tube *loosely* and then to melt the camphor by direct *gentle* heating: this should be done very carefully and slowly, the aim of the operation being to get a clear solution of the naphthalene in the molten camphor *at as low a temperature as possible.* Swirl the molten material gently around the bottom of the tube to ensure good mixing, and then allow to

---

* This is clearly seen in large classes, where the values obtained for the "Constant" may vary over a wide range, but the values for the molecular weight of a given substance are (usually) remarkably consistent.

cool. When quite cold, either remove the contents of the tube with a spatula, or, if this is not possible, break the tube, removing all fragments of glass from the solid camphor. Grind up the camphor in a mortar in order further to ensure a homogeneous mixture, and then fill a melting-point tube precisely as in (1) above. The melting-point is determined precisely as before—namely, by first rapidly melting the entire contents of the capillary tube in the melting-point apparatus, allowing to cool until resolidification occurs, and then increasing the temperature *very slowly*, again noting as the melting-point the temperature at which the last trace of crystalline matter just disappears. Repeat with a further portion of the same material until consistent results are obtained.

Molecular Weight of Naphthalene, 128. Then if:

g gms. of naphthalene in G gms. of camphor depress F.P. by t°C., 128 gms. of naphthalene in 100 gms. of camphor depress F.P. by

$$\frac{t \times 128 \times G}{g \times 100}°C.$$

This value is the Molecular Depression Constant (K) of Camphor.

(3) DETERMINATION OF MOLECULAR WEIGHT OF A GIVEN SUBSTANCE, *e.g.*, ACETANILIDE, using the above Molecular Depression Constant of Camphor.

Proceed precisely as in (2), but use pure powdered acetanilide instead of naphthalene.

Then if:

g^1 gms. of acetanilide in G^1 gms. of camphor depress F.P. by T°C.,

then $\dfrac{g^1 \times 100 \times K}{G^1 \times T}$ gms. acetanilide in 100 gms. of camphor depress F.P. by K°C.

= Molecular Weight of Acetanilide.

Example of Results Obtained.

F.P. of Camphor   .   .   176·0, 176·0, 176·0°.   Mean, 176·0°

Determination of Constant, using Naphthalene

Weight of naphthalene used   .   .   .   .   0·1990 gm.
Weight of camphor used .   .   .   .   .   2·0590 gms.
F.P. of mixture   .   .   146·5, 146·5, 146·4°.   Mean, 146·5°
∴ Depression of F.P. .   .   29·5°

Molecular Depression Constant $= \dfrac{29·5 \times 128 \times 2·0590}{0·1990 \times 100} = \underline{391}$

Molecular Weight of Acetanilide.

Weight of acetanilide used   .   .   .   .   0·2053 gm.
Weight of camphor used .   .   .   .   .   2·0750 gms.
F.P. of mixture   .   .   147·1, 147·0, 147·0.   Mean, 147·0°
∴ Depression of F.P. .   .   29·0°

Molecular Weight of acetanilide $= \dfrac{0·2053 \times 100 \times 391}{2·0750 \times 29·0} = \underline{133}$

Theoretical for acetanilide, $C_6H_5NHCOCH_3$; 135.

Molecular Weight by Elevation of the Boiling-point.

This method is strictly parallel in principle to that for the determination of molecular weight by depression of the freezing-point. When a substance is dissolved in a solvent, the boiling-point is raised, and the **Molecular Elevation Constant** (K) of a solvent is the elevation of the boiling-point produced when 1 gram-molecule of a substance is dissolved in 100 grams of the solvent. This Constant again can be either calculated, or determined experimentally using a number of solutes of known molecular weight.

The solvents most frequently employed are:

SOLVENT	BOILING-POINT	MOLECULAR ELEVATION CONSTANT (K)	CONSTANT (K[1]) FOR LANDS-BERGER-WALKER METHOD
Ether	35°	21·0	30·2
Acetone	56	17·0	22·6
Chloroform	61	36·6	26·0
Ethyl Acetate	77	27·5	33·2
Rectified Spirit* (95·6%)	78	11·5	15·5
Carbon Tetrachloride	78	48·0	32·4
Benzene	80	27·0	33·0
*Cyclo*hexane	81	27·5	38·1
Water	100	5·2	5·4
Ethylene Dibromide	130	64·0	—

The method is used to determine the molecular weight primarily of those compounds which are too slightly soluble in the usual cold solvents for the more efficient freezing-point method to be employed.

The apparatus is shown in cross-section in Fig. 66. **T** is a glass tube similar to that used for freezing-point determinations, except that a short piece of stout platinum wire should be fused through the base as shown. A Beckmann thermometer **B** is fitted to the tube **T**, and a condenser (either a short light water-condenser or a spiral air-condenser) to the side-arm. The tube **T** is supported within a glass jacket **J** which carries a similar condenser: a supply of the pure solvent is boiled in **J** during the determination to ensure a uniform temperature and to protect the contents of **T** from loss of heat by radiation. The jacket **J** stands on an asbestos tray **A**, which has in the centre a small hole covered with fine wire gauze: the tray **A** has in addition at diagonally opposite corners two asbestos chimneys **D** and **E** to conduct away the hot air. The apparatus is heated by means of a Bunsen burner, and the supply of gas must be capable of delicate adjustment by a screw-clip or some similar means.

For use, clean and dry the tube **T** and weigh it with both necks corked. Now add about 20–25 ml. of the solvent, and weigh again. Add

---

* Rectified spirit should always be used in preference to absolute alcohol which is strongly hygroscopic.

either a number of glass beads or (preferably) some fragments of un-glazed porcelain, and adjust the thermometer **B** in position: the bulb of **B** should be amply covered by the solvent and should just not touch the

beads. It is advisable now to wrap some asbestos cord **CC**[1] loosely in a spiral round the lower portion of **T**, and then fit **T** into the jacket **J**, finally plugging the top of the annular space be-tween **T** and **J** loosely with the upper end of the cord: by these means the direct ascent of hot gases in the annular space is prevented, and the tube **T** cannot come in direct contact with **J**. Place sufficient solvent in **J** to bring it approximately level with the top of the beads in **T**. Adjust the condenser, and then sur-round the whole appar-atus with wind-screens so that it is completely protected from draughts.

Fig. 66.

Now start the heating so that the solvent in both **T** and **J** is boiling steadily, and that the con-densed liquid is falling back into **T** from the condenser at about 1 drop per second. When the boiling is quite steady, take readings on the Beckmann thermometer every 2–3 minutes, tapping it gently about 5 seconds before each reading to ensure that the mercury meniscus is not "sticking" and so giving an inaccurate reading.

When three consistent readings are obtained, add a weighed pellet of the solute to **T**: for this purpose it is important that the thermometer is not withdrawn, and the boiling is not interrupted. It is best to hold the pellet ready in a pair of forceps near the mouth of the side-arm of **T**, and then momentarily to remove the condenser, drop in the pellet and replace the condenser: when the condenser is removed a small quantity of cold air entering the side-arm will cause slight condensation of the hot vapour, none of which will therefore escape.

Wait a few minutes after the pellet has completely dissolved, and then continue taking readings as before until three consistent values are obtained. A second weighed pellet may then be added if desired, and the process repeated.

Then as before if:

g gms. of solute in G gms. of solvent elevate B.P. by T°C.,

$\dfrac{g \times 100 \times K}{G \times T}$ gms. of solute in 100 gms. of solvent elevate B.P. by K°C.

= Molecular Weight of the solute.

NOTE. (1) The success of this method depends primarily on obtaining smooth steady boiling of the liquid in **T** with an absolute minimum of superheating. It is advisable before starting the determination to roughen the end of the platinum wire inside **T** by means of a piece of emery paper wrapped around the end of a glass rod. If, in spite of the presence of this wire and the glass beads, steady boiling is not obtained, better results can sometimes be obtained by preparing a fine roll (2–3 mm. diameter) of thin platinum foil **F** (Fig. 66), and then cutting it completely across (as shown on the dotted lines) to make a number of triangular cross-sections: add about ten of these to the glass beads

(2) It should be borne in mind that any variation of the rate of heating will affect appreciably the boiling-point of the solvent or that of the solution, and the rate of heating must therefore remain constant throughout the experiment. Students frequently make the mistake of boiling the pure solvent *too gently*: hence when the solute is added, the temperature of the solution barely reaches the new boiling-point, and the gas pressure has to be increased. If, on the other hand, the solvent is boiled too vigorously, slight superheating alternating with "bumping" will occur, and an irregular boiling-point will result. The rate of boiling noted above (giving 1 drop of condensate per second) is usually the most suitable.

(3) The use of water as a solvent should be avoided whenever possible, as its Molecular Elevation Constant is so low that only a small elevation of the boiling-point is obtained.

(4) The same considerations with regard to association in solution apply here as in the freezing-point method (p. 341).

Example of Calculation.

Molecular Weight of Benzoic Acid in Benzene.

Weight of benzene used	. . . . .	29·30 gms.
B.P. of benzene	. . 4·162, 4·163, 4·160.	Mean, 4·162°
Weight of benzoic acid added	. . . .	1·133 gm.
B.P. of solution	. . 3·720, 3·725, 3·722.	Mean, 3·722°

Elevation of B.P. = 0·440°

∴ Molecular Weight of benzoic acid $= \dfrac{1·133 \times 100 \times 27}{29·3 \times 0·440} = \underline{237}$

Theoretical for $C_7H_6O_2$; 122.

Hence benzoic acid forms bi-molecular associates in benzene solution.

Molecular Weight by the Landsberger-Walker Method.

The Landsberger-Walker Method is essentially a modification of the preceding boiling-point elevation method, the solution being now heated by the passage of vapour from the pure boiling solvent. The Landsberger-Walker

Method has the advantage over the preceding method in that it is quicker, that super-heating of the solvent cannot occur, and that several readings can be made for one addition of the solute: the results are, however, less accurate. although they are sufficiently accurate for most purposes in organic chemistry.

FIG. 67.

The apparatus consists of a tube **T** (Fig. 67) having a small hole **H** near the top: the lower part of the tube is graduated in ml. Into **T** is fitted the delivery-tube **A**, and a thermometer **B** which should be graduated to o·1°C. The tube **T** fits into an outer jacket **J**, at the base of which is an outlet tube leading to a condenser. A conical flask **F** is usually used to generate the vapour of the boiling solvent: this flask carries an open safety-tube **S** rising at least 25 cm. above the flask, and also a delivery-tube for connection with **A**.

For an actual determination, assemble the apparatus, placing about 10 ml. of the pure solvent in **T** and about 150 ml. in **F**: add some unglazed porcelain to

F to ensure steady boiling. Now heat **F** until a steady stream of vapour is passing through the solvent in **T**, and is then escaping through **H** and passing downwards through **J** to the condenser: adjust the heating of **F** so that the condensed liquid is emerging from the condenser at about 1 drop per second. Note the boiling-point of the solvent.

Now arrest the boiling in **F**, and pour sufficient solvent out of **T** so that about 10 ml. remain. Add a weighed pellet of the solute, and reassemble the apparatus. adding additional porcelain to **F**. Again boil the solvent in **F**, and adjust the rate of boiling until the condensed liquid is leaving the condenser at the same rate as before. The solute rapidly dissolves in the solvent in **T**, and the thermometer registers a higher boiling-point. Note this boiling-point, and *at once* slip off the rubber connection between the two delivery-tubes, turning out the gas below **F** if the solvent is inflammable. Carefully lift off the cork carrying the tube **A** and the thermometer **B**, allowing the solution to drain from the ends. Now read the volume of the solution in **T**, ensuring at the same time that the apparatus has been clamped accurately in a vertical position.

Reassemble the apparatus and continue blowing the vapour through the same solution. The boiling-point is now lower, owing to the increasing dilution of the solution. After a few minutes, note this temperature and then the volume of the solution as before.

A third and fourth determination can usually be made.

The calculation is precisely the same as that for the preceding method, except that, since the volume and not the weight of the solution is now measured the former Molecular Elevation Constants must be divided by the density of the corresponding solvents at their boiling-points. The Constants (K^1) so obtained for the Landsberger-Walker method (*i.e.*, the elevation given by 1 gram-molecule of solute in 100 ml. of solvent) are given in the right-hand column of the table on p. 345.

NOTE. Acetone and alcohol are the best solvents to use when possible. Both benzene and *cyclo*hexane have such low latent heats of vaporisation that considerable condensation occurs in **T**, and more than two readings can only rarely be obtained. The Constant for water is so low that (as before) only a very small elevation of the boiling-point occurs, and inaccurate results are therefore usually obtained.

Example of Results Obtained.

Molecular Weight of Benzoic Acid in Rectified Spirit.

Boiling-point of pure solvent	77·60°
Weight of benzoic acid added	0·885 gm.
Boiling-point of solution	78·13°
Volume of this solution	20·0 ml.
Elevation of boiling-point	0·53°

$$\therefore \text{ Molecular Weight of benzoic acid} = \frac{0·885 \times 100 \times 15·6}{20·0 \times 0·53} = \underline{130}$$

Theoretical for $C_7H_6O_2$; 122.

Molecular Weights by Chemical Methods.

Molecular Weight of an Acid by Analysis of its Silver Salt.

The silver salts of most carboxylic acids are only sparingly soluble in cold water, and hence are readily prepared. Moreover they very rarely contain water of crystallisation, and therefore when dried can be analysed without further treatment. The analysis itself is simple, rapid and accurate, because gentle ignition of a weighed quantity of the silver salt in a crucible drives off the organic matter, leaving a residue of pure metallic silver.

Since the silver salts of the carboxylic acids are usually soluble in dilute nitric acid, they must be prepared by treating an aqueous solution of a *neutral salt* of the acid (and not the free acid itself) with silver nitrate solution. It is not practicable to attempt to neutralise the acid with sodium or potassium hydroxide solution, because the least excess of alkali would subsequently cause the white silver salt to be contaminated with brown silver oxide. The general method used therefore to obtain a neutral solution is to dissolve the acid in a small excess of ammonia solution, and then to boil the solution until all free ammonia is driven off. The solution of the pure ammonium salt is now cooled and treated with a small excess of silver nitrate solution, when the silver salt of the acid is precipitated.

Dissolve 1·5 c.c. of glacial acetic acid in about 50 c.c. of distilled water and then* add dilute ammonia solution until the well-stirred mixture smells of ammonia. Boil the solution *gently* until no odour of ammonia can be detected in the steam and until a red litmus-paper placed in the steam gives no blue coloration. Then cool and add dilute (*e.g.*, 10%) silver nitrate solution with stirring until no further precipitation of the white silver acetate occurs. Filter through a *small* Buchner funnel, drain well and then wash at least three times with small quantities of water to remove excess of silver nitrate. Then drain thoroughly, transfer to a small evaporating-basin, cover with a watch-glass and dry either in a steam oven or in a vacuum desiccator. Powder the cold

dry salt in a small clean mortar: if the salt does not readily form a fine dry powder, continue the drying for a further period.

Meanwhile clean and dry a porcelain crucible and lid, selecting for this purpose a crucible of the tall narrow type (Fig. 68): heat the crucible and lid on a pipe-clay triangle over a Bunsen flame and allow to cool in an atmospheric desiccator. Weigh the crucible and lid when quite cold, add about 0·5 gm. of the powdered silver salt,

FIG. 68.

and weigh again. Place the crucible and lid in an inclined position (Fig. 68) in a pipe-clay triangle, and then gently heat the upper portion

---

* Alternatively, to prevent undue hydrolysis, make the solution just alkaline to phenolphthalein with sodium hydroxide, then *just* acid with dilute nitric acid, and finally, add a slight excess of ammonia.

of the crucible with a very small Bunsen flame as shown. After 5–10 minutes, increase the size of the flame somewhat in order to heat the whole of the upper portion of the crucible and the lid. The silver salt below becomes heated by conduction and largely decomposes at this stage. Now slowly bring the flame down to the base of the crucible, and then after several minutes heat far more strongly until eventually the whole crucible becomes red hot. Then stop the heating, allow the crucible to cool somewhat and replace it in the desiccator until quite cold. Weigh again. Repeat the ignition until the weight of the crucible and its metallic contents is constant (if the first heating has been carefully performed, one reheating should be sufficient).

Then, since Atomic Weight of silver = 107·9,

if g gm. silver is obtained from G gm. silver salt,

107·9 gms. silver are obtained from $\dfrac{G \times 107·9}{g}$ gms. silver salt

= Molecular Weight of silver salt.

The Molecular weight of the acid itself is clearly equal to that of the silver salt *minus* the atomic weight of silver *plus* the weight of hydrogen displaced by the silver, *i.e.*, to $\left(\dfrac{G \times 107·9}{g} \right) - 107·9 + 1.$

Silver acetate is one of the most soluble of the silver salts of the carboxylic acids. When determining the molecular weight of one of the aromatic acids, *e.g.*, benzoic acid, a larger volume of water should be taken for the preparation of the silver salt, otherwise a thick cream of precipitated material is obtained and is difficult to filter and wash efficiently. For benzoic acid, therefore, add 1 gm. of the powdered acid to about 50 ml. of water, and then add dilute ammonia until the acid has dissolved and the solution smells of ammonia. Boil and cool as before, and then dilute (if necessary) so that the solution has a volume of at least 75 ml. Precipitate the silver salt as before, filter, drain, and wash *thoroughly* before drying. Use 0·6–0·7 gm. for the analysis. The silver salts of the aromatic acids give much free carbon on heating in a crucible, and the ignition must therefore be carefully and thoroughly performed.

· NOTE. (1) It is clear that the above calculation is based on the knowledge that the acid is monobasic. If the acid had been dibasic, one gram-molecule of the silver salt would have contained two atoms of silver and the calculation, based on this fact, would have given twice the previous value. The method can therefore be used to determine molecular weights *only* if the basicity of the acid is already known: otherwise only the *equivalent weight* of the acid (*i.e.*, the weight in grams of the acid equivalent to 1 gram-atom of silver) can be calculated from the above analysis.

(2) The method cannot be applied to acids which contain halogens or sulphur: the silver salts of the former on ignition would give silver halide and those of the latter would give silver sulphide containing some silver sulphate, *etc.* Certain

acids moreover give silver salts which on being heated decompose too vigorously for accurate results, *e.g.*, silver oxalate, which decomposes suddenly with the evolution of carbon dioxide: $(COOAg)_2 = 2Ag + 2CO_2$.

(3) The above method of preparing a neutral solution of the ammonium salt cannot be applied to *extremely* weak acids (*e.g.*, some amino-acids), the ammonium salts of which dissociate in boiling aqueous solution.

Molecular Weight of an Acid by Titration with Standard Alkali Solution.

The molecular weight of many carboxylic acids which are freely soluble in cold water (*i.e.*, chiefly the aliphatic acids) can readily be obtained by titrating a known weight of the acids in aqueous solution with standard sodium or potassium hydroxide solution, using phenolpthalein as an indicator. To avoid the use of unduly large quantities of the acid, it is advisable to use $N/2$ caustic alkali solution, and in order to obtain a sharp end-point, this alkali solution should be prepared from CO_2-free water* and pure (alcohol-washed) caustic alkali free from carbonate.

Weigh out accurately about 2·5 gms. of pure powdered succinic acid, transfer to a 100 ml. graduated flask, dissolve in distilled water, make the solution up to the graduation mark and mix well. Now, by means of a pipette, transfer 25 ml. of the solution to a 150 ml. conical flask, add a drop of phenolphthalein solution and titrate with $N/2$ NaOH or KOH solution. Repeat with two further quantities of 25 ml. of the acid solution to obtain consistent results.

If the acid had been monobasic, then clearly the molecular weight would be the weight in grams which neutralises 1000 ml. of *normal* alkali solution: the molecular weight of the dibasic succinic acid is the weight which neutralises 2000 ml. of the normal alkali solution. Hence this method, like the preceding silver salt method, presupposes a knowledge of the basicity of the acid concerned: if the basicity is unknown, then only the equivalent weight (*i.e.*, the weight which neutralises 1000 ml. of the normal alkali solution) can be calculated.

Example of Calculation.

Weight of succinic acid taken . . . . 2·627 gms.

Solution made up to 100 ml.

25 ml. of this solution required 22·2, 22·1, 22·1

$= 22·1$ ml. $N/2$ NaOH solution

---

* To prepare CO_2-free water, almost fill a large aspirator or bottle with distilled water, and then securely close the neck with a rubber stopper carrying two delivery-tubes, one passing just through the stopper into the aspirator and the other passing right down to the bottom: connect the former delivery-tube to a water-pump. Join three wash-bottles in series, the first two containing 50% aqueous KOH solution and the third containing distilled water to a depth of at least 10 cm.: connect this wash-bottle to the long delivery-tube of the aspirator. When the water-pump is in operation, air is drawn through the two KOH wash-bottles (where CO_2 and all other acid gases are absorbed), then through the water wash-bottle (which absorbs any alkali spray) and finally through the distilled water in the aspirator, from which all CO_2 is slowly extracted. Using a moderately vigorous stream of air, about 12 litres of CO_2-free water can be prepared in 3 hours with this apparatus.

∴ 100 ml. of this solution require 88·4 ml. $N/2$ NaOH solution

$$= 44·2 \text{ ml. } N/\text{NaOH solution}$$

2·627 gms. succinic acid (dibasic) are equivalent to 44·2 ml. N/NaOH

∴ $\dfrac{2·627 \times 2000}{44·2}$ gms. succinic acid (dibasic) are equivalent to 2000 ml. N/NaOH

$= \underline{119}$

Theoretical for succinic acid, $C_4H_6O_4$; 118.

Molecular Weight of a Base by Analysis of its Chloro-platinate.

When platinum is dissolved in aqua regia it is first converted to platinic chloride, $PtCl_4$, and the latter at once unites with the excess of hydrochloric acid to give the stable soluble dibasic chloroplatinic acid, H_2PtCl_6.

When an amine, or a solution of its hydrochloride, is added to an aqueous solution of chloroplatinic acid, a salt of the base with the chloroplatinic acid, of general formula B_2,H_2PtCl_6 (where B is one molecule of the base) is formed and usually crystallises out, for these chloroplatinates have normally a rather low solubility in cold water. The chloroplatinate can be filtered off, dried, and then analysed by direct ignition, when only the metallic platinum ultimately remains. Knowing the percentage of platinum in the chloroplatinate, the molecular weight of the latter, and hence of the constituent base, can readily be calculated.

Dissolve 0·5 ml. of pure aniline (or 0·5 gm. of powdered p-toluidine) in 10 ml. of dilute hydrochloric acid (warming if necessary to obtain a clear solution). Pour this solution with stirring into a slight excess of chloroplatinic acid solution, e.g., into about 10 ml. of a solution containing 10% of platinum as the chloroplatinic acid. The orange-yellow chloroplatinate of the amine at once crystallises out. Cool in ice-water for about 10 minutes, and then filter through a small Buchner funnel (preferably one of the cone-shaped type). Drain the chloroplatinate and then wash it twice, using about 5 ml. of ice-cold distilled water for each washing. Again drain thoroughly, transfer to a small basin,*

---

* When the chloroplatinate has been transferred to the basin, wash out the Buchner funnel, filter-paper and flask with hot water until all remaining traces of the chloroplatinate have been dissolved: add the united washings to the original filtrate and place in the platinum residue bottle. The platinum can be readily recovered from these aqueous residues as follows. Heat the solution in a large beaker on a water-bath, and then add a coil of pure magnesium ribbon, pressing the latter to the bottom of the beaker with a heavy glass rod. Cover the beaker with a watch-glass. After several minutes, the colour of the solution begins to fade, and spongy platinum is deposited: the process then rapidly becomes complete and, on stirring, the platinum settles to the bottom of the colourless solution. Filter off the metal at the pump, wash with very dilute hydrochloric acid, and then thoroughly with water. Drain, and dry in a desiccator (and not by washing with alcohol and ether, as these solvents may ignite in contact with the finely divided platinum).

Alternatively, the bulk of the platinum in the aqueous residues can be precipitated by ammonium chloride as ammonium chloroplatinate, the latter filtered off, and the filtrate evaporated to dryness. The chloroplatinate and the residue from the evaporation are then ignited.

N

cover with a watch-glass and dry either in a steam oven or (preferably) in a vacuum desiccator.

Now analyse 0·4–0·5 gm .by ignition *precisely* as described for the ignition of silver salts (p. 350).

Then, since Atomic Weight of platinum = 195·2,
if g gm. platinum is obtained from G gm. chloroplatinate,

195·2 gms. platinum are obtained from $\dfrac{G \times 195\cdot2}{g}$ gms.

$$= \text{Molecular Weight of chloroplatinate.}$$

Then, since $B_2, H_2PtCl_6 = \dfrac{G \times 195\cdot2}{g}$, and $H_2PtCl_6 = 410$.

$$2B = \dfrac{G \times 195\cdot2}{g} - 410$$

NOTE. (1) The above calculation (similarly to that of the silver salt of an acid) is based on the knowledge that the amine is monacidic and therefore forms a chloroplatinate of formula B_2, H_2PtCl_6. If the amine is diacidic (*e.g.*, ethylene diamine, phenylene diamine, *etc.*), the chloroplatinate would have the general formula B, H_2PtCl_6, and the calculated result would have twice the above value. Hence the molecular weight of an amine can be determined by this method only if the acidity of the amine is known: otherwise, the calculated result gives only the *equivalent weight* of the base (*i.e.*, the weight in grams equivalent to 1 gram-atom of platinum).

(2) The chloroplatinates prepared as above are sufficiently pure for direct analysis without recrystallisation. The chloroplatinates of the amines are usually freely soluble in hot water, but recrystallisation (when required) should not be attempted until the process has been found to be successful with a small test-portion of the chloroplatinate. The chloroplatinates of many primary and secondary amines decompose in hot water, the amine being oxidised, and the chloroplatinate reduced to the metal: some amines furthermore co-ordinate readily with the metal when the chloroplatinate is boiled with water and a mixed product is obtained on cooling.

(3) Many chloroplatinates separate from aqueous solution with water of crystallisation. If this is suspected, the chloroplatinate should be dried to constant weight in the oven before analysis, to ensure elimination of water of crystallisation. Aniline, *p*-toluidine and pyridine all give anhydrous chloroplatinates, and can be conveniently used in the above determination: no attempt should be made to recrystallise their chloroplatinates.

Estimation of the Number of Hydroxyl Groups in a given Polyhydric Alcohol or Phenol.

Method. A known weight of the alcohol is heated with a definite volume of a mixture of acetic anhydride and pyridine until acetylation is complete:

$$R(OH)_n + nCH_3CO\cdot O\cdot COCH_3 = R(O\cdot COCH_3)_n + nCH_3COOH$$

The excess of unchanged acetic anhydride is then hydrolysed by the addition of water, and the total free acetic acid estimated by titration with standard NaOH solution. Simultaneously a control experiment* is performed identical with the above except that the alcohol is omitted. The difference in the volumes of NaOH solution required in the two experiments is equivalent to the difference in the amount of acetic acid formed, *i.e.*, to the acetic acid used in the actual acetylation. If the molecular weight of the alcohol is known, the number of hydroxyl groups can then be calculated.

1. DETERMINATION OF NUMBER OF HYDROXYL GROUPS IN PHENOL. C_6H_5OH. Molecular Weight, 94.

Prepare the acetylating mixture by adding 1 volume of acetic anhydride to 4 volumes of pure anhydrous pyridine, and shaking thoroughly. Immediately before use, transfer the mixture to a clean dry burette having a well-fitting glass tap, and then close the top of the burette by means of a soda-lime tube.

Fit two similar 100 ml. conical flasks, **A** and **B**, with reflux water-condensers, using preferably rubber stoppers for this purpose. Connect up the water-condensers in series. Weigh the flask **A**, add about 2 gms. of pure *dry* powdered phenol and weigh again. Now add 20 ml. of the acetylating mixture to the flask **A**, and also to the control flask **B**. Connect the flasks to the reflux condensers and heat both flasks on briskly boiling water-baths for 30 minutes. Then remove the water-baths, and pour 25 ml. of distilled water down each condenser, shaking the contents of each flask gently to ensure complete hydrolysis of the unchanged acetic anhydride. Finally cool each flask thoroughly in cold water and allow to stand for 10 minutes. Then titrate the contents of each flask with N.NaOH solution, using phenolphthalein as an indicator. A fine emulsion of phenyl acetate will form when the contents of the flask **A** are diluted, and should therefore be vigorously stirred throughout the titration to ensure that all the free acetic acid is extracted by the N.NaOH solution.

Example of Calculation.

Weight of phenol used	.	.	1·930 gms.
Flask **A** requires .	.	.	67·7 ml. N.NaOH solution
Flask **B** (Control) requires	.	.	87·6 ml. N.NaOH solution

Difference in N.NaOH solution required for **A** and **B** = 19·9 ml.

---

* Control or blank experiments have frequently to be employed in organic estimations. Their value is twofold:

(1) The *absolute* concentration of a reagent (*e.g.*, the exact amount of acetic anhydride in the above pyridine solution) need not be determined, since if the same amount of the reagent is used in the actual and in the control experiments, the *difference* gives at once the actual amount used.

(2) Adventitious losses of the reagent, due, *e.g.*, to the chemical action of the alkaline glass vessels, slight absorption by the corks, *etc.*, are almost identical for the actual and the control experiments and therefore do not affect the *difference* in result between the two experiments.

1000 ml. N.NaOH $\equiv$ 1 Gm.Mol.NaOH $\equiv$ 1 Gm.Mol.CH_3COOH $\equiv$ 1 Hydroxyl group.

$\therefore$ 19·9 ml. N.NaOH $\equiv$ 19·9/1000 Hydroxyl group

$\therefore$ 1·930 gms. phenol contain 19·9/1000 Hydroxyl group

and 94 gms. (1 Gm.Mol.) phenol contain $\dfrac{19·9}{1000} \times \dfrac{94}{1·930}$ Hydroxyl group

$= $ 0·97 Hydroxyl group.

NOTE. (1) In view of the large volume of N.NaOH solution required in the above titrations, the contents of the flask **A** after hydrolysis may alternatively be washed carefully into a 100 ml. graduated flask, and the solution made up to the mark and well mixed. 25 ml. of the solution are then withdrawn with a pipette, and titrated with the N.NaOH solution. The 100 ml. flask is then washed out repeatedly with distilled water, and used similarly for the contents of the flask **B**.

(2) The use of reflux condensers during the acetylation is not absolutely essential, since very little evaporation of the acetylating mixture from an open conical flask would occur during heating on the water-bath. The use of the condensers is desirable however, both for training in sound analytical practice, and also to protect the contents of the flask from condensed steam, *etc.*

2. DETERMINATION OF THE NUMBER OF HYDROXYL GROUPS IN (ii) GLYCOL. $C_2H_4(OH)_2$. Molecular Weight, 62.

Carry out the determination precisely as for phenol, but add about 1 ml. (approximately 1 gm.) of glycol to the flask **A**, and weigh as before by difference.

(iii) GLYCEROL. $C_3H_5(OH)_3$. Molecular Weight, 92.

Use approximately 1 ml. of glycerol, and cork the flask **A** securely when weighing the glycerol by difference, owing to the very hygroscopic nature of the latter. Heat on the water-bath for 60 minutes instead of 30 minutes. Excellent results are obtained by this method if a freshly opened sample of anhydrous glycerol is available: a sample which has been exposed to the air for even a short period will absorb sufficient water to give inaccurate results.

(iv) MANNITOL. $C_6H_8(OH)_6$. Molecular Weight, 182.

Take approximately 1 gm. of the finely powdered mannitol, using either a weighing bottle, or else weighing directly in the flask **A** as before. Heat on the water-bath for 60 minutes. During the titration with the NaOH solution, a fine precipitation of the hexacetyl-mannitol may occur, but will not affect the titration. The results are excellent.

(v) GLUCOSE. $C_6H_7O(OH)_5$. Molecular Weight, 180.

Use approximately 1 gm. of the finely powdered *anhydrous* glucose, heating for 60 minutes. Slightly low results (*e.g.*, 4·7–4·8 Hydroxyl groups) are usually obtained.

NOTE. (1) It is clear that the molecular weight of the alcohol or phenol must be known before the above determinations are carried out. The molecular weight if unknown must be determined by one of the methods given on pp. 328–349.

(2) The method can be used to determine the amount of a known alcohol or phenol present in a crude sample, provided that the impurities do not themselves contain hydroxyl groups.

Estimation of the Number of Amino Groups in Aniline. First Method.

This method is precisely similar to the previous method used for the estimation of the number of hydroxyl groups in a polyhydric alcohol. A known weight of aniline is heated with a mixture of acetic anhydride and pyridine until acetylation is complete; the excess of acetic anhydride remaining is

$$C_6H_5NH_2 + CH_3CO \cdot O \cdot COCH_3 = C_6H_5NHCOCH_3 + CH_3COOH$$

then hydrolysed with water and the total free acetic acid estimated by titration with standard NaOH solution, the result being compared with that obtained in a control or blank experiment.

If the molecular weight of the aniline is known, the number of amino groups can be calculated: alternatively, if the aniline is known to be a monacidic base, its molecular weight can be calculated. If the molecular weight and the acidity of the aniline are both known, then clearly the method can be used to estimate the amount of aniline in a given sample. The method is general for many primary and secondary amines, aniline being used solely as a typical member of the former class.

Proceed *precisely* as in the Determination of the Number of Hydroxy Groups in Phenol, except that after weighing the flask **A**, run in about 2 ml. of pure aniline, and weigh again. Then continue exactly as before. The acetanilide which is formed usually remains in solution when the contents of the flask **A** are diluted with water for hydrolysis.

Example of Calculation.

Weight of aniline used	.	.	.	2·015 gms.
Flask **A** requires	.	.	.	63·5 ml. N.NaOH solution
Flask **B** (Control) requires	.	.	85·3 ml. N.NaOH solution

Difference in N.NaOH solution required for **A** and **B** = 21·8 ml.

To calculate number of amino groups, knowing Mol. Weight of aniline (93):

1000 ml. N.NaOH ≡ 1 Gm. Mol. CH_3COOH ≡ 1 NH_2 group

∴ 21·8 ml. N.NaOH are equivalent to 21·8/1000 NH_2 group

∴ 2·015 gms. aniline contain   21·8/1000 ,, ,,

∴ 93 gms. aniline contain $\dfrac{21·8 \times 93}{1000 \times 2·015} = 1·01\ NH_2$ group.

Alternatively, to calculate Molecular Weight of aniline, knowing latter to be a monacidic amine:

21·8 ml. N.NaOH are equivalent to 2·015 gms. aniline

1000 ml. N.NaOH are equivalent to $\dfrac{2·015 \times 1000}{21·8} = 92·4$ gms. aniline.

Second Method.

Although the above method gives excellent results and is to be strongly recommended, its use in large classes entails the consumption of large quantities of the comparatively costly pyridine. This difficulty can be overcome by acetylating the aniline with a mixture of acetic anhydride and glacial acetic acid. For this purpose a mixture of 2 volumes of the anhydride and 1 volume of acetic acid is used: this mixture contains more acetic anhydride than that previously used for acetylations (p. 79) in order to ensure that quantitative acetylation occurs in a reasonably short time. If acetic anhydride alone is used high results are obtained, presumably owing to the formation of diacetyl-aniline.

Fit two similar 250 ml. conical flasks, **A** and **B**, with reflux water-condensers (again preferably using rubber stoppers) and connect the condensers in series as before over two water-baths. Prepare a mixture of 2 volumes of acetic anhydride and 1 volume of glacial acetic acid, and shake it thoroughly. Weigh the flask **A**, run in about 1·5 ml. of pure aniline, and weigh again. Now chill the flask **A** in ice-water, and then carefully run in 4 ml. of the acetylating mixture, using for this purpose either an accurate burette or (better) a small pipette: unless the aniline is thus kept chilled during the addition, the heat of the reaction may send up a fine spray of the acetylating mixture which will be largely lost. Run 4 ml. of the acetylating mixture also into the control flask **B**. Fit the flasks to the condensers and heat on the briskly boiling water-baths for 30 minutes, occasionally shaking the contents of the flasks gently around. Then pour about 50 ml. of hot water down each condenser. (In spite of the cooling action of the condenser, the water enters the flask **A** sufficiently hot to precipitate the acetanilide as an oil, which subsequently forms a suspension of fine crystals: if cold water is added, the acetanilide may separate as a hard crystalline lump, which will interfere with the subsequent titration.) Continue heating the flasks on the water-baths for a further 10 minutes to ensure complete hydrolysis of unchanged acetic anhydride. Then remove the water-baths, wash the condensers again with a small quantity of cold water, detach the flasks and wash the base of the corks also with water, allowing all washings to fall into their respective flasks.

Cool the flasks in cold water, and then titrate the contents of each with N.NaOH solution, using phenolphthalein as an indicator. Shake the contents of the flask **A** repeatedly during the titration in order to keep the fine crystals of acetanilide dispersed in the aqueous solution.

The acetylations may alternatively be performed in 100 ml. conical flasks, and the contents after dilution and hydrolysis with water can then be carefully washed into 250 ml. beakers for the titration with alkali. The calculation is precisely similar to that of the first method. Excellent results are obtained.

Estimation of Aniline Hydrochloride.

Aniline hydrochloride, being a salt formed from a very weak base and a strong acid, undergoes considerable hydrolysis in aqueous solution to aniline

$$C_6H_5NH_2,HCl \rightleftharpoons C_6H_5NH_2 + HCl$$

and hydrochloric acid. The latter can be titrated with standard alkali solution, in which case the progressive neutralisation of the free hydrochloric acid causes the hydrolysis of the aniline hydrochloride to be ultimately complete. If phenolphthalein is used as an indicator, the end-point is unaffected by the free aniline present.

The method can therefore be used to estimate the percentage of aniline hydrochloride in a crude sample, provided the impurities are not themselves salts of other similar amines. Alternatively, if aniline is known to be a monacidic base (forming therefore a mono-hydrochloride) the molecular weight of aniline can be determined, since the molecular weight of the aniline hydrochloride is clearly that weight which is neutralised by 1000 ml. of N.NaOH solution.

Weigh out accurately about 4 gms. of the finely powdered aniline hydrochloride on a watch-glass. Place a small funnel (having preferably only a very short stem) in the neck of a 100 ml. graduated flask, and transfer the hydrochloride through the funnel into the flask, pushing the powder if necessary gently down the stem of the funnel with a fine glass rod. Rinse the watch-glass, rod and funnel with distilled water, dissolve the hydrochloride completely, make the solution up to the mark and mix well. Withdraw 25 ml. of the solution with a pipette, and titrate with $N/5$ NaOH solution, the latter having been prepared by diluting N.NaOH solution with CO_2-free water (see footnote, p. 352). Repeat the titration with a further 25 ml. of the solution to ensure consistent results.

Estimation of the Number of Acetyl Groups in an Acetyl Ester.

Method. This method is essentially the reverse of the estimation of the number of hydroxyl groups in a polyhydric alcohol by quantitative acetylation (p. 354). A known weight of the acetyl compound is hydrolysed by boiling with a known volume of N.NaOH solution, this volume being in excess of that required for complete hydrolysis. The excess of NaOH is then estimated

$$R(O \cdot COCH_3)_n + nNaOH = R(OH)_n + nCH_3COONa$$

by titration with N.HCl or N.H$_2$SO$_4$ solution, and the volume of N.NaOH solution used actually to hydrolyse the acetyl compound thus determined. If the molecular weight of the acetyl compound is known, the number of acetyl groups in the molecule can then be calculated.

1. DETERMINATION OF NUMBER OF ACETYL GROUPS IN TRIACETIN (TRIACETYL-GLYCEROL) $C_3H_5(O \cdot COCH_3)_3$. Molecular Weight, 218.

Fit two 200 ml. conical flasks, **A** and **B**, with reflux water-condensers again using preferably rubber corks for this purpose. Weigh the flask **A**, add about 2 ml. of triacetin, and weigh again. (Alternatively, in large classes it is sufficiently accurate to run in 2·0 ml. of triacetin, *i.e.*, 2·3 gms., from a burette.) Then by means of a pipette add 50 ml. of *N*.NaOH solution to each flask (the flask **B** acting as a control), and finally add a few *minute* fragments* of unglazed porcelain to each flask to ensure steady boiling subsequently. Boil each solution under reflux *very gently* for 30 minutes, heating the solutions over a gauze with a small flame for this purpose. Then stop the heating, pour about 10 ml. of distilled water down each condenser to wash any solution back into the flasks, and then remove the latter and cool in cold water. Titrate the contents of each flask with *N*.HCl solution, using phenolphthalein as an indicator.

Example of Calculation.

    Weight of triacetin taken = 2·300 gms.

    Flask **A** requires   .   .   .   .   18·3 ml. *N*.HCl solution

    Flask **B** (Control) requires .   .   .   49·7 ml. *N*.HCl solution

    Difference in volume of *N*.HCl required = 31·4 ml.

1000 ml. *N*.HCl ≡ 1000 ml. *N*.NaOH ≡ 1 Gm. Mol. NaOH ≡ 1 Acetyl group

∴ 31·4 ml. *N*.HCl ≡ 31·4 ml. *N*.NaOH ≡ 31·4/1000 Gm. Mol. NaOH

                                           ≡ 31·4/1000 Acetyl groups

    Thus 2·300 gms. triacetin contain 31·4/1000 Acetyl groups,

$$218 \text{ gms. (1 Gm. Mol.) triacetin contain } \frac{31·4}{1000} \times \frac{218}{2·300} \text{ Acetyl groups}$$

$$= \underline{2·97} \text{ Acetyl groups.}$$

2. DETERMINATION OF THE NUMBER OF ACETYL GROUPS IN:

(ii) HEXACETYL-MANNITOL. $C_6H_8(O \cdot COCH_3)_6$. Molecular Weight, 434.

Continue precisely as for triacetin, but since hexacetyl-mannitol (p. 114) is a crystalline compound, weigh out 2·0–2·5 gms. of the finely powdered substance, either from a weighing-bottle, or by direct weighing in the flask **A**. The results are excellent.

(iii) PENTACETYL-GLUCOSE. $C_6H_7O(O \cdot COCH_3)_5$. Molecular Weight, 390.

A modification of the above method is required for acetylated sugars, because on alkaline hydrolysis the liberated sugar, *e.g.*, glucose, undergoes slight resinification by the alkali present, giving a brown solution, in which the end-point of the titration is difficult to detect accurately. If however $N.H_2SO_4$ solution is used instead of *N*.NaOH solution, hydrolysis occurs rapidly, and the acidic solution remains colourless, giving therefore an excellent end-point when the mixture of acetic acid

* Larger fragments of porcelain would absorb appreciable quantities of the sodium hydroxide, which would be only slowly extracted by the acid during the subsequent titration.

and unchanged sulphuric acid is back-titrated with N.NaOH solution, using phenolphthalein as an indicator.

Weigh out approximately 1·5 gms. of powdered pentacetyl-glucose (p. 112) in the flask **A**, and then add 25 ml. of $N.H_2SO_4$ solution to each of the flasks **A** and **B**, together with a fragment of porcelain. Boil under reflux gently for 30 minutes, then wash each condenser down as before with 10 ml. of distilled water, cool, and titrate the solutions with N.NaOH solution.

Example of Calculation.

Weight of pentacetyl-glucose taken = 1·500 gms.

Flask **A** requires . . . . 44·3 ml. N.NaOH solution

Flask **B** (Control) requires . . 25·1 ml. N.NaOH solution

Difference in volume of N.NaOH required = 19·2 ml.

1000 ml. N.NaOH solution $\equiv$ 1 Acetyl group

19·2 ml. N.NaOH solution $\equiv$ 19·2/1000 Acetyl group

1·500 gms. pentacetyl-glucose contain 19·2/1000 Acetyl group

$\therefore$ 390 gms. (1 Gm. Mol.) pentacetyl-glucose contain $\dfrac{19·2}{1000} \times \dfrac{390}{1·500}$ Acetyl group

= 4·99 Acetyl groups

NOTE. (1) The above method (pp. 359–361) is sometimes used in preference to that given on p. 354 in order to determine the number of hydroxyl groups in an unidentified polyhydric alcohol. The alcohol is acetylated by any of the standard methods, a marked excess of the acetylating reagent being used to ensure complete acetylation of all hydroxyl groups present. The polyacetyl compound is then purified and its molecular weight determined: the number of acetyl groups present (and therefore the number of hydroxyl groups in the original alcohol) is then estimated by the above method. The advantage of this longer method is chiefly that the estimation of the number of acetyl groups by quantitative hydrolysis is more accurate (particularly for a substance of unknown constitution) than that of the number of hydroxyl groups by quantitative acetylation.

(2) The same method can clearly be applied to the quantitative saponification or hydrolysis of most esters. Hence it may equally well be used for the quantitative estimation of a known ester in a crude sample.

Estimation of Formaldehyde.

Method. Formaldehyde may be estimated in solution by oxidising it to formic acid by means of a known quantity (in excess) of iodine dissolved in an excess of NaOH solution. The oxidation is, in effect, carried out by the sodium hypo-iodite formed by the action of the iodine on the alkali, the formic acid being then neutralised by the alkali present:

$$I_2 + 2NaOH = NaI + NaIO + H_2O$$
$$HCHO + NaIO = HCOOH + NaI$$

When the oxidation is complete, the excess of hypo-iodite is estimated by acidifying the solution, and then titrating the iodine thus formed against

$$NaIO + NaI + 2HCl = 2NaCl + H_2O + I_2$$

N*

standard sodium thiosulphate solution. It will be seen that each molecule of iodine used in the original oxidation corresponds to one molecule of formaldehyde.

Formalin Solution. The method has frequently to be applied to the estimation of formaldehyde in commercial formalin solution. The latter must, however, first be diluted until it contains about 0·2% of formaldehyde, before the above method is applied. Therefore first weigh accurately a corked conical flask of about 75–100 ml. capacity. Then run in about 2·5 ml. of the formalin using preferably a dropping-tube or a pipette for this purpose, to ensure that the neck of the flask is kept free from the solution. Re-weigh the corked flask. Now add about 50 ml. of water to the formalin in the flask, and then pour the mixed solution carefully through a small funnel into a 500 ml. graduated flask. Rinse out the conical flask and then the funnel thoroughly with water, make the solution in the graduated flask up to the mark and mix well.

Transfer 25 ml. of this dilute solution by means of a pipette to a conical flask, and add similarly 50 ml. of $N/10$ iodine solution. Now add 10% sodium hydroxide solution until the liquid becomes pale yellow in colour, and allow the solution to stand, with occasional shaking, at room temperature for at least 10 minutes. Then acidify with dilute hydrochloric acid (free from chlorine) in order to liberate the remaining iodine. Titrate the latter with $N/10$ sodium thiosulphate solution, using starch as an indicator in the usual way.

From the above equations, it will be seen that 1 ml. of the $N/10$ iodine solution used in the oxidation is equivalent to 0·00150 gm. of formaldehyde.

Example of Calculation.

Weight of formalin solution used . . . 2·520 gms.
Diluted to 500 ml.

50 ml. of $N/10$ I_2 solution added to 25 ml. of this dilute formalin solution. After oxidation in the presence of sodium hydroxide, and subsequent acidification, the excess of iodine liberated required 17·3 ml. $N/10$ $Na_2S_2O_3$ solution.

$$17·3 \text{ ml. } N/10 \text{ } Na_2S_2O_3 \equiv 17·3 \text{ ml. } N/10 \text{ } I_2 \text{ solution}$$

Therefore the iodine used to oxidise the formaldehyde

$$= 50 - 17·3 = 32·7 \text{ ml. } N/10 \text{ } I_2 \text{ solution}$$
$$\equiv 32·7 \times 0·00150 \text{ gm. HCHO}$$

25 ml. of the dilute formalin contain $32·7 \times 0·00150$ gm. HCHO
∴ 500 ml. of the dilute formalin contain $32·7 \times 0·00150 \times 20$ gms. HCHO
i.e., 2·520 gms. of the original formalin contain $32·7 \times 0·00150 \times 20$ gms. HCHO
∴ 100 gms. of the orig. formalin contain $\dfrac{13·1 \times 0·00150 \times 20 \times 100}{2·520}$ gms. HCHO

$$= \underline{38·9\%} \text{ HCHO.}$$

NOTE. The above method can be successfully applied only to dilute solutions of formaldehyde which are free in particular from other aliphatic aldehydes, since the latter, if present, would undergo a similar oxidation. Formaldehyde, if mixed with other aldehydes, should be estimated by quantitative addition of potassium cyanide: for details, see advanced text-books of quantitative organic analysis.

Estimation of Urea (Hypobromite Method).

Method. There are two standard methods for the estimation of urea, (i) the hypobromite method, (ii) the urease method (p. 419). The chief merit of the hypobromite method is the rapidity of the analysis: the results obtained are considered sufficiently accurate for most medical requirements, *e.g.*, for the estimation of urea in urine. For accurate metabolic work, however, the urease method should be employed.

Urea is decomposed by alkaline sodium hypobromite solution according to the equation:

$$CO(NH_2)_2 + 3NaBrO + 2NaOH = 3NaBr + N_2 + Na_2CO_3 + 3H_2O$$

Thus 1 gram-molecule of urea (60 gms.) should give 22·4 litres of nitrogen at N.T.P., or 1 gm. of urea should give 373 ml. of nitrogen. Actually however urea in solution always gives a small amount of ammonium cyanate with which it is in equilibrium, and consequently the full amount of nitrogen (in accordance with the above equation) is not evolved: it is found that 1 gm. of urea gives actually 357 ml. of nitrogen at N.T.P. (*i.e.*, 95·7% of the theoretical), and all calculations should therefore be based on this value.

A convenient form of apparatus, particularly for large classes, is shown in Fig. 69; it is identical with that used for the determination of the equivalent weight of metals by hydrogen evolution. **A** and **H** are glass tubes connected together by the rubber tubing **J** and securely fastened to the board **B**. The tube **A** is graduated from the top downwards. The tube **H** carries near its base a short outlet tube, to which is connected a piece of rubber tubing closed by the clip **T**. A gas-tight rubber tube **R** joins **A** to a short length of glass tubing **G**, which can be fitted securely by the rubber stopper **D** to the 250 ml. conical flask **C**. **F** is a bath containing water at the temperature of the laboratory. Care must be taken to ensure that all connections are gas-tight.

Fig. 69.

The estimation may be made to determine the amount of urea in a crude sample, or the amount of urea in a sample of urine. Place about 30 ml. of freshly prepared sodium hypobromite solution (p. 426) in the flask **C**. Now weigh out accurately about 0·15 gm. of urea into a small test-tube **E**, and then place the latter as shown in the flask **C**. (Alternatively, if the estimation is being carried out on urine, which usually contains about 2% of urea, measure out exactly 5 ml. of the sample into the tube **E**.) In each case, take great care not to spill any of the contents of **E** into the hypobromite solution. Now fit the stopper **D** securely into **C** and immerse the latter in the water-bath **F**. When thermal equilibrium is attained, run water from **T** or add it through the open end of **H** until the level of the water is the same in both limbs of the U-tube. Note the volume in **A**, reading the bottom of the meniscus. Now tilt **C** so that the urea and hypobromite are thoroughly mixed: a copious evolution of nitrogen follows. Allow water to run from **T** so that approximately the same level is maintained in the tubes **A** and **H**. After the evolution of nitrogen has ceased, allow **C** to cool to the temperature of the bath by moving the flask about in the water. Next bring the water to the same level in each limb **A** and **H** as before. Again note the reading in **A**, and so determine the volume of gas evolved. Note the temperature of the water in **F** and the barometric pressure.

A Hempel gas-burette (Fig. 60, p. 329) may be used in place of the tubes **A** and **H**: for this purpose it is manipulated precisely as described on p. 331.

Example of Calculation.

Weight of urea taken . . . . . . 0·144 gm.
Volume of nitrogen obtained . . . . . 53·2 ml.
Barometric pressure, 757 mm. Temperature, 18°C.
Vapour pressure of water at 18°C., 15·4 mm. (Table II, p. 433).
53·2 ml. of nitrogen reduced to N.T.P. become

$$\frac{53\cdot2 \times 273 \times (757 - 15\cdot4)}{291 \times 760} = 48\cdot7 \text{ ml.}$$

357 ml. of nitrogen are given by 1 gm. of pure urea.
∴ 48·7 ml. of nitrogen are given by 48·7/357 gms. of pure urea
i.e., 0·144 gm. of urea contains . 48·7/357 gms. of pure urea
∴ 100 gms. of urea contain . $\dfrac{48\cdot7 \times 100}{357 \times 0\cdot144}$ gms. of pure urea
= <u>94·7%</u> urea.

Estimation of Sugars.

Three methods are in use for the estimation of sugars:
(i) Chemical, depending upon the reducing properties of certain sugars.
(ii) Polarimetric, depending upon the optical activity of the sugars concerned.
(iii) Fermentation methods.

The third method is of limited application and is used only in special cases. The second is the most accurate and rapid method, and is of considerable technical importance. The chemical method (described below), although less accurate than the polarimetric method, is of great value for the estimation of sugars in biological fluids. In fact, for such purposes, it is often to be preferred to the polarimetric method owing to the probable presence of other substances having high optical rotations.

Several variations of the chemical method are in use. In the one described below, a freshly prepared Fehling's solution is standardised by titrating it directly against a standard solution of pure anhydrous glucose: when the end-point is reached, *i.e.*, when the cupric salt in the Fehling's solution is completely reduced to cuprous oxide, the supernatant solution becomes completely decolorised. Some difficulty is often experienced at first in determining the end-point of the reaction, but with practice accurate results can be obtained. The titrations should be performed in daylight whenever possible, unless a special indicator is used (see under Methylene-blue, p. 427).

The standardised Fehling's solution can then be used to determine, for example, the percentage amount of glucose in a crude sample. The method clearly can be applied only to reducing sugars: hence those disaccharides and polysaccharides which are non-reducing must first be hydrolysed to monosaccharides, and the estimation carried out on the hydrolysed product. It should be noted that solutions containing about 0·5% of reducing sugar give the most consistent and accurate results, and all sugar solutions should therefore be made up to approximately this concentration.

PREPARATION AND STANDARDISATION OF FEHLING'S SOLUTION.

Solution A. Dissolve 17·320 gms. of powdered crystalline copper sulphate, $CuSO_4,5H_2O$, in water and make the solution up to 250 ml. in a graduated flask.

Solution B. Dissolve 86·5 gms. of crystalline sodium potassium tartrate ("Rochelle salt," $C_4H_4O_6NaK,4H_2O$) in warm water. Dissolve 30 gms. of pure sodium hydroxide in water. Mix the tartrate and hydroxide solutions, cool and make up to 250 ml. in a graduated flask.

When the Fehling's solution is required, transfer equal volumes of solutions A and B (at room temperature) to a dry flask, and mix thoroughly by shaking. Since however Fehling's solution deteriorates slowly on keeping, only sufficient of the solutions A and B should be mixed together to meet immediate requirements.

To standardise this solution, weigh out accurately about 1·25 gms. of pure anhydrous glucose ("Analar"), dissolve in water and make up the solution to 250 ml. in a graduated flask. By means of a pipette, place 25 ml. of the freshly prepared Fehling's solution in a porcelain evaporating-basin, dilute with an equal volume of distilled water and boil *very gently* over a gauze. Now run the standard glucose solution from a burette, 1 ml. at a time, into the boiling Fehling's solution until the blue colour has entirely disappeared. Do this by allowing the solution to cool at intervals and so permitting the precipitate of cuprous oxide to settle: then tip the basin on one side and look through the supernatant liquid on to the white background of the basin. Bring the solution to the boil again during each addition of the sugar solution. Having thus determined approximately how much sugar solution is required, carry out more accurate titrations, running the glucose solution steadily into the boiling Fehling's solution until the end-point is approached, and then continuing by adding 0·1 ml. of the glucose solution at a time.

Repeat the titrations until consistent values (*i.e.*, values which do not differ by more than 0·1 ml. of glucose solution) are obtained. Then calculate the weight of glucose equivalent to 1 ml. of the Fehling's solution.

It is usually found that 1 ml. of the above Fehling's solution ≡ 0·0050 gm. of glucose.

The weights of other monosaccharides and reducing disaccharides which will reduce 1 ml. of this standard Fehling's solution are: galactose, 0·00511 gm.; fructose, 0·00514 gm.; mannose, 0·00431 gm.; lactose, 0·00678 gm.; maltose, 0·00807 gm.

ESTIMATION OF GLUCOSE IN A GIVEN SAMPLE.

This is clearly the reverse of the standardisation of the Fehling's solution described above.

Weigh out accurately about 1·25 gm. of the sample, dissolve it in water and make the solution up to 250 ml. Titrate this solution against 25 ml. of the standard Fehling's solution, precisely as before.

Example of Calculation.

Weight of sample taken, 1·250 gms. Dissolved in 250 ml. of water.

25 ml. of Fehling's solution required 26·7 ml. of glucose solution.

But 1 ml. of Fehling's solution ≡ 0·005 gm. of pure glucose.

i.e., 26·7 ml. of glucose solution contain 25 × 0·005 gm. of pure glucose.

∴ 250 ml. of glucose solution contain $\dfrac{25 \times 0\cdot005 \times 250}{26\cdot7}$ gm. pure glucose

∴ Sample contains $\dfrac{25 \times 0\cdot005 \times 250 \times 100}{26\cdot7 \times 1\cdot250}$% of pure glucose

$= \underline{93\cdot7\%}$ glucose.

ESTIMATION OF CANE SUGAR (SUCROSE).

This is done by estimating the reducing power of the sugar after hydrolysis (or "inversion") by acid, the glucose and fructose thus formed having very nearly the same reducing power.

The calculation is based on the equation:

$$C_{12}H_{22}O_{11} + H_2O = 2C_6H_{12}O_6$$

∴ 342 gms. of cane sugar ≡ 360 gms. of invert sugar

0·00475 gm. of cane sugar ≡ 0·005 gm. of invert sugar

≡ 1 ml. of the Fehling's solution

Weigh out accurately about 1·3 gms. of the sample of cane sugar, dissolve it in about 15 ml. of distilled water in a boiling-tube, add 5 ml. of *N*.HCl and stand the tube in a briskly boiling water-bath for 10 minutes. Cool, add 5 ml. of *N*.NaOH solution, and transfer to a 250 ml. graduated flask. Rinse out the boiling-tube thoroughly with water, transfer the washings to the graduated flask and make the solution up to the mark. Place 25 ml. of the standardised Fehling's solution in a porcelain basin, bring to the boil and add the "invert" sugar from a burette until the Fehling's solution is decolorised, observing all the precautions described above. Repeat the titrations until consistent results are obtained.

Example of Calculation.

Weight of sample = 1·310 gms. Dissolved in 250 ml. of water.

25 ml. of Fehling's solution required 23·4 ml. of invert sugar solution.

But 1 ml. of Fehling's solution ≡ 0·005 gm. of invert sugar.

$$\equiv 0·00475 \text{ gm. of cane sugar.}$$

i.e., 23·4 ml. of the sugar solution contain 25 × 0·00475 gm. of cane sugar.

∴ 250 ml. of the sugar solution contain $\dfrac{25 \times 0·00475 \times 250}{23·4}$ gm. of the cane sugar

∴ Sample contains $\dfrac{25 \times 0·00475 \times 250 \times 100}{23·4 \times 1·310}$ % cane sugar

$$= \underline{96·8\%} \text{ cane sugar.}$$

NOTE. The use of methylene-blue has been recommended to mark more accurately the complete reduction of Fehling's solution by a reducing sugar. This indicator is prepared by dissolving 1 gm. of powdered methylene-blue in water and diluting to 500 ml. It is used as an internal indicator, a few drops of the methylene-blue solution being added to the Fehling's solution just before reduction is complete. The end-point is indicated by the disappearance of the methylene-blue colour, the dye being reduced to a colourless substance immediately an excess of sugar is present. The use of this indicator enables a sharper end-point to be obtained, and its use is specially recommended if the titrations have to be carried out by artificial light.

Estimation of Amino-acids, e.g., Glycine.

Method. An amino-acid such as glycine, NH_2CH_2COOH, cannot be estimated by direct titration with standard alkali solution, owing to the opposing effects of the basic and the acidic groups. If, however, the amino-acid is first

$$HCH\vert O + H_2\vert NCH_2COOH = CH_2{:}NCH_2COOH + H_2O$$

treated with neutral formaldehyde solution, it can be titrated directly with standard sodium hydroxide solution.

Glycine is present in aqueous solution as the "zwitterion" $\overset{+}{N}H_3CH_2C\overset{-}{O}O$ which is incapable of reacting with formaldehyde. When, however, sodium hydroxide solution is added, the glycine is converted into $NH_2CH_2C\overline{O}O$ which condenses with formaldehyde to give a stable cation. The overall changes may be represented by the following equations, although the precise reactions are probably more complicated:

$$\overset{+}{N}H_3CH_2C\overline{O}O + \overline{O}H \rightleftharpoons NH_2CH_2C\overline{O}O + H_2O$$

$$CH_2\vert O + H_2\vert NCH_2C\overline{O}O \longrightarrow CH_2 : NCH_2C\overline{O}O + H_2O$$

Since formaldehyde solutions almost invariably contain formic acid, and amino-acids themselves are seldom exactly neutral,* it is very important that both the formaldehyde solution and the glycine solution should before mixing be brought to the same pH (see footnote, p. 407), and for this purpose each solution is first made *just* alkaline to phenolphthalein by means of dilute sodium hydroxide solution. This preliminary neutralisation must not be confused with the subsequent *titration* with standard sodium hydroxide, using phenolphthalein as an indicator.

Place about 50 ml. of 40% "formalin solution" in a conical flask and add *at least* 10 drops of phenolphthalein solution. Now add very carefully from a burette dilute sodium hydroxide solution ($N/10$ will serve the purpose) until the solution is *just* faintly pink.

Weigh out accurately about 2 gms. of glycine, transfer to a 250 ml. graduated flask, dissolve in distilled water, make up to the mark, and mix well. Transfer 25 ml. of the solution to a conical flask, add 2 drops of phenolphthalein, and then again add dilute sodium hydroxide very carefully until the solution is *just* faintly pink. Now add about 10 ml. (*i.e.*, an excess) of the neutralised formaldehyde solution: the pink colour of the phenolphthalein disappears immediately and the solution becomes markedly acid. Titrate with $N/10$ sodium hydroxide solution until the pink colour is just restored. Repeat the process with at least two further quantities of 25 ml. of the glycine solution in order to obtain consistent readings.

The calculation depends simply on the fact that 1000 ml. N.NaOH $\equiv$ 1 gm. molecule of glycine. The method can clearly be used either to determine the molecular weight of an amino-acid of known basicity, or to estimate an amino-acid of known molecular weight.

Example of Calculation. Glycine, Molecular Weight, 75.

Weight of glycine taken = 2·029 gm. Glycine solution made up to 250 ml.
   25 ml. require 26·5 ml. $N/10$ NaOH solution.
∴ 250 ml. glycine solution require 26·5 ml. N.NaOH solution.
   But 1000 ml. N.NaOH = 75 gms. glycine.

$$\therefore 26\cdot5 \text{ ml. } N.\text{NaOH} = \frac{75 \times 26\cdot5}{1000} \text{ gms. glycine.}$$

$$\therefore \text{ Sample used contains } \frac{75 \times 26\cdot5 \times 100}{1000 \times 2\cdot029}\% \text{ glycine}$$
$$= \underline{98\cdot0\%} \text{ glycine.}$$

The above method, due to Sorensen, is of great importance in following the course of hydrolysis of proteins by enzymes (p. 417). For example, if the protein and its hydrolysis are represented thus:

* Glycine itself is almost neutral, and requires very little sodium hydroxide to give a pink colour with phenolphthalein; some other amino-acids, *e.g.*, glutamic acid, aspartic acid, *etc.*, are definitely more acidic and consequently require more alkali for this purpose (*cf.* footnote, p. 288).

$$H_2N \cdot CHR_1CO\text{–}NH \cdot CHR_2CO\text{–}NH \cdot CHR_3COOH$$
$$\downarrow 2H_2O$$
$$H_2N \cdot CHR_1COOH + H_2N \cdot CHR_2COOH + H_2N \cdot CHR_3COOH$$

it will be clear that if the above estimation is carried out on the original protein and on the hydrolysis product, then the latter will require three times as much sodium hydroxide for neutralisation as the former.

SECTION B

SEMI-MICROANALYSIS

The Balance and Weighing.

Precautions. Undoubtedly the most important factor in carrying out semi-micro determinations effectively is to have a balance that is sufficiently accurate. For such determinations it is necessary to weigh to not less than the nearest 0·05 mgm. An ordinary analytical balance of good quality can often be adjusted to such a sensitivity but it is necessary to keep the case and pans scrupulously clean, to shield the balance from draughts, vibration and direct sunlight and to operate the balance with considerable care. A true semi-micro balance is certainly less likely to give trouble but is not essential; a prismatic recording ring-rider balance is almost ideal for the purpose, particularly for rapidity of weighing, but is expensive and is again not essential.

Provided that the balance is functioning correctly, the main source of error is in the weights themselves; these should be calibrated by one of the standard methods so that their relative values are known, and they should be carefully cleaned with tissue paper and checked from time to time. To make the best use of the balance, weighing should be carried out by the method of swings, but for this purpose it is necessary first to determine the sensitivity of the balance.

The sensitivity of the balance. The sensitivity of the balance may conveniently be defined as the deflection of the balance pointer over the scale caused by an excess of 1 mgm. on one of the pans. This factor differs according to the actual load on the pans, and it is usual to plot the sensitivity at a series of loads over the range within which the balance is to be used; the sensitivity at any particular load may then be determined at once by reference to the curve.

Assume for purposes of illustration that the whole balance beam corresponds to 10 mgm. and is graduated over its whole length in 10 divisions; on such a beam a 5 mgm. rider is used. It is very important that the rider should sit exactly upright on any notch-mark on the beam and it should, if necessary, be bent so that this is the case. The balance pointer-scale is commonly graduated in 10 divisions on each side of the centre, and it is conventional mentally to divide each of these main divisions into 10 parts; deflections to the left are written −, those to the right +. Thus a deflection of 5 whole divisions to the left is written as − 50, and one of nearer 4 than 3 whole divisions to the right may, perhaps, be estimated as +37. It is important that the swings of the balance should not be too large and a deflection of 50 is probably quite sufficient for most purposes.

It is necessary first to determine the rest-point of the balance. This may be done by setting the balance swinging (it is essential that the balance case should be closed when the balance is swinging and when the rider is being used), with the rider on the zero mark on the beam, ignoring the first three swings, then taking the average deflection of two swings to the left and adding it (*i.e.*, algebraically, the signs being taken into account) to the deflection of the inter-mediate swing to the right; the result is the rest-point of the balance. Thus if the swings are − 47, +40, − 45, the rest-point is 0·6 of a large division on the left of the zero mark on the pointer-scale (*i.e.*, − 6). The rest-point of the balance need not be exactly at the zero mark on the pointer-scale but it should not be more than one large scale division off. If necessary, adjustment should be made with the screws at the ends of the balance beam.

For determining the sensitivity of the balance, the rider is now moved to the 1 mgm. notch on the beam (*i.e.*, the first large beam division), the balance pans being without load. The balance is set swinging and the rest-point again determined, as described above; it will now, of course, have moved further to the left. If it is now − 48 (*i.e.*, − 4·8 large divisions), then the sensitivity is − 48 − (− 6) = − 42 units of deflection per mg. when the balance is unloaded. A sensitivity in the neighbourhood of 50 units per mg. is convenient, and if the observed value is widely different from this it may be adjusted by raising or lowering the "gravity" screw on the balance, the sensitivity being increased by raising the screw or nut. The sensitivity should be checked after each adjustment (the rest-point with the rider at zero and on the 1 mgm. notch being determined each time), until a satisfactory value is obtained. The determination is then repeated with 1 gm., 2 gm., 5 gm., 10 gm., and 20 gm. weights on each pan and the sensitivity plotted against load.

Weighing by swings. Before any series of weighings the rest-point should be determined (the rider being on the zero notch on the beam); the object to be weighed is then placed on the left-hand pan of the balance and the weights on the right. It is important in this connection that the weights should be placed as centrally as possible on the pan. Weights are added in the usual way until their sum is seen to be within 10 mgm. of the weight of the object; the rider is then used in the normal way until the milligram division nearest to the point of balance is found (this may be the division above or below the point of balance, depending on which is nearest). The beam is then allowed to swing and after neglecting the first three swings, the deflection of two swings to the left is noted (and their average taken), and of the intermediate swing to the right, and their algebraic sum determined. The difference between this and the original rest-point gives the mean deflection; looking up the sensitivity at this load from the graph, this may be translated into a weight in mgm., thus, in conjunction with the weights on the pan and the rider reading, giving the weight of the object. It is very important to check the sum of the weights whilst on the balance pan and again as they are put away in their box.

Example. Suppose for illustration that the weights on the pan amount to 18·54 gms. and that the rider is balanced on the 7 mgm. graduation on the beam and that the observed rest-point is +17 units, the original rest-point of the balance, before weighing was started, being +4 units. Then the mean deflection is +13 units and if the sensitivity of the balance at a load of *ca.* 18 gms. (read off from the load/sensitivity curve) is 39 units per mgm., then this deflection corresponds to a weight of $\frac{13}{39}$ = 0·33 mgm. Thus the total weight of the object is 18·54 gms. (weights on pan) + 0·007 gm. (rider on beam scale) +0·00033 gm. (calculated from swings)=18·54733 gms. If the rider reading had happened to be on the notch above the weight of the object, and a similar-sized deflection to the left (the original rest position of the balance still being + 4 units) had been obtained, then the mean deflection would have been − 21 units, corresponding to a weight of $\frac{-21}{39}$ = −0·54 mgm., and this would have to be *subtracted* from the weight indicated on the pan and rider. Thus the weight of the object would be 18·54 gms. + 0·007 gm. − 0·00054 gm. = 18·54646 gms.

Conclusion. It is unnecessary to correct the weight of the object for the original rest-point of the balance where only weighings by difference are being carried out, unless there has been an actual change in the rest-point over the period during which the weighings have been made; this is very unlikely to happen if the balance is properly situated and functioning correctly. Any necessary correction, derived from the calibration of the weights, should, however, be applied where, as usually happens, the weights on the pan are not identical at the initial and final weighings, when weighing by difference. It should finally be emphasised that the secret of accurate weighing is care and patience; weighing cannot be rushed!

Estimation of Carbon and Hydrogen.

Principle. A definite amount of substance (*ca.* 25 mgm.) is weighed into a small boat, placed in a combustion tube and heated in a stream of oxygen with a bunsen flame; the resulting products of incomplete combustion are passed through a part of the tube packed with an oxidising filling heated in a furnace. The resulting products of complete combustion, water and carbon dioxide, are absorbed in weighed tubes containing anhydrous magnesium perchlorate and soda-lime respectively, and these are weighed again after absorption is complete, thus giving the weight of water and carbon dioxide produced, and hence the percentages of carbon and hydrogen in the original compound.

It will be apparent that this method depends for its success on the fact that all organic compounds, if oxidised under sufficiently vigorous conditions, may be converted quantitatively to water and carbon dioxide.

Apparatus.

The oxygen used in the combustion is supplied by a small cylinder (120 Atm.) fitted with a pressure reduction valve, pressure gauge (to avoid the risk of the cylinder becoming exhausted during an actual determination) and fine control knob. It is important that the valve is kept free from oil or grease of any kind.

In order to ensure the complete purity of the oxygen it is first passed through a purification train.

The purification train. The oxygen is led from the cylinder through ordinary flexible rubber condenser tubing to the constant level device **A** (Fig. 70). This consists of two concentric tubes (approximately 2 cm. and 0·5 cm. respectively, in diameter) immersed in 50% aqueous potassium hydroxide contained in the outer vessel (diameter 3·5 cm.). Then by adjusting the liquid level in **A** the pressure of oxygen may be kept constant, and at a maximum of about 8 cm. of water. The constant pressure stream of oxygen is delivered to the apparatus through the side-arm **B**, and any excess from the cylinder escapes around the outside of the outer tube and through the hole **C**. When the apparatus is in use there should be a small but regular excess of bubbles escaping through the liquid and out at **C**. The potash in **A** serves to remove the greater part of any carbon dioxide that may occur in the oxygen.

The side-arm **B** is connected by a length of narrow-bore pressure tubing to a small open-ended manometer **D**. This rubber tubing, and all the rest employed up to the point **V**, have previously been impregnated with paraffin wax by immersing the lengths of tubing in paraffin wax boiling under reduced pressure. By this means the wax is driven into the pores of the tubing, which is rendered quite impermeable to the passage of gas through its walls. The orifice of the tube is usually found to be blocked with wax, and after removal of the obvious blockage, the tubing should be thoroughly cleared by the use of a narrow glass rod, followed by pipe cleaners; otherwise when the rubber is used to connect glass tubes, these will scrape slivers of wax from the tube-pores and will become blocked. All joints in the apparatus are made so that the two glass portions are touching inside the rubber tube and the latter acting only like a sleeve to hold them together—this avoids any possibility of minute particles of wax being carried over into the combustion tube.

The manometer **D** contains a small quantity of dilute sodium hydroxide solution coloured with phenolphthalein and is backed by a scale graduated in cm The length of impregnated pressure-tubing joining **B** and **D** passes through a rigidly mounted pinch-cock **E** fitted with a fine adjustment screw. This is used to reduce the oxygen pressure slightly so that about 6 cm. head is indicated on **D**.

The manometer **D** is connected with impregnated pressure-tubing, and by a glass-to-glass joint, with the side-arm **F** of a U-tube (each limb being about 1 cm. in diameter and 12 cm. long). Before filling, the U-tube should be washed with distilled water, alcohol, then ether and finally dried in an oven. The first limb of the U-tube contains soda-lime (B.D.H. Micro-analytical reagent grade Carbasorb is very convenient) whose purpose is to remove any carbon dioxide from the oxygen stream. A drawback of the soda-lime is that it readily takes up water vapour (a little comes from the pressure gauge) becoming first sticky and then forming a hard impermeable crust that greatly slows the oxygen stream. This difficulty may be overcome by putting a small quantity of magnesium perchlorate (Anhydrone—M.A.R. grade) in the top of the U-tube limb; this also absorbs water, but tends to contract as it does so, drawing away from the wall of the tube and hence not impeding the oxygen flow. Thus in filling the U-tube a small plug of glass wool is put at the bottom of the limb, the limb two-thirds filled with soda-lime, a further plug of glass wool inserted, the top third of the tube filled with magnesium perchlorate and topped with a plug of glass wool that comes just opposite the side-arm. The open end of the limb which projects (5 cm.) above the side-arm is then sealed off. Sealing off the limb has been found to be most satisfactory, as stoppers, taps, *etc.*, tend to leak or to give other trouble. After being used for many determinations the absorbent gradually "cakes," seriously impeding the passage of oxygen, and has to be replaced. This is easily effected by carefully cutting the top off the limb, cleaning it out, refilling and sealing once again. By having the projecting length above the side-arm in the first instance this process may be repeated several times without modifying the tube; when the edge finally gets too near to the side-arm a fresh length of tube may be fused on and the whole series repeated.

The second limb of the U-tube is similarly filled with magnesium perchlorate and sealed off; this packing ensures the final removal of any traces of water vapour from the oxygen stream. It is essential when the limbs are being filled and sealed that the operations are carried out as rapidly as possible and that the side-arms are stoppered (by means of a short length of impregnated tubing blocked with a glass rod) as both substances absorb water vapour from the air very readily. The two limbs of the U-tube are separated by a ground-glass tap T_2. This serves to keep the two absorbents out of contact with each other except when oxygen is flowing and also to shut the oxygen stream off from the combustion tube.

It is an advantage to have all the components of the purification train mounted on a small rigid framework. Thus pure, dry oxygen is delivered at the combustion tube.

Fig. 70.

The combustion tube. The oxygen is led through the side-arm **G** (Fig. 70) into the combustion tube **L** via the horizontal side-arm **H** which is fused into the combustion tube about 4 cm. from the end (the joint between **G** and **H** is also made with impregnated rubber tubing with the two glass tubes touching inside the rubber). The position of **H** thus allows the combustion boat **M** to be introduced into the tube through the end (normally sealed by a tight-fitting rubber bung **J**) while oxygen is flowing.

The combustion tube **L** is made preferably of transparent silica (though hard glass can be used) and is 60 cm. long and 1 cm. in diameter; at the further end it has a short fine beak (2 cm. long, *ca.* 0·25 cm. in diameter). A small square of asbestos board **K** is placed up against the combustion tube side-arm to screen the rubber bung **J** from heat and thus avoid any possibility of its evolving volatile carbon compounds during the combustion.

The combustion tube is empty, with the exception of the boat, up to the furnace mouth. The packing of the tube will be considered in detail below.

The furnace and thermostatic mortar. For heating the tube packing, a small electric furnace **N** has been found to be more satisfactory than a row of gas burners. The type used consists of a porcelain tube (1·5 cm. in diameter and 25 cm. long) wound with nichrome wire and contained in an asbestos cylinder, the annular space being lagged; the ends of the asbestos cylinder being closed by asbestos semi-circles built round the porcelain furnace tube. The furnace is controlled by a Simmerstat that has been calibrated at 680° against a bimetal pyrometer, and the furnace temperature is checked by this method from time to time. The furnace is equipped with a small steel bar attached to the asbestos and is thus mounted on an ordinary laboratory stand; the Simmerstat may then be placed immediately underneath it on the baseplate of this stand.

The thermostatic mortar **P**, whose function is described below, is a small electrical heating unit (1·5 cm. in diameter and 7 cm. long) kept constant at 180°. The temperature may be kept constant by an ordinary mercury contact thermostat, mounted in the mortar itself and operating directly on the supply current to the heating-coil; though another Simmerstat may be used if desired. The right-hand end of the mortar bore is only wide enough to take the drawn-out beak end of the combustion tube, which is thus held in place.

There is a tendency for the water produced by the combustion to condense in the narrow neck of the combustion tube, instead of passing right over into the absorption tube. To avoid this, two movable copper hooks **Q** are mounted on a copper rod, which can slide in and out of the mortar **P**; these may be placed over the beak of the combustion tube and conduct sufficient heat from the mortar to vaporise the water once again so that it is driven over by the oxygen stream into the absorption tube **R**.

The absorption tubes. The water from the combustion is absorbed by magnesium perchlorate (anhydrone) in the tube **R** and the carbon dioxide by soda-lime (Carbasorb) in the tube **S**. It is convenient to use absorption tubes having two taps each, which may be closed at the end of the experiment. The tubes may then be immediately weighed full of oxygen, thus avoiding the necessity for sweeping them out with air before weighing. Before filling, both tubes are washed in turn with distilled water, alcohol, then ether and finally dried in the oven.

In filling the tube **R**, one tap is inserted after being carefully greased with a high-vacuum grease. The taps are provided with scored grooves (that run completely around them near their outer end) which act as a trap to prevent any grease reaching the uncovered portion of the tap where it may attract dirt, or be wiped off during weighing or otherwise change the weight of the tube. The taps are, in effect, hollow stoppers having at the side a small hole of approximately the same bore as the side-arms of the absorption tube (cf. **T₄**, Fig. 71). A small plug of glass wool is inserted into the tube which is then filled nearly to the end with perchlorate and topped with a second plug of glass wool. The second tap is then greased and inserted; both taps are naturally kept closed when the tube is not in use. It is important that the same end of the water absorption tube is always attached to the beak of the combustion tube so that the oxygen always flows through in the same direction, and absorption takes place evenly from one end. After some absorption has taken place it is easy to recognise the "absorbing end" as the perchlorate contracts from the sides of the tube and congeals. In order to label the absorbing end previous to this indication, the perchlorate packing is not continued quite to the top of the tube so that the ends are distinguishable. Absorption of water indiscriminately at either end tends to cause "channelling" in the packing with consequent risk of some water escaping absorption.

The type of carbon dioxide obsorption tube **S** (Fig. 70) which is recommended is shown in detail in Fig. 71. In this tube the composite filling of soda-lime and a small packing of magnesium perchlorate are kept in separate chambers which are put in contact only while gas is flowing, by rotating a ground-glass joint tap which divides the tube into two compartments; the perchlorate being packed in what is virtually an enlarged hollow tap-stopper **a** (Fig. 71) at one end of the tube. By keeping these two elements of tube-packing out of contact with each other except when the tube is being used to absorb carbon dioxide, the "life" of the tube, before repacking becomes necessary, is much increased. In filling the carbon dioxide absorption tube **S** of this type (Fig 71), the hollow stopper **a**, having a small hole at the lower end, is charged in turn with a glass-wool plug **b**, perchlorate **c**, and a second glass-wool plug **d**, and the glass stopper **e** is then fixed into **a** with warm glass cement. The neck of the absorption stopper **a** is carefully greased and fitted into the main absorption tube **S** like an ordinary tap: the unit now constitutes the tap **T₃**. The main soda-lime chamber **f** is then filled from the other end of **S** with a glass-wool plug **g**, soda-lime **h**, and a second glass-wool plug **j**, and the greased tap **T₄** finally inserted. The presence of perchlorate is necessary as the soda-lime contains a little moisture which is driven off by the continued passage

FIG. 71.

of oxygen, and this would cause low results for carbon if the water were not prevented from leaving the tube by the "safety" layer of perchlorate.

When in position, the side-arm **k** of the carbon dioxide absorption tube is attached to the T_5 side-arm of the water absorption tube **R** (Fig. 70) by impregnated rubber pressure tubing over a glass-to-glass joint. The side-arm **l** (Fig. 71) of the carbon dioxide absorption tube is attached by a similar joint to a small guard-tube **V** containing perchlorate to prevent any water vapour reaching the perchlorate in the absorption tube. This end of the absorption train is supported by a small wire hook attached to a stand.

The Mariotte bottle. The perchlorate guard tube is attached by a length of ordinary rubber condenser tubing to the Mariotte bottle **W**. This is, in effect, a siphon bottle, and the lead-in tube **X** is a capillary provided with a tap T_1. The bent capillary **Y** serves as exit tube; it is fitted into **W** by a rubber bung and its level may be adjusted.

By the time the oxygen stream has reached the absorption tubes its initial excess pressure (*ca.* 6 cm. of water) has been almost completely dissipated by the resistance afforded to its passage by the packing of the combustion tube. The purpose of the Mariotte bottle is to create a slightly reduced pressure on the far side of the absorption train and so to draw the gas through the absorption tubes. The fact that the pressure inside the apparatus is equal to atmospheric pressure at the place where absorption begins, reduces the chance of leakage of carbon dioxide out of the apparatus and of leakage of water vapour into it. The reduced head in the Mariotte bottle is the difference in level between the bottom of **X** and the tip of **Y**, and is adjusted so as to give an initial flow of oxygen through the apparatus of 5 ml./min.

Packing of combustion tube. The exact filling used in the combustion tube depends on the elements other than carbon, hydrogen and oxygen that are present in the substances to be analysed. On combustion, halogens and sulphur, and to some extent nitrogen, all produce acid gases that would be absorbed by the soda-lime in the carbon dioxide absorption tube; thus if reliable results are to be obtained the packing of the combustion tube has to be of such a nature that these products are not permitted to emerge from the tube.

(*a*) *For compounds containing carbon, hydrogen, oxygen, nitrogen and halogens.* Before filling, the combustion tube is washed with conc. nitric acid, distilled water, alcohol, ether and finally dried in an oven. A 15 mm. roll of silver gauze, which has been etched in pure nitric acid, washed with distilled water, dried and heated to dull redness, is first introduced into the tube; it should be of such a diameter that it just fits in the tube and slides easily down to the "beak" end. The purpose of this, and of another roll of silver gauze to be inserted later, is to convert any halogens or hydrogen halides produced in the combustion to non-volatile silver halides and thus prevent their being carried out of the tube. Next a small plug (2–3 mm.) of ignited asbestos is inserted; this should be pushed in firmly, but not tightly, by means of a glass rod. These asbestos plugs, of which there are a number of others yet to be mentioned, serve to confine the elements of tube-filling in small separate compartments. Next comes 30 mm. of M.A.R. grade lead peroxide (it is very important that this reagent is of high quality), care being taken that this is not tightly packed otherwise too much resistance will be offered to the passage of oxygen when the combustion tube is in use. Any lead peroxide adhering to the walls of the tube is pushed down by an asbestos wool plug fastened to a copper wire. These elements of tube-filling will be heated, not by the furnace but by the thermostatic mortar which is maintained at 180°. The main purpose of the lead peroxide is to absorb any oxides of nitrogen produced in the combustion of nitrogen-containing substances. It is maintained at 180°, which is about its optimum temperature for this purpose. Lead peroxide also absorbs appreciable quantities of water at this temperature but it is allowed to absorb its complement before an actual determination is carried out in the tube. When an actual combustion is then carried out there is a smooth exchange of water through the lead peroxide, provided the temperature of the mortar is kept constant, and the theoretical amount of water vapour emerges from the combustion tube and is absorbed in the absorption tube. Lead peroxide also absorbs some CO_2 but this is at a minimum around 180° and again it is allowed to absorb its complement before an actual determination is carried out. The remainder of the filling of the combustion tube is heated to 680° by the furnace.

Another small asbestos plug is then inserted to confine the lead peroxide (it is very important that the lead peroxide is not tamped down or it will almost completely prevent passage of gas through the tube) followed by a 30 mm. roll of silver gauze, treated in the same way as the first one inserted. This is the main halogen-absorbent, the one already inserted serving as a trap (at 180°) to catch any halogen lost by the hot (680°) silver halide first formed. Next about 25–30 mm. of ignited asbestos is added; this is known as a "choking plug" as it is this element of filling that offers the major part of the resistance to the flow of oxygen in the apparatus. The exact dimensions and compression of the choking plug are determined by trial and error. The amount of asbestos is so adjusted that, when the combustion tube is completely packed, the apparatus assembled, the absorption tubes in place, the furnace and thermostatic mortar at their equilibrium temperatures, and also when there is a pressure of 60 mm./water registered on the pressure gauge and a reduced head of about 20 mm. of water on the Mariotte bottle, the rate of flow of oxygen through the apparatus is about 5 ml. per min. It is essential to have the furnace and mortar on while this adjustment is being made as temperature greatly affects the rate at which gas will flow at a given pressure difference (hot tubes generally "run" noticeably faster than cold).

The choking plug is followed by 200 mm. of M.A.R. "wire-form" copper oxide; this is the main oxidative packing of the tube. Partially combusted material reacts with the heated copper oxide to form carbon dioxide and water, leaving copper behind which is re-oxidised by the oxygen passing over the heated metal. The copper oxide is confined by a small plug (2–3 mm.) of ignited asbestos, followed by a 10 mm. roll of silver gauze. This just protrudes from the furnace and acts as a catalytic surface on which a good deal of the initial combustion takes place, the heated vapour of the substance reacting with the stream of hot oxygen. The remainder of the combustion tube is empty except for the boat holding the material to be analysed.

A tube filled in this fashion will last for about a hundred combustions of substances containing C, H, O, N, and halogens.

(b) *For compounds containing carbon, hydrogen, oxygen, nitrogen, halogens and sulphur.* If the compound to be analysed contains sulphur in addition to the elements considered above, then oxides of sulphur will be formed, and a new substance will have to be introduced into the combustion tube in order to prevent these acid oxides from reaching the soda-lime in the absorption tube. This is effected by replacing the 200 mm. length of M.A.R. "wire-form" copper oxide with a 1:1 mixture of the oxide with M.A.R. lead chromate in fine granules. The oxides of sulphur are then converted to non-volatile lead sulphate and so prevented from passing out of the tube and reaching the absorption train.

Burning out of combustion tube. The combustion tube **L** and also the materials with which it has been filled, have not been specially dried in any way and it is now necessary to burn out the combustion tube and packing till no more water vapour or carbon dioxide can be driven off. To do this the side-arm **H** (Fig. 70) is attached to the end of the purification train **G** in the usual way. This joint should be made really tight fitting and there should be no need to disturb it subsequently until either the purification train or combustion tube need repacking. The beak of the combustion tube is then attached to the bottle **W** via the guard-tube **V**—the absorption tubes **R** and **S** not being put on at this stage. The oxygen is then turned on, all the taps opened, the gauge **D** adjusted to 60 mm. of water and the furnace and thermostatic mortar then turned on. It generally requires about 20 minutes for the two heated portions of the combustion tube to reach the equilibrium temperatures; at the end of this period the side-arm **Y** of the bottle may be adjusted so as to give a rate of flow of 5 ml./min. This can be tested sufficiently accurately by collecting the flow over one minute in a 5 or 10 ml. measuring cylinder.

The board **K** is now placed over the end of the combustion tube (Fig. 70) and the tube is heated with the hottest part of a Bunsen flame, starting just to the right of **K**. The burner should be put only gradually under the tube otherwise the sudden expansion of hot gas will blow the fluid out of the gauge **D**. It is an advantage to have a small metal cone held by a wire support fixed to the top of the burner; this serves to concentrate the flame and the combustion tube may be kept "cupped" in the hottest part of the flame. The flame is slowly moved to the right along the tube until it reaches the furnace mouth, the complete transit taking about 15 minutes. The process should then be repeated, heating the tube with the burner from **K** up to the furnace mouth. After the heating is complete, a further 250 ml. of oxygen, as measured by the water displaced from **W** and collected directly in a 250 ml. measuring cylinder below, is passed through the apparatus. The tap **T₁** is then closed, the furnace and mortar shut off, and the apparatus allowed to cool down with the end **H** of the combustion tube open to the oxygen supply. The tap **T₂** and the oxygen supply are turned off when the combustion tube is cold.

The whole process is then repeated exactly as described above. The absorption tubes are then weighed and attached to the apparatus (full details will be given below when a complete combustion is described), and the above process repeated. The absorption tubes are detached and reweighed. They should not have gained in weight by more than 0·05 mgm. If either or both have changed by more than this amount, the whole process is repeated until each shows no further gain in weight (of more than 0·05 mgm.).

One of the dangers in burning out a combustion tube is that of burning it out too thoroughly; so that when a substance is then ignited in it, the results obtained will be low as the tube filling will take up as much carbon dioxide and water vapour as it requires in order to come to equilibrium at the furnace and thermostatic mortar temperatures. This difficulty is overcome by doing two or three "equilibrium" combustions of known substances in a new combustion tube, after it has been burnt out and before a real estimation is carried out in it. The combustion tube thus has opportunity to come to equilibrium and the water absorption tube may also pick up the very small quantity of carbon dioxide that it normally retains. The operations leading up to the carrying out of a combustion will now be described.

Weighing of absorption tubes. During the processes of attaching the tubes **R** and **S** to the apparatus and subsequently detaching them after a combustion, they will pick up a certain amount of grease and water vapour from the fingers of the operator. This would be no drawback if the amount that was wiped on or off was the same in every case, *i.e.*, if there was no resultant change in weight. This is found not to be the case, and as the water absorption tube **R** usually gains less than 20 mgm. as the result of a combustion, steps have to be taken to avoid what would otherwise be a very considerable source of error.

In practice the closed tubes are carefully polished to remove all grease, moisture, *etc.*, and are then allowed to stand for a definite period of time in the air, to pick up a definite amount of water vapour—this process is known as maturing. Unless the atmospheric conditions change very considerably during the experiment (about 2 hours), the amount of water vapour deposited on the tubes before and after the combustion will be the same and any systematic error will have been avoided. Unless the tubes have been used in the combustion tube burning-out process, and so are full of oxygen, they must be filled with oxygen before weighing by connecting to the apparatus and passing oxygen through for 20 minutes. (It is very important not to forget this when a spent absorption tube is replaced by a freshly-packed one.)

Chamois cloths are used to polish the tubes and it is essential to have a carefully controlled scheme of polishing, so that any tube is always polished in the same way and for the same length of time. Before polishing is started, one of the taps of the absorption tube should be opened momentarily in order to equalise the gas pressure inside and outside the tube. It is probably simplest to use two cloths and start polishing in the middle of the tube, outwards, first towards one end and then towards the other (always starting towards the same end first) and including the side-arms and taps, care being taken not to dislodge the latter. Once polishing has started, the tubes should no on account be touched with the fingers.

The polishing process should take between thirty seconds and one minute and the tube should then be placed on a small wire stand. The time at which polishing ended should be noted. The other tube is then treated similarly and the time at which polishing was completed again noted; the two tubes should always be polished in the same order.

The tubes are left on their rack until ten minutes have elapsed since the completion of polishing of the first one; the latter is then transferred to a small aluminium rider which holds it firmly and evenly on the balance pan. This transfer may best be accomplished by using a pair of thin metal tweezers of wide aperture, whose ends have been slightly bent inwards, to grip the tube firmly and easily. The time at which the final counterpoising and reading is made is noted. At the end of the combustion when the tubes have been momentarily opened to the air, repolished exactly as before and are reweighed, their weight will be known to within a few milligrams and the weighing will therefore be rather more rapid in the second case than in the first; hence the tube is allowed to mature for a slightly longer time in the second case so that exactly the same length of time elapses, between the end of polishing and the final counterpoising, as before the combustion.

Some authorities recommend that the inside of the side-arms of the absorption tubes should also be polished by rubbing with "pipe-cleaner." This, however, is rather unsatisfactory with the type of absorption tube that has greased taps as there is always the danger of removing traces of grease from the tap and hence of changing the weight of the tube. Although the side-arm interiors are not, therefore, specially polished, care should be taken that no minute pieces of rubber or wax from the impregnated tubing find their way into them. If this does take place, the offending particles should be carefully removed with a piece of very fine copper wire.

A little practice in polishing and weighing the absorption tubes is desirable before an actual analysis is carried out. It is important that when the taps on the absorption tubes are "off," they should be as far "off" as possible (i.e., hole in tap is 180° away from side-arm hole).

Weighing out the sample. The combustion is carried out in a flat-bottomed boat (40 mm. × 5 mm.) provided with a small lip at one end for easy handling. It is an advantage to have a long, narrow boat both for ease of introduction into the combustion tube and also for smooth combustion. The boat is preferably made of platinum but one of hard glazed porcelain is satisfactory. The boat is ignited in a Bunsen flame, so that all of it has been heated red-hot and then placed on an aluminium block in a desiccator over perchlorate or calcium chloride; the block has preferably a narrow groove into which the boat just fits. The block is used so that the heat is very rapidly conducted away from the hot boat, which thus attains the temperature of its surroundings almost instantaneously.

The boat is then transferred to the balance pan (narrow-ended metal tweezers are most suitable for this purpose) and weighed: the weight of the empty boat should never vary by more than 0·05 mgm. during its working life. The boat is transferred to the grooved block (removed from the desiccator) and 25–30 mgm. of the sample to be analysed are then transferred to it. This is best carried out using a very small, narrow-ended spatula, and it is essential that only a small amount of material is put in the boat at a time—the 25–30 mgm. should be transferred in about six operations. The boat is then gripped firmly with the tweezers and carefully tapped on the aluminium block; this serves to remove any small particles of substance that may possibly be adhering to the outside of the boat and also to settle the charge of substance thinly and evenly along the whole length of the boat. The block is then carefully wiped with a polishing cloth and returned to the desiccator; the boat is transferred to the balance pan and reweighed. It is finally returned to the block in the desiccator.

This operation of weighing out the sample of substance to be analysed may conveniently be carried out while waiting for the absorption tubes to mature after polishing.

Carrying out a combustion. The apparatus (Fig. 70, p. 373) will have been left with the bottle **W** connected to the beak of the combustion tube via the guard tube **V** and with all the taps shut; the combustion tube, which is always allowed to cool down while connected to the oxygen source, will therefore be full of oxygen at slightly above atmospheric pressure, thus guarding against any possible leaking in of carbon dioxide or water vapour from the air.

The furnace **N** and the thermostatic mortar **P** are turned on, and the tap T_1 of the bottle **W** opened to allow for the thermal expansion of the oxygen in the tube **L** as the latter is heated up to its equilibrium temperature. The apparatus can conveniently be allowed to attain its equilibrium temperature over the period of about 20 minutes while the absorption tubes are being polished and weighed and the specimen for analysis weighed out: it is thus ready for immediate use as soon as the weighings have been completed.

The tap T_1 is then closed, the tap T_2 opened and the oxygen turned on. The bung **J** is then removed from the combustion tube and the charged combustion boat inserted. This is best carried out by raising the aluminium block, with the boat in place, to the level of the combustion tube floor and then gently pushing the boat, the lip pointing away from the furnace, into the combustion tube with a length of stout, rigid, copper wire. The boat should be inserted till its front end is about 8 cm. away from the furnace; the boat may be guided by leverage of the copper rod on the lip, thus keeping it flat on the floor of the combustion tube and avoiding any chance of its being overturned. The rubber bung is then firmly inserted. It is an advantage to remove the asbestos square **K** during this operation to leave a little more room for manipulation, but it should be replaced as soon as the bung has been reinserted. By having the oxygen turned on and the far end of the system closed by the tap **T₁** oxygen is flowing out of the open back-end of the combustion tube all the time the above operation is in progress, and the risk of any carbon dioxide or water vapour getting into the tube from the air is thus very small.

The absorption tubes **R** and **S** are next joined together by a 20 mm. length of impregnated rubber tubing, the side-arms forming a glass-to-glass join inside the rubber; the side-arm at the "non-absorbing" end of the tube **R** being attached to the side-arm of the "absorbing" end of the tube **S**. The exit of the tube **S** is now attached to the guard tube **V** in the usual way and the pair of tubes finally attached by a 15 mm. piece of impregnated tubing, and glass-to-glass joint, to the beak of the combustion tube. As short a piece of tubing as is compatible with a gas-tight join is used for this connection so that as much as possible of the beak of the combustion tube and of the side-arm of **R** may be heated directly by the heating hooks **Q** attached to the thermostatic mortar. These hooks are next placed in position, both initially being on the combustion tube beak between the mortar and the rubber connection to the tube **R**.

The tap **T₂** is now turned off and the apparatus tested for leaks. If the siphon **Y** is not running, then there is no leak between **Y** and the tap **T₁** of the bottle **W**. The tap **T₁** is now opened and the siphon observed again. A more delicate indication of a leak is gained if the drop on the end of the tube **X** is shaken off; the meniscus in **X** will then rise a few mm., and its movements may be studied. Rapid cessation of flow indicates no leak up to the first tap **T₃** on the carbon dioxide absorption train. The process is repeated for the other taps, **T₄**, **T₅**, and **T₆**, of the absorption tubes; water may flow for a few seconds on opening **T₆** as the Mariotte bottle has then been put in contact with with the whole length of the hot combustion tube up to the tap **T₂** of the purification train. If any leak is encountered at any stage all the taps should be closed, the faulty tap or tube adjusted, and the process repeated. The tap **T₂** is then opened and the oxygen stream allowed to pass through the apparatus. If necessary the level on the pressure gauge **D** is adjusted to 6 cm. by the micro screw-clip **E**, and then the side-arm **Y** of the Mariotte bottle lowered until there is a rate of flow of 5 ml./min. If it is found necessary to lower **Y** more than a few centimetres there is an obstruction in the system and this is nearly always caused by one or more of the taps on the absorption tubes being not quite completely open; when opening the taps it is essential to look carefully to see that side-arm and hole in the tap are exactly in line, as the thumb-grip on the top of the tap is not always set exactly at right-angles to the tap hole. A 5 or 10 ml. measuring cylinder should be used when adjusting the rate of flow so that the value is measured with reasonable accuracy.

A beaker is placed under **Y** and the combustion may now be started. The Bunsen burner,* with the air-hole wide open, and the cone in place, is carefully introduced under the combustion tube so that liquid is not driven out of the pressure gauge by the sudden thermal expansion. The heating is started about 2 cm. to the right of the asbestos square **K**; care should be taken that the burner is not left at this end of the tube long enough for the bung **J** to become appreciably warmed, otherwise errors will arise due to the evolution of volatile carbon-containing compounds. The Bunsen should be moved slowly along the combustion tube so that each part of the tube has been heated to a bright red heat. Particular care should be taken as the burner approaches the boat.

When burning the majority of organic compounds, an attempt should be made to drive the substance out of the boat, by heating, in an only partially combusted state, the greater part of the combustion taking place catalytically on the small piece of silver gauze that is just protruding from the furnace mouth. Exceptions to this are non-volatile substances such as glucose which may largely be oxidised in the boat.

The chief danger and main source of error in a combustion is that of moving the Bunsen forward a little too rapidly and so causing much of the substance to burn very rapidly, so that a "flash-back" occurs. This usually causes an explosion wave to travel back along the tube towards the purification train, some carbon dioxide and water vapour being carried with it. If these reach the packing of the purification train they will, of course, be absorbed there and the results of the estimation will necessarily be low.

There are two main warning signs of a "flash-back" which, if observed, allow sufficient time for remedial measures. During the combustion, the height of the pressure gauge fluctuates very little, but as soon as a flash-back, due to over-heating, is imminent the pressure begins to rise. Immediately this is seen to occur the Bunsen should be moved back several cm. along the tube, and if the pressure still rises, right back to where heating was originally started.

The second indication is a faint smoke-like cloudiness in the zone of the tube which is being heated by the Bunsen; this is quite readily visible as the interior of the tube is normally quite clear and bright. This is a later stage of development of the flash-back than the rise of pressure, already mentioned, and should be counteracted by moving the Bunsen immediately to the point of the combustion tube where heating was commenced. In either case the Bunsen should then be moved slowly forwards as before. A flash-back is attended by the deposition of carbon particles, carried back by the explosion wave, on the cold walls of

* Various small moving electric heaters and other devices have been invented for carrying out the combustion, including methods by which it is done automatically, but it should be remembered that all substances behave differently and each combustion is, in the strict sense of the word, a new experiment. For this reason, carrying out the combustion with a Bunsen burner is preferred as it allows great sensitivity of control and, more important, allows the student to see exactly what is taking place at each stage.

the tube. Care should be taken that these are completely burnt off as the Bunsen is slowly moved forward again.

As the substance is heated in the boat—it usually melts before the Bunsen quite reaches the boat itself and runs forward to the front end— it distils out and forms a ring round the combustion tube and finally a clearly visible drop of liquid on the floor of the tube. The boat is carefully heated bright red-hot throughout its length to ensure that any particles of carbon left by partial combustion are completely burned away in the stream of oxygen. Care should be taken not to heat too rapidly when the boat is reached or the substance is rapidly vaporised, may catch fire, and a flash-back result. As the burner approaches the end of the boat, the drop of partially burnt material will move slowly down the tube in front of it. As the material approaches the silver gauze at the furnace mouth it is being driven forward into a heated zone, instead of a cold one as previously, and its rate of progress is slowed down; this means that the chance of the Bunsen catching up the material with the consequent danger of a "flash-back" is increased, and great care should be taken. During the whole of the passage of the Bunsen it is important that the combustion tube should be cupped evenly in its flame; there is a danger of the operator moving the Bunsen slightly towards himself all the time, and the position of the burner should therefore be occasionally checked by looking at it from above.

Finally the material is driven on to the silver gauze and the combustion of the partially broken-down substance begins to take place catalytically. The Bunsen should not now be moved forward for several minutes and then only very slowly. At this point a drop in the rate of flow of water from the siphon will be noticed as a considerable proportion of the oxygen passing into the tube will be used up in the combustion and will thus not pass the absorption tubes. It is important that the flow of water should never actually stop and if it becomes very slow the burner should be moved slightly away from the furnace mouth; it should be realised that there is a time lag between the actual "over-combustion" taking place and the arrival of the products of combustion at the absorption tubes with consequent fall in the rate of flow; thus the Bunsen should be moved back slightly as soon as any really noticeable fall in the rate of flow takes place.

The end of the combustion is nearly always marked by the difference of levels registered on the pressure gauge sinking momentarily to zero. When this takes place the Bunsen is gently moved forward until it is on the silver gauze and this is then heated to bright redness. The catalytic combustion that has taken place nearly always leaves some particles of unburnt carbon on the gauze and these now burn off in the oxygen stream with tiny flashes of light. When the burner has heated the tube right up to the furnace mouth it is removed and carefully replaced at the far end of the combustion tube where heating began. At the same time the beaker is removed from under the siphon of the Mariotte bottle and replaced by a 250 ml. measuring cylinder. The Bunsen is now moved slowly along the exposed length of the combustion tube as before; the second heating taking about 15 minutes. It is then removed and extinguished. The passage of oxygen through the apparatus is continued until 250 ml. have been passed. This operation is designed to ensure that the carbon dioxide and water vapour are swept out of the combustion tube and transferred quantitatively to the absorption tubes. The carbon dioxide is swept out and absorbed more rapidly than the water vapour. This is due in large part to the tendency of the water vapour to condense in the beak of the combustion tube and/or the side-arm of the water absorption tube **R**. The two heating hooks **Q** are left in their original position until 130 ml. of water have been collected, they are then separated and placed one on each side of the piece of rubber tube which connects beak and side-arm, and just touching it. They remain here while a further 60 ml. pass and are finally placed on the absorption tube side-arm while the last 60 ml. pass, thus ensuring that all the water is driven over from the side-arm into the absorption tube **R**.

At the end of the sweeping out, the tap T_1 is first closed, and then the taps T_3, T_4, T_5 and T_6 in this order. The tubes **R** and **S** are then detached from the beak of the combustion tube, the guard tube **V** is then detached from them and replaced on the combustion tube beak. The furnace and thermostatic mortar are then switched off and the combustion tube allowed to cool with the tap to the oxygen supply open. The bung **J** is removed, and the boat withdrawn by means of a piece of rigid copper wire with a small hook in the end that fits into the small hole in the lip at the back of the boat; the bung is then replaced and the boat transferred to its block in the desiccator.

The absorption tubes are then detached from each other, transferred to their stand, and polished, matured and weighed exactly as at the beginning of the experiment. They must be repolished, matured and reweighed before they are used for a further determination. Finally when the tube is cool the tap T_2 of the purification train may be closed and the oxygen supply shut off.

Example of Calculation.

Estimation of C and H in acetanilide.

0·02170 gm. of acetanilide gave 0·05651 gm. CO_2 and 0·01271 gm. H_2O

∴ 0·02170 gm. of acetanilide contains $\dfrac{0·05651 \times 12}{44}$ gm. of carbon

and $\dfrac{0·01271}{9}$ gm. of hydrogen

∴ 100 gms. of acetanilide contains $\dfrac{0·05651 \times 12 \times 100}{44 \times 0·02170}$ gms. of carbon

and $\dfrac{0·01271 \times 100}{9 \times 0·02170}$ gms. of hydrogen.

= 71·0% C and 6·51% H.

Theoretical for C_8H_9ON; C = 71·1%, H = 6·67%.

O

Substances suitable for the estimation: acetanilide, sucrose, glucose, cinnamic acid, diphenylamine, salicylic acid, vanillin, *p*-bromoacetanilide, toluene *p*-sulphonamide.

Estimation of Nitrogen.

The two chief methods for estimating nitrogen in organic compounds are (i) the *Dumas* method, which can be applied to all organic compounds; (ii) the *Kjeldahl* method, which is of restricted application, but which is frequently used in biochemical and physiological work. Its limitations are indicated in the description of the method (p. 396).

The Dumas Method.

Principle. A definite amount of the substance (*ca.* 30 mgm.) is weighed out, transferred to a combustion tube and is burnt with a Bunsen flame in an atmosphere of air-free carbon dioxide, an oxidative filling (cupric oxide) of the tube being used as a source of oxygen. The carbon present is converted to carbon dioxide, the hydrogen to water, any sulphur to sulphur dioxide, and nitrogen and halogens are evolved in the free state. This resulting nitrogen is swept out of the heated tube by a stream of air-free carbon dioxide and collected in a graduated vessel (nitrometer) over 50% potassium hydroxide solution which absorbs the carrier gas. Any oxides of nitrogen that may have been produced during the combustion are reconverted to nitrogen by a heated copper spiral. From the measured volume of gas, reduced to normal temperature and pressure, the amount of nitrogen in the substance may be calculated.

The method depends for its success on the quantitative liberation of the nitrogen content of substances as molecular nitrogen; this can be rather difficult in certain cases (*e.g.*, polynitro compounds) but satisfactory determinations can be carried out by slight modification of the conditions under which the experiment is carried out.

Apparatus.

The source of carbon dioxide. The main requirement of the carbon dioxide supply is that it shall be air-free. It is, however, almost impossible to generate carbon dioxide, by any fairly simple method, so that it is completely free from air. Nevertheless, it is possible to obtain the gas sufficiently pure so that no serious error is introduced into the determination.

The gas is usually generated by the action of hydrochloric acid on marble chips in a Kipp's apparatus **A** (Fig. 72). (It is advantageous to generate the carbon dioxide by using the Tucker all-glass apparatus, which, although more expensive, is extremely reliable.)

Before use, the marble chips are washed repeatedly with hot water, and then de-aerated by first etching them with concentrated hydrochloric acid and then boiling them with air-free water under reduced pressure. The chips are then rapidly transferred to the generator; small chips should be used and the bulb of the generator nearly filled so that there is as little air space left as possible. The acid to be used is made up from equal parts of concentrated hydrochloric acid (A.R. standard) and air-free water. Before the acid is transferred to the generator, a number of de-aerated marble chips are dissolved in it in order to expel any residual dissolved air and also to saturate it with carbon dioxide. The top portion of the generator **A** is then lifted several times in order to cause a rapid evolution of carbon dioxide so as to sweep out the air from the middle bulb. A number of pieces of marble, of such a size that they will not slip down the acid funnel, are then added to the acid in the upper bulb in order to sweep out any residual air in this part of the vessel. The stopper of this top bulb is provided with a non-return valve (a thin layer of mercury on a sintered

FIG. 72.

glass plate in a small funnel) to allow the escape of any excess of carbon dioxide and to prevent the leak of any air into the acid. Both these de-aeration processes are repeated a number of times over a period of hours. All bungs and stoppers should be tight-fitting and the bung carrying the gas delivery tap T_1 (Fig. 72) attached to the middle bulb should be wired in place; the gas take-off from this middle bulb should be by a glass tube bent round and reaching up to the top of the bulb to prevent, so far as possible, the carrying over of acid spray. Finally the generator should be allowed to deliver a slow stream of carbon dioxide until this is found to be sufficiently free of air (see below how to test the gas stream for this condition) for use in the estimation. If the generator, after standing, fails to supply sufficiently pure carbon dioxide, it should be allowed to flush several times, then run slowly until the pure gas is obtained.

The relatively concentrated hydrochloric acid is employed so that with ordinary use of the apparatus, spent liquor does not accumulate very rapidly; the concentrated acid also ensures a brisk and delicately controlled flow of gas. When the generator is replenished with acid, marble or both, the de-aeration procedure detailed above is repeated until a sufficiently air-free gas supply is obtained.

Z-tube. The tube **B** is made of capillary tubing (3 mm. internal bore) bent into the shape of a *Z*. It is attached by a length (5 cm.) of very tight-fitting rubber pressure tubing to the tap T_1. a glass-to-glass join being made inside the rubber tubing. The purpose of **B** is to act as a trap for any small droplets of liquid that may be carried over in the gas stream from the generator **A**. The tube **B** is placed horizontally (*i.e.*, so that T_1 and the tube **D** are in the same horizontal plane—an arrangement which cannot be adequately indicated in Fig. 72): its further end is attached by a very tight-fitting rubber bung **C** to the end of the combustion tube **D**. This end of the capillary is drawn out into a beak 2·5 mm. long and 4 mm. in external diameter.

Combustion tube. This tube **D** is made of transparent silica or hard glass (50 cm. long and 1 cm. in diameter) and is provided at the right-hand end with a short, fine beak (3 cm. long, *ca.* 5 mm. in external diameter). The packing of the tube will be considered in detail below. The tube carries at the left-hand end a small square of asbestos board **L** which prevents the heat of the Bunsen used during combustion from affecting the rubber bung **C**.

The furnace. For heating the tube packing, a small electric furnace **E** is used, similar to that described in the carbon and hydrogen determination. It is 22 cm. in length and 1·5 cm. in diameter. The furnace is maintained at 680°C., as before, by a calibrated Simmerstat and its temperature is checked from time to time with a bimetal pyrometer.

The angle tube. The beak of the combustion tube which protrudes from the furnace is attached to the side-arm of the nitrometer through an angle tube **F** made of thick-walled capillary glass tubing (30 cm. long by 2 mm. internal diameter). The tube forms a straight continuation of the combustion tube and is bent two-thirds of the way along at such an angle that it forms a straight join with the side-arm **G** of the nitrometer. The joints at both ends are made glass-to-glass with tight-fitting rubber pressure tubing (3 cm. lengths) to hold them in place. Both ends of the angle tube are drawn out into beaks 3 cm. long and 1 mm. internal diameter. A small square of asbestos board **K** is placed on the beak of the combustion tube in order to prevent the heat of the furnace reaching the rubber tubing joint and thus causing it to swell and perhaps to leak.

The Nitrometer. Before use the glass nitrometer should be well washed with warm conc. nitric acid, followed by distilled water, alcohol, and ether, and allowed to dry. The taps T_2 and T_3 should then be lightly greased with vaseline and turned until no striations are apparent. The bottom of the nitrometer fits into a metal or porcelain stand with a cork lining. This is carried by the baseplate of an ordinary metal clamp-stand and the nitrometer is held upright by a clamp gripping the upper part of its stem. A thermometer may be hung from this clamp with wire. The bottom part of the nitrometer stem is supplied with two side-arms; one which is attached by a length of pressure tubing to a glass reservoir **J**, is used for adjusting levels. As the pressure tubing will be in contact with very concentrated alkali for long periods, it is advisable to let it soak for some hours in a bath of aqueous potassium hydroxide before attaching to the apparatus. If this is omitted, sulphur is extracted from the rubber and then reacts with the mercury that is subsequently to be introduced into the apparatus, with formation of black particles of mercuric sulphide, which make reading of the gas volume difficult. The tubing should be wired on where it joins both the reservoir and the nitrometer side-arm. The other side-arm **G** is drawn out and carries a tap T_2 for attachment to the angle tube **F**. The tap T_2 should have a length of glass rod fused to it so that it is capable of fine adjustment.

The main stem of the nitrometer widens into a bulb and then narrows to form a graduated tube. The usual graduation is of 8 ml. in 0·02 ml. divisions. The graduations continue to the tap T_3 at the top of the stem. Above T_3 there is a small reservoir **H** to prevent splashing of the concentrated alkali when gas is expelled from the nitrometer and also to ensure that a small excess of potash is left as a liquid seal above the tap T_3.

Clean dry mercury is first put into the nitrometer till it has just reached the bend in the lower side-arm **G**. 50% Aqueous potassium hydroxide is then run into the reservoir **J** until the whole of the nitrometer is filled, and a little liquid has passed through the tap T_3 into the reservoir **H** above. The bulb **J** should be about one-third full of the potash when raised to the height of the liquid in the nitrometer. The stand to which the nitrometer is attached is provided with a ring that slides up and down for adjusting the level of **J**. The mercury acts as a seal and prevents any potassium hydroxide reaching the side-arm **F**. The reservoirs **H** and **J** are provided with rubber bungs (not shown in Fig. 72), penetrated by short lengths of capillary tubing, so that even when the apparatus is in use, the concentrated potassium hydroxide solution may be kept almost out of contact with the atmosphere. If this is not done, the potassium hydroxide absorbs carbon dioxide from the air extremely rapidly and therefore soon requires replenishing. The concentrated potash gradually attacks the glass, ultimately causing the tap T_3 to leak, but effective greasing will in some part prevent this.

Packing of combustion tube. Before use, the silica tube **D** (Fig. 72) is washed in turn with warm concentrated nitric acid, distilled water, alcohol, ether and dried in an oven. A bit of ignited asbestos is first introduced and pushed along to the beak end of the combustion tube so that it forms a plug about 5 mm. in length. This is followed by a 100 mm.-long layer of M.A.R. "wire-form" copper oxide followed by a 3 mm. asbestos plug to hold it in place. Next a 50 mm. freshly reduced copper spiral is added. This prepared by winding the correct width of copper gauze round a stout copper wire until the requisite thickness is attained: the wire is provided with small loops at both ends to prevent the gauze cylinder slipping off, and also to ensure easy removal of the spiral from the combustion tube. It is reduced by heating to a uniform red heat in a Bunsen flame and then dropping while still red hot into a little hot methyl alcohol in a boiling-tube. The alcohol vapour reduces the spiral to the characteristic rose colour and itself ignites at the top of the tube. The flame is blown out and an excess of methyl alcohol added to chill and immerse the spiral. The spiral is then withdrawn, washed well with dry ether and dried in an evacuated desiccator. This element of filling is followed by a further 3 mm. asbestos plug to hold it in place.

The above constitutes the permanent filling of the tube and need only be replaced at rare intervals. It is possible to perform up to 50 combustions before again reducing the copper spiral, but indication of the spiral being spent is afforded by the loss of its bright coppery appearance and, when more pronounced, by high values from the estimation. The purpose of this heated copper spiral is to reduce any oxides of nitrogen that may be formed in the course of the combustion. The main danger in this respect is the formation of nitric oxide. This, like nitrogen, is a neutral gas and is not absorbed by the potash in the nitrometer; every molecule of nitrogen derived from the original sample being estimated will form *two* molecules of nitric oxide, thus more than the theoretical volume of gas will be collected and high results will be obtained. This occurs to a marked extent with nitro-compounds and the reduced copper spiral may then be exhausted far more rapidly than usual.

The temporary filling of the combustion tube **D** is now inserted; this is in part replaced after every combustion. Sufficient "wire-form" copper oxide is added so that it just emerges to the left of the furnace **E** when the tube is protruding 10–15 mm. at the beak end; this constitutes the main oxidative packing of the tube. This is followed by 25 mm. of M.A.R. "powder-form" copper oxide, followed by the sample suspended in more copper oxide, and backed by an oxidised copper spiral, 50 mm. in length.

Weighing of sample. Two separate tubes are used for weighing the sample and for mixing it subsequently with copper oxide: they may conveniently be mounted in two holes cut in a large flat cork. The smaller tube, used for the actual weighing, is 7·5 cm. long and 9 mm. in diameter, and is fitted with a ground-glass stopper. It is supported on the balance pan by a small notched aluminium rider. This tube is roughly weighed and approximately 25 mgm. of the material whose nitrogen content is to be estimated is transferred to the tube by means of a micro-spatula. The tube is then carefully weighed. It must be touched only with forceps and not with the fingers or its weight will be altered by the grease picked up from the hands. The contents are then transferred to the larger or mixing tube (7·5 cm. long and 1–2, cm. wide) which is also provided with a ground-glass stopper and which already contains a 20 mm. layer of "powder-form" copper oxide. The weighing tube is now carefully reweighed, again being handled only with forceps, and hence the weight of substance transferred to the mixing tube is known by difference. A further 10 mm. layer of "powder-form" copper oxide is now added to the mixing tube, the stopper carefully replaced and the mixture well shaken so that the sample is spread evenly throughout the whole of the mass of copper oxide. It is now ready to be transferred to the combustion tube.

Transferring the sample to the combustion tube. If we are dealing with the combustion tube **D** (Fig. 72) as it will have been left from a previous combustion, we have first to remove some proportion of the temporary element of the filling. The oxidised spiral is first removed, then all the "powder-form" copper oxide that had contained the original sample. This sometimes cakes and may be difficult to dislodge from the walls of the tube; a rigid copper or steel rod is useful for ensuring that all is removed. It will be found that a portion of the "wire-form" copper oxide that was situated just inside the furnace will have been converted to metallic copper; it is this portion of the packing that has provided the oxygen necessary for the combustion to take place. It is essential that this spent "wire-form" copper oxide is removed and a little more of the oxide beyond it, but it is not necessary to remove all the "wire-form" copper oxide on each occasion. The tube filling is replenished by adding fresh "wire-form" copper oxide until the packing would just protrude from the furnace if the beak end protruded about 10–15 mm. at the far end of the furnace.

When adding the fine "powder-form" copper oxide to the combustion tube it is an advantage to have the tube clamped upright and to add the powder through a small glass funnel, part of whose stem has been cut off, the resulting butt end just fitting into the wide end of the combustion tube.

A layer of 25 mm. of "powder-form" copper oxide is now added.

Its purpose is twofold; first of all to prevent any particles of the analysis sample, which is to be added next, from percolating through the coarse porous "wire-form" copper oxide and so into that portion of the tube heated by the furnace; and secondly as a heat insulator, to prevent the sample being heated too rapidly by the nearby furnace. Both these safeguards are required, as otherwise some portion of the sample would be ignited as soon as the furnace was switched on and the nitrogen produced would be carried away during the initial sweeping of the air out of the tube with the carbon dioxide stream, and would not be collected; low results would thus be obtained.

A chalk mark is now made on the tube to indicate the point reached by the filling. The copper oxide containing the dispersed sample in the mixing tube is now transferred to the combustion tube via the small funnel; the powder should be poured carefully down the hole at the bottom of the funnel so that as little as possible spreads on the sloping sides. A further chalk mark is now made on the combustion tube to indicate the point reached by the filling. A 10 mm. layer of "powder-form" copper oxide is placed in the mixing tube, the stopper replaced, the whole well shaken, and this charge, in turn, transferred to the combustion tube. When removing the ground-glass stopper from the mixing tube at any time, care should be taken that no powder caught at the bottom of the ground-glass seal is removed with it; this is best prevented by carefully loosening the stopper, gently turning it round and then removing it. The copper oxide washings are repeated twice more, thus ensuring the removal of all the sample from the mixing tube and the effective washing of any particles adhering to the funnel down into the combustion tube. After each washing, the funnel should be gently tapped in the top of the combustion tube, thus causing any particles that may be adhering to the funnel or the inside walls of the tube to settle down on to the rest of the filling. The copper oxide spiral is finally regenerated by heating it red-hot in a Bunsen flame and allowing it to cool in air; when cold it is added to the combustion tube which is then ready for use. The portion of the tube occupied by very nearly all the sample is clearly chalk-marked, which is a useful guide when carrying out the combustion with a burner.

As the tube ages it becomes opaque and it is not possible to see, at any stage, to what level the tube packing has reached. This may be overcome by using a steel rod as a "dip-stick" and making temporary chalk marks on the tube; these are removed as filling progresses and only the two indicating the position of the sample are left. Care should be taken that the metal rod is tapped well on the inside wall of the tube before withdrawal so that no portion of the copper oxide containing the sample is left adhering to it. The spent copper oxide of both varieties removed from the tube after each estimation may be regenerated by heating in a crucible or silica dish to 700–800° in air or in a muffle furnace for about half an hour. After cooling it is sieved through suitable sieves and then used again as "wire or powder-form" copper oxide.

Assembling the apparatus. The combustion tube **D** (Fig. 72) is now placed in the cold furnace so that the first chalk mark is not less than 25 mm. from the furnace mouth. Connection is first made to the Z-tube **B** by pushing a tight-fitting, bored rubber bung as far as it will go into the wide end of the combustion tube and then inserting the drawn-out beak of **B** with a screwing motion until the glass tube has penetrated right through the bung and is clearly visible on the far side. This is the only means by which a satisfactory gas-tight joint may be obtained. The beak at the far end of the combustion tube is now attached to the drawn-out end of the tube **F**, which has previously been attached to the side-arm of the nitrometer. Both these joints are glass-to-glass and are made with impregnated pressure tubing. The small asbestos squares **K** and **L** are now placed on the combustion tube as shown (Fig. 72).

Testing the CO₂ supply. The furnace **E** is now switched on and takes about 20 minutes before the combustion tube packing has reached the required temperature. As the combustion tube has been handled and packed in the air it will at this stage be full of air which requires sweeping out before the combustion takes place; this may be carried out very satisfactorily while the furnace is heating up. The sweeping-out process usually takes longer with a freshly packed tube as the packing gives up its occluded air rather slowly. If a stream of carbon dioxide is passed into the nitrometer full of potash, the alkali will very rapidly be exhausted; so when sweeping out it is usual to lower the reservoir **J**, open the tap **T₃** and allow the potash to sink so that the gas traverses a column of only 20–30 mm. of alkali before passing through the empty nitrometer and out at the tap **T₃**. After the level has been so lowered, the generator is turned on and the nitrometer tap **T₂** opened wide. After gas has passed for 5 minutes, most of the air will have been swept out of the combustion tube. This may be tested by closing tap **T₂**, raising the reservoir **J** till the alkali emerges into the bulb **H**, closing **T₃** and lowering the reservoir to its original position. Care should be taken to see that tap **T₂** is *always* closed before the reservoir **J** is raised or lowered (apart from the final adjusting of levels before reading the volume of nitrogen collected at the end of the experiment, it is easier to lift the reservoir **J** out of its ring for raising and lowering, rather than running the ring up and down the central stand on each occasion). Tap **T₂** is now cautiously opened to such an extent that not more than one bubble of gas per second passes, and these bubbles are observed carefully as they rise in the nitrometer tube. Bubbles containing a large proportion of air are not absorbed, suffer little diminution in size and rise rapidly up the tube. Bubbles of carbon dioxide, however, are absorbed, diminish in size and rise more and more slowly as they ascend. When all the air has been swept out of the combustion tube, the so-called micro-bubbles are obtained; these should almost disappear and not be larger than a fine dust; they swirl in the wide part of the nitrometer as they rise, instead of travelling straight upwards, and they rise extremely slowly. These bubbles are so small that it should be possible to collect them for upwards of half an hour before any detectable volume is registered on the nitrometer graduations. If these micro-bubbles are not at first obtained, the sweeping out should be continued till a subsequent test shows all the air to have been swept out of the combustion tube.

The original adjustment of the generator for production of air-free carbon dioxide may be tested in a similar manner by attaching the generator **A** through the Z-tube **B** and angle-tube **F** to the nitrometer without the combustion tube being in place and allowing the gas to run until micro-bubbles are obtained, thus showing that air-free carbon dioxide is being produced. It sometimes proves unusually difficult to get to the stage of producing micro-bubbles; this is very often due to the potash in the nitrometer becoming exhausted. As a first step, this should be changed before further search is made for any leak or other source of the trouble.

Now that the combustion-tube packing is heated up to the required temperature and the apparatus filled with nitrogen, all air being swept out, the combustion may be started.

The combustion. The tap T_2 is closed, T_3 opened and the reservoir **J** raised (Fig. 72), to make sure that no air has been collected at the top of the nitrometer tube; a small quantity of potash is left in **H** when tap T_3 is closed and the reservoir **J** then lowered again. The carbon dioxide generator is switched off and tap T_2 slowly turned on until it is *fully* opened.

A lighted Bunsen burner, with the air-hole fully open and the barrel fitted with a metal cone, is now gently placed under the combustion tube just at the beginning of the oxidised copper spiral (Fig. 72). Care should be taken that the burner is applied gradually to the tube at the start to prevent a sudden rush of expanding gas through the potash in the nitrometer, for if carbon dioxide passes too rapidly through the alkali it may not be completely absorbed. Care should also be taken that the Bunsen is not placed so near the rubber bung **C** that any charring takes place.

The rate at which bubbles of gas enter the nitrometer is now determined solely by the rate at which the heating is carried out; it should be controlled so as never to exceed one bubble of gas per second. The oxidised copper spiral is carefully heated to redness by very slowly moving the burner along it, and the heating of the powder copper oxide, containing the washings from the mixing tube, is then started. Up to this point, any gas that enters the nitrometer will be carbon dioxide, and even while heating the initial portion of copper oxide, the amount of nitrogeneous material contained in it is so small that very little nitrogen will be evolved. As the burner approaches the first chalk mark, however, extra care is required as very nearly all the sample is

O*

contained in this small section of tube filling, and overheating will cause rapid combustion with a consequent rapid stream of gas bubbles in the nitrometer. The great danger here is that these bubbles containing both nitrogen and carbon dioxide may rise rapidly through the potash and a considerable proportion of the constituent carbon dioxide will then never be absorbed by the alkali, thus leading to high results. Nearly all the errors made in nitrogen determinations arise from this source and the importance of a slow, regular evolution of gas controlled by careful combustion, cannot be overstated. As soon as there is any sign of too rapid an evolution of gas the burner should immediately be moved 5 cm. back along the tube; rapidity of this movement is particularly important as there is usually a time lag between any overheating and the emergence of the offending bubbles in the nitrometer. Heating is continued until the burner arrives at the furnace mouth and gas evolution ceases. The burner may then be extinguished.

Sweeping out. Although the combustion is now finished, a considerable proportion of the evolved nitrogen will still be left in the combustion tube and it is necessary to sweep this completely into the nitrometer. The tap T_2 on the nitrometer is closed, the tap T_1 on the carbon dioxide generator opened and then tap T_2 reopened to such an extent that one bubble of gas per second is passing. The sweeping out is continued until micro-bubbles, similar to those obtained at the beginning of the experiment, are again attained. This generally takes about ten minutes.

It sometimes happens that two or more bubbles coalesce to form one that hardly rises at all in the narrow part of the nitrometer tube; this may be driven up to the rest of the collected gas at the top of the tube by gently squeezing the rubber pressure tubing connecting the movable reservoir **J** with the nitrometer proper.

The tap T_2 is now closed and the nitrometer disconnected from the angle-tube **F**. The angle-tube is also disconnected from the combustion tube, the end of which is sealed by putting on a piece of rubber pressure tubing, having one end blocked with a length of glass rod. The furnace is now switched off and the carbon dioxide generator left switched on until the combustion tube is cold; this ensures that the reduced copper spiral, by cooling in carbon dioxide, is maintained in the reduced state. (Despite this precaution it does become spent and should be replaced from time to time. A spent copper spiral leads to high results, but before this takes place there is usually sufficient indication by dulling and loss of colour of the spiral.) Finally the generator is switched off.

Reading the volume. The nitrometer is removed to a place of reasonably constant temperature, and the levelling bulb **J** raised on its carriage and clamped at the same level as the liquid in the graduated tube of the nitrometer. After standing for 10 minutes, the levels are finally adjusted and the volume of nitrogen evolved read off with the aid of a lens. (If the meniscus is obscured by small bubbles which have collected at the gas-liquid interface, these may be dispersed as before by gently squeezing the rubber pressure tubing connecting the reservoir **J** with the nitrometer.) The temperature is read on the thermometer suspended from a clamp at the side of the graduated tube and the atmospheric pressure read off from an accurate barometer.

Blank on tube. It is advisable with a newly packed tube to carry out a determination on A.R. glucose (*ca.* 25 mgm.); this serves to burn out the tube by removing occluded air from the permanent filling and also as an additional check on the quality of the carbon dioxide supply.

Example of Calculation.

Before using the observed gas volume to calculate the percentage of nitrogen in the sample being analysed, a correction has to be made for the vapour pressure of the potassium hydroxide solution and for the retention of some liquid near the top of the nitrometer due to the slow draining of the rather viscous potash solution down the narrow walls of the nitrometer tube. Both these factors will have the effect of making the observed value *larger* than the theoretical value; Pregl found that both could be adequately corrected for empirically by *subtracting* 2% from the measured volume before carrying out the calculation.

Estimation of N in acetanilide.

0·02375 gm. of acetanilide gave 2·21 ml. of N_2 at 18°C. and 754 mm.

∴ 0·02375 gm. of acetanilide gave

$$\frac{2 \cdot 21 \times 0 \cdot 98 \times 273 \times 754}{291 \times 760} \text{ ml. (corrected) at N.T.P.}$$

∴ 0·02375 gm. of acetanilide contain

$$\frac{2 \cdot 21 \times 0 \cdot 98 \times 273 \times 754 \times 28}{291 \times 760 \times 22,400} \text{ gm. of nitrogen}$$

∴ 100 gms. of acetanilide contain

$$\frac{2 \cdot 21 \times 0 \cdot 98 \times 273 \times 754 \times 28 \times 100}{291 \times 760 \times 22,400 \times 0 \cdot 02375} \text{ gms. of nitrogen}$$
$$= \underline{10 \cdot 6\%}.$$

Theoretical for C_8H_9ON; 10·4%.

Substances suitable for the estimation: acetanilide, diphenylamine, glycine, benzanilide.

The Kjeldhal Method.

Principle. A definite amount of the substance (*ca.* 25 mgm.) is weighed out and transferred to a special Kjeldhal flask; it is decomposed by digesting with concentrated sulphuric acid and the nitrogen thereby converted quantitatively to ammonium sulphate. The acid solution is then transferred to a steam-distillation apparatus, made alkaline and the ammonia steam-distilled into saturated boric acid solution and finally titrated against standard acid.

The more easily the nitrogen is converted to ammonia, the more satisfactorily can the method be carried out. This method was originally utilised for the determination of nitrogen in amines, amino-acids, *etc.*, and was particularly useful for the nitrogen analysis of biological material. The sulphuric acid digestion may be expedited and improved by the use of catalysts such as selenium and mercuric sulphate. The direct method is unsuitable for a number of substances, especially azo compounds and substances where oxygen is attached to nitrogen as in the nitro and nitroso compounds, as there is a tendency to lose some of the nitrogen as gaseous nitrogen or as an oxide. Such compounds may still be estimated by this method, however, if they are first reduced with hydrogen iodide and red phosphorus before undergoing the digestion process. It is indeed sometimes sufficient merely to add an excess of glucose to the digestion mixture thus avoiding the separate operation of reduction. Unless such substances can be reduced easily and without waste of time, it is probably desirable that more elementary students should use the Dumas method for the nitrogen determination in these compounds.

Apparatus.

Steam-distillation unit. This consists of a steam generator **A** (Fig. 73) which is a 1-litre round-bottomed flask with a tight-fitting rubber bung wired in. The bung carries a tube **B** for delivering steam to the apparatus proper and a

FIG. 73.

tap-funnel **C** for refilling the flask with water. Tube **B** is connected to a steam-trap **D** which is provided with a tap T_1 (or rubber tube and screw-clip) at the bottom for releasing any condensed water. The trap has a side-arm, also provided with a tap T_2, which is connected to the glass tube E (28 cm. $\times$ 3 mm.) reaching down to the bottom of the 150 ml. distillation bulb F. The end of this tube is bent down as shown to prevent the splashing over of liquid droplets. The tube E is provided with a small tap-funnel G which is closed either by the tap T_3 or by a rubber tube carrying a screw-clip. The solution to be steam-distilled is subsequently introduced through G.

The distillation bulb F is connected by a length of glass tubing (15 cm. $\times$ 2·5 cm.) to a double-bulb splash-head H which prevents any liquid droplets being carried right over during a distillation. The upper bulb carries an exit tube of transparent quartz Q (1 cm. in diameter) which is bent over twice at right angles. The short vertical limb is 10 cm. long and is bent as shown to form a further splash precaution. The horizontal limb is 20 cm. long and the vertical limb 40 cm. long; the latter is provided wth a 30 cm. water-jacket, converting it into a condenser, whose lower end K dips into a 100 ml. conical flask J, the level of which may be raised and lowered. It is necessary to make this part of the apparatus of quartz as the steam will dissolve traces of alkali from even hard glass. It is most convenient to have the apparatus arranged so that it may all be clamped around the same stand.

Before assembling, the constituent parts of the apparatus should be washed in turn with warm conc. nitric acid, distilled water, acetone, and dried in an oven.

Digestion apparatus. The Kjeldhal flasks L of Pyrex glass are shaped as shown with a 50 ml. capacity bulb and a long neck (10 cm. $\times$ 1·5 cm.), provided with a small lip or spout. When digestion is proceeding they are supported over a micro-burner by an asbestos-centred gauze, and the top end is lightly clamped so that the flask is tilted slightly to the vertical. The flasks should be supplied with loosely fitting glass stoppers, made by drawing out and sealing off the bottom end of a hard glass boiling-tube. Digestions should *always* be carried out in a fume-cupboard as considerable quantities of sulphur di- and tri-oxides may be evolved.

Digestion. 20–25 mgm. of the substance whose nitrogen content is to be estimated are weighed out in a stoppered weighing-tube and then transferred to the flask L that has been previously dried in an oven at 120°C. With care, the substance may be transferred directly into the bulb of the flask without any adhering to the sides. If any material sticks on the way down, the flask should be tapped gently to cause the substance to fall to the bottom. 2 Gms. of the catalyst mixture (32 gms. potassium sulphate, 5 gms. mercury sulphate and 1 gm. of selenium powder, well mixed) are added and 3 ml. of A.R. conc. sulphuric acid are measured out carefully and poured into the digestion flask. The acid should be poured straight into the bulb without touching the sides unless any of the nitrogenous sample has adhered to the walls of the flask, in which case the acid may be used to wash the particles down into the bulb of the digestion flask.

The loose stopper is now inserted into the flask with the drawn-off end downwards. The mixture is heated over the micro-burner so that the solution boils *gently* for 5 minutes, the heating is then increased so that the solution boils vigorously, and digestion continued for a further 45 minutes; the liquid should then be colourless. Many substances will have been decomposed quantitatively on shorter heating but the above period should suffice for all substances for which the method is suitable; the vigorous heating should in no circumstances be continued for longer than 45 minutes. As well as this Kjeldhal flask, another should be put on to digest at the same time, prepared in exactly the same way except that approximately 30 mgm. of A.R. glucose (only roughly weighed out) are substituted for the nitrogenous material. This serves as a blank for the method and a test for the purity of the reagents.

As has been mentioned above, many substances which do not give satisfactory nitrogen analyses by this method can be made to do so if, before digestion, they are reduced with red phosphorus and hydrogen iodide. This procedure is rather tedious, however, and satisfactory results can often be obtained if 500 mgm. of A.R. glucose are added to the digestion mixture—the digestion then being carried out in the usual way (Elek and Sobotka, *J. Amer. Chem. Soc.*, 1926, **48**, 501). Substances that do not yield to this modified procedure are best estimated by the Dumas method.

Steaming-out the steam-distillation apparatus. After the cleaned steam-distillation apparatus (Fig. 73) has been assembled, it is essential to pass steam through it for some time to remove readily soluble alkali. All the taps on the apparatus are opened and the water in the steam generator boiled vigorously. The steam will gradually pass into the apparatus. After a few minutes, the tap of the tap-funnel **C** may be closed and soon afterwards the tap T_1 of the steam-trap; finally the tap T_3 of the funnel **G** may be closed. Steaming-out should then be continued for not less than one hour, the receiver **J** not being in place.

During this process some water will have condensed in the steam-trap **D** and also in the distillation bulb **F**. If at the end of the steaming-out process, the Bunsen burner is removed from the generator **A**, the pressure in **A** will be reduced owing to steam condensation, and the liquid in **F** will be sucked back into **D**; provided that the bent-over tube is carefully adjusted, the bulb **F** may be almost completely emptied of liquid as desired. Finally the condensed water in the steam-trap **D** may be run out by opening the tap T_1.

Before each experiment the steam-distillation apparatus should be steamed-out for about half an hour; this may be carried out while the digestion is taking place.

Charging the steam-distillation apparatus. After steaming-out, and when the digestion in **L** is complete, the Bunsen burner is replaced under the steam-generator **A** and the tap on the tap-funnel **C**, and taps T_2 and T_3 closed; as steam is generated it is allowed to pass out of the steam-trap through T_1. Exactly 20 ml. of a freshly mixed solution of 40% sodium hydroxide* and 40%

* These solutions are obtained by dissolving 40 gms. of the solid in water so that the final volume of the cold *solution* is 100 ml. With pure sodium hydroxide, the alkaline solution should be quite clear and free from insoluble material. The sodium sulphide used is the crystalline Na_2S, $9H_2O$.

sodium sulphide are run into the funnel **G**. (The 40% alkali and 40% sulphide solutions are made up in bulk and freshly mixed in the proportion of 9 vols. of alkali to 1 vol. of sulphide as required.) The tap T_3 is opened and the alkali run into the bulb **F**. The tap is then closed and the funnel washed carefully round with a fine jet of distilled water; when washing is complete, T_3 is opened and the wash-water allowed to run into **F**. The process is then repeated—the *total* washings being not more than 5–10 ml. Tap T_3 is then left closed. 10 ml. of saturated boric acid solution are poured into **J** which is then adjusted (setting at an angle if necessary) so that the end of the condenser is 2–3 mm. below the surface of the liquid but not touching the bottom of the flask.

The digestion mixture is allowed to cool in the Kjeldhal flask and then diluted with 10 ml. of distilled water. It is then carefully poured into the funnel **G** (Fig. 73), the last drop on the lip of the flask being washed off with a few drops of distilled water from a wash-bottle. The tap T_3 is then carefully opened and the acid solution allowed to run down into the bulb **F**. A small quantity of the solution is prevented from flowing through T_3 by closing the tap; this is to prevent the possibility of any of the ammonia, liberated when the acid ammonium sulphate solution is run into an excess of alkali, from escaping through T_3 and thus introducing a large error into the determination. The flask **L** is now carefully washed out with 5 ml. of distilled water from a wash-bottle and the washings transferred to the funnel **G**. The washings are run into the bulb **F** by opening the tap T_3, but again a small liquid seal is left in **G** by closing T_3 before all the liquid has passed through. This washing is repeated twice more; each time a small liquid seal being left in the funnel **G**. Finally, the walls of the funnel are washed with 5 ml. of distilled water and the wash allowed to flow through T_3 into the bulb **F**; a small liquid seal is still left at T_3 above the closed tap. The liquid in the bulb will now be black owing to the precipitation of mercury sulphide by the interaction of the sodium sulphide solution and the mercuric sulphate of the catalyst mixture— this prevents the possible formation of any mercury-ammonia complexes that might prevent the quantitative distillation of the latter.

Distillation of the ammonia. The ammonia which has been liberated quantitatively in the bulb **F** must now be distilled completely into the receiver **J**. The tap T_1 on the steam-trap is therefore closed and tap T_2 opened so that the steam is delivered into the bulb **F**, which at the same time is heated directly with the flame of a micro-Bunsen burner. This prevents any considerable increase in the volume of liquid in the bulb **F** due to steam condensation. If too great a volume of liquid collects in **F**, the chance of minute droplets of concentrated sodium hydroxide splashing over into the receiver is much increased, and very small quantities of this alkaline liquid will introduce very large errors.

The steam-distillation is continued for 5 minutes after steam can first be seen entering the condenser; the ideal rate of distillation is about 4–5 ml. of distillate per minute, but this is not critical and may be varied within reasonable limits. The receiver **J** is then lowered from the lip **K** of the condenser and the steam-distillation continued for a further two minutes, thus ensuring that no traces of liquid containing ammonia are left on the inside of the condenser. At the end of this time any liquid on the lip **K** is rinsed with distilled water into **J**, which is then ready for titration. It is important that the receiver and its contents are kept cold during the distillation and it is advisable to interpose a piece of asbestos board or other screen so that it is not exposed to the heat from the burner under the steam generator.

Titration. The solution of ammonia absorbed in saturated boric acid may now be titrated as an alkali directly with 0·025 N.HCl (best obtained by dilution of commercially available standard N.HCl in a graduated flask). Three drops of indicator (mixed methyl-red/methylene-blue being most satisfactory) are added to the liquid in the receiver and the 0·025 N.HCl run in from an accurate burette.

Blank estimation. The distillation bulb is now emptied, as already described, by removing the burner from under the steam generator, only tap **T₂** being left open; the spent charge from **F** is thereby forced over into **D** and may be run out through **T₁**. The complete experiment, including titration, is then repeated with the digestion mixture from *ca.* 30 mgm. of A.R. glucose in place of the nitrogenous material. The volume of acid used is *subtracted* from the titre obtained in the real experiment. The blank estimation serves as a check on (i) the purity of the reagents, (ii) any droplets of alkali that may have splashed over in the steam, and (iii) any other sources of error.

Example of Calculation.
Estimation of N in glycine.
0·02035 gm. of glycine yielded an amount of NH_3 that required 10·96 ml. of 0·025 N.HCl. A blank estimation carried out on A.R. glucose (30 mgm.) resulted in a titre of 0.20 ml. of 0·025 N.HCl.

$$10·76 \text{ ml. } 0·025 \ N.\text{HCl} = 10·76 \text{ ml. } 0·025 \ N.\text{NH}_3 \text{ solution}$$
$$= \frac{10·76 \times 14 \times 0·025}{1000} \text{ gm. nitrogen}$$

$\therefore$ 0·02035 gm. glycine contains $\dfrac{10·76 \times 14 \times 0·025}{1000}$ gm. nitrogen

$\therefore$ 100 gms. glycine contain $\dfrac{10·76 \times 14 \times 0·025 \times 100}{1000 \times 0·02035}$ gms. nitrogen

$$= \underline{18·5\%}.$$

Theoretical for $C_2H_5O_2N$; 18·7% N.

Substances suitable for the estimation: acetanilide, diphenylamine, glycine, benzanilide.

Estimation of Methoxyl (CH_3O-) Groups. (Zeisel's Method.)

Principle. A definite amount of the substance (*ca.* 25 mgm.) is weighed out and transferred to the reaction bulb of the apparatus where it is decomposed by refluxing with constant-boiling hydriodic acid, the essential reaction being:

$$R \cdot OCH_3 + HI \longrightarrow R \cdot OH + CH_3I$$

The methyl iodide is transferred quantitatively (by means of a stream of a carrier gas such as carbon dioxide) to an absorption vessel where it either reacts with alcoholic silver nitrate solution and is finally estimated gravimetrically as AgI, or it is absorbed in an acetic acid solution containing bromine. In the latter case, iodine monobromide is first formed, further oxidation yielding iodic acid, which on subsequent treatment with acid KI solution liberates iodine which is finally estimated with thiosulphate (*cf.* p. 405). The advantage of this latter method is that six times the original quantity of iodine is finally liberated.

This method is not confined to methoxyl groups but can be used for ethoxyl as well, but higher alkyl groups do not yield iodides that are sufficiently volatile. The method may also be used for the estimation of methyl and ethyl groups attached to nitrogen, but the reaction with hydrogen iodide must now be carried out at a rather higher temperature. Sufficient control can readily be exercised so that the $-OCH_3$ and $-NCH_3$ groups in a compound containing both may be separately estimated; this is of particular value in the field of alkaloid chemistry where such compounds are often encountered.

The chief potential source of error to be avoided is the passing over of any of the concentrated hydrogen iodide with the methyl iodide, thus causing high results. This is prevented by a small water-condenser which does not keep back the methyl iodide, and also a gas-trap containing a suspension of red phosphorus in water. Another potential error is introduced by the low solubility of some methyl ethers in the aqueous hydrogen iodide, leading to incomplete decomposition and low results; this can be overcome, for instance, by the addition of a small quantity of phenol to the reaction mixture, thus increasing the solubility. A difficulty not so easy to surmount is the ease with which a number of ethers will sublime out of the hot hydrogen iodide before they have been decomposed (β-naphthyl methyl ether is a particularly marked example of this). It is also important that the flow of carrier gas should be slow to avoid any chance of some of the methyl iodide passing so rapidly through the absorbing liquid as to escape into the air. This is prevented by inserting a glass spiral into the receiver in order to increase the length of path the iodide must traverse.

Apparatus. The apparatus is made of Pyrex glass, in one piece. It consists of a shaped bulb **A** (Fig. 74) of about 30 ml. capacity in which the reaction takes place, provided with an inclined inlet **B** at the side and a vertical ascension tube **D**. **B** serves not only as an inlet for the admission of the carrier gas but also as the route by which the reagents and test sample are introduced into the apparatus. A length of solid glass rod **C**, rounded at both ends, is inserted into the inlet **B**. It is made of such a size that it is only loose-fitting, thus allowing carbon dioxide to pass around it, but preventing any methyl iodide vapour or hot hydrogen iodide from distilling up the side tube when the experiment is in progress. At the top end **C** is broadened into a narrow collar so that it is held in place against the end of the tube **B**. Several deep scorings are cut with a file through this collar so as to allow the free passage of gas, and the end of tube **B** is cut obliquely so that the collar cannot, in any case, impede the flow of gas too greatly.

FIG. 74.

The inlet tube **B** is connected with rubber tubing of about 6 mm. bore to the carbon dioxide Kipp, via a wash-bottle containing sodium carbonate solution (to remove any dilute hydrochloric acid spray). The use of Pregl's device to ensure an even and easily controlled flow of gas is a great advantage. It consists in inserting a few pieces of string into the rubber tube for a distance of about 10 cm., i.e., from the upper end of **C** to the point where the screw pinchcock **P** is attached to the tube. It is very important, when the apparatus is in use, that there should be no constriction or bend in the rubber tube between the end of the inlet tube **B** and the wash-bottle. This is particularly to be avoided where the end of the glass rod **C** comes into the rubber tube. If these precautions are taken, a slow, even, and easily controlled flow of gas can be obtained, particularly if the screw pinchcock **P** is attached to a rigid mounting with the tube running through it instead of merely hanging on the tube itself.

The ascension tube **D** (*ca.* 1 cm. in diameter*) rises for about 8 cm. above **A**, then narrows (5 mm. in diameter) to form a small condenser **E** (8 cm. long). The ascension tube then bends over in a flattened U-shape and descends into the

----

* The dimensions given for the various tubes are those which have been found most suitable: they may however be varied within narrow limits.

gas-washer **F** (*ca.* 8 cm. long). The tube continues to the bottom of the washer, leaving a gap of only 1–2 mm. when **F** is closed by the insertion of the rubber bung **M**. The tube in this section is 2–3 mm. in diameter. The outlet tube (5 mm.) from the top of **F** is bent as shown in Fig. 74, being about 10 cm. in length and joining on to the gas delivery-tube **H**. This is about 4 mm. in diameter in its upper end, which bears two pairs of internal constrictions as shown; the introduction of a drop of water converts these into a seal impermeable to methyl iodide vapour and the sealing is completed with a loosely fitting bung **N** in the top of the tube. The lower end of **H** is made of capillary tube of about 1 mm. internal diameter and is approximately 20 cm. in length. The tube dips down to the bottom of the receiver **K** (the narrow portion of which is *ca.* 15 cm. in length, and 1·5 cm. smaller in diameter than the top): the space between **H** and **K** is filled with a glass spiral **J**. This ensures that the methyl iodide vapour emerging from the bottom of **H** has to traverse a longer path through the liquid in **K** and thus has very little opportunity to escape absorption. **L** is a split bored cork by which the apparatus may be clamped to a single stand; the receiver **K** is supported at the right height by a block.

Cleaning of apparatus. It is very important that the apparatus should be clean and dry and in particular that it should be free from any traces of grease. Before each analysis the apparatus is therefore immersed in concentrated nitric acid for a few minutes and then washed well with water. The inlet tube **B** is then connected to a water-pump, the rubber bungs **M** and **N** inserted and 400 ml. of water are drawn through the apparatus by way of the tube **H**. This is followed by 200 ml. of distilled water and then 200 ml. of acetone. The receiver **K**, containing the spiral **J**, should be washed with the same series of solvents and the whole apparatus, without the rubber bungs, then well dried in an oven at 120°. If several sets of apparatus are being used by a class, it is very important that the main apparatus, the receiver, the spiral and the glass rod **C**, of each set should bear a distinguishing mark, as corresponding parts of different sets are rarely identical in size, and it is most important for accurate work that they should be well-fitting.

Preparation of sample and assembly of apparatus. The gas-washer **F** (Fig. 74) is first filled by placing the apparatus on its side and introducing sufficient 5% cadmium sulphate solution, containing suspended red phosphorus, into the lower bulb so that when the apparatus is placed upright after the insertion of the bung **M**, the gas delivery-tube is a few mm. below the surface of the liquid. A drop of distilled water is then introduced into the top end of the delivery-tube **H** to form a seal at the constriction **G**, and the bung **N** is then inserted. The apparatus is then clamped upright so that the reaction flask is about 2 cm. above a micro-burner: this should be provided with a metal chimney **Q**, a little wider than the reaction vessel and of sufficient height to reach the bottom of the tube **B**; a small hole should be cut in the bottom of the chimney to allow the passage of the gas-tubing to the burner.

The spiral **J** is now placed in **K** and 10 ml. of a 20% solution of sodium acetate in glacial acetic acid, followed by 15 drops of bromine, then added. (The bromine should be of the best grade obtainable, preferably micro-analytical reagent, and should be free from iodine; it should be stored in small containers so that the contents of each newly opened bottle are not left standing about too long.) To prevent bromine vapour spreading unduly in the laboratory, a lightly fitting plug of cotton-wool, moistened with 1–2 drops of formic acid, is inserted just into the wide part of the receiver **K**. The latter is then drawn up over the delivery-tube, so that there is a gap of only 1–2 mm. between the lower end of **H** and the bottom of **K**, and it is then held in place by a wooden block.

The test sample is now weighed out. This is best done by weighing 20–25 mgm. into a small tinfoil cup: (the cup is best made by cutting the corners off a small square of tinfoil, and then pressing this circle into a cup by rubbing it into shape round the end of a glass rod). After the material has been introduced, the cup should be gently tapped on a metal block, while held with balance tweezers, to ensure that no particles of the sample are adhering to its outside edge; this also serves to settle the material down on to the floor of the cup. The cup, after weighing, is lightly closed by pinching the edges together and then slid carefully down the side-arm **B** into the reaction vessel **A**. For many substances it is quite satisfactory to weigh the material on a small square of cigarette paper (any gummed edge being cut off), which is finally folded over as before. If this is done, however, it is necessary to introduce a few minute pieces of unglazed porcelain into **A** in order to promote smooth boiling. With the tin cup this is unnecessary, as the stannic iodide produced by the dissolution of the cup promotes steady boiling and prevents bumping. About 20 mgm. of pure phenol are then added. Finally 5 ml. of hydriodic acid* M.A.R. grade, d 1·7, are added from a pipette, the end of which should be inserted well into vessel **A**, and care taken in withdrawal so that no hydrogen iodide is left in the side-arm **B**. The glass plug **C** is now inserted into the side-arm and the rubber tube from the Kipp and wash-bottle attached. The screw pinchcock is now fully closed and the Kipp tap opened. The pinchcock is now very carefully unscrewed until carbon dioxide begins to pass and adjusted so that not more than two bubbles are rising round the spiral in the receiver **K** at one time. It is very important to ensure at this stage that the rate is quite satisfactory, as too rapid a flow will almost certainly result in some methyl iodide escaping absorption. Finally a very slow stream of water is allowed to flow through the condenser **E**.

The Evolution of Methyl Iodide. The flask **A** (Fig. 74) is now heated with the non-luminous flame of the micro-burner. The immedi-

---

* This should be free from sulphur, and obtained in small containers so that a specimen is rapidly used; it should be in dark bottles and stored in the dark. When withdrawing a specimen, the acid should be exposed to the air for as short a time as possible, as both air and light promote its decomposition to iodine.

ate result of the heating will be an increase in the rate of bubbles passing up the absorption spiral; no endeavour should be made to decrease this flow, however, as it will return to the original rate as soon as the hydrogen iodide begins to boil. The mixture is kept boiling gently for 40 minutes. At the end of this period the vessel **K** containing the spiral **J** is lowered from the tube **H**, which is then rinsed inside and out with small quantities of distilled water from a wash-bottle provided with a fine nozzle; these washings are caught in **K**.

Titration. The contents of the receiver **K** (Fig. 74, p. 402) are then washed quantitatively into a 100 ml. conical flask containing 10 ml. of 20% sodium acetate solution; the sodium acetate/acetic acid is present in order to buffer the hydrobromic acid formed in Equation 2 (*b*) below. (It is an advantage to have these conical flasks provided with ground-in stoppers; alternatively, well-fitting dry rubber bungs can be used. In the latter case the flasks should be swirled well rather than shaken so that the liquid does not touch the rubber.) To destroy the excess of bromine, two drops of formic acid (not less than 80% concentration) are now added and the solution shaken; if necessary, more formic acid is added, one drop at a time, each addition being followed by shaking, until both the colour and smell of bromine have disappeared. 5 Ml. of 10% potassium iodide solution are added, the solution swirled, and then acidified with 10 ml. of $2N.H_2SO_4$. The solution is immediately stoppered, gently swirled, allowed to stand for 3 minutes and then titrated against 0.025 $N.Na_2S_2O_3$ solution from an accurate burette. The thiosulphate is run in rapidly, the titration flask being swirled until a faint yellow colour is obtained; the burette reading is then noted and the solution carefully titrated till colourless, using a white glazed tile underneath the flask and another one behind it.

Blank estimation. A blank estimation in which A.R. glucose is used should be carried out exactly as above as a check on the method and on the purity of the reagents employed.

Reactions involved:

1. $R \cdot OCH_3 + HI \longrightarrow R \cdot OH + CH_3I$
2. (*a*) $CH_3I + Br_2 \longrightarrow CH_3Br + IBr$

   (*b*) $IBr + 3H_2O + 2Br_2 \longrightarrow HIO_3 + 5HBr$
3. $HIO_3 + 5KI + H_2SO_4 \longrightarrow 3I_2$
4. $3I_2 + 6Na_2S_2O_3 \longrightarrow 3Na_2S_4O_6 + 6NaI$

∴ **$-OCH_3 \equiv CH_3I \equiv HIO_3 \equiv 3I_2 \equiv 6Na_2S_2O_3$**

Example of Calculation.

Estimation of methoxyl group in vanillin.

0.02445 gm. of vanillin yielded a solution that required 38.10 ml. 0.025 $N.Na_2S_2O_3$ solution.

$6 \times 40,000$ ml. 0.025 $N.Na_2S_2O_3$ solution $\equiv 31$ gms. CH_3O group.

∴ 38.10 ml. 0.025 $N.Na_2S_2O_3$ solution $\equiv \dfrac{31 \times 38.10}{240,000}$ gm. CH_3O group.

Hence 0·02445 gm. of vanillin contains $\dfrac{31 \times 38\cdot10}{240,000}$ gm. CH_3O group

∴ 100 gms. of vanillin contain $\dfrac{31 \times 38\cdot10 \times 100}{240,000 \times 0\cdot02445}$ gms. CH_3O group

$$= 20\cdot1\% \text{ Methoxyl Group.}$$

Theoretical for $C_8H_8O_3$; 20·4% CH_3O.

Alternatively, since Molecular Weight of vanillin is 152·1,

152·1 gms. vanillin contain $\dfrac{31 \times 38\cdot10 \times 152\cdot1}{240,000 \times 0\cdot02445}$ gms. CH_3O group.

(Weight $CH_3O = 31$)

$$= \dfrac{38\cdot10 \times 152\cdot1}{240,000 \times 0\cdot02445} \ CH_3O \text{ group}$$

$$= 0\cdot99 \ CH_3O \text{ group.}$$

Substances suitable for the estimation: vanillin, veratrole.

PART V

SIMPLE ENZYME REACTIONS

In the following pages an account is given of some of the more simple reactions which enzymes catalyse. The reactions have been selected partly because they are of particular interest to the organic chemist, and partly because they are capable of simple and ready demonstration in the laboratory.

The student who is unacquainted with the study of enzymes should first read the following brief theoretical introduction.

Enzymes may be described as organic catalysts of biological origin. The majority are obtained from the interior of cells, but some are obtained from natural secretions such as the digestive juices and milk. For a full discussion of the nature of enzymes and the mechanism of their reactions the student should consult a work such as *Chemistry and Methods of Enzymes*, by J. B. Sumner and G. F. Soames (Academic Press, New York). The following points should however be noted:

(1) Enzymes are nitrogenous organic substances, very few of which have been isolated in a pure state; consequently their precise nature is in many instances still obscure. They form solutions in water and in dilute salt solutions, and are precipitated when such solutions are saturated with ammonium sulphate.

(2) They are highly specific in their reactions, *e.g.*, zymase ferments *d*-glucose, but does not affect *l*-glucose.

(3) The effect of temperature is complex, but the majority of enzymes are most active about $45°$ and all are completely destroyed at $100°$. At $0°$ the activity is reduced considerably, but the enzyme is not destroyed.

(4) The activity of an enzyme varies considerably with acidity and there is generally a marked optimum pH* for each enzyme. Thus pepsin of the stomach has an optimum pH of $1·4$, *i.e.*, it works best in a decidedly acid medium. It is inactive in neutral or alkaline solutions and the latter rapidly destroy it.

(5) Enzyme action is frequently accelerated or retarded by the presence of other substances both organic and inorganic. Such substances have been divided into three categories: (*a*) co-enzymes, without which certain enzymes are unable to function; (*b*) activators and inhibitors; (*c*) anti-enzymes.

---

* The pH of a solution is defined as minus the logarithm of the hydrogen ion concentration: $pH = - \log [H]$. Thus if $[H] = 10^{-4}$, then $pH = 4$. Also if $[H] = 2 \times 10^{-4}$, then $[H] = 10^{0·3010} \times 10^{-4} = 10^{-3·699}$; $\therefore pH = 3·699$. In any aqueous solution $[H] [OH] = 10^{-14}$ at ordinary temperatures. Therefore in a neutral solution $[H] = 10^{-7}$, or the pH of a neutral solution is 7. Hence the pH of an acid solution is < 7, and the pH of an alkaline solution > 7.

Nomenclature The compound on which the enzyme acts is known as the *substrate*. The name of the enzyme is now usually obtained by adding the termination -*ase* to the name of the substrate. Thus an enzyme which hydrolyses an ester is known as an *esterase*. Nevertheless the older names of many enzymes still persist owing to their early discovery. In some cases the name of the enzyme indicates the reaction which it catalyses, *e.g.*, *oxidase*.

The isolation of enzymes in a pure state is frequently a matter of great difficulty owing to their instability, their low concentrations in plant and animal tissues, and also to their colloidal nature. The methods employed depend upon the physical and chemical nature of the enzyme in question. In the following experiments, no attempt has been made to isolate enzymes in a high state of purity.

The accompanying table gives details of a few of the simpler reactions which enzymes catalyse. Those for which practical directions are given in the following pages are marked with an asterisk.

It should be noted that a number of different enzyme preparations can now be purchased directly from manufacturing chemists. It must be emphasised that the activity of an enzyme, whether purchased or prepared in the laboratory, may vary between rather wide limits. The activity is dependent on the source of the enzyme, the presence of poisons and also on the temperature. It appears, for example, that the quality of horseradish peroxidase depends upon the season of the year at which the root is obtained from the ground. It cannot be expected therefore that all the experiments described below will work always with the precision characteristic of an organic reaction proceeding under accurately known conditions.

Lipase.

The action of esterases consists essentially in the hydrolysis (or synthesis) of carboxylic acid esters according to the equation:

$$RCOOR^1 + H_2O \rightleftharpoons RCOOH + R^1OH$$

If RCOOH is a comparatively simple organic acid and R^1OH a monohydric alcohol then the enzyme is called an esterase. Examples of such esters are ethyl butyrate, $C_3H_7COOC_2H_5$, and ethyl mandelate, $C_6H_5CH(OH)COOC_2H_5$.

If, on the other hand, RCOOH is a higher fatty acid and R^1OH a polyhydric alcohol, then the enzyme is called a lipase. Stearin or glyceryl tristearate (a fat) is

$$CH_2 \cdot O \cdot CO \cdot C_{17}H_{35}$$
$$|$$
$$CH \cdot O \cdot CO \cdot C_{17}H_{35}$$
$$|$$
$$CH_2 \cdot O \cdot CO \cdot C_{17}H_{35}$$

an example of this type of ester. The difference, however, is one of degree rather than kind. Thus the lipases which split natural fats are also capable of hydrolysing simple esters, although very much more slowly. Conversely esterases can hydrolyse fats, but only feebly.

A convenient source of the enzyme is castor oil seeds. The oil of the seeds is itself an ester, and therefore if the action of the enzyme is to be demonstrated on an extraneous ester, the castor oil must first be completely removed by extraction with ether. This, however, is a long process and may require several days for completion. The hydrolysing action of the enzyme on the oil in the seed can however be demonstrated as described on p. 410.

Enzyme	Origin	Substrate	Products	Optimum pH
*Pancreatic lipase	pancreas	fats and other organic esters	organic acid and alcohol (often glycerol)	7·0
*Plant lipase	seeds rich in oil, e.g. castor oil seeds	,,	,,	5·0
*Diastase (or amylase)	liver, etc., malt	starch (amylum)	maltose and dextrin	6·0 (liver) 5·2 (malt)
*Ptyalin	saliva	,,	,,	6·7
Maltase	pancreas, small intestine, yeast	maltose	glucose	6·1 (gut) 6·6 (yeast)
*Invertase (sucrase)	small intestine, yeast	sucrose	glucose and fructose	6·2 (gut) 4·8 (yeast)
*Emulsin (β-glycosidase)	almond nuts	β-glucosides	glucose and a non-carbohydrate	4·1–4·5
*Zymase (a mixture)	yeast	d-glucose, l-fructose	alcohol, CO_2 and small quantities of glycerol	4·5–6·5
Carboxylase	yeast	keto-acids	aldehydes and CO_2	4·8
Pepsin	stomach	proteins	peptones	1·4
*Trypsin (a mixture)	duodenum	proteins, peptones, polypeptides	amino-acids	8–11
*Urease	soya bean, jack bean	urea	ammonium carbonate	7·2–7·9
*Aldehyde oxidase	milk	aldehydes	fatty acid	approx. 7·0
*Peroxidase	horseradish, turnips, milk	activates H_2O_2 and a suitable substrate, e.g., aniline	quinone-imine dyes, induline, mauveine, aniline-black	4·5 varies with substrate
Catalase	living tissues of plants and animals	hydrogen peroxide	H_2O and inactive molecular O_2	7·0
*Carbonic anhydrase	red blood corpuscles	carbonic acid	CO_2 and H_2O	6·8

ACTION OF LIPASE ON CASTOR OIL.

Remove the shells from 1 gm. of the seeds* (about 5) and then grind up the latter thoroughly in a mortar. Add a few ml. of water and work into a paste. Proceed in this way adding a few c.c. at a time until in all 25 ml. of water have been added. If this has been done thoroughly, a cream of uniform consistency will be obtained. Using a small measuring-cylinder, transfer 10 ml. of the lipase cream to each of two boiling-tubes **A** and **B**. Then using a 1 ml. pipette, add exactly 1 ml. of $N/10$ acetic acid to each and mix well: this activates the enzyme. Boil the contents of **B** for 2 minutes in order to destroy the enzyme, then place both tubes in a water-bath maintained at $40°$, shaking well from time to time. After 45 minutes remove the tubes, cool, add 2 drops of phenolphthalein to each and titrate with $N/10$ sodium hydroxide solution. It will be found that more alkali is required to neutralise the acid in **A** than in **B**, showing that acid has been produced by enzymatic hydrolysis. An interesting feature, usually observable in the titration of **A**, is that when the end-point is approached the suspension becomes almost clear. This is due to the fact that the ester of the seeds has been hydrolysed to a fatty acid and an alcohol. The insoluble fatty acid is gradually replaced by its soluble sodium salt as the titration proceeds. The contents of **B** will of course remain cloudy.

The following are typical results using a lipase cream of average activity:

A required 6·9 ml. of $N/10$ NaOH solution.

B required 1·3 ml. of $N/10$ NaOH solution.

Diastase.

Diastase or amylase is formed when malt is produced by the germination of barley grains. Malt is therefore a good source of the enzyme. Diastase is also secreted by the salivary glands (when it is known as ptyalin), and also by the pancreas. Its function is to hydrolyse† starch to a mixture of maltose and dextrin:

$$(C_6H_{10}O_5)_n + H_2O = C_{12}H_{22}O_{11} + (C_6H_{10}O_5)_{n-2}$$

The optimum pH for ptyalin is 6·7 and that of malt diastase is 4·9. Hence it would seem that the enzyme differs in some way according to its origin.

Preparation of an extract containing malt diastase.

Grind 10 gms. of malt‡ thoroughly in a mortar so that the grains are completely pulverised, add 50 c.c. of water and macerate well. Allow to stand for about one hour, grinding up the mixture thoroughly from time to time, and then filter through a Buchner funnel.

* Care must be taken not to inhale dust from the seeds as they contain a poisonous protein: the grinding should therefore be carried out in a fume-cupboard.

† It has been shown that diastase consists of two distinct enzymes, α- and β-amylase, both of which are concerned with the hydrolysis of starch.

‡ Usually obtainable from a brewery.

(1) HYDROLYSIS OF STARCH BY DIASTASE.

Mix 3 gms. of starch well with 10 c.c. of water in a test-tube and pour the mixture into 90 c.c. of boiling water contained in a 300 c.c. conical flask, stirring at the same time. Cool to about 70° and then place in a water-bath maintained at 65–70°, but not higher. Now add 2–3 c.c. of the malt extract prepared as above,* mix well and allow the hydrolysis to proceed. Take a series of test-tubes and in each put 10 c.c. of water and 2 drops of a 1% iodine solution. At intervals of about 4 minutes (depending upon the activity of the enzyme solution), remove 1 c.c. of the reaction mixture, cool and add it to one of the test-tubes and note the colour obtained. At the beginning of the experiment the colour will be blue due to the starch alone. As the reaction proceeds, the colour gradually becomes violet, reddish, yellowish and finally colourless.

The reason for this is that the starch is hydrolysed successively to dextrins of varying degrees of complexity and these give characteristic colours with iodine: for example, erythro-dextrin gives a reddish colour. The dextrin ultimately obtained, namely achroo-dextrin, gives no colour with iodine, as its name suggests. When this stage is reached, remove a few c.c. of the reaction product and boil with Fehling's solution: a marked reduction takes place. This is due to maltose, the presence of which can be further demonstrated as follows.

To 50 c.c. of the reaction product add 200 c.c. of alcohol: a white precipitate of dextrin is produced. Stir well, allow to stand for about 15 minutes, and then filter through a Buchner funnel and transfer the filtrate to a 500 c.c. distilling-flask. (The filtration is usually very slow and it may be found advantageous to use two Buchner funnels.) Add a few pieces of unglazed porcelain to the solution and distil off the alcohol (and some water) using a sand-bath. Transfer the residual liquid (about 40 c.c.) to a 100 c.c. conical flask, add a solution of 1 c.c. of phenylhydrazine in 2 c.c. of glacial acetic acid, and mix thoroughly. Heat in a boiling water-bath for 30 minutes. (If at the end of this period the solution is not absolutely clear, filter through a small fluted filter-paper into a previously warmed flask.) In either case allow to cool very slowly, preferably in a hot water-bath with the flame removed. Malto-sazone crystallises out when the solution is cold, and may be identified as described on p. 110.

(2) HYDROLYSIS OF STARCH BY PTYALIN.

When ptyalin acts on starch *in vitro*, the final product consists of about 80% of maltose and 20% of dextrin. The enzyme is destroyed in markedly acid solution, as it is also during full digestion in the stomach. But the presence of proteins, which act as buffers, prevents the hydrochloric acid secreted in the early stages of digestion from causing so high a concentration of hydrogen ions that the action of ptyalin is inhibited. This, together with the absence of active mechanical movement in the cardiac end of the stomach, permits the

---

* Or alternatively add 0·1–0·2 gm. of the diastase obtainable from chemical dealers.

ptyalin to function in the stomach for about half an hour after the ingestion of food. Ptyalin works only in the presence of electrolytes, the chloride ion being the most effective.

Warm about 100 c.c. of distilled water in a beaker to about 40° and with a portion of this thoroughly rinse out the mouth and reject the liquid. Again introduce about 20 c.c. of the warm water into the mouth and mix with the saliva as completely as possible. Transfer the liquid so obtained into another beaker and then filter through a small fluted filter-paper into a small conical flask or boiling-tube.

Place 10 c.c. of 1% starch solution (prepared as described above) in a boiling-tube, add 2 c.c. of 1% sodium chloride solution and place the tube in a water-bath maintained at 38–40°. Place about 5 c.c. of water in a series of test-tubes and to each add a few drops of 1% iodine solution. Now add 4 c.c. of the diluted saliva solution to the starch solution, mix well and note the time. At intervals of about 30 seconds transfer 2 drops of the reacting mixture, by means of a dropping-tube, to one of the test-tubes, mix and note the colour. As in the previous experiment, the colour, which is blue at first, changes to blue-violet, red-violet, red-brown, pale brown, and finally disappears: at this stage the solution will reduce Fehling's solution. If the reaction proceeds too quickly for the colour changes to be observed, the saliva solution should be diluted.

Invertase (sucrase).

Yeast contains a number of enzymes, more particularly invertase and zymase. Invertase catalyses the hydrolysis of sucrose to glucose and fructose (*cf.* the catalysis of this reaction by acids, p. 279).

$$C_{12}H_{22}O_{11} + H_2O = C_6H_{12}O_6 + C_6H_{12}O_6$$
$$\text{sucrose} \qquad\qquad \text{glucose} \quad\; \text{fructose}$$

Sucrose is dextro-rotatory. Fructose shows a laevo-rotation greater in magnitude than the dextro-rotation shown by glucose. Hence as the hydrolysis of sucrose proceeds, the dextro-rotation gradually falls to zero and the solution finally shows a laevo-rotation. This hydrolysis is therefore sometimes called "inversion" and so the enzyme which catalyses the reaction is known as "invertase." Its more systematic name is, however, sucrase.

Preparation of an invertase solution.

Grind together in a mortar 25 gms. of brewers' or of commercial pressed yeast and about an equal weight of silver sand, adding gradually 10 c.c. of water. After the mixture has been well ground up and the yeast cells effectively ruptured, add about 50 c.c. of water slowly with thorough mixing. Allow the mixture to stand for about 20 minutes, stirring from time to time. Filter through a Buchner funnel until a reasonably clear filtrate is obtained.

It is important to note that this solution does not contain any zymase.

In order to obtain an extract containing zymase, more complex methods of treatment must be employed.

HYDROLYSIS OF CANE SUGAR.

Dissolve 10 gms. of cane sugar in water and make up to approximately 100 c.c. Label three boiling-tubes **A**, **B** and **C**, and in them place the following:

(A) 20 c.c. of sugar solution and 2 c.c. of the invertase solution obtained above.

(B) 10 c.c. of sugar solution and 1 c.c. of the invertase solution which has previously been boiled thoroughly for 2–3 minutes.

(C) 10 c.c. of sugar solution, 1 c.c. of the invertase solution, and 1 c.c. of 10% NaOH solution.

Mix each solution well and place the boiling-tubes in a water-bath maintained at 50°. After 10 minutes, transfer 1 c.c. of each of the reaction mixtures to separate test-tubes, add 2 c.c. of Fehling's solution to each and boil. A marked reduction is obtained in **A***, no reduction is obtained in **B**, and no reduction or only very slight reduction is obtained in **C**. This shows that the activity of the invertase is destroyed both by heat and alkali.

At the end of 30 minutes treat the mixture in **A** as follows: Dissolve 8 c.c. of glacial acetic acid in 10 c.c. of water, add 4 c.c. of phenylhydrazine and mix well in order to obtain a clear solution. Add this to the solution in **A** and mix thoroughly: a slightly cloudy solution may be obtained, but this will clear on heating. Place the mixture in a boiling water-bath and note the formation of yellow crystals of glucosazone after about 15 minutes. At the end of about 1 hour, cool, filter off the precipitate and identify as directed on p. 110.

Emulsin.

Emulsin, an enzyme readily obtained from almonds, has the property of hydrolysing β-glycosides.

An account has been given on p. 115 of the α- and β-methylglucosides, formed by replacing the hydrogen atoms of the terminal OH groups of α- and β-glucose respectively by methyl groups. These hydrogen atoms can be replaced by various other radicals, and the compounds so formed belong to the general class of glycosides. A number of glycosides occur naturally and these are usually β-glycosides. For example, salicin (I) is a combination of salicyl alcohol (or saligenin) and glucose. Amygdalin (II) is a combination of two molecules of glucose, one molecule of hydrogen cyanide and one molecule

---

* Actually the optimum pH for the invertase reaction is about 4·8, and under these conditions the reaction proceeds even more rapidly. The solution can be adjusted approximately to this pH by adding 6 c.c. of 1% acetic acid at the beginning of the experiment.

HOCH$_2$C$_6$H$_4$O   H

$$
\begin{array}{c}
\text{C} \\
\text{HCOH} \\
\text{HOCH} \quad \text{O} \\
\text{HCOH} \\
\text{HC} \\
\text{CH}_2\text{OH} \\
\text{(I)}
\end{array}
$$

C$_6$H$_5$CH(CN) – O   H
$$C_{12}H_{20}O_{10}$$
(II)

HOC$_6$H$_4$O   H
$$C_6H_{10}O_5$$
(III)

of benzaldehyde. Arbutin (III) is a combination of glucose with hydro-quinone (1:4-dihydroxy-benzene).

Emulsin does not hydrolyse α-methylglucoside, whereas it readily hydrolyses β-methylglucoside, salicin, amygdalin and arbutin. This is an excellent example of the specificity of enzymes:

$$C_6H_{11}O_5\text{--}OCH_3 + H_2O = C_6H_{12}O_6 + CH_3OH$$
β-methyl glucoside   glucose

$$C_6H_{11}O_5\text{--}OC_6H_4CH_2OH + H_2O = C_6H_{12}O_6 + HOC_6H_4CH_2OH$$
salicin   glucose   salicyl alcohol

Since an enzyme is a biological catalyst and therefore merely accelerates a reaction, it cannot alter the position of equilibrium in a reversible reaction. The hydrolysis of β-methylglucoside is reversible and emulsin should therefore be capable also of synthesising this compound from glucose and methyl alcohol. This synthesis can actually be carried out by the action of the enzyme on glucose dissolved in an excess of methyl alcohol, the excess of alcohol throwing the equilibrium over to the left. Owing to experimental difficulties, this reaction is not here described.

In aqueous solution, the hydrolysis of a glucoside by emulsin goes to completion on account of the large proportion of water present.

Preparation of emulsin from almonds.

Place about 15 sweet almonds in boiling water for one minute. Pour off the water and remove the brown skins which have been loosened by the hot water. Grind up the "blanched" almonds in a mortar as thoroughly as possible. Add 40 c.c. of water and grind into a paste, then add 10 c.c. of 10% acetic acid and mix well: this causes the coagulation of the proteins present. Allow to stand for 10 minutes, stirring at intervals. Filter through a Buchner funnel: wash the residue in the funnel with a few c.c. of water (allowing the washings to enter the filtrate) and drain well. Add 1 drop of 10% acetic acid to the filtrate; the solution should remain clear: if it does not, add the dilute acetic acid drop by drop until no more precipitate is formed, and then re-filter.

The clear filtrate is very active and may be used directly for the following experiments. Alternatively the solid enzyme may be isolated as follows. To the filtrate add an equal volume of alcohol to precipitate the enzyme: filter off the latter through a small Buchner funnel, wash with alcohol and then ether, and dry in a vacuum desiccator.

HYDROLYSIS OF SALICIN BY EMULSIN.

Salicin is a colourless crystalline substance, soluble in water. It does not reduce Fehling's solution nor does it give a coloration with ferric chloride. On hydrolysis with emulsin, glucose and salicyl alcohol are produced: the former reduces Fehling's solution and the latter gives a violet coloration with ferric chloride.

By gentle warming, dissolve 5 gms. of salicin in 100 c.c. of water contained in a 250 c.c. conical flask. Add about 20 c.c. of the emulsin solution as prepared above or 0·2–0·3 gm. of the solid enzyme preparation,* mix well and place the flask in a water-bath maintained at 45°. Shake the mixture well from time to time and at the end of about 30 minutes transfer 1 c.c. to a test-tube, cool and add ferric chloride solution: a violet coloration is produced. Also boil 1 c.c. of the reaction mixture with Fehling's solution and note the reduction.

At the end of about an hour,† filter the solution and transfer 20 c.c. of the clear filtrate to a boiling-tube. Dissolve 2·5 c.c. of phenylhydrazine in 3 c.c. of glacial acetic acid diluted with 3 c.c. of water, and add this solution to that in the boiling-tube. Mix well and place the tube in a boiling water-bath. After about 15 minutes, crystals of glucosazone begin to separate. At the end of about 1 hour, filter off the precipitate and identify (p. 110).

Cool the remainder of the filtrate and extract three times with ether, using 20–30 c.c. for each extraction. Dry the combined ethereal extracts over powdered anhydrous sodium sulphate. Filter into a small flask and distil off the ether on a water-bath. Pour the residual oil into a small dish or beaker: crystallisation takes place almost immediately. The salicyl alcohol so obtained is almost pure, but it may, if so desired, be recrystallised from a small quantity of benzene. It is a colourless crystalline solid, m.p. 86°, readily soluble in water; it gives a violet coloration with ferric chloride.

Zymase.

Yeast contains invertase, maltase and zymase as well as other enzymes. The enzyme primarily concerned with alcoholic fermentation is zymase, which causes the breakdown of the naturally occurring monosaccharides, glucose, fructose and mannose, and produces mainly ethyl alcohol and carbon dioxide. It was the production of this gas which led to the term fermentation (*fervere* = to boil) being applied to this particular enzyme reaction, although of course the reaction is carried out at, or just above, room temperature. The equation for the reaction can be written simply:

$$C_6H_{12}O_6 = 2C_2H_5OH + 2CO_2$$

* 0·2–0·3 gm. of the manufacturer's product also works satisfactorily.

† The time required for complete hydrolysis will naturally depend upon the activity of the emulsin, but preparations of average activity give a satisfactory yield of products after 1 hour.

Zymase has been shown to consist of several component enzymes and a co-enzyme called co-zymase, all of which are concerned with alcoholic fermentation.

During alcoholic fermentation small quantities of other substances are formed such as glycerol, succinic acid and fusel oil (a mixture of higher aliphatic alcohols). Of these, only glycerol is a true decomposition product of the monosaccharide, the other substances being breakdown products of the amino-acids present in the yeast.

The monosaccharide is broken down by a complicated series of reactions to pyruvic acid, $CH_3COCOOH$, and glycerol. The pyruvic acid in turn is converted by the enzyme carboxylase into carbon dioxide and acetaldehyde, the latter being reduced to alcohol at the expense of one of the precursors of glycerol. Therefore as soon as any acetaldehyde is formed, the production of glycerol is stopped. If however the acetaldehyde is fixed by the addition of sodium sulphite, the precursor is again released and the production of glycerol is thus unhindered.

ALCOHOLIC FERMENTATION OF CANE SUGAR.

Fit a 2-litre flask with a delivery-tube bent twice at right angles so that it leads vertically downwards. Place 50 gms. of cane sugar and 500 c.c. of water in the flask, and warm very gently to dissolve; then add about 20 gms. of either brewers' or bakers' yeast. If any yeast adheres to the neck of the flask, wash down with a small quantity of water. Shake the mixture well and then attach the delivery-tube to the flask. Allow the flask to stand in a warm place (about 20–25°) for 2–3 days—a position near a hot-water radiator is admirable for this purpose. The mixture froths considerably and carbon dioxide is evolved: this can be demonstrated by allowing the open end of the delivery-tube to dip just below the surface of some lime-water contained in a test-tube. As soon as all the air has been displaced from the flask, each bubble of gas will produce a cloud of calcium carbonate as it passes through the lime-water. (Alternatively, if the flask is shaken, the sudden liberation of carbon dioxide will cause a copious precipitation in the lime-water.) When the evolution of gas appears to have stopped, filter the mixture through a Buchner funnel, then distil the clear filtrate from a 750 c.c. distilling-flask, collecting the fraction boiling up to about 97° (approximately 50 c.c.). With the distillate, carry out the tests for ethyl alcohol (p. 251).

Trypsin.

The so-called "trypsin," obtainable from pancreatic juice and from fresh extracts of the pancreas, is not a simple enzyme but a mixture of trypsin proper (which hydrolyses proteins to proteoses and peptones) and a series of enzymes which hydrolyse these breakdown products to their constituent amino-acids. The term "trypsin," when used below, refers to this mixture.

Since trypsin is a mixture, it has no well-defined optimum pH. It should also be noted that trypsin is the only hydrolytic enzyme which is at all active in alkaline solution.

The course of tryptic digestion of proteins.

On hydrolysing a protein, both NH_2 groups and COOH groups are set free in equal numbers by the splitting of – CONH – groups, and therefore the reaction cannot be followed by simple titration. One method of estimating the breakdown products (peptones, peptides, amino-acids, *etc.*) is Sorensen's formaldehyde titration method, the theory of which has been fully discussed under the Estimation of Glycine (p. 367). From the description given there it is obvious that the quantitative value of the formaldehyde titration will increase as the digestion proceeds, until finally a value is obtained which corresponds (theoretically at least) to the constituent amino-acids of the original protein.

Another important method of following protein hydrolysis is that due to Van Slyke, and consists in estimating the free amino groups liberated by treatment with nitrous acid, whereby gaseous nitrogen is evolved and measured in a special apparatus.

$$NH_2CH_2COOH + HNO_2 = HO \cdot CH_2COOH + N_2 + H_2O$$

Only Sorensen's method is employed in the following experiments. The student should therefore first acquaint himself with the theory of the estimation of glycine (p. 367).

It must be emphasised that these experiments are only roughly quantitative, for owing to the slight opalescence of the digesting mixture, accurate end-points using phenolphthalein can be obtained only by using an instrument known as a comparator.

HYDROLYSIS OF CASEIN.

Prepare a solution of casein as follows. Weigh out 15 gms. of casein into a dry 500 ml. conical flask and add about 150 ml. of water. Dissolve 1·5 gms. of anhydrous sodium carbonate and 1·5 gms. of borax in about 20 ml. of hot water and add this solution to the casein. Warm until a solution is obtained, filter if necessary, and make up to a total volume of about 250 ml. with water. Add a few drops of toluene (to prevent putrefaction) and shake the solution.

Remove 25 ml. by means of a pipette, add a few drops of phenolphthalein: the colour is pink. Now add very cautiously, *drop by drop*, dilute acetic acid (say $N/100$) until the pink colour has *just* not disappeared. It is important not to add too much acid, otherwise the casein will be precipitated. Now add 5 ml. of neutralised formalin (see p. 368) and then titrate with $N/10$ NaOH solution. Note the amount required.

To the remainder of the casein solution add 0·5 to 0·8 gm. of finely powdered commercial trypsin, shake to dissolve, and place in a thermostat (or in an incubator) at 40°. After 15 minutes, remove 25 ml. and add a few drops of phenolphthalein: it will now be found that the solution remains colourless. Run in carefully $N/10$ NaOH solution until the colour of the solution is just pink, add 5 ml. of neutralised formalin and then titrate against $N/10$ NaOH solution until the pink colour is just restored: note the amount required. Remove further quantities of 25 ml. at intervals which must be determined by the speed of the reaction. The following will probably make a suitable series: $\frac{1}{2}$, $\frac{3}{4}$, 1, 2, 3, 6 and 24 hours. It will be found that, as the reaction proceeds, the titration value increases fairly rapidly at first and then more slowly.

P

HYDROLYSIS OF GELATIN.

Dissolve 6 gms. of gelatin in about 250 ml. of warm water. Carry out the formaldehyde titration on 25 ml. of the solution: note in this case that the solution is acid to phenolphthalein.

To the remainder of the gelatin solution, add 0·5 to 0·8 gm. of finely powdered commercial trypsin and incubate at 40°. Carry out the formaldehyde titration on 25 ml. samples at intervals as above.

Note that the original solution sets to a gel on standing, but is fluid at 40°, and when removed from the bath usually remains so sufficiently long for a titration to be carried out. It is interesting to observe that, after several hours' digestion, the mixture no longer sets to a gel on standing at room temperature, showing that the gelatin is now replaced by completely water-soluble amino-acids.

Urease.

The chief sources of this important enzyme are (a) the jack bean (*Canavalia ensiformis*), (b) the soy (or soja) bean (*Glycine hispida*). The enzyme is of great value in identifying and estimating urea. The action of urease on urea is absolutely specific, the reaction catalysed being:

$$(NH_2)_2CO + 2H_2O = (NH_4)_2CO_3$$

Urease is one of the enzymes which have been obtained in the crystalline state. This has been done by stirring jack bean meal with 30% aqueous acetone, filtering and allowing the filtrate to remain at 0° for several hours. The urease which crystallises out is separated by centrifuging and is then recrystallised. Like crystalline pepsin and trypsin, it is a protein.

SPECIFIC UREASE TEST FOR UREA.

The principle of this test is as follows: The liquid suspected of containing urea is treated with dilute acid or alkali until its pH is about 7. A solution of the enzyme is also made and its pH adjusted to 7. The two solutions are mixed and the resulting conversion of urea to ammonium carbonate causes the pH of the solution to rise to over 8; this change is noted by the use of a suitable indicator, phenol-red being the one usually employed. Proteins do not interfere with the test, but the reaction is inhibited by traces of heavy metals.

Place about 0·2 gm. of jack-bean meal in a test-tube, add 2 c.c. of water and about 5 drops of phenol-red. Mix thoroughly and allow to stand while the urea solution is being made up.

Dissolve about 0·2 gm. of urea in 5 c.c. of water, add about 5 drops of phenol-red and 1 drop of dil. HCl: the colour is now yellow. Divide the solution into two portions. To one portion, add very dilute (about 1%) NaOH solution until the colour is red: now add the second portion, *drop by drop*, until the red colour is *just* discharged. The solution is now at about pH 7.

To this solution add the enzyme solution, mix well and allow to stand at room temperature. The mixture becomes red as the pH rises to 8.

ESTIMATION OF UREA BY UREASE.

This method of estimating urea is more accurate than the hypobromite method (p. 363) and is used extensively for accurate metabolic work.

The method is based on the conversion of urea to ammonium carbonate and the estimation of the latter by titration with standard acid. For this purpose, two equal quantities of urea (or urine) are measured out into two flasks **A** and **B**. **A** is treated with 10 c.c. of a strong urease preparation and some phenolphthalein, warm water is added and the mixture is adjusted by the addition of $N/10$ HCl from a burette **A**[1] until the red colour is just discharged. This brings the mixture to about pH 8 (the optimum for urease) and also prevents loss of ammonia.

The contents of **B**, which act as a control, are treated with mercuric chloride in order to inhibit the action of the enzyme, and then 10 c.c. of urease solution are added. The solution is diluted with water and ammonium chloride added (in order to balance the ammonium chloride subsequently formed in **A**). Methyl-red is then added and the solution is titrated with $N/10$ HCl from a second burette **B**[1] until a bright red colour is obtained.

The solution in **A** is now treated with mercuric chloride and methyl-red, and then titrated with $N/10$ HCl until its colour matches that of the solution in **B**. The difference in the volume of HCl run in from the burettes **A**[1] and **B**[1] is a measure of the amount of urea present.

Urease solution. Place about 5 gms. of jack-bean meal in a mortar and grind up with about 10 c.c. of water. Then add about 90 ml. of water, mix *thoroughly* and allow to stand for some time in order to deposit starch and other insoluble substances. Decant off the supernatant liquid into a conical flask and cork the latter.

The estimation. Label two 250 ml. conical flasks **A** and **B**, and into each measure 5 ml. of urine solution (or about 0·1 gm. of solid urea, accurately weighed). Add to each about 20 ml. of water and bring the temperature to about 60°. To **A** add 3 drops of phenolphthalein solution and to **B** add 1 ml. of 0·5% mercuric chloride solution. Now to each solution, add 10 ml. of the urease solution and mix well. The mixture **A** soon turns red.

Fill two burettes **A**[1] and **B**[1] with $N/10$ HCl. Run in from **A**[1], drop by drop, sufficient $N/10$ hydrochloric acid *just* to discharge the red colour in **A**. Maintain the temperature at about 60° and keep the colour just discharged by cautiously adding the HCl from time to time. Care must be taken not to add an excess of acid, otherwise the proteins will be precipitated and the enzyme rendered inactive. The reaction is complete in about 5 minutes, but allow the mixture to stand for a further 5 minutes after the final discharge of the colour.

Meanwhile add 4 drops of methyl-red and 1 ml. of 10% ammonium chloride solution to **B**. The colour will normally be yellow; if so, add $N/10$ HCl from **B**[1], drop by drop, until a red colour is just obtained.

Now add 1 ml. of the mercuric chloride solution to **A** and 4 drops of methyl-red. Run in $N/10$ HCl from the first burette **A**[1] until a red colour is obtained identical with that in **B**. Note the difference in the volume of acid run in from **A**[1] and **B**[1].

Calculation.

The equations for the above reactions are:

$$CO(NH_2)_2 + 2H_2O = (NH_4)_2CO_3$$
$$(NH_4)_2CO_3 + 2HCl = 2NH_4Cl + CO_2 + H_2O$$

1 gram-molecule of urea ≡ 2000 ml. of *N*.HCl solution

i.e., 60 gms. of urea ≡ 2000 ml. of *N*.HCl solution

∴ 0·003 gm. of urea ≡ 1 ml. of *N*/10 HCl solution

Aldehyde oxidase (or dehydrogenase).

This enzyme, sometimes also called the Schardinger enzyme, occurs in milk. It is capable of "oxidising" acetaldehyde to acetic acid, and also the purine bases xanthine and hypoxanthine to uric acid. The former reaction is not a simple direct oxidation and is assumed to take place as follows. The enzyme "activates" the hydrated form of the aldehyde so that it readily parts with two hydrogen atoms in the presence of a suitable hydrogen acceptor such as methylene-blue, the latter being reduced to the colourless leuco-compound. The oxidation of certain substrates will not take place in the absence of such a hydrogen acceptor.

$$CH_3CH{<}^{OH}_{OH} \quad + \quad M \quad \longrightarrow \quad CH_3COOH \; + \; MH_2$$

$$\text{methylene-blue} \qquad\qquad \text{leuco-methylene-blue}$$

Make up an approximately 5% solution of acetaldehyde in water, add a few drops of phenolphthalein and then add dilute Na_2CO_3 until the solution just turns pink, thus removing any free acid.

Make up a methylene-blue solution by grinding 0·1 gm. with water and making up to 1 litre with water.

Place 5 c.c. of milk in each of two test-tubes **A** and **B**. Boil the milk in **B** thoroughly for 2 minutes to destroy the enzyme, and cool. Then in each test-tube place 1 c.c. of the acetaldehyde solution and 1 c.c. of the methylene-blue solution. Mix gently by inverting the tubes: avoid shaking with air. Now place **A** and **B** in a water-bath maintained at 40–50°. After a time (usually about 20 minutes) the dye in **A** is completely decolorised except at the surface, while **B** is unaffected.

This reaction can also be carried out in the absence of air or oxygen, *i.e.*, anaerobically.

Peroxidase.

This enzyme is widely distributed, more particularly in plants. Three important sources of the enzyme are horse-radish, turnips and milk. Peroxidase is capable of activating both hydrogen peroxide and a suitable substrate so that the latter is oxidised, although hydrogen peroxide alone may be incapable of affecting this change. It sometimes happens that hydrogen peroxide alone does, in fact, oxidise a given substrate slowly and feebly, but on adding the enzyme the reaction is not only accelerated, but appears to have its course altered and thus gives rise to entirely different end-products. An interesting example of this is shown by aniline, which under certain conditions is oxidised by hydrogen peroxide alone to azobenzene, azoxybenzene and nitrobenzene: in the presence of peroxidase, however, entirely different substances are produced, *viz.*, a quinone-imine dye, an induline, a mauveine and aniline-black.

Other substances can activate hydrogen peroxide, for example, ferrous iron (p. 284). The products however are usually different from those obtained when using peroxidase.

The function of peroxidase is not yet known, but it may be of considerable importance in many oxidation processes. In view of recent work, it may also be of great value as a synthetic agent.

Isolation of Peroxidase.

The activity of the specimen isolated will depend largely upon the extent and thoroughness of the extraction. By following the details outlined below, a specimen of peroxidase sufficiently active for all ordinary purposes is obtained.

Cut the tops off some turnips, wash the latter if necessary and then weigh out 300 gms. Cut up into small pieces and mince in a small mincing-machine. Place the macerated product in a 1-litre beaker or jar, add 300 c.c. of water and stir thoroughly with a strong glass rod at intervals during 20 minutes. Decant off as much as possible of the supernatant liquid on to a Buchner funnel, transferring as little of the pulp as possible to the filter-paper. Now place the pulp in a strong cotton cloth and extract as much liquid as possible by squeezing. Combine this liquid with the filtrate in the Buchner funnel, measure the total volume and transfer to a beaker. Saturate with ammonium sulphate by adding about 70 gms. of powdered ammonium sulphate for each 100 c.c. of filtrate. Stir well and then allow to stand. After a few minutes the crude peroxidase is precipitated, and may rise to the surface or sink to the bottom of the liquid. If the latter happens, decant off as much of the supernatant liquid as possible and filter off the remainder through a small Buchner funnel. If the precipitate rises to the top of the liquid, it is usually advisable to transfer to a separating-funnel, allow to settle, run off as much of the lower liquid as possible, and then filter the remainder through a Buchner funnel. Place the funnel in a vacuum desiccator and allow to dry overnight. Detach as much of the dried precipitate as possible from the filter-paper, grind up in a mortar and preserve in a small stoppered tube. This preparation will retain its activity for several months.

It should be noted that the aqueous extract of the turnips shows weak peroxidase activity before precipitation with ammonium sulphate.

QUALITATIVE TESTS FOR AROMATIC AMINES.

Place about 0·2 gm. (or 0·2 c.c.) of the amine in a test-tube, add 0·2 c.c. of glacial acetic acid to dissolve the amine and then add water until the test-tube is half-full. Next place about 0·3 gm. of the peroxidase preparation in a very small mortar and grind up with about 15 c.c. of water. Filter through a small fluted filter-paper into a test-tube.

With the aid of a small pipette or a fine-bore dropping-tube (Fig. 22, p. 42), add about 4 drops of the filtered enzyme solution to the amine acetate solution. Using another dropping-tube add 1 drop of "20 volume" hydrogen peroxide solution and shake well. Note the colour change which takes place.

The rate of colour change will depend upon the activity of the enzyme preparation. The changes enumerated below are usually, however, easily observable.

Aniline. Purple, gradually turning brown. A brown precipitate on standing.

o-*Toluidine.* Transient green, deep blue and then a deep blue precipitate. Usually a very fast reaction.

m-*Toluidine.* Reddish-purple, gradually darkening.

p-*Toluidine.* Orange-red, then a deep blood red: finally a red precipitate is formed.

α-*Naphthylamine.* Opalescent indigo blue.

β-*Naphthylamine.* Brown solution with a very slight pale blue fluorescence.

Monomethylaniline. Deep blue, changing to a slate blue.

Dimethylaniline. Yellow, changing through olive green to a deep green. On long standing becomes bluish green.

Diphenylamine (suspension). Bluish-purple changing to a deep permanganate colour.

Triphenylamine (suspension). Almost negative. A very pale rose-pink coloration may slowly form.

o-*Phenylene diamine.* Yellow, darkening to the colour of dichromate.

m-*Phenylene diamine.* Dark brown. Not an easily observable change, as the original solution is usually brown.

p-*Phenylene diamine.* A transient yellow which almost immediately changes to a deep green. On standing the solution turns brown. A very sensitive test for peroxidase. In fact, a slice of turnip or horse-radish will develop a green colour when treated with hydrogen peroxide and a solution of p-phenylene diamine in dilute acetic acid.

Repeat one or two of the above experiments using however, in place of the active enzyme, a sample of the enzyme solution which has been thoroughly boiled for 2 minutes. Note that the above colour changes do not now occur.

Peroxidase in milk.

Dissolve about 0·1 gm. of p-phenylene diamine in about 10 c.c. of water. Place 5 c.c. of milk in each of two test-tubes **A** and **B**. Boil the milk in **B** thoroughly for 2 minutes and then cool. In each test-tube place 5 drops of the phenylene diamine solution and then add 1 drop of "20 vol." hydrogen peroxide solution, and mix. A green coloration is produced in **A**, and then very rapidly changes to a slate-blue. No coloration is produced in **B**. This test therefore readily differentiates fresh from boiled milk.

Carbonic Anhydrase.

Carbon dioxide is carried in the blood chiefly as bicarbonate. By the series of reversible reactions given below sodium bicarbonate can be converted into carbon dioxide and water:

$$NaHCO_3 + HP \rightleftharpoons NaP + H_2CO_3 \qquad\qquad H_2CO_3 \rightleftharpoons CO_2 + H_2O$$

HP represents weak protein acids and NaP the sodium salts of such acids. In the lungs the reaction proceeds from left to right. It is known, however, that the reaction $H_2CO_3 \rightleftharpoons CO_2 + H_2O$ proceeds far too slowly at the pH and temperature of the blood to account for the actual rate of CO_2 evolution in expired air, and therefore must be accelerated catalytically. The cause of this acceleration is an enzyme, called carbonic anhydrase, which occurs in the red blood corpuscles.

Apart from its great importance in respiration, it is interesting from the chemical standpoint in that both the forward and reverse reactions can be readily demonstrated merely by altering the conditions of the experiment.

I. DECOMPOSITION OF CARBONIC ACID.

Fit up the apparatus shown in Fig. 75. **A** is a small glass vessel of about 20 ml. capacity, into the side of which is blown a small tube **B** of about 5 ml. capacity. **A** is closed by a well-fitting rubber stopper through which passes a glass tube **C**, which is connected by narrow-bore pressure tubing, at least 0·5 metre in length, to a micro gas-burette **DE**, which is conveniently attached to a vertical board **G**. **D** has a capacity of 1 ml. and is graduated downwards in 0·01 ml. divisions; it is fixed in position, while the limb **E** is capable of adjustment in a vertical direction. The liquid used in the burette is alcohol coloured with methyl-red. The vessel **A** is fixed securely in a cylindrical jar **F**, of large capacity,

FIG. 75.

filled with water. **F** acts as a thermostat for **A**, and therefore the latter must be immersed as completely as possible in **F**.

Now, by means of a pipette, transfer 1 ml. of 0·2 molar $NaHCO_3$ solution into **A** (do not blow). Using a graduated 1 m.l. pipette, place 0·8 ml. of 0·2 molar phosphate buffer solution (pH = 6·8)* in **B**. Using another graduated pipette, place 0·1 ml. of a blood solution (blood diluted 1 in 100 with water) in **A**. Place the stopper securely in **A** and adjust **E** so that the alcohol is the same level in each limb.

* Made by adding 23·65 ml. of 0·2 N.NaOH solution to 50 ml. of 0·2 molar KH_2PO_4 solution and making up to 200 ml. 0·2 Molar KH_2PO_4 contains 27·23 gms. per litre.

Now place **F** on its side on the bench and mix the solutions by rotating. At the precise moment when the solutions are mixed start a stop-watch.* Now roll **F** backwards and forwards on the bench at a uniform rapid rate (to and fro, about three times a second). A brisk evolution of CO_2 occurs and depresses the

FIG. 76.

alcohol in **D**: take readings at the end of 15, 30, 45 and 60 seconds. (If the rolling is slower than the above, the rate of CO_2 evolution will be affected in part by diffusion, and not solely by the chemical reaction velocity which this experiment is designed to demonstrate.)

Wash out **A** and **B** thoroughly and repeat the experiment as before, omitting however the blood solution. The reaction now takes place at a much slower rate. Plot the results obtained in each case. Curves of the type shown (Fig. 76) will be obtained: the first reading is sometimes anomalous owing to various factors, e.g., the time taken for the two liquids to mix.

II. COMBINATION OF CARBON DIOXIDE WITH WATER.

Make up a mixed solution containing 1·68 gms. $NaHCO_3$ and 0·212 gm. anhydrous Na_2CO_3 per litre, i.e., 0·02 molar $NaHCO_3$ and 0·002 molar Na_2CO_3. Place 5 ml. of this solution in each of two test-tubes **A** and **B**, and to each add 6 drops of thymol-blue. The pH of the solution is about 9 and the colour of the indicator is greyish-blue. With the aid of a dropping-pipette, add 0·25 ml. of blood solution (1 ml. in 100 c.c. of water) to **A**. Now place two narrow delivery-tubes in each test-tube at such a height that the former do not quite touch the surfaces of the solutions. Fill the test-tubes simultaneously through the delivery-tubes with alveolar air. This is done by closing the nose (by pinching with the fingers) after a normal inspiration, and then expiring deeply through the mouth. Remove the delivery-tubes, place a thumb over each test-tube and shake each at the same uniform rate. The colour changes through green to yellow as the pH falls (due to the formation of carbonic acid), but it will be observed that this change in colour occurs much more rapidly in **A** than in **B**.

* It is obviously desirable for two people to carry out this experiment, one to do the shaking and the other to take readings.

APPENDIX

PREPARATION OF REAGENTS

Throughout this book, the reagents referred to, unless otherwise stated, have been prepared as described below.

ACIDS.

ACETIC ACID, DILUTE. Approx. $4N$. Dilute 230 c.c. of glacial acetic acid with water until total volume is 1 litre.

HYDROCHLORIC ACID, DILUTE. 1 vol. of conc. HCl to 3 vols. of water.

NITRIC ACID, DILUTE. 1 vol. of conc. HNO_3 to 10 vols. of water.

SULPHURIC ACID, DILUTE. 1 vol. of conc. H_2SO_4 to 8 vols. of water.

SULPHUROUS ACID. Water saturated with SO_2.

BASES.

AMMONIUM HYDROXIDE SOLUTION, DILUTE. 1 vol. of conc. ammonia (d, 0·880) to 3 vols. of water.

POTASSIUM HYDROXIDE, ALCOHOLIC. Reflux 10 gms. of powdered KOH with 100 c.c. of rectified spirit for 30 minutes. Cool and if solid material remains, decant through a filter of glass-wool.

SODIUM HYDROXIDE, 10% AQUEOUS. 100 gms. NaOH dissolved in water, and the cold solution diluted to 1 litre.

SODIUM HYDROXIDE, 30% AQUEOUS. As above, using 300 gms. NaOH.

SALTS.

BARIUM CHLORIDE. 10% solution, *i.e.*, 100 gms. of $BaCl_2,2H_2O$ dissolved in water and the solution made up to 1 litre.

BLEACHING POWDER. Shake a mixture of 125 gms. of bleaching powder and 1 litre of water at intervals for 2 hours, then filter.

CALCIUM CHLORIDE. Dissolve 100 gms. of $CaCl_2,6H_2O$ (or 50 gms. of anhydrous $CaCl_2$) in water and make up to 1 litre.

COPPER SULPHATE. 10% solution of $CuSO_4,5H_2O$.

FERRIC CHLORIDE. Approx. 4·5%. Dissolve 75 c.c. of "liquid $FeCl_3$"* in water and make up to 1 litre. Alternatively, dissolve 75 gms. of $FeCl_3,6H_2O$ in water, add 10 c.c. of conc. HCl, and make up to 1 litre.

FERROUS SULPHATE. Dissolve 10 gms. of $FeSO_4,7H_2O$ in water, add 10 c.c. of dil. H_2SO_4 and make up to 100 c.c. with water. It should, whenever possible, be prepared immediately before use.

MERCURIC CHLORIDE. Saturated aqueous solution (approx. 6%).

MERCURIC NITRATE. 5% solution of $Hg(NO_3)_2$.

* As supplied by chemical dealers; a concentrated solution of $FeCl_3$ acidified with HCl.

P*

MERCUROUS NITRATE. 5% solution of $HgNO_3,H_2O$.

POTASSIUM IODIDE. 10% solution.

POTASSIUM PERMANGANATE. 1% solution.

SILVER NITRATE. 2% solution.

SODIUM BISULPHITE. Dissolve 600 gms. of $NaHSO_3$ in water, make up to 1 litre and pass in SO_2 for a few minutes to ensure absence of Na_2SO_3.

SODIUM CARBONATE. 20% solution of $Na_2CO_3,10H_2O$.

SODIUM HYPOBROMITE. Dissolve 200 gms. of NaOH in water, make up to 1 litre, chill in ice-water, and slowly add 50 c.c. of bromine with stirring.

SODIUM HYPOCHLORITE. $2N$. This may be prepared with sufficient accuracy by dissolving 100 gms. of NaOH in 200 c.c. of water in a large beaker, cooling the solution, and then adding about 500 gms. of crushed ice. Now counterpoise the beaker on a rough set of scales, and pass in chlorine from a cylinder until an increase in weight of 72 gms. is obtained. Make up the solution to 1 litre and stir well. The solution must be kept in a cool dark place, but even then slowly decomposes.

SODIUM NITROPRUSSIDE. Dissolve a few crystals in water as required.

SPECIAL REAGENTS.

ACETYLATING MIXTURE. Equal vols. of acetic anhydride and glacial acetic acid. (A special mixture is used for quantitative acetylation; see p. 358.)

AMMONIACAL SILVER NITRATE. Add 1 drop of 10% aqueous NaOH solution to about 5 c.c. of silver nitrate solution in a test-tube: then add *dilute* NH_3 drop by drop with shaking until only a trace of undissolved Ag_2O remains. A number of reductions require the presence of Ag^+ ions. It is often advisable, therefore, after adding the ammonia to add silver nitrate solution until a faint but permanent precipitate is obtained. The solution should always be prepared in small quantities immediately before use, and any unexpended solution thrown away afterwards. If the solution is kept for some time, it may form explosive by-products.

BROMINE-WATER. Shake about 5 c.c. of bromine with 100 c.c. of water, and decant off the clear aqueous solution as required (concentration about 3%).

CHLORINE-WATER. Water saturated in the cold with chlorine gas (about 0·7%).

FEHLING'S SOLUTION. *Solution* **A**. Dissolve 69·28 gms. of $CuSO_4,5H_2O$ in water and make up to 1 litre.

Solution **B**. Dissolve 346 gms. of sodium potassium tartrate ($C_4H_4O_6NaK,4H_2O$, "Rochelle salt") and 120 gms. of NaOH in water and make the mixed tartrate and hydroxide solution up to 1 litre.

To prepare Fehling's solution, mix equal volumes of Solutions

A and **B**. Fehling's solution should be prepared only in sufficient quantity for immediate needs, as it slowly deteriorates on standing, while Solutions **A** and **B** keep almost indefinitely.

HYDROGEN PEROXIDE. "10 volumes" solution (as purchased).

IODINE SOLUTION. Cold saturated aqueous solution. (If a more concentrated solution is required, add 1 gm. of powdered iodine to a solution of 2 gms. of potassium iodide in a minimum of water, and dilute the solution to 100 c.c.)

α-NAPHTHOL, ALCOHOLIC, 1%. Dissolve 1 gm. of α-naphthol in methylated spirit and make up to 100 c.c. with spirit.

α-NAPHTHOL, ALCOHOLIC, 20%. As above, using 20 gms. of α-naphthol.

SCHIFF'S REAGENT. Dissolve 1 gm. of rosaniline in 50 c.c. of water with gentle warming. Cool, saturate with SO_2, add about 1 gm. of animal charcoal, shake and filter: make up to 1 litre with water. If the pink colour reappears on standing, add a few drops of SO_2-water carefully with stirring until the colour *just* disappears.

2:4-DINITROPHENYLHYDRAZINE. Dissolve 2 gms. of 2:4-dinitrophenyl-hydrazine in 30 c.c. of methyl alcohol and 10 c.c. of water. Add slowly, with shaking, 4 c.c. of conc. H_2SO_4. Cool the solution, and filter.

INDICATORS.

METHYLENE-BLUE. Dissolve 1 gm. of powdered methylene-blue in water and make up to 500 c.c.

METHYL-ORANGE. Dissolve 1 gm. of methyl-orange in 1·5 litres of boiling water.

METHYL-RED. Dissolve 1 gm. in 1 litre of alcohol.

THYMOL-BLUE. Dissolve 0·266 gm. in 50 c.c. of alcohol, and add 100 c.c. of water.

PHENOLPHTHALEIN. Dissolve 1 gm. of phenolphthalein in 100 c.c. of methylated spirit.

PHENOL-RED. Grind up 0·1 gm. of phenol-red with 29 c.c. of $N/100$ NaOH and make up to 250 c.c. with water.

LABORATORY FIRST-AID, TREATMENT OF FIRES, Etc.

A First-Aid Box should be kept in a readily accessible place in the laboratory, and should contain the following articles. *All bottles and packages should be clearly labelled.*

Bandages, lint, gauze, cotton-wool, adhesive plaster, and a sling.

Delicate forceps, needles, thread, safety-pins, and scissors.

Fine glass dropping-tube. Glass eye-bath.

Vaseline, salt, mustard (powder). Castor oil. Olive oil. Sal volatile. Zinc oxide ointment. Boracic acid (powder). Chloramine-T (fine hydrated crystals, *not* pellets).

Bottles of the following:
Acriflavine or Euflavine Emulsion (in quantity).
Saturated aqueous picric acid solution (in quantity).
Lime-water (in quantity).
2% Iodine solution. 1% Boric acid. 1% Acetic acid.
8% Sodium bicarbonate solution (*i.e.*, saturated in the cold).
1% Sodium bicarbonate solution.

BURNS

(1) *Caused by Dry Heat* (*i.e.*, by Flames, Hot Metal, *etc.*)
    (*a*) For very small burns, hold the burn in cold saturated (8%) sodium bicarbonate solution for some time, then cover freely with zinc oxide ointment (or, failing this, with vaseline) and bandage to exclude air.
    (*b*) For large burns, *do not put on oil or ointment*, but always apply the acriflavine emulsion freely and without delay. If the burn is on the hand or arm, after applying the emulsion, cover the burn *lightly*, with a layer of cotton-wool also soaked in the acriflavine emulsion.
[Alternatively, a saturated aqueous solution of picric acid can be used. This should be poured freely on to the burn, and also on to a pad of cotton-wool, which should then be applied *lightly* to the burn.
Of the two treatments, the acriflavine or euflavine treatment is the more efficacious. Either treatment, however, should be regarded as solely preliminary to qualified medical attention.]
(2) *Scalds* (by boiling water). Apply at once the acriflavine or picric acid treatment.
(3) *Acid Burns.* Wash *immediately* and *thoroughly* with cold water, and then with dilute (8%) sodium bicarbonate solution.
    If burn is severe, wash again with water and then apply the acriflavine or picric acid treatment.
(4) *Caustic Alkali Burns.* The same as for acid burns, except that after *thorough* washing with water, wash with very dilute (*e.g.*, 1%) acetic acid solution in place of sodium bicarbonate. Then continue as before.
(5) *Bromine Burns.* When experiments involving the use of liquid bromine are being performed, small bottles of petrol (b.p. 80–100°) should be available on the bench. If bromine is spilt on the hands, *immediately* wash it off with an ample supply of petrol, when the bromine will be completely removed from the skin. (If subsequently, the skin which has been in contact with the petrol feels tender and "smarts" owing to the removal of the normal film of grease, cover gently with olive oil.)
    If petrol is not immediately available, wash under a steady stream of water for some time, and then wash with dilute (8%) sodium bicarbonate solution. Water followed by bicarbonate is not

however as effective as petrol for removing the bromine which has already started to penetrate the skin.

(6) *Phosphorus Burns.* Wash in cold water, and then immerse in aqueous silver nitrate solution. If serious, wash again with water and apply the acriflavine treatment.

(7) *Sodium Burns.* Most frequently caused by small molten pellets flying out of heated tubes. If a small solidified pellet of sodium can still be seen, remove carefully with forceps. Then wash the burn thoroughly in water, then in dilute (1%) acetic acid, and then cover with gauze soaked in olive oil. For serious burns apply the acriflavine treatment.

(8) *Methyl sulphate.* If spilt on the hands: wash *immediately* with an ample supply of concentrated ammonia solution. Then rub *gently* with a wad of cotton-wool soaked in the ammonia solution.

EYE ACCIDENTS.

In all cases, the patient should see a doctor. If the accident appears serious, a doctor should be sent for immediately, *while* first aid is applied. If the accident appears to be of a minor character, the patient should be sent to a doctor after first-aid has been applied.

(1) *Acid in Eye.* If acid is dilute, wash the eye repeatedly with 1% sodium bicarbonate solution. If the acid is concentrated, first wash the eye well with water, and then continue with the bicarbonate solution.

(2) *Caustic Alkali in Eye.* Proceed just as for acid in the eye, but wash with 1% boric acid solution in place of bicarbonate solution.

(3) *Bromine in Eye.* Wash well with water, and then *at once* with 1% sodium bicarbonate solution.

(4) *Glass in Eye.* Remove loose glass either with forceps, or by washing with water in an eye-bath.

If glass has penetrated the eye, remove the fragments with forceps *only* if the glass has entered the white of the eye away from the immediate neighbourhood of the iris and pupil, and if the glass can readily be removed without danger of increasing the damage. If glass is not removed, place patient on his back and hold eye gently open until doctor arrives.

Whilst awaiting medical attention, acute pain in the damaged eye may be rapidly relieved by adding 1–2 drops of a cocaine-castor oil mixture prepared in accordance with the prescription:

Cocain. Alk. gr. i.
Ol. ricini puriss. fl. dr. ii.
Pro oculis. Mitte fl. dr. ii.

(In view of the composition of this mixture, the prescription requires a qualified medical signature before it can be made up by a pharmacist.)

Soreness which may follow very minor accidents to the eye may be relieved by placing 1 drop of castor oil in the corner of the eye.

Cuts.

If only a minor cut, wash well in 1% aqueous Chloramine-T solution or in 2% iodine solution. Remove dirt or glass, wash again, and apply sterilised dressing firmly bandaged to check bleeding.

For serious cuts, send at once for a doctor, and meanwhile endeavour to check bleeding whenever possible, *e.g.*, in the case of a cut limb, by pressure immediately above the cut.

Most cuts which occur in the laboratory are caused either by glass tubing, condensers, *etc.*, snapping while they are being forced through perforated corks, with the result that the broken jagged end cuts the hand holding the cork, or by test-tubes and boiling-tubes breaking whilst being too forcibly corked, with similar results. Such accidents in either case are avoided by careful working.

Poisons.

Solids and Liquids.

(*a*) *In the mouth but not swallowed.* Spit out at once, and wash the mouth out repeatedly with water.

(*b*) *If swallowed.*

(i) Acids generally (including oxalic) or alkalis. Dilute by drinking much water. Then for acids follow by drinking much lime-water. Milk may then be given, but no emetics.

(ii) Salts of heavy metals. Give milk or white of egg.

(iii) Arsenic or Mercury Compounds. Give emetic without delay, *e.g.*, one teaspoonful of mustard, or 1 tablespoonful of salt, in a tumbler of *warm* water.

[(iv) Potassium Cyanide. Immediately fatal.]

Gas Poisoning.

Remove patient to fresh air, and loosen clothing at neck. If breathing has stopped, give artificial respiration until the doctor arrives.

To counteract chlorine or bromine fumes if inhaled in only small amounts, inhale ammonia vapour, or gargle with sodium bicarbonate solution. Afterwards suck eucalyptus pastilles, or drink warm dilute peppermint or cinnamon essence, to soothe the throat and lungs.

Electric Shock.

Switch off, and treat for burns and shock.

TREATMENT OF FIRES.

Clothes. Laboratories should be equipped with a sufficient number of fireproof blankets, so that a blanket is available at any point of the laboratory at a few seconds' notice. Each blanket should be kept in a clearly labelled box, the lid of which is closed *by its own weight* and not by any mechanical fastening, which might delay removal of the blanket. The box itself should be kept in some open and unencumbered position in the laboratory.

The blanket when required should be at once wrapped firmly around the person whose clothes are on fire, the person then placed in a prone position on the floor with the ignited portion upwards, and the blanket pressed firmly over the ignited clothes until the fire is extinguished.

BENCH FIRES.

Most of the available fire-extinguishers are unsuitable for chemical laboratory use. Those which give a stream of water are useless for extinguishing burning ether, benzene, petrol, *etc.*, and exceedingly dangerous if metallic sodium or potassium are present. Those which give a vigorous and fine stream of carbon tetrachloride, although of greater use than the water type, frequently serve merely to fling the burning material (and particularly burning solvents) along the surface of the bench without extinguishing the fire, the area of which is thus actually increased.

The following methods should therefore generally be used:

(1) *Sand.* Buckets of dry sand for fire-extinguishing should be available in the laboratory and should be *strictly reserved* for this purpose, and not encumbered with sand-baths, waste-paper, *etc.* Most fires on the bench may be quickly smothered by the ample use of sand. Sand once used for this purpose should always be thrown away afterwards, and *not* returned to the buckets, as it may contain appreciable quantities of inflammable, non-volatile materials (*e.g.*, nitrobenzene), and be dangerous if used a second time.

(2) *Carbon tetrachloride.* Although sand is of great value for extinguishing fires, it has the disadvantage that any glass apparatus around which the fire centres is usually smashed under the weight of the sand. Alternatively, therefore, for *small* fires carbon tetrachloride may be poured in a copious stream from a Winchester Bottle on to the fire, when the "blanketing" effect of the heavy carbon tetrachloride vapour will quickly extinguish the fire. In such cases it should be remembered, however, (*a*) not to use carbon tetrachloride if metallic sodium or potassium is present, as violent explosions may result, (*b*) to ventilate the laboratory immediately after extinguishing the fire, in order to disperse the phosgene vapour which is always formed when carbon tetrachloride is used in this way.

(3) If a liquid which is being heated in a beaker or a conical flask catches fire, it is frequently sufficient to turn off the gas (or other source of heating) below and then at once to stretch a clean duster tightly over the mouth of the vessel. The fire quickly dies out from lack of air, and the (probably valuable) solution is recovered unharmed.

Students should bear in mind that the majority of bench fires arise from one of two causes, both of which result from careless manipulation by the student himself. These causes are : (1) the cracking of glass vessels which are being heated (usually for distillation purposes) whilst containing inflammable liquids. This cracking may occasionally be due to faulty apparatus, but is almost invariably caused by an unsuitable method of heating, the latter furthermore being often hastily applied. (2) The addition of unglazed porcelain to a heated liquid which is "bumping" badly—with the result that the previously superheated liquid suddenly froths over and catches fire. Porcelain should never be added to a "bumping" liquid until the latter has been allowed to cool for a few minutes and therefore has fallen in temperature below its boiling-point.

The most dangerous solvent in the laboratory is carbon disulphide, the flash-point of which is so low that its vapour is ignited, *e.g.*, by a gas-ring 3–4 minutes after the gas has been turned out. Carbon disulphide should therefore never be used in the laboratory unless an adequate substitute as a solvent cannot be found. Probably the next most dangerous liquid for general manipulation is ether, which, however, has frequently to be employed. If the precautions described on pp. 54, 123, are *always* followed, the manipulation of ether should however be quite safe.

EXPLOSIONS.

Gaseous explosions also rank among those accidents which are almost invariably due to careless work. They are usually caused by:

(i) Faulty condensation of a heavy inflammable vapour, such as ether. The precautions mentioned in the previous paragraph if observed will prevent this occurrence.

(ii) Igniting an inflammable gas before all air has been removed from the containing vessel. Whenever an inflammable gas is collected, a sample in a small test-tube should first be ignited at a safe distance from the main experiment. If it burns quietly, without any sign of even a gentle explosion, the main body of the gas can be safely ignited —although even then, this should be done with the smallest volume of gas suitable for the purpose concerned.

(iii) Experiments in which metallic sodium has been used (*e.g.*, the preparation of ethyl acetoacetate), and in which the product has subsequently to be treated with water. Great care should be taken to ensure that no unchanged sodium remains when the water is added.

TABLE I. ATOMIC WEIGHTS.

	Symbol	At. Wt.		Symbol	At. Wt.
Antimony	Sb	121·76	Manganese	Mn	54·93
Arsenic	As	74·91	Mercury	Hg	200·61
Barium	Ba	137·36	Nitrogen	N	14·01
Bromine	Br	79·92	Oxygen	O	16·00
Calcium	Ca	40·08	Phosphorus	P	31·02
Carbon	C	12·00	Platinum	Pt	195·23
Chlorine	Cl	35·46	Potassium	K	39·10
Chromium	Cr	52·01	Silver	Ag	107·88
Copper	Cu	63·57	Sodium	Na	23·00
Hydrogen	H	1·008	Strontium	Sr	87·63
Iodine	I	126·92	Sulphur	S	32·06
Iron	Fe	55·84	Tin	Sn	118·70
Lead	Pb	207·22	Zinc	Zn	65·38
Magnesium	Mg	24·32			

TABLE II. VAPOUR PRESSURE (p) OF WATER AT VARIOUS TEMPERATURES (t).

t (°C)	8	9	10	11	12	13	14	15	16
p (mm.)	8·0	8·6	9·2	9·8	10·5	11·2	11·9	12·7	13·5
t (°C)	17	18	19	20	21	22	23	24	25
p (mm.)	14·4	15·4	16·3	17·4	18·5	19·7	20·9	22·2	23·6

TABLE III. CONVERSION FACTORS FOR GRAVIMETRIC ANALYSIS.

Sought.	Weighed as	Factor.	Log. of Factor.
C	CO_2	0·2727	1·4357
H	H_2O	0·1119	1·0488
Cl	AgCl	0·2474	1·3934
Br	AgBr	0·4256	1·6290
I	AgI	0·5406	1·7329
S	$BaSO_4$	0·1374	1·1379
CH_3O	AgI	0·1321	1·1209

The factor represents the fraction by weight of the element sought (Column 1) in the final compound weighed (Column 2), e.g., the weight of carbon in x gms. of carbon dioxide is therefore $0·2727x$ gms.

TABLE IV. PHYSICAL CONSTANTS OF ORGANIC COMPOUNDS.

The following classes of organic compounds are arranged approximately in the order of the Sections 9-25 given on pp. 234–235. In the case of compounds having more than one reactive group, the derivatives noted are the fully substituted derivatives that would normally be obtained if an excess of reagent were used: *e.g.*, the methyl ether of a dihydric phenol is the di-methyl ether, the benzoyl derivative of a diamine is the dibenzoyl derivative, *etc.* The following abbreviations are used: *anhyd.*, anhydrous; *dec.*, with decomposition; *subl.*, sublimes.

When, in a column headed "M.p.," a value is given in parenthesis, it indicates that the compound is liquid at room temperature and that the value given is consequently the boiling-point. Conversely in a column headed "B.p.," values given in parenthesis are those of the melting-point. A blank space indicates that the compound has not apparently been recorded.

Alcohols and Derivatives

	d.	B.p.	Acetate *d.*	Acetate B.p.	Benzoate *d.*	Benzoate B.p.	3:5-Dinitro benzoate M.p.	Phenyl urethane deriv. M.p.
Methyl .	0·796	65°	0·945	57°	1·090	198°	109°	47°
Ethyl .	0·794	78	0·920	77	1·050	213	93	52
n-Propyl .	0·808	97	0·900	101	1·025	230	73	58
iso- ,, .	0·795	83	0·905	91	1·010	218	122	90
n-Butyl .	0·815	116	0·885	126	1·010	249	64	61
iso- ,, .	0·805	108	0·880	116	1·005	241	87	80
sec- ,, .	0·810	99	0·875	112	1·002	235	75	65
iso-Amyl .	0·812	131	0·870	139	0·990	262	61	55
Allyl . .	0·858	97	0·923	104	1·055	230	50	70
Glycol .	1·110	197	1·115	187	(m.p. 73)		169	157
Glycerol .	1·265	290	1·161	258	(m.p. 76)			160–180
Benzyl .	1·045	205	1·062	216	(m.p. 21)	323	114	78
Mannitol (d)	(m.p. 166)		(m.p. 120)		(m.p. 124)			303
Cyclohexanol	0·947	160		175	1·068	193	112	82

For Saligenin, see under Phenols

Phenols and Derivatives

	M.p.	B.p.	Acetyl deriv. M.p.	Benzoyl deriv. M.p.	3:5 Dinitro-benzoate M.p.	Toluene-p-Sulphonyl deriv. M.p.	Methyl ether M.p.	B.p.
Phenol . .	43°	182°	(196°)	69°	145°	95°	Liq.	154°
Catechol . .	104	245	63	84	152		15	207
Resorcinol .	118	276	(278)	117	201	80	Liq.	214
Hydroquinone .	170		123	204	250		56	212
Pyrogallol (1:2:3)	133	309	165	89	205		47	241
Phloroglucinol (1:3:5) .	218		105	185	162	53	53	256
o-Cresol . .	31	190	(208)	(307)	138	53	Liq.	171
m- ,, .	Liq.	202	(212)	54	165	51	,,	177
p- ,, .	35	201	(214)	71	189	69	,,	176
Guaiacol .	32	205	(240)	57	141	85	23	206
Carvacrol* .	Liq.	237	(246)	(260)	83		Liq.	217
Thymol† .	50	230	(244)	32	130		,,	216
Eugenol .	Liq.	247	30	69	131	55	,,	248
Saligenin .	82			51			,,	230
p-Chloro-phenol	41	217	,,	93		71	,,	197
p-Bromo-phenol	63	235	21	104		94	,,	223
sym-Trichloro-phenol .	69	246	(261)	75			60 Subl.	
sym-Tribromo-phenol .	95		87	81			88	
Salicylic acid .	157		137	132		155	100	
α-Naphthol .	95	278	49	56	217	88	Liq.	263
β-Naphthol .	122	285	71	107	210	125	72	274

* Pr:Me:OH = 1:4:3   † Pr:Me:OH = 1:4:2

For Nitro-phenols and Amino-phenols see under Nitro-derivatives and Amines respectively.

Aldehydes, Ketones and Acetals

	d.	M.p.	B.p.	Oxime M.p.	Phenyl-hydra-zone M.p.	2:4-Dinitro-phenyl-hydrazone M.p.	Semi-carba-zone M.p.
Formaldehyde .	—	Gas	(−21°)	Liq.	145°	167°	169°
Acetaldehyde .	0·800	Liq.	21	47 anti	99	162	162
Paraldehyde .	0·998	,,	128	—	—	—	—
Propionaldehyde	0·810	,,	49	40	Liq.	155	{ 89 / 154
Butyraldehyde .	0·817	,,	74	Liq.		121	126
Crotonaldehyde	0·860	,,	104	119	56	190	199
Chloral* . .	1·510	,,	98	40			90
Benzaldehyde .	1·050	,,	179	{ 35 anti / 128 syn	157	237	214
Salicylaldehyde	1·171	,,	196	63	141	252	231
Cinnamaldehyde	1·055	,,	252 dec.	{ 64 anti / 138 syn	168	255	215
Anisaldehyde .	1·125	,,	248	{ 45,64 anti / 133 syn	120	254	210
Vanillin . .	—	80	285	121	105	267	229
Furfural . .	1·163	Liq.	162	{ 76 anti / 92 syn	97	202	202
Acetone . .	0·798	,,	56	60	42 (anhyd.)	128	187
Methyl ethyl ketone . .	0·810	,,	80	Liq. b.p. 152	Liq.	115	148
Diethyl ketone .	0·816	,,	102	23 (b.p. 165)	,,	156	139
Acetylacetone .	0·930	,,	139	149	—	209	—
Acetophenone .	—	20	203	60	105	242	201
Benzophenone .	—	48	305	143	137	239	167
Benzoin . .	—	137	343	{ 151 anti / 99 syn	159	245	206
Benzil . .	—	95	347	237 (α)	225	{ 134 mono / 225 di	{ 174 mono / 243 di
Cyclohexanone .	0·947	Liq.	155	88	81	162	167
Methylal $CH_2(OCH_3)_2$.	0·872	,,	42				
Ethylal $CH_2(OC_2H_5)_2$	0·830	,,	88				
Dimethyl-acetal $CH_3CH(OCH_3)_2$	0·865	,,	64				
Acetal $CH_3CH(OC_2H_5)_2$	0·835	,,	104				

* Chloral gives *hydrate*, m.p. 57°, and *alcoholate*, m.p. 56°.

Aliphatic Carboxylic Acids and Derivatives

Acid	M.p.	B.p.	Methyl ester		Ethyl ester		Phenyl ester M.p.	Benzyl ester B.p.	Amide M.p.	Anilide M.p.	Nitrile B.p.	Chloride B.p.	Anhydride B.p.
			d.	B.p.	d.	B.p.							
Formic	8°	100°	0·985	32°	0·935	54°	—	203°	Liq.	50	Gas	—	—
Acetic	18	118	0·950	57	0·920	77	(196°)	216	82	122	82	55	138
Propionic	−19	141	0·920	79	0·897	99	20	222	79	105	98	80	162
n-Butyric	Liq.	163	0·905	102	0·885	120	(228)	239	115	96	117	100	198
Monochloro-acetic	63	189	1·240	130	1·160	144	45	Liq.	119	137	126	103	m.p. 46
Dichloro-acetic	Liq. (10)	194		143	1·290	158	33	„	98		113	110	215 dec.
Trichloro-acetic	58	196	1·100	152	1·385	168	(254)	„	141	94	83	118	223 „
Cyano-acetic	66	dec.	1·067	200	1·065	207			120		m.p. 30		
Carbonic	—	—		89	0·980	126	78		132		—	Gas	Gas
Oxalic	101*	dec.	m.p. 51	163	1·080	186	130	(80)	subl.	245	gas, b.p. −21	64	
Malonic	135	„	1·156	181	1·060	198	50		170		m.p. 30	dec.	gas, b.p. 7
Succinic	185	„	(m.p. 18)	195	1·046	216	118	(42)	254†	226	m.p. 54	191	m.p. 120
Lactic	18 (liq.)	„	1·094	145	1·035	154		(ca. 50)	74	59	183		
Tartaric (d)	169	„	(m.p. 48)‡	280	1·201	280	101		195				173
Citric	153 (anhyd.)	„	(m.p. 79)		1·140	294	124		210-215				
Glutaric	97	303		214		236			174¶	224		217	

* M.p. of dihydrate.   † Succinimide, m.p. 125°.   ‡ Second form, m.p. 61°.   ¶ Glutarimide, m.p. 154°.

Aromatic Carboxylic Acids and Derivatives

Acid	M.p.	B.p.	Methyl ester d.	Methyl ester B.p.	Ethyl ester d.	Ethyl ester B.p.	Phenyl ester M.p.	Benzyl ester M.p.	Amide M.p.	Anilide M.p.	Nitrile B.p.	Chloride B.p.	Anhydride M.p.
Benzoic	121	249°	1·101	200°	1·050	213°	69°	(323)	130°	164°	190°	198°	42°
Salicylic*	157	dec.	1·186	224	1·135	232	42	(320)	139	134	98	m.p. 19	
m-Hydroxy-benzoic	200		(m.p. 70)		(m.p. 73)	295	176		171	197	m.p. 82	Liq.	
p-Hydroxy-benzoic	213		(m.p. 131)		(m.p. 116)	298			162	250	,, 113	,,	
Phthalic	196	dec.	1·198	282	1·119	298	70	42	219†		,, 142	275	130
Cinnamic	133	dec.	(m.p. 36)	263	1·050	271	72	39	141	153	254	m.p. 35	(135)
Phenyl-acetic	76	266	1·045	220	1·045	227	42	(318)	157	117	231	180	(72)
Mandelic (dl)	118	dec.	(m.p. 52)	250	(m.p. 37)	253	84	(318)	133	114	m.p. 22		
o-Chloro-benzoic	142	subl.		234		243	37		142	119	,, 43	237	79
m- ,,	158		(m.p. 21)	231		245			134	124	,, 41	225	95
p- ,,	243	,,	(m.p. 44)			238			179	194	,, 95	220	194
o-Bromo-benzoic	150	,,		244		254			155	141	,, 53	245	75
m- ,,	155		(m.p. 31)			261			155	137	,, 38	243	149
p- ,,	251		(m.p. 81)			264	117		189	197	,, 113	m.p. 42	219
o-Toluic	104	254		207		221			142	125		211	
m- ,,	110	263							94	126			
p- ,,	117	275	(m.p. 32)	217		228			158	144		224	
o-Nitrobenzoic	148			275	(m.p. 30)				174	155			
m- ,,	141		(m.p. 78)		(m.p. 47)				142	154		m.p. 30	
p- ,,	240		(m.p. 96)		(m.p. 57)				201	211		m.p. 75	

* Acetyl-salicylic acid, m.p. 137°; for other derivatives, see under Phenols.   † Phthalimide, m.p. 232°.

Sulphonic Acids and Derivatives

	M.p.	Chloride M.p.	Amide M.p.	Anilide M.p.
Benzene sulphonic . .	65° (anhyd.)	14°	153°	105°
,, m-disulphonic .	dec.	63	229	
Sulphanilic . . .	dec.		163	200
o-Sulpho-benzoic . .	134 (anhyd.)	40 and 79	*	195
Toluene o-sulphonic .	57	10	153	136
Toluene p-sulphonic .	92	69	137	103
Naphthalene α-sulphonic .	85–90	68	150	112
Naphthalene β-sulphonic .	124	76	217	132

* Imide (saccharin) has m.p. 224°.

Carbohydrates

In view of the indefinite melting-points of many sugars and of their readily obtainable derivatives (e.g., osazones, cf. p. 111), their identification should be based primarily on their chemical properties. Their rotatory power can often be used for identification purposes, but is not considered in this book.

Quinones

	Colour	M.p.	Oxime M.p.	Semi-carbazone M.p.
Benzoquinone . .	Yellow	115°	240°	243°
α-Naphthoquinone .	,,	125	207	247
β-Naphthoquinone .	Red	115–120 dec.	169	184
Anthraquinone . .	Pale yellow	273	224	
Phenanthraquinone .	Orange	202	202	
Camphorquinone . .	Pale yellow	198	140	147

M.p.'s of oximes and semicarbazones are those of the di-derivatives.

Amines and Derivatives

	$d.$	M.p.	B.p.	Acetyl deriv. M.p.	Benzoyl deriv. M.p.	Toluene p-Sulphonyl deriv. M.p.	Picrate M.p.
Aniline . . .	1·025	Liq.	184°	113°	163°	103°	165°
Benzylamine .	0·985	,,	185	60	105	116	199
o-Toluidine .	1·005	,,	198	112	143	108	212–5
m- ,,	0·991	,,	203	65	125	114	195
p- ,, . .	—	45	200	153	158	117	181
o-Phenylene-diamine	—	102	257	185	301	201	
m- ,, ,,	—	65	283	191	240	172	
p- ,, ,,	—	147	267	304	>300	266	
Monomethyl-aniline	0·976	Liq.	193	102	63	94	145
Monoethyl- ,,	0·970	,,	206	54	60	87	138
Dimethyl- ,,	0·960	,,	193	—	—	—	163
Diethyl- ,,	0·940	,,	216	—	—	—	142
o-Amino-phenol .	—	174		123	182	139	
m- ,, ,, .	—	122		101	153		
p- ,, ,, .	—	184		150	234		
o-Chloro-aniline .	1·215	Liq.	207	87	99	105	134
m- ,, ,, .	1·218	,,	230	72	120	138	
p- ,, ,, .	—	70	230	179	192	95	187
o-Bromo- ,, .	—	31	250	99	116		165
m- ,, ,, .	—	18	251	87	120		187
p- ,, ,, .	—	66	245	167	204		
sym-Trichloro-aniline	—	77	262	204	174		83
,, -Tribromo- ,,	—	120	300	232	204		
o-Anisidine . .	1·095	Liq.	218	84	60	127	200
m- ,, .	—	,,	251	81		68	169
p- ,, .	—	57	243	127	153	114	170
Diphenylamine .	—	54	302	101	180	141	
Triphenylamine .	—	127	348	—	—	—	
Hexamethylene-tetramine . .	—	dec.	—	—	—	—	179
α-Naphthylamine .	—	50	300	159	160	157	181
β- ,, .	—	111	294	132	162	133	195
Piperidine . .	0·861	Liq.	105	Liq.	48	—	152
Pyridine . .	0·989	,,	115	—	—	—	167
Quinoline . .	1·095	,,	236	—	—	—	203
iso- ,, . .	—	24	240	—	—	—	222
Quinaldine . .	1·063	Liq.	247	—	—	—	191

Pyridine methiodide m.p. 117°
Quinoline ,, 134
iso- ,, ,, 159
Quinaldine ,, 195

Nitroso-compounds

	Formula	M.p.
Phenyl-methyl-nitrosamine . .	$C_6H_5(CH_3)N \cdot NO$	Liq.
,, -ethyl- ,, . .	$C_6H_5(C_2H_5)N \cdot NO$	,,
Nitroso-benzene	$C_6H_5 \cdot NO$	$67°$
p-Nitroso-phenol	$HO \cdot C_6H_4 \cdot NO$	125 dec.
p-Nitroso-monomethyl-aniline .	$NO \cdot C_6H_4 \cdot NH \cdot CH_3$	118
p- ,, -dimethyl- ,, . .	$NO \cdot C_6H_4 \cdot N(CH_3)_2$	93
p- ,, -monoethyl- ,, . .	$NO \cdot C_6H_4 \cdot NH \cdot C_2H_5$	78
p- ,, -diethyl- ,, . .	$NO \cdot C_6H_4 \cdot N(C_2H_5)_2$	87
Diphenyl-nitrosamine . . .	$(C_6H_5)_2N \cdot NO$	67
p-Nitroso-diphenylamine . .	$NO \cdot C_6H_4NH \cdot C_6H_5$	144
α-Nitroso-β-naphthol . . .	$NO \cdot C_{10}H_6 \cdot OH$	109
β- ,, -α- ,, . . .	,,	163
4- ,, -α- ,, . . .	,,	198

Azo-compounds

	Formula	M.p.
Azo-benzene	$C_6H_5 \cdot N{:}N \cdot C_6H_5$	$68°$
p-Amino-azo-benzene . .	$NH_2 \cdot C_6H_4 \cdot N{:}N \cdot C_6H_5$	126
p-Dimethylamino-azo-benzene .	$(CH_3)_2N \cdot C_6H_4 \cdot N{:}N \cdot C_6H_5$	115
Benzene-azo-(p)-phenol . .	$C_6H_5 \cdot N{:}N \cdot C_6H_4OH$	152
Benzene-azo-β-naphthol . .	$C_6H_5 \cdot N{:}N \cdot C_{10}H_6OH$	131
Azo-o-toluene	$CH_3C_6H_4 \cdot N{:}N \cdot C_6H_4CH_3$	55
Azo-p-toluene	,,	144

Amino-acids and Derivatives

	Formula	M.p.	Methyl ester M.p.	Ethyl ester M.p.	Acetyl deriv. M.p.	Benzoyl deriv. M.p.	3:5-Dinitrobenzoyl deriv. M.p.
Glycine	$NH_2 \cdot CH_2COOH$	232° dec.	Liq.	Liq.	206°	187°	179°
Alanine (dl)	$CH_3 \cdot CH(NH_2)COOH$	295 ,,	,,	,,	138	165	177
Sarcosine	$CH_3 \cdot NH \cdot CH_2COOH$	212 ,,	,,	,,	135	104	154
Phenyl glycine	$C_6H_5NH \cdot CH_2COOH$	127	48	58	194	63	—
Aspartic (l)	$HOOC \cdot CH_2 \cdot CH(NH_2)COOH$	*271 dec.	Liq.	Liq.		185	—
Cystine (l)	$[-S \cdot CH_2 \cdot CH(NH_2)COOH]_2$	*260 ,,	,,			180	180
Valine (dl)	$(CH_3)_2CH \cdot CH(NH_2)COOH$	*298 ,,				132	
,, (l)	,,	*315 ,,		Liq.		127	158
Leucine (l)	$(CH_3)_2CH \cdot CH_2 \cdot CH(NH_2)COOH$	*294 ,,			181	106 anhyd.	187
Phenyl alanine (dl)	$C_6H_5CH_2 \cdot CH(NH_2)COOH$	256	,,	,,		187	
,, ,, (l)	,,	*283 dec.				145	93
Hippuric	$C_6H_5CO \cdot NH \cdot CH_2COOH$	187	85	67			—
Tyrosine (l)	$p\text{-}HOC_6H_4 \cdot CH_2 \cdot CH(NH_2)COOH$	314	135	108	172	166	—
Anthranilic	$NH_2 \cdot C_6H_4COOH$	144	25	Liq.	185	181	278
m-Amino-benzoic	,,	174	37	,,	250	248	270
p- ,, ,,	,,	186		89	252	278	>290

* The m.ps. of these acids vary with the rate of heating, and the values given are those obtained on rapid heating in sealed tubes.

Nitro-compounds

	M.p.	B.p.		M.p.	B.p.
Nitro-methane . .	Liq.	101°	o-Nitro-benzylchloride .	48°	
Nitro-ethane . .	,,	114	m- ,, ,, .	45	
Nitrobenzene . .	,,	210	p- ,, ,, .	71	
m-Dinitrobenzene .	90	302	p-Nitro-benzyl bromide .	99	
o-Nitro-toluene .	Liq.	220	p-Nitro ,, iodide .	127	
p- ,, ,, .	52	238	o-Nitro-benzaldehyde .	44	
sym-Trinitro- ,, .	82		m- ,, ,, .	58	
o-Nitro-phenol .	46	216	p- ,, ,, .	106	
m- ,, ,, .	97		o-Nitro-benzoic acid .	144	
p- ,, ,, .	114		m- ,, ,, ,, .	141	
Picric acid . .	122		p- ,, ,, ,, .	241	
o-Nitro-aniline .	71		o-Nitro-benzoyl chloride .	20	
m- ,, ,, .	114	285	m- ,, ,, ,, .	30	
p- ,, ,, .	148		p- ,, ,, ,, .	75	
o-Nitro-acetanilide .	92		3:5-Dinitro-benzoyl		
m- ,, ,,	155		chloride . . .	70	
p- ,, ,,	212		p-Nitro-chloro-benzene .	83	242
o-Nitro-benzyl alcohol .	74	270	p- ,, -bromo- ,, .	126	259
m- ,, ,, ,, .	27		p- ,, -iodo- ,, .	172	
p- ,, ,, ,, .	93		α-Nitro-naphthalene .	61	304
			β- ,, ,, .	79	

Azoxy-compounds

	Formula	M.p.
Azoxybenzene	$C_6H_5N{:}NO{\cdot}C_6H_5$	36°
o-Azoxytoluene	$CH_3C_6H_5N{\cdot}NO{\cdot}C_6H_4CH_3$	59
p- ,, ...	,,	75

Ureas and Thioureas

(for Amides, see under Carboxylic acids)

	Formula	M.p.
Urea	NH_2CONH_2	$132°$
Guanidine	$NH_2C(:NH)NH_2$	dec.
Semicarbazide	$NH_2CONH \cdot NH_2$	96
Biuret	$NH_2CONH \cdot CONH_2$	192 dec.
Phenyl-urea	$C_6H_5 \cdot NHCONH_2$	147
sym-Diphenyl-urea . . .	$C_6H_5 \cdot NHCONH \cdot C_6H_5$	237
Tetraphenyl-urea	$(C_6H_5)_2NCON(C_6H_5)_2$	183
Benzyl-urea	$C_6H_5CH_2 \cdot NHCONH_2$	149
o-Tolyl-urea	$CH_3C_6H_4 \cdot NHCONH_2$	191
p- ,, - ,, ...	,,	181
Thiourea	NH_2CSNH_2	180
Thio-semicarbazide . . .	$NH_2CSNH \cdot NH_2$	182
Phenyl-thiourea	$C_6H_5 \cdot NHCSNH_2$	154
Thio-carbanilide	$C_6H_5 \cdot NHCSNH \cdot C_2H_5$	153
Tetraphenyl-thiourea . . .	$(C_6H_5)_2NCSN(C_6H_5)_2$	195

Substituted Hydrazines

	Formula	M.p.	B.p.	Acetyl deriv. M.p.	Benzoyl deriv. M.p.
Phenyl-hydrazine . .	$C_6H_5NH \cdot NH_2$	$23°$	$243°*$	$128°$	$168°$
Phenyl-methyl-hydrazine	$C_6H_5(CH_3)N \cdot NH_2$	Liq.	227 *	92	153
p-Tolyl-hydrazine . .	$CH_3C_6H_4NH \cdot NH_2$	65	242 *	121	146
Diphenyl-hydrazine .	$(C_6H_5)_2N \cdot NH_2$	34		184	192
Hydrazobenzene . .	$C_6H_5NH \cdot NHC_6H_5$	131		105	138
2:4-Dinitrophenylhydrazine	$(NO_2)_2C_6H_3NH \cdot NH_2$	198		197	206

*With partial decomp.

Halogeno-hydrocarbons

	d.	B.p.		d.	B.p.
Methyl chloride .	Gas	−24°	Benzyl chloride .	1·105	179°
,, bromide .	,,	4·5	,, bromide .	1·440	198
,, iodide .	2·285	43	,, iodide .	(m.p.	dec.
Ethyl chloride . .	—	12·5		24)	
,, bromide .	1·450	38	Benzal chloride .	1·296	207
,, iodide .	1·943	72	Benzo-trichloride .	1·380	213
n-Propyl chloride .	0·805	46	Chloro-benzene .	1·110	132
,, bromide .	1·354	71	Bromo- ,,	1·495	156
,, iodide : .	1·746	102	Iodo- ,,	1·835	188
iso-Propyl chloride .	0·860	37	o-Dichloro-benzene .	1·315	179
,, bromide .	1·312	60	m- ,, ,, .	1·290	172
,, iodide .	1·706	89	p- ,, ,, .	(m.p.	172
n-Butyl chloride .	0·890	77		53)	
,, bromide .	1·280	100	o-Dibromo-benzene .	1·978	224
,, iodide .	1·615	130	m- ,, ,, .	1·955	219
iso-Butyl chloride .	0·880	68	p- ,, ,, .	(m.p.	219
,, ,, bromide .	1·273	91		89)	
,, ,, iodide .	1·611	120	o-Chloro-toluene .	1·085	159
Allyl chloride .	0·940	46	m- ,, ,, .	1·075	162
,, bromide .	1·436	70	p- ,, ,, .	1·075	162
,, iodide .	1·845	104	o-Bromo-toluene .	1·425	181
Methylene dichloride .	1·364	42	m- ,, ,, .	1·415	183
,, dibromide .	2·498	97	p- ,, ,, .	(m.p.	185
,, di-iodide .	3·285	180		28)	
		dec.	o-Iodo-toluene .	1·700	207
Chloroform .	1·504	61	m- ,, ,, .	1·702	204
Bromoform .	2·904	151	p- ,, ,, .	(m.p.	211
Iodoform . .	(m.p.	dec.		35)	
	120)		α-Chloro-naphthalene	1·196	259
Carbon tetrachloride .	1·606	77	β ,, ,,	(m.p.	265
,, tetrabromide .	(m.p.	189		56)	
	92)	dec.	α-Bromo-naphthalene	1·490	281
,, tetra-iodide .	(subl.)	dec.	β- ,, ,,	(m.p.	281
Ethylene dichloride .	1·254	83		59)	
,, dibromide .	2·180	130	α-Iodo-naphthalene .	1·734	303
,, di-iodide .	(m.p.		β- ,, ,, .	(m.p.	309
	81)			54)	
Ethylidene dichloride .	1·186	60			

Ethers

	d.	B.p.		d.	B.p.
Diethyl . . .	0·720	35°	Anisole . . .	0·990	154°
Di-*n*-propyl . .	0·740	91	Phenetole . .	0·980	171
Di-*n*-butyl . .	0·775	140	*o*-Chloro-anisole .		195
Di-*iso*-amyl . .	0·781	170	*m*- ,, ,, .		193
Glycol mono-methyl .	0·969	125	*p*- ,, ,, .		198
,, ,, -ethyl .	0·935	135	*o*-Bromo-anisole .		220
,, ,, -*n*-propyl	0·914	153	*m*- ,, ,, .		213
,, ,, -*n*-butyl	0·901	172	*p*- ,, ,, .		220
Glycol dimethyl .	0·869	83	Catechyl-mono-		
,, diethyl .	0·850	124	methyl* .	(m.p. 32)	205
Glycerol trimethyl .	0·947	148	Catechyl-dimethyl†	,, 15	207
,, triethyl .	0·947	181	Resorcinol-mono-		
Methyl benzyl . .	0·970	169	methyl . .		243
Ethyl ,, .	0·953	189	Resorcinol-dimethyl .	1·065	216
Dibenzyl . . .	1·037	295	Hydroquinone-		
Monochloro-dimethyl	15·06	59	monomethyl .	(m.p. 53)	243
1:1'-Dichloro-dimethyl	1·328	105	Hydroquinone-		
2-Monochloro-diethyl	1·045	107	dimethyl . .	,, 56	212
2:2'-Dichloro-diethyl .	1·217	177	Methyl-*o*-cresyl .	0·985	171
			,, -*m*- ,, .	0·972	177
			,, -*p*- ,, .	0·970	176
			Diphenyl . .	(m.p. 28)	252
			Methyl-α-naphthyl .	1·095	263
			,, -β- ,, .	(m.p. 72)	274
			Ethyl-α- ,, .	1·060	276
			,, -β- ,, .	(m.p. 37)	282

* Guaiacol. † Veratrole.

Aromatic Hydrocarbons

	d.	M.p.	B.p.	Picrate M.p.
Benzene	0·877	5°	81°	
Toluene	0·871	Liq.	110	
o-Xylene	0·885	,,	142	
m- ,, ...	0·870	,,	139	
p- ,, ...	0·865	15	137	
Mesitylene	0·870	Liq.	164	
Ethylbenzene . . .	0·874	,,	134	
Styrene	0·915	,,	146	
Naphthalene . . .	—	80	218	152
Anthracene . . .	—	216	351	139
Phenanthrene . . .	—	100	340	143
Diphenyl	—	70	254	
Dibenzyl	—	52	284	
Diphenyl-methane . .	—	26	261	
Triphenyl-methane . .	—	92		

LOGARITHMS

	0	1	2	3	4	5	6	7	8	9	1	2	3	4	5	6	7	8	9
10	·0000	0043	0086	0128	0170	0212	0253	0294	0334	0374	4	8	12	17	21	25	29	33	37
11	·0414	0453	0492	0531	0569	0607	0645	0682	0719	0755	4	8	11	15	19	23	26	30	34
12	·0792	0828	0864	0899	0934	0969	1004	1038	1072	1106	3	7	10	14	17	21	24	28	31
13	·1139	1173	1206	1239	1271	1303	1335	1367	1399	1430	3	6	10	13	16	19	23	26	29
14	·1461	1492	1523	1553	1584	1614	1644	1673	1703	1732	3	6	9	12	15	18	21	24	27
15	·1761	1790	1818	1847	1875	1903	1931	1959	1987	2014	3	6	8	11	14	17	20	22	25
16	·2041	2068	2095	2122	2148	2175	2201	2227	2253	2279	3	5	8	11	13	16	18	21	24
17	·2304	2330	2355	2380	2405	2430	2455	2480	2504	2529	2	5	7	10	12	15	17	20	22
18	·2553	2577	2601	2625	2648	2672	2695	2718	2742	2765	2	5	7	9	12	14	16	19	21
19	·2788	2810	2833	2856	2878	2900	2923	2945	2967	2989	2	4	7	9	11	13	16	18	20
20	·3010	3032	3054	3075	3096	3118	3139	3160	3181	3201	2	4	6	8	11	13	15	17	19
21	·3222	3243	3263	3284	3304	3324	3345	3365	3385	3404	2	4	6	8	10	12	14	16	18
22	·3424	3444	3464	3483	3502	3522	3541	3560	3579	3598	2	4	6	8	10	12	14	15	17
23	·3617	3636	3655	3674	3692	3711	3729	3747	3766	3784	2	4	6	7	9	11	13	15	17
24	·3802	3820	3838	3856	3874	3892	3909	3927	3945	3962	2	4	5	7	9	11	12	14	16
25	·3979	3997	4014	4031	4048	4065	4082	4099	4116	4133	2	3	5	7	9	10	12	14	15
26	·4150	4166	4183	4200	4216	4232	4249	4265	4281	4298	2	3	5	7	8	10	11	13	15
27	·4314	4330	4346	4362	4378	4393	4409	4425	4440	4456	2	3	5	6	8	9	11	13	14
28	·4472	4487	4502	4518	4533	4548	4564	4579	4594	4609	2	3	5	6	8	9	11	12	14
29	·4624	4639	4654	4669	4683	4698	4713	4728	4742	4757	1	3	4	6	7	9	10	12	13
30	·4771	4786	4800	4814	4829	4843	4857	4871	4886	4900	1	3	4	6	7	9	10	11	13
31	·4914	4928	4942	4955	4969	4983	4997	5011	5024	5038	1	3	4	6	7	8	10	11	12
32	·5051	5065	5079	5092	5105	5119	5132	5145	5159	5172	1	3	4	5	7	8	9	11	12
33	·5185	5198	5211	5224	5237	5250	5263	5276	5289	5302	1	3	4	5	6	8	9	10	12
34	·5315	5328	5340	5353	5366	5378	5391	5403	5416	5428	1	3	4	5	6	8	9	10	11
35	·5441	5453	5465	5478	5490	5502	5514	5527	5539	5551	1	2	4	5	6	7	9	10	11
36	·5563	5575	5587	5599	5611	5623	5635	5647	5658	5670	1	2	4	5	6	7	8	10	11
37	·5682	5694	5705	5717	5729	5740	5752	5763	5775	5786	1	2	3	5	6	7	8	9	10
38	·5798	5809	5821	5832	5843	5855	5866	5877	5888	5899	1	2	3	5	6	7	8	9	10
39	·5911	5922	5933	5944	5955	5966	5977	5988	5999	6010	1	2	3	4	5	7	8	9	10
40	·6021	6031	6042	6053	6064	6075	6085	6096	6107	6117	1	2	3	4	5	6	8	9	10
41	·6128	6138	6149	6160	6170	6180	6191	6201	6212	6222	1	2	3	4	5	6	7	8	9
42	·6232	6243	6253	6263	6274	6284	6294	6304	6314	6325	1	2	3	4	5	6	7	8	9
43	·6335	6345	6355	6365	6375	6385	6395	6405	6415	6425	1	2	3	4	5	6	7	8	9
44	·6435	6444	6454	6464	6474	6484	6493	6503	6513	6522	1	2	3	4	5	6	7	8	9
45	·6532	6542	6551	6561	6571	6580	6590	6599	6609	6618	1	2	3	4	5	6	7	8	9
46	·6628	6637	6646	6656	6665	6675	6684	6693	6702	6712	1	2	3	4	5	6	7	7	8
47	·6721	6730	6739	6749	6758	6767	6776	6785	6794	6803	1	2	3	4	5	5	6	7	8
48	·6812	6821	6830	6839	6848	6857	6866	6875	6884	6893	1	2	3	4	4	5	6	7	8
49	·6902	6911	6920	6928	6937	6946	6955	6964	6972	6981	1	2	3	4	4	5	6	7	8
50	·6990	6998	7007	7016	7024	7033	7042	7050	7059	7067	1	2	3	3	4	5	6	7	8
51	·7076	7084	7093	7101	7110	7118	7126	7135	7143	7152	1	2	3	3	4	5	6	7	8
52	·7160	7168	7177	7185	7193	7202	7210	7218	7226	7235	1	2	3	3	4	5	6	7	7
53	·7243	7251	7259	7267	7275	7284	7292	7300	7308	7316	1	2	2	3	4	5	6	6	7
54	·7324	7332	7340	7348	7356	7364	7372	7380	7388	7396	1	2	2	3	4	5	6	6	7
	0	**1**	**2**	**3**	**4**	**5**	**6**	**7**	**8**	**9**	**1**	**2**	**3**	**4**	**5**	**6**	**7**	**8**	**9**

LOGARITHMS

	0	1	2	3	4	5	6	7	8	9	1	2	3	4	5	6	7	8	9
55	·7404	7412	7419	7427	7435	7443	7451	7459	7466	7474	1	2	2	3	4	5	5	6	7
56	·7482	7490	7497	7505	7513	7520	7528	7536	7543	7551	1	2	2	3	4	5	5	6	7
57	·7559	7566	7574	7582	7589	7597	7604	7612	7619	7627	1	2	2	3	4	5	5	6	7
58	·7634	7642	7649	7657	7664	7672	7679	7686	7694	7701	1	1	2	3	4	5	5	6	7
59	·7709	7716	7723	7731	7738	7745	7752	7760	7767	7774	1	1	2	3	4	4	5	6	7
60	·7782	7789	7796	7803	7810	7818	7825	7832	7839	7846	1	1	2	3	4	4	5	6	6
61	·7853	7860	7868	7875	7882	7889	7896	7903	7910	7917	1	1	2	3	4	4	5	6	6
62	·7924	7931	7938	7945	7952	7959	7966	7973	7980	7987	1	1	2	3	3	4	5	6	6
63	·7993	8000	8007	8014	8021	8028	8035	8041	8048	8055	1	1	2	3	3	4	5	5	6
64	·8062	8069	8075	8082	8089	8096	8102	8109	8116	8122	1	1	2	3	3	4	5	5	6
65	·8129	8136	8142	8149	8156	8162	8169	8176	8182	8189	1	1	2	3	3	4	5	5	6
66	·8195	8202	8209	8215	8222	8228	8235	8241	8248	8254	1	1	2	3	3	4	5	5	6
67	·8261	8267	8274	8280	8287	8293	8299	8306	8312	8319	1	1	2	3	3	4	5	5	6
68	·8325	8331	8338	8344	8351	8357	8363	8370	8376	8382	1	1	2	3	3	4	4	5	6
69	·8388	8395	8401	8407	8414	8420	8426	8432	8439	8445	1	1	2	2	3	4	4	5	6
70	·8451	8457	8463	8470	8476	8482	8488	8494	8500	8506	1	1	2	2	3	4	4	5	6
71	·8513	8519	8525	8531	8537	8543	8549	8555	8561	8567	1	1	2	2	3	4	4	5	5
72	·8573	8579	8585	8591	8597	8603	8609	8615	8621	8627	1	1	2	2	3	4	4	5	5
73	·8633	8639	8645	8651	8657	8663	8669	8675	8681	8686	1	1	2	2	3	4	4	5	5
74	·8692	8698	8704	8710	8716	8722	8727	8733	8739	8745	1	1	2	2	3	4	4	5	5
75	·8751	8756	8762	8768	8774	8779	8785	8791	8797	8802	1	1	2	2	3	3	4	5	5
76	·8808	8814	8820	8825	8831	8837	8842	8848	8854	8859	1	1	2	2	3	3	4	5	5
77	·8865	8871	8876	8882	8887	8893	8899	8904	8910	8915	1	1	2	2	3	3	4	4	5
78	·8921	8927	8932	8938	8943	8949	8954	8960	8965	8971	1	1	2	2	3	3	4	4	5
79	·8976	8982	8987	8993	8998	9004	9009	9015	9020	9025	1	1	2	2	3	3	4	4	5
80	·9031	9036	9042	9047	9053	9058	9063	9069	9074	9079	1	1	2	2	3	3	4	4	5
81	·9085	9090	9096	9101	9106	9112	9117	9122	9128	9133	1	1	2	2	3	3	4	4	5
82	·9138	9143	9149	9154	9159	9165	9170	9175	9180	9186	1	1	2	2	3	3	4	4	5
83	·9191	9196	9201	9206	9212	9217	9222	9227	9232	9238	1	1	2	2	3	3	4	4	5
84	·9243	9248	9253	9258	9263	9269	9274	9279	9284	9289	1	1	2	2	3	3	4	4	5
85	·9294	9299	9304	9309	9315	9320	9325	9330	9335	9340	1	1	2	2	3	3	4	4	5
86	·9345	9350	9355	9360	9365	9370	9375	9380	9385	9390	1	1	1	2	3	3	4	4	5
87	·9395	9400	9405	9410	9415	9420	9425	9430	9435	9440	0	1	1	2	2	3	3	4	4
88	·9445	9450	9455	9460	9465	9469	9474	9479	9484	9489	0	1	1	2	2	3	3	4	4
89	·9494	9499	9504	9509	9513	9518	9523	9528	9533	9538	0	1	1	2	2	3	3	4	4
90	·9542	9547	9552	9557	9562	9566	9571	9576	9581	9586	0	1	1	2	2	3	3	4	4
91	·9590	9595	9600	9605	9609	9614	9619	9624	9628	9633	0	1	1	2	2	3	3	4	4
92	·9638	9643	9647	9652	9657	9661	9666	9671	9675	9680	0	1	1	2	2	3	3	4	4
93	·9685	9689	9694	9699	9703	9708	9713	9717	9722	9727	0	1	1	2	2	3	3	4	4
94	·9731	9736	9741	9745	9750	9754	9759	9763	9768	9773	0	1	1	2	2	3	3	4	4
95	·9777	9782	9786	9791	9795	9800	9805	9809	9814	9818	0	1	1	2	2	3	3	4	4
96	·9823	9827	9832	9836	9841	9845	9850	9854	9859	9863	0	1	1	2	2	3	3	4	4
97	·9868	9872	9877	9881	9886	9890	9894	9899	9903	9908	0	1	1	2	2	3	3	4	4
98	·9912	9917	9921	9926	9930	9934	9939	9943	9948	9952	0	1	1	2	2	3	3	4	4
99	·9956	9961	9965	9969	9974	9978	9983	9987	9991	9996	0	1	1	2	2	3	3	3	4
	0	1	2	3	4	5	6	7	8	9	1	2	3	4	5	6	7	8	9

ANTI-LOGARITHMS

	0	1	2	3	4	5	6	7	8	9	1	2	3	4	5	6	7	8	9
·00	1000	1002	1005	1007	1009	1012	1014	1016	1019	1021	0	0	1	1	1	1	2	2	2
·01	1023	1026	1028	1030	1033	1035	1038	1040	1042	1045	0	0	1	1	1	1	2	2	2
·02	1047	1050	1052	1054	1057	1059	1062	1064	1067	1069	0	0	1	1	1	1	2	2	2
·03	1072	1074	1076	1079	1081	1084	1086	1089	1091	1094	0	0	1	1	1	1	2	2	2
·04	1096	1099	1102	1104	1107	1109	1112	1114	1117	1119	0	1	1	1	1	2	2	2	2
·05	1122	1125	1127	1130	1132	1135	1138	1140	1143	1146	0	1	1	1	1	2	2	2	2
·06	1148	1151	1153	1156	1159	1161	1164	1167	1169	1172	0	1	1	1	1	2	2	2	2
·07	1175	1178	1180	1183	1186	1189	1191	1194	1197	1199	0	1	1	1	1	2	2	2	2
·08	1202	1205	1208	1211	1213	1216	1219	1222	1225	1227	0	1	1	1	1	2	2	2	3
·09	1230	1233	1236	1239	1242	1245	1247	1250	1253	1256	0	1	1	1	1	2	2	2	3
·10	1259	1262	1265	1268	1271	1274	1276	1279	1282	1285	0	1	1	1	1	2	2	2	3
·11	1288	1291	1294	1297	1300	1303	1306	1309	1312	1315	0	1	1	1	2	2	2	2	3
·12	1318	1321	1324	1327	1330	1334	1337	1340	1343	1346	0	1	1	1	2	2	2	2	3
·13	1349	1352	1355	1358	1361	1365	1368	1371	1374	1377	0	1	1	1	2	2	2	3	3
·14	1380	1384	1387	1390	1393	1396	1400	1403	1406	1409	0	1	1	1	2	2	2	3	3
·15	1413	1416	1419	1422	1426	1429	1432	1435	1439	1442	0	1	1	1	2	2	2	3	3
·16	1445	1449	1452	1455	1459	1462	1466	1469	1472	1476	0	1	1	1	2	2	2	3	3
·17	1479	1483	1486	1489	1493	1496	1500	1503	1507	1510	0	1	1	1	2	2	2	3	3
·18	1514	1517	1521	1524	1528	1531	1535	1538	1542	1545	0	1	1	1	2	2	2	3	3
·19	1549	1552	1556	1560	1563	1567	1570	1574	1578	1581	0	1	1	1	2	2	3	3	3
·20	1585	1589	1592	1596	1600	1603	1607	1611	1614	1618	0	1	1	1	2	2	3	3	3
·21	1622	1626	1629	1633	1637	1641	1644	1648	1652	1656	0	1	1	2	2	2	3	3	3
·22	1660	1663	1667	1671	1675	1679	1683	1687	1690	1694	0	1	1	2	2	2	3	3	3
·23	1698	1702	1706	1710	1714	1718	1722	1726	1730	1734	0	1	1	2	2	2	3	3	4
·24	1738	1742	1746	1750	1754	1758	1762	1766	1770	1774	0	1	1	2	2	2	3	3	4
·25	1778	1782	1786	1791	1795	1799	1803	1807	1811	1816	0	1	1	2	2	2	3	3	4
·26	1820	1824	1828	1832	1837	1841	1845	1849	1854	1858	0	1	1	2	2	3	3	3	4
·27	1862	1866	1871	1875	1879	1884	1888	1892	1897	1901	0	1	1	2	2	3	3	3	4
·28	1905	1910	1914	1919	1923	1928	1932	1936	1941	1945	0	1	1	2	2	3	3	4	4
·29	1950	1954	1959	1963	1968	1972	1977	1982	1986	1991	0	1	1	2	2	3	3	4	4
·30	1995	2000	2004	2009	2014	2018	2023	2028	2032	2037	0	1	1	2	2	3	3	4	4
·31	2042	2046	2051	2056	2061	2065	2070	2075	2080	2084	0	1	1	2	2	3	3	4	4
·32	2089	2094	2099	2104	2109	2113	2118	2123	2128	2133	0	1	1	2	2	3	3	4	4
·33	2138	2143	2148	2153	2158	2163	2168	2173	2178	2183	0	1	1	2	2	3	3	4	4
·34	2188	2193	2198	2203	2208	2213	2218	2223	2228	2234	1	1	2	2	3	3	4	4	5
·35	2239	2244	2249	2254	2259	2265	2270	2275	2280	2286	1	1	2	2	3	3	4	4	5
·36	2291	2296	2301	2307	2312	2317	2323	2328	2333	2339	1	1	2	2	3	3	4	4	5
·37	2344	2350	2355	2360	2366	2371	2377	2382	2388	2393	1	1	2	2	3	3	4	4	5
·38	2399	2404	2410	2415	2421	2427	2432	2438	2443	2449	1	1	2	2	3	3	4	4	5
·39	2455	2460	2466	2472	2477	2483	2489	2495	2500	2506	1	1	2	2	3	3	4	5	5
·40	2512	2518	2523	2529	2535	2541	2547	2553	2559	2564	1	1	2	2	3	4	4	5	5
·41	2570	2576	2582	2588	2594	2600	2606	2612	2618	2624	1	1	2	2	3	4	4	5	5
·42	2630	2636	2642	2649	2655	2661	2667	2673	2679	2685	1	1	2	2	3	4	4	5	6
·43	2692	2698	2704	2710	2716	2723	2729	2735	2742	2748	1	1	2	3	3	4	4	5	6
·44	2754	2761	2767	2773	2780	2786	2793	2799	2805	2812	1	1	2	3	3	4	4	5	6
·45	2818	2825	2831	2838	2844	2851	2858	2864	2871	2877	1	1	2	3	3	4	5	5	6
·46	2884	2891	2897	2904	2911	2917	2924	2931	2938	2944	1	1	2	3	3	4	5	5	6
·47	2951	2958	2965	2972	2979	2985	2992	2999	3006	3013	1	1	2	3	3	4	5	5	6
·48	3020	3027	3034	3041	3048	3055	3062	3069	3076	3083	1	1	2	3	4	4	5	6	6
·49	3090	3097	3105	3112	3119	3126	3133	3141	3148	3155	1	1	2	3	4	4	5	6	6
	0	**1**	**2**	**3**	**4**	**5**	**6**	**7**	**8**	**9**	**1**	**2**	**3**	**4**	**5**	**6**	**7**	**8**	**9**

ANTI-LOGARITHMS

	0	1	2	3	4	5	6	7	8	9	1	2	3	4	5	6	7	8	9
·50	3162	3170	3177	3184	3192	3199	3206	3214	3221	3228	1	1	2	3	4	4	5	6	7
·51	3236	3243	3251	3258	3266	3273	3281	3289	3296	3304	1	2	2	3	4	5	5	6	7
·52	3311	3319	3327	3334	3342	3350	3357	3365	3373	3381	1	2	2	3	4	5	5	6	7
·53	3388	3396	3404	3412	3420	3428	3436	3443	3451	3459	1	2	2	3	4	5	6	6	7
·54	3467	3475	3483	3491	3499	3508	3516	3524	3532	3540	1	2	2	3	4	5	6	6	7
·55	3548	3556	3565	3573	3581	3589	3597	3606	3614	3622	1	2	2	3	4	5	6	7	7
·56	3631	3639	3648	3656	3664	3673	3681	3690	3698	3707	1	2	3	3	4	5	6	7	8
·57	3715	3724	3733	3741	3750	3758	3767	3776	3784	3793	1	2	3	3	4	5	6	7	8
·58	3802	3811	3819	3828	3837	3846	3855	3864	3873	3882	1	2	3	4	4	5	6	7	8
·59	3890	3899	3908	3917	3926	3936	3945	3954	3963	3972	1	2	3	4	5	5	6	7	8
·60	3981	3990	3999	4009	4018	4027	4036	4046	4055	4064	1	2	3	4	5	6	6	7	8
·61	4074	4083	4093	4102	4111	4121	4130	4140	4150	4159	1	2	3	4	5	6	7	8	9
·62	4169	4178	4188	4198	4207	4217	4227	4236	4246	4256	1	2	3	4	5	6	7	8	9
·63	4266	4276	4285	4295	4305	4315	4325	4335	4345	4355	1	2	3	4	5	6	7	8	9
·64	4365	4375	4385	4395	4406	4416	4426	4436	4446	4457	1	2	3	4	5	6	7	8	9
·65	4467	4477	4487	4498	4508	4519	4529	4539	4550	4560	1	2	3	4	5	6	7	8	9
·66	4571	4581	4592	4603	4613	4624	4634	4645	4656	4667	1	2	3	4	5	6	7	9	10
·67	4677	4688	4699	4710	4721	4732	4742	4753	4764	4775	1	2	3	4	5	7	8	9	10
·68	4786	4797	4808	4819	4831	4842	4853	4864	4875	4887	1	2	3	4	6	7	8	9	10
·69	4898	4909	4920	4932	4943	4955	4966	4977	4989	5000	1	2	3	5	6	7	8	9	10
·70	5012	5023	5035	5047	5058	5070	5082	5093	5105	5117	1	2	4	5	6	7	8	9	11
·71	5129	5140	5152	5164	5176	5188	5200	5212	5224	5236	1	2	4	5	6	7	8	10	11
·72	5248	5260	5272	5284	5297	5309	5321	5333	5346	5358	1	2	4	5	6	7	9	10	11
·73	5370	5383	5395	5408	5420	5433	5445	5458	5470	5483	1	3	4	5	6	8	9	10	11
·74	5495	5508	5521	5534	5546	5559	5572	5585	5598	5610	1	3	4	5	6	8	9	10	12
·75	5623	5636	5649	5662	5675	5689	5702	5715	5728	5741	1	3	4	5	7	8	9	10	12
·76	5754	5768	5781	5794	5808	5821	5834	5848	5861	5875	1	3	4	5	7	8	9	11	12
·77	5888	5902	5916	5929	5943	5957	5970	5984	5998	6012	1	3	4	5	7	8	10	11	12
·78	6026	6039	6053	6067	6081	6095	6109	6124	6138	6152	1	3	4	6	7	8	10	11	13
·79	6166	6180	6194	6209	6223	6237	6252	6266	6281	6295	1	3	4	6	7	9	10	11	13
80	6310	6324	6339	6353	6368	6383	6397	6412	6427	6442	1	3	4	6	7	9	10	12	13
·81	6457	6471	6486	6501	6516	6531	6546	6561	6577	6592	2	3	5	6	8	9	11	12	14
·82	6607	6622	6637	6653	6668	6683	6699	6714	6730	6745	2	3	5	6	8	9	11	12	14
·83	6761	6776	6792	6808	6823	6839	6855	6871	6887	6902	2	3	5	6	8	9	11	13	14
·84	6918	6934	6950	6966	6982	6998	7015	7031	7047	7063	2	3	5	6	8	10	11	13	15
·85	7079	7096	7112	7129	7145	7161	7178	7194	7211	7228	2	3	5	7	8	10	11	13	15
·86	7244	7261	7278	7295	7311	7328	7345	7362	7379	7396	2	3	5	7	8	10	12	13	15
·87	7413	7430	7447	7464	7482	7499	7516	7534	7551	7568	2	3	5	7	9	10	12	14	16
·88	7586	7603	7621	7638	7656	7674	7691	7709	7727	7745	2	4	5	7	9	11	12	14	16
·89	7762	7780	7798	7816	7834	7852	7870	7889	7907	7925	2	4	5	7	9	11	13	14	16
·90	7943	7962	7980	7998	8017	8035	8054	8072	8091	8110	2	4	6	7	9	11	13	15	17
·91	8128	8147	8166	8185	8204	8222	8241	8260	8279	8299	2	4	6	8	9	11	13	15	17
·92	8318	8337	8356	8375	8395	8414	8433	8453	8472	8492	2	4	6	8	10	12	14	15	17
·93	8511	8531	8551	8570	8590	8610	8630	8650	8670	8690	2	4	6	8	10	12	14	16	18
·94	8710	8730	8750	8770	8790	8810	8831	8851	8872	8892	2	4	6	8	10	12	14	16	18
·95	8913	8933	8954	8974	8995	9016	9036	9057	9078	9099	2	4	6	8	10	12	15	17	19
·96	9120	9141	9162	9183	9204	9226	9247	9268	9290	9311	2	4	6	8	11	13	15	17	19
·97	9333	9354	9376	9397	9419	9441	9462	9484	9506	9528	2	4	7	9	11	13	15	17	20
·98	9550	9572	9594	9616	9638	9661	9683	9705	9727	9750	2	4	7	9	11	13	16	18	20
·99	9772	9795	9817	9840	9863	9886	9908	9931	9954	9977	2	5	7	9	11	14	16	18	20
	0	1	2	3	4	5	6	7	8	9	1	2	3	4	5	6	7	8	9

INDEX

452

Pyknometer, 340
Pyramidon, 213
Pyridine, reactions of, 282, 287
  use in acetylation, 82, 211, 354, 357
  use in bromination, 135
Pyridine ethiodide, 298
    methiodide, 298
    picrate, 134, 287
Pyruvic acid, action of carboxylase on, 416

Qualitative analysis of a compound, 305 et seq.
  of a mixture, 301 et seq.
Quantitative analysis, 319 et seq.
Quicklime—see Calcium oxide
Quinoline, preparation, 229
  reactions of, 282, 287
Quinoline chlorozincate, 229
Quinoline picrate, 134, 298
Quinones, reactions of, 280

Rapid furfural test, 278 et seq.
Rast's camphor method, 342
Reactions and identification of organic compounds, 234 et seq.
Reagents, preparation, 425
Recrystallisation, 13
  experimental directions, 15
  semi-micro, 44
Rectified spirit, as solvent, 14, 345, 349
Reducing agent, test for, by ammoniacal silver nitrate, 311
  by Fehling's solution, 311
Reduction, of anthraquinone, 281
  azo-compounds, 165
  azoxybenzene, 168
  benzene-azo-β-naphthol, 166
  benzoquinone, 281
  diazonium compounds, 147, 155, 157
  m-dinitrobenzene to m-nitro-aniline 128
  to m-phenylene diamine, 292
  nitro-anilines, 295
  nitrobenzene to aniline, 121, 292
  nitrobenzene to azoxybenzene, 167
  nitro-ethane, 102
  nitrophenols, 294
  oximes, 67
  phenylhydrazine, 157
Reflux condenser, 17
  semi-micro, 42–43
Reformatsky reaction, 223
Resorcinol, reactions of, 253
Rochelle salt, 87, 365, 426

Salicin, hydrolysis of, by emulsin, 413, 414
Salicyl alcohol, 413, 414, 415
Salicylaldehyde, reactions of, 256, 259
Salicylamide, reactions of, 271, 274
Salicylic acid, acetylation, 82, 266
  reactions of, 261, 266
Saligenin—see Salicyl alcohol
Salts, ammonium, reactions of, 271
  metallic, effect of heat on, 237, 308
  reactions of, 263
  of amines, reactions of, 282
Sand, use for extinguishing fires, 431
Sandmeyer's method for preparation of benzonitrile, 149
  chlorobenzene, 147
  p-tolunitrile, 152
Saponification, 71, 361
Saunders, action of phosphorus trichloride on alcohols, 69
  identification of amino-acids, 289
  iodoform reaction, 65
Scalds, treatment of, 428
Schardinger enzyme—see Aldehyde oxidase
Scheme, for the identification of an organic compound, 305 et seq.
  for the separation of a mixture, 301 et seq.
Schiff's Bases, 178
  nitrometer, 388
  Reagent, use of, 257, 260
    preparation, 427
  test for uric acid, 296
Schotten-Baumann reaction, benzoylation, 189
  sulphonylation, 193
Secondary aromatic amines, reactions of, 284
"Seeding" of solutions, for crystallisation, 17
Semicarbazide, use in preparation of semicarbazones, 203
Semicarbazone formation, 203
Semi-microanalysis, 369
Separation, of simple binary mixtures, 301 et seq.
Separating-funnels, 36
Side-chain, oxidation of, 186
Silica gel, as drying agent, 19
Silver acetylide, 59
Silver nitrate
  ammoniacal, preparation, 426
  ammoniacal, treatment of compounds with, 311
Silver oxalate, thermal decomposition, 352